REASON IN REVOLT
Marxist Philosophy and Modern Science

Alan Woods and Ted Grant

Wellred Publications
London

Reason in Revolt – Marxist Philosophy and Modern Science
By Alan Woods & Ted Grant

Volumen one in the series *Marxism in the New Millennium*

First published May 1995
Second edition July 2007

Copyright © Alan Woods

ISBN-13 978 1 900007 29 0
ISBN-10 1 900007 29 0

Published and distributed by Wellred Publications, P.O. Box 50525,
London E14 6WG Tel: 020 7515 7675
Typeset and Printed by Intypelibra

Cover design by Melanie MacDonald

If you wish to contact the author for any comments or suggestions, please write
via the publisher's address. This book is also available in Spanish, Italian,
German, Greek, Turkish, Urdu, Bahasa Indonesia, Portuguese and additional
translations are being prepared in French and Dutch.

Contents

About the authors

Alan Woods was born in Swansea, South Wales, in 1944 in a working class family with strong Communist traditions. He is a graduate of Sussex University where he studied Russian, and also studied as a postgraduate in Moscow and Sofia. Alan became a Marxist at an early age and joined the Labour Party Young Socialists at the age of 16.

He met Ted Grant in 1960 and joined what later became the Militant Tendency. This was a collaboration that lasted for over 40 years, until Ted's death in 2006. In the 1970s he went to Spain where he participated in the underground struggle against the Franco dictatorship and helped set up the Spanish Marxist Tendency. In recent years he has devoted a lot of attention to Latin America and especially Venezuela.

For over 40 years, as a prolific writer and journalist, he has published many articles and books on Marxism. Among these works are *Lenin and Trotsky – What They Really Stood For* (co-authored with Ted Grant), *Bolshevism, the Road to Revolution*, *Marxism and the National Question*, *Marxism and the United States*, *The Venezuelan Revolution, a Marxist Perspective and Ireland: Republicanism and Revolution*. He is also currently preparing two books: *History of Philosophy* and *Marxism and Art*.

Alan lives in London and is the editor of the popular website www.marxist.com

Ted Grant (1913-2006) was one of the most outstanding figures in the world Trotskyist movement. He emigrated to Britain from South Africa in 1934, where he joined the Independent Labour Party, and subsequently the Labour Party. In 1938 he helped to found the Workers International League which later fused to form the Revolutionary Communist Party. In the 1960s he founded the Militant Tendency, which was the most successful and influential Trotskyist movement in the world. Right till the end of his life, he has played a leading role in the revolutionary movement in Britain and internationally. He is regarded by many as the principal theoretician of Trotskyism. His selected writings, entitled *The Unbroken Thread*, was published in 1989. A collected edition of his works is now under preparation and can be visited on www.tedgrant.org

Acknowledgements

In producing the present work, we were fortunate to count on the active help and encouragement of friends and collaborators, whose advice and criticism were invaluable to us. We take this opportunity to express our thanks to the following people for their kind assistance.

Ana Muñoz, for her painstaking and tireless work on the book from start to finish; Rob Sewell, whole boundless enthusiasm sustained a long and difficult project, and whose research was fundamental to the sections on biology, genetics and evolution; Bryan Beckenham and John Pickard for their invaluable help with the section on chaos theory; we are indebted to Thanassis Olympios (Greece) for the section on geology and the evolution of life; Bosse Öberg (Sweden) for the material on religion; we would especially like to thank Eric J. Lerner (USA) for his valuable comments on the "Big Bang" and related matters; Julianna Grant for her assistance with "The Language and Thought of the Child" and Anne Tanner for her material on genetics. Finally, we would like to thank Gareth Pilkington, Sue Norris, Ruth Fallon, Michael Roberts, Steve Jones, Hamish McLaren, Dan Morley and Harry Whittaker for proof-reading, technical work and comments, and Melanie MacDonald for the cover design.

Author's preface to the second English edition

"Philosophers have only interpreted the world in different ways:
the point, however, is to change it." (Marx)

More than a decade has passed since *Reason in Revolt* was first published in English. The response to it has surpassed our greatest expectations. Sadly, Ted Grant, my old friend, comrade and teacher will not see the publication of the second edition. After a lifetime of tireless service to the cause of Marxism and the working class, he passed away last year at the ripe old age of 93.

Ted always had a passionate interest in Marxist theory, and philosophy in particular. He also followed all the developments of modern science very closely. In addition to the *Financial Times* and *The Economist*, he subscribed to *The New Scientist*, which he used to devour from cover to cover. He would often be infuriated by the mystical and idealist slant that some scientists gave to the discoveries of modern science. He would look up from the pages of his journal and shake his head in disbelief: "These people confuse science with science fiction," he would exclaim indignantly.

There was one remark that struck me as particularly profound. He said that in the human mind, "matter has finally become conscious of itself". A more beautiful way of expressing philosophical materialism would be difficult to imagine.

It is a matter of great satisfaction to me that in the last years of his life Ted could see the tremendous interest in our ideas that has been expressed in many countries. So far *Reason in Revolt* has been translated into Spanish, Italian, German, Greek, Urdu, Bahasa Indonesia, Portuguese and Turkish, and new translations are being prepared in French and Dutch. In addition, it has appeared in an "American" translation in the USA, and has also been published in separate editions in Venezuela, Mexico, Cuba and India.

Many of the discoveries made by science over the last decade have confirmed the positions of dialectical materialism defended in *Reason in Revolt*. In particular, the Human Genome Project has completely undermined the position of the reactionaries who sought to use genetics to justify racism, homophobia and creationism. This is a colossal advance for science and for socialism.

Other discoveries have made us reconsider some of our original opinions. In the first edition we were still unsure about the existence of black holes—those mysterious objects in which the compression of matter has reached such an extremity, that not even light can be emitted. These black giants suck in all surrounding matter, so that nothing can approach them without being crushed and devoured. Until recently there was little hard evidence for it. But the observations made possible by the Hubble telescope have shown that black holes play a fundamental role in the formation of galaxies.

They are present at the centre of every galaxy and serve to hold galaxies together, giving them the cohesion without which life, and ourselves, would be impossible. Thus, what appeared to be the most destructive force in the universe turns out to have colossal creative powers. The dialectical conception of the unity of opposites thus received powerful confirmation from a most unexpected source!

Role of dialectics

The recognition of the pioneering role of dialectical materialism is long overdue. The theory of chaos, and its derivatives complexity and ubiquity, has provided a striking confirmation of many of the main tenets of dialectical materialism, but this debt has never been acknowledged. This is unfortunate, since knowledge of the dialectical method would have helped avoid a number of pitfalls into which science has occasionally strayed as a result of incorrect assumptions. This fact was acknowledged by the late Stephen Jay Gould, who wrote that if scientists had paid attention to Engels' *The Role of Labour in the Transition of Ape to Man*, they could have avoided a hundred years of errors.

The great advantage of dialectics is that it deals with things in their motion and development, and moreover shows how all development takes place through contradictions. The dialectical method explains how quite small changes can, at a critical point, produce enormous transformations: the law of the transformation of quantity into quality. The importance of this law has only recently been recognised by science through chaos theory. Engels deals at length with the three fundamental laws of dialectics, which he specifies as:

The law of the transformation of quantity into quality and *vice versa*;
The law of the interpenetration of opposites;
The law of the negation of the negation.

This does not mean, of course, that philosophy—any philosophy—must dictate to science, as did the Church in the Middle Ages, or as the bureaucracy in Stalinist Russia. Science has its own methods of investigation, observation and experiment, and must follow these and these alone. Engels writes in *The Dialectics of Nature*:

"All three are developed by Hegel in his idealist fashion as mere laws of *thought*: the first, in the first part of his *Logic*, in the *Doctrine of Being*; the second fills the whole of the second and by far the most important part of his *Logic,* the *Doctrine of Essence*; finally the third figures as the fundamental law for the construction of the whole system. *The mistake lies in the fact that these laws are foisted on nature and history as laws of thought, and not deduced from them.* This is the source of the whole forced and often outrageous treatment; the universe, willy-nilly, is made out to be arranged in accordance with a system of thought which itself is only the product of a definite stage of evolution of human thought. If we turn the thing round, then everything becomes simple, and the dialectical laws that look so extremely mysterious in idealist philosophy at once become simple and clear as noonday." (My emphasis, AW.)

Scientists necessarily approach their subject matter with certain assumptions, of which they are usually unaware. These assumptions invariably have a philosophical character. Behind every hypothesis there are always many assumptions, not all of them derived from science itself. For example, what led geneticists to conclude that humans possessed far more genes than is, in fact, the case? It is the method of *reductionism*, which flows from the mechanical assumption that nature knows only *purely quantitative relations.* Biological determinism considers humans as a collection of genes, and not as complex organisms, processes, the product of a dialectical interrelation between genes and the environment.

In reality, in nature changes in quantity eventually end in a qualitative leap. Very small modifications can produce huge changes. Tiny genetic mutations can give rise to huge differences. This is what explains the apparent contradiction between the size and complexity of humans and the relatively small number of genes involved. In *Reason in Revolt*, this was our criticism of the method of Richard Dawkins in *The Selfish Gene*. Later, Dawkins himself retreated from his earlier position, shocked by the way in which it had been used by right-wing reactionaries.

The genetic difference between humans and chimpanzees is less than two per cent and most of the genetic material present in modern humans is very old. Organic matter has evolved from inorganic matter, and higher life forms have evolved from lower ones. We share most of our genes, not just with monkeys and dogs, but with fishes and roundworms. This is quite sufficient to demolish all the arguments of the Creationists and "intelligent design" merchants.

'Intelligent design'

The decay of capitalism is an expression of its inability to develop the productive forces as it did in the past. This inevitably has serious intellectual consequences. Dialectics teaches us that human consciousness in general is not revolutionary but profoundly conservative. It tends to lag behind the development of the productive forces. Men and women initially react to change by clinging to the old, familiar ideas, habits, traditions and routine. It requires great historic events to shake them out of this routine and impel them on the road to revolution. This process is neither simple nor painless.

As incredible as it may seem, in the first decade of the twenty first century, religion is experiencing a revival, not only in the form of Islamic fundamentalism, but also of Christian, Jewish and Hindu fundamentalism. The President of the United States firmly believes that God created the world in six days, that man was created from dust and that the first woman was made out of one of his ribs, and so on. The Founding Fathers of the United States were rationalists and products of the French Enlightenment. Many of them were agnostics or even atheists. But if we were able to open the brain of George W. Bush and peer inside, we would see all the accumulated rubbish of the last 2,000 years.

At a time when the discoveries of science—particularly in the United States—are unlocking all the secrets of nature and establishing the material conditions for a new stage in human civilization, we are witnessing on all sides a monstrous regression of culture. It is as if capitalism in its phase of senile decay is returning to its childhood. And there can be few spectacles as nauseating as a decrepit old man who has lost his powers of reason and has become mentally childish.

"Intelligent design" is merely the resurrection under a more plausible name of the Creationist movement, which in the USA involves millions of people and is backed by some scientists. The ideas of Darwin are being challenged in the USA by supporters of the so-called intelligent design theory. They demand that American schoolchildren be made to read the First Book of Genesis as an alternative "theory" to Darwinism. If this movement were to succeed, we would be back in the Dark Ages when men and women prostrated themselves before graven idols and burnt witches at the stake.

The revelations of the Human Genome Project have cut the ground from under the feet of the reactionaries. It has decisively settled the old "nature" versus "nurture" controversy. It shows that the number of genes in humans is not more than 23,000. This has shattered the case for biological-genetic determinism at a single stroke. The relatively small number of genes rules out the possibility of individual genes controlling and shaping behaviour patterns such as criminality and sexual preference.

We share our genes with other species going far back into the mists of time. Evolution is very economical. It constantly fashions new genes from old parts. Thus, the idea of the supporters of "intelligent design" theory that humans are a special creation of God is exploded. Human beings have only about 3,000 more genes than the humble roundworm, a creature with a body of 959 cells, of which 302 are neurons in what passes for its brain. By contrast, humans have 100 trillion cells in their body, including 100 billion brain cells.

Thus, the human genome holds important philosophical and political implications. The biological determinists insisted that in some way genes are responsible for things, like homosexuality and criminality. They attempted to reduce all social problems to the level of genetics. We criticised these false theories in *Reason in Revolt*, but at that time we had no means of knowing that in a few years their unscientific character would be so clearly demonstrated. As I wrote in the preface to the second Spanish edition in 2001:

"The latest discoveries have finally exploded the nonsense of Creationism. It has comprehensively demolished the notion that every species was created separately, and that Man, with his eternal soul, was especially created to sing the praises of the Lord. It is now clearly proved that humans are not at all unique creations. The results of the Human Genome Project show conclusively that we share our genes with other species—that ancient genes helped to make us who we are. In fact, a small part of this common genetic inheritance can be traced back to primitive organisms such as bacteria."

Marxism and optimism

Ted Grant was an incorrigible optimist all his life. Marxists are optimistic by their very nature because of two things: the philosophy of dialectical materialism, and our faith in the working class and the socialist future of humanity. Most people look only at the surface of the events that shape their lives and determine their destiny. Dialectics teaches one to look beyond the immediate, to penetrate beyond the appearance of stability and calm, and to see the seething contradictions and ceaseless movement that lies beneath the surface. The idea of constant change, in which sooner or later everything changes into its opposite enables a Marxist to rise above the immediate situation and to see the broader picture.

In the 15 years since the fall of the Soviet Union, we have witnessed an unprecedented ideological offensive against the ideas of Marxism. Ted and I wrote *Reason in Revolt* to answer the critics of Marxism. And history has not taken long to prove us right. In the space of little more than a decade not one stone upon another is left of the absurd delusions of the bourgeoisie. On a world scale the capitalist system is in crisis. War follows war. Terrorism spreads like an uncontrollable epidemic. Millions of people live in poverty on the edge of starvation. In one country after another elements of barbarism are appearing. The very future of the planet is threatened by global ecological degradation.

In the period of the decline of the Roman Empire people believed that the end of the world was approaching. This idea had its clearest expression in the Christian religion and the *Book of Revelation*. In the period of the decline of feudalism the same idea was revived by the Flagellants and other millenarian sects who confidently awaited the Day of Judgement when the earth and all its inhabitants would be consumed with fire. But in reality what was approaching was not the end of the world but only the end of a particular socio-economic system that had exhausted its potential for progress.

In the first decade of the twenty first century the capitalist system, together with its values, morality, politics and philosophy, finds itself in a blind alley. The ingrained pessimism of the bourgeoisie and its ideologues in this period is manifested in the poverty of its thought, the triviality of its art and the emptiness of its spiritual values. It is expressed in the wretched philosophy of post-modernism, which imagines itself to be superior to all previous philosophy, when in reality it is vastly inferior.

In its youth the bourgeoisie was capable of producing great thinkers: Locke, Hobbes, Kant, Hegel, Adam Smith and Ricardo. In the period of its decline, it is only capable of producing what Marx describes as flea-crackers. They talk of the end of ideology and the end of history in the same breath. They do not believe in progress because the bourgeoisie has long since ceased to be progressive. When they talk of the end of history it is because they have ended in an historical dead-end and can see no way out. When they talk of the end of ideology it is because they are no longer capable of producing one.

Capitalism is not something eternal, as its defenders would like us to believe. It is a very recent phenomenon with a turbulent past, a shaky present, and no future at all. The comforting illusions of the past, the notion that the free market economy held the key that could unlock all doors barring the way to progress and universal happiness, have all been shattered. In a vague way, the ideologues of the bourgeoisie sense that the system they defend is reaching its end. Naturally, they cannot accept this. A man on the edge of a precipice is not capable of rational thought. The spread of irrational tendencies, mysticism and religious fanaticism reflect the same thing.

It did not take long for all the contradictions to come to the surface. On a world scale the situation is characterised by extreme turbulence and volatility. This is expressed in the turbulence on world stock markets. The present slowdown shows that the boom is running out of steam, and this is preparing the way for a global recession, as Greenspan was recently compelled to admit. At bottom, what this expresses is the revolt of the productive forces against the straitjackets of private ownership and the national state. The system is being shaken by one shock after another. The earlier confidence has evaporated. The articles in the bourgeois press are full of foreboding.

The crisis of capitalism has produced an opposite reaction. There is now a growing interest in Marxist ideas. The so-called anti-globalization movement and the wave of "anti-capitalist" demonstrations show the existence of a ferment among the petit-bourgeois youth. The student and middle-class youth reflect the contradictions that are maturing in the bowels of society. Even before the crisis has properly matured, there is a general questioning of the kind of society that could generate such horrors.

In the next period ideas that now are listened to by small groups will be eagerly sought by hundreds of thousands and millions. The proof of this can be seen by what is happening in Venezuela, where socialist and Marxist ideas are being enthusiastically debated in every factory and village. It is no accident that *Reason in Revolt* is a best-seller in Venezuela, and has been warmly recommended by Hugo Chávez. What has happened in Venezuela today will happen tomorrow in Britain, in Russia, in China and the USA itself.

The main contradiction is that the big battalions of the proletariat in the industrialised capitalist countries have still not moved. The crisis of humanity can be reduced to the crisis of leadership of the proletariat. The right-wing leaders of the workers' parties and trade unions—the product of decades of reformist degeneration—are holding the movement back. But that will change. In the next period these organizations will be shaken from top to bottom. At a certain stage mass left-wing tendencies will emerge, which will move in the direction of Marxism.

The discussion of socialism of the 21st century in Venezuela is an important development, which has led to an enormous interest in the ideas of Marxism. It is true that the revisionists of the Heinz Dieterich type are moving heaven and earth to erect a barrier between the masses and Marxism, alleging that Marxism is out of date and that we need to create a new and entirely novel system of ideas that will, they assure us, be the authentic "socialism of the 21st century". But on closer inspection we see that this brand of ideas is neither new nor socialist, but only a rehash of the utopian attempts of the reformists to create "capitalism with a human face".

We do not need to reinvent socialism, just as we do not need to reinvent the wheel. The most modern analysis of the world of the 21st century is the *Communist Manifesto*, written by Marx and Engels over 150 years ago. For in the pages of the *Manifesto* we have a precise description of the world, not as it was in 1848, but as it is today. This fact, in and of itself, is a striking proof of the superiority of the scientific method of Marxism, which is rooted in the method of dialectical materialism.

Does this mean that Marxism admits of no modification and change? Of course, not! Marxism must take into account all the changes in the objective situation, or else it would not be a scientific method but a lifeless dogma. But what is really remarkable is how few adjustments we have to make to the ideas that were worked out by Marx and Engels in the 19th century and developed and enriched by Lenin and Trotsky in the 20th century. We may make this or that change, but in all the fundamentals the basic ideas retain all their vigour and actuality.

In writing *Reason in Revolt*, I was deeply impressed by the fact that the discoveries of modern science furnish us with many more examples of the truth of dialectics than the examples that were available to Engels in the 19th century. The method of Marxism provides one with all the basic tools needed to analyse and understand living reality. Dialectical materialism allows us to study reality, not as a series of dry, unconnected, senseless events or "facts", but as a dynamic process, driven by its internal contradictions, ever changing and with an infinitely rich content. Marxism is much more than a political doctrine, or a theory of economics. It is the philosophy of the future.

London, March 15, 2007

Authors' foreword

"A spectre is haunting Europe."
(*The Communist Manifesto*)

Mark Twain once joked that rumours of his death had been exaggerated. It is a striking fact that, every year for approximately the last 150 years, Marxism has been pronounced defunct. Yet, for some unaccountable reason, it maintains a stubborn vitality, the best proof of which is the fact that the attacks upon it not only continue, but actually tend to multiply both in frequency and acrimony. If Marxism is really irrelevant, why bother even to mention it? The fact is that the detractors of Marxism are still haunted by the same old spectre. They are uncomfortably aware that the system they defend is in serious difficulties, riven by insurmountable contradictions; that the collapse of a totalitarian caricature of socialism is not the end of the story.

In the last few years, ever since the fall of the Berlin Wall, there has been an unprecedented ideological counter-offensive against Marxism, and the idea of socialism in general. Francis Fukuyama went so far as to proclaim the "End of History". But history continues, and with a vengeance. The monstrous regime of Stalinism in Russia has been replaced by an even greater monstrosity. The real meaning of "free-market reform" in the former Soviet Union has been a frightful collapse of the productive forces, science and culture, on a scale that can only be likened to a catastrophic defeat in war.

Despite all this—or maybe because of it—the admirers of the alleged virtues of capitalism are dedicating considerable resources to affirm that the collapse of Stalinism proves that socialism does not work. It is alleged that the entire body of ideas worked out by Marx and Engels, and later developed by Lenin, Trotsky and Rosa Luxemburg, have been completely discredited. Upon closer examination, however, what is becoming increasingly obvious is the crisis of the so-called free-market economy, which currently condemns 22 million human beings to a life of enforced inactivity in the industrialised nations alone, wasting the creative potential of a whole generation. The whole of Western society finds itself in a blind alley, not only economically, politically and socially, but morally and culturally. The fall of

Stalinism, which was predicted by Marxists decades ago, cannot disguise the fact that, in the final decade of the 20th century, the capitalist system is in a deep crisis on a world scale. The strategists of Capital look to the future with profound foreboding. And at bottom the more honest among them ask themselves the question they dare not answer: Was old Karl right after all?

Whether one accepts or rejects the ideas of Marxism, it is impossible to deny the colossal impact that they have exercised on the world. From the appearance of *The Communist Manifesto*, down to the present day, Marxism has been a decisive factor, not only in the political arena, but in the development of human thought. Those who fought against it were nevertheless compelled to take it as their starting point. And, irrespective of the present state of affairs, it is an indisputable fact that the October Revolution changed the entire course of world history. A close acquaintance with the theories of Marxism is therefore a necessary precondition for anyone who wishes to understand some of the most fundamental phenomena of our times.

Engels' role

August 1995 marks the centenary of the death of Frederick Engels, the man who, together with Karl Marx developed an entirely new way of looking at the world of nature, society and human development. The role played by Engels in the development of Marxist thought is a subject that has never been given its due. This is partly the result of the towering genius of Marx, which inevitably overshadows the contribution made by his lifelong friend and comrade. In part it flows from the innate humility of Engels, who always played down his own contribution, preferring to emphasise Marx's pre-eminence. At his death, Engels gave instructions that his body be cremated and his ashes cast into the sea at Beachy Head, because he wanted no monument. Like Marx, he heartily detested anything remotely resembling a cult of the personality. The only real monument they wished to leave behind was the imposing body of ideas, which provides a comprehensive ideological basis for the fight for the socialist transformation of society.

Many people do not realise that the scope of Marxism extends far beyond politics and economics. At the heart of Marxism lies the philosophy of dialectical materialism. Unfortunately, the immense labour of writing *Capital* prevented Marx from writing a comprehensive work on the subject, as he had intended. If we exclude the early works, such as *The Holy Family* and *The German Ideology*, which represent important, but still preparatory, attempts to develop a new philosophy, and the three volumes of *Capital*, which are a classic example of the concrete application of the dialectical method to the particular sphere of economics, then the principal works of Marxist philosophy were all the work of Engels. Whoever wants to understand dialectical materialism must begin by a thorough knowledge of *Anti-Dühring*, *The Dialectics of Nature*, and *Ludwig Feuerbach*.

To what extent have the philosophical writings of this man who died in August 1895 stood the test of time? That is the starting point of the present work. Engels defined dialectics as "the most general laws of motion of nature, society, and human thought". In *The Dialectics of Nature*, in particular, Engels based himself on a careful study of the most advanced scientific knowledge of the day, to show that "in the last analysis, the workings of nature are dialectical". It is the contention of the present work that the most important discoveries of 20th century science provide a striking confirmation of this.

What is most amazing is not the attacks on Marxism, but the complete ignorance of it which is displayed by its detractors. Whereas no one would dream of practising as a car mechanic without studying mechanics, everyone feels free to express an opinion about Marxism, without any knowledge of it whatsoever. The present work is an attempt to explain the basic ideas of Marxist philosophy, and show the relation between it and the position of science and philosophy in the modern world. The intention of the authors is to produce a trilogy, which will cover the three main component parts of Marxism: 1) Marxist philosophy (dialectical materialism), 2) the Marxist theory of history and society (historical materialism), and 3) Marxist economics (the labour theory of value).

Originally, we intended to include a section on the history of philosophy, but in view of the length of the present work we have decided to publish this separately. We begin with a review of the philosophy of Marxism, dialectical materialism. This is fundamental because it is the method of Marxism. Historical materialism is the application of this method to the study of the development of human society; the labour theory of value is the result of the application of the same method to economics. An understanding of Marxism is impossible without a grasp of dialectical materialism.

The ultimate proof of dialectics is nature itself. The study of science occupied the attention of Marx and Engels all their lives. Engels had intended to produce a major work, outlining in detail the relation between dialectical materialism and science, but was prevented from completing it because of the heavy burden of work on the second and third volumes of *Capital*, left unfinished when Marx died. His incomplete manuscripts for *The Dialectics of Nature* were only published in 1925. Even in their unfinished state, they provide a most important source for the study of Marxist philosophy, and provide brilliant insights into the central problems of science.

One of the problems we faced in writing the present work is the fact that most people have only a second-hand knowledge of the basic writings of Marxism. This is regrettable, since the only way to understand Marxism is by reading the works of Marx, Engels, Lenin and Trotsky. The great majority of works that purport to explain "what Marx meant" are worthless. We have therefore decided to include a large number of quite lengthy quotes, particularly from Engels, partly to give the reader direct access to these ideas without any "translation", and partly in the hope that it will stimulate people to read the originals for themselves. This method does not make the book easier to read, but was, in our opinion, necessary. In the same way, we felt obliged to reproduce some lengthy quotes of authors with whom we disagree, on the principle that it is always better to allow one's opponents to speak for themselves.

London, May 1st 1995

Part one:
Reason and unreason

1. Introduction

We are living in a period of profound historical change. After a period of 40 years of unprecedented economic growth, the market economy is reaching its limits. At the dawn of capitalism, despite its barbarous crimes, it revolutionised the productive forces, thus laying the basis for a new system of society. The First World War and the Russian Revolution signalled a decisive change in the historical role of capitalism. From a means of developing the productive forces, it became transformed into a gigantic fetter upon economic and social development. The period of upswing in the West in the period of 1948-73 seemed to promise a new dawn. Even so, the benefits were limited to a handful of developed capitalist countries. For two-thirds of humanity living in the Third World, the picture was one of mass unemployment, poverty, wars and exploitation on an unprecedented scale. This period of capitalism ended with the so-called oil crisis of 1973-74. Since then, they have not managed to get back to the kind of growth and levels of employment they had achieved in the post-war period.

A social system in a state of irreversible decline expresses itself in cultural decay. This is reflected in a hundred different ways. A general mood of anxiety and pessimism as regards the future spreads, especially among the intelligentsia. Those who yesterday talked confidently about the inevitability of human progress and evolution, now see only darkness and uncertainty. The 20th century is staggering to a close, having witnessed two terrible world wars, economic collapse and the nightmare of fascism in the period between the wars. These were already a stern warning that the progressive phase of capitalism was past.

The crisis of capitalism pervades all levels of life. It is not merely an economic phenomenon. It is reflected in speculation and corruption, drug abuse, violence, all-pervasive egotism and indifference to the suffering of others, the breakdown of the bourgeois family, the crisis of bourgeois morality, culture and philosophy. How could it be otherwise? One of the symptoms of a social system in crisis is that the ruling class increasingly feels itself to be a fetter on the development of society.

Marx pointed out that the ruling ideas of any society are the ideas of the ruling class. In its heyday, the bourgeoisie not only played a progressive role in pushing back the frontiers of civilisation, but was well aware of the fact. Now the strategists of capital are seized with pessimism. They are the representatives of an historically doomed system, but cannot reconcile themselves to the fact. This central contradiction is the decisive factor which sets its imprint upon the mode of thinking of the bourgeoisie today. Lenin once said that a man on the edge of a cliff does not reason.

Lag in consciousness

Contrary to the prejudice of philosophical idealism, human consciousness in general is extraordinarily conservative, and always tends to lag far behind the development of society, technology and the productive forces. Habit, routine, and tradition, to use a phrase of Marx, weigh like an Alp on the minds of men and women, who, in "normal" historical periods cling stubbornly to the well-trodden paths, from an instinct of self-preservation, the roots of which lie in the remote past of the species. Only in exceptional periods of history, when the social and moral order begins to crack under the strain of intolerable pressures do the mass of people start to question the world into which they have been born, and to doubt the beliefs and prejudices of a lifetime.

Such a period was the epoch of the birth of capitalism, heralded by the great cultural re-awakening and spiritual regeneration of Europe after its lengthy winter sleep under feudalism. In the period of its historical ascent, the bourgeoisie played a most progressive role, not only in developing the productive forces, and thereby mightily expanding humanity's power over nature, but also in extending the frontiers of science, knowledge and culture. Luther, Michelangelo, Leonardo, Dührer, Bacon, Kepler, Galileo and a host of other pathfinders of civilisation shine like a galaxy illuminating the broad highroad of human cultural and scientific advance opened by the Reformation and Renaissance. However, such revolutionary periods do not come into being easily or automatically. The price of progress is struggle—the struggle of the new against the old, the living against the dead, the future against the past.

The rise of the bourgeoisie in Italy, Holland, England and later in France was accompanied by an extraordinary flourishing of culture, art and science. One would have to look back to ancient Athens to find a precedent for this. Particularly in those countries where the bourgeois revolution triumphed in the 17th and 18th centuries, the development of the forces of production and technology was accompanied by a parallel development of science and thought, which drastically undermined the ideological domination of the Church.

In France, the classical country of the bourgeois revolution in its political expression, the bourgeoisie in 1789-93 carried out its revolution under the banner of Reason. Long before it toppled the formidable walls of the Bastille, it was necessary to overthrow the invisible but no less formidable walls of religious superstition in the minds of men and women. In its revolutionary youth the French bourgeoisie was rationalist and atheist. Only after installing themselves in power did the men of property, finding themselves confronted by a new revolutionary class, jettison the ideological baggage of their youth.

Not long ago France celebrated the two hundredth anniversary of its great revolution. It was curious to note how even the memory of a revolution two centuries ago fills the establishment with unease. The attitude of the French ruling class to their own revolution vividly recalled that of an old libertine who tries to gain a ticket to respectability—and perhaps admittance to heaven—by renouncing the sins of his youth, which he is no longer in a position to repeat. Like all established privileged classes, the capitalist class seeks to justify its existence, not only to society at large, but to itself. In its search for ideological points of support, which would tend to justify the *status quo* and sanctify existing social relations, they rapidly rediscovered the enchantments of Mother Church, particularly after the mortal terror they experienced at the time of the Paris Commune. The church of Sacré Coeur is a concrete expression of the bourgeois' fear of revolution translated into the language of architectural philistinism.

Karl Marx (1818-83) and Frederick Engels (1820-95) explained that the fundamental driving force of all human progress is the development of the productive forces—industry, agriculture, science and technique. This is a truly great theoretical generalisation without which it is impossible to understand the movement of human history in general. However, it does not mean, as dishonest or ignorant detractors of Marxism have attempted to show, that Marx "reduces everything to economics". Dialectical and historical materialism takes full account of phenomena such as religion, art, science, morality, law, politics, tradition, national characteristics and all the other manifold manifestations of human consciousness. But not only that. It shows their real content and how they relate to the actual development of society, which in the last analysis clearly depends upon its capacity to reproduce and expand the material conditions for its existence. On this subject, Engels wrote the following:

"According to the materialist conception of history, the *ultimately* determining element in history is the production and reproduction of real life. More than this neither Marx nor I have ever asserted. Hence, if someone twists this into saying that the economic element is the *only* determining one, he transforms that position into a meaningless, abstract, senseless phrase. The economic situation is the basis, but the various elements of the superstructure—political forms of the class struggle and its results, to wit: constitutions established by victorious classes after a successful battle, etc., judicial forms, and the reflexes of all these actual struggles in the brains of the participants, political, juristic, philosophical theories, religious views and their further development into systems of dogmas also exercise their influence upon the course of the historical struggles, and in many cases predominate in determining their *form*." [1]

The affirmation of historical materialism that, in general, human consciousness tends to lag behind the development of the productive forces seems paradoxical to some. Yet it is graphically expressed in all kinds of ways in the United States where the achievements of science have reached their highest level. The constant advance of technology is the prior condition for bringing about the real emancipation of men and women, through the establishment of a rational socio-economic system, in which human beings exercise conscious control over their lives and environment. Here, however, the contrast between the rapid development of science and technology and the extraordinary lag in human thinking presents itself in its most glaring form.

In the USA nine persons out of ten believe in the existence of a supreme being, and seven out of ten in a life after death. When the first American astronaut who succeeded in circumnavigating the world in a spacecraft was asked to broadcast a message to the inhabitants of the earth, he made a significant choice. Out of the whole of world literature, he chose the first sentence of the book of *Genesis*: "In the beginning, God created heaven and the earth." This man, sitting in his spaceship, a product of the most advanced technology ever seen, had his mind full to the brim with superstitions and phantoms handed down with little change from the primeval past.

In the notorious "monkey trial" of 1925, a teacher called John Scopes was found guilty of teaching the theory of evolution, in contravention of the laws of the state of Tennessee. The trial actually upheld the state's anti-evolution laws, which were not abolished until 1968, when the US Supreme Court ruled that the teaching of creation theories was a violation of the constitutional ban on the teaching of religion in state schools. Since then, the creationists changed their tactics, trying to turn creationism into a "science". In this, they have the support, not only of a wide layer of public opinion, but of not a few scientists, who are prepared to place their services at the disposal of religion in its most crude and obscurantist form.

In 1981 American scientists, making use of Kepler's laws of planetary motion, launched a spacecraft that made a spectacular rendezvous with Saturn. In the same year an American judge had to declare unconstitutional a law passed in the state of Arkansas, which imposed on schools the obligation to treat so-called creation-science on equal terms with the theory of evolution. Among other things, the creationists demanded the recognition of Noah's flood as a primary geological agent. In the course of the trial, witnesses for the defence expressed fervent belief in Satan and the possibility that life was brought to earth in meteorites, the variety of species being explained by a kind of meteoric shuttle-service! At the trial, Mr. N.K.

♦ For reasons of convenience, where the same work is cited several times in immediate sequence we have placed the reference number at the end of the last quote.
(1) Karl Marx and Frederick Engels, *Selected Correspondence, Letter to Bloch*, 21st-22nd September 1890, henceforth referred to as MESC.

Wickremasinge of the University of Wales was quoted as saying that insects might be more intelligent than humans, although "they're not letting on...because things are going so well for them." [2]

The religious fundamentalist lobby in the USA has mass support, access to unlimited funds, and the backing of congressmen. Evangelical crooks make fortunes out of radio stations with a following of millions. The fact that in the last decade of the 20th century there are a large number of educated men and women—including scientists—in the most technologically advanced country the world has ever known who are prepared to fight for the idea that the book of *Genesis* is literally true, that the universe was created in six days about 6,000 years ago, is, in itself, a most remarkable example of the workings of the dialectic.

'Reason becomes unreason'

The period when the capitalist class stood for a rational world outlook has become a dim memory. In the epoch of the senile decay of capitalism, the earlier processes have been thrown into reverse. In the words of Hegel, "Reason becomes Unreason". It is true that, in the industrialised countries, "official" religion is dying on its feet. The churches are empty and increasingly in crisis. Instead, we see a veritable "Egyptian plague" of peculiar religious sects, accompanied by the flourishing of mysticism and all kinds of superstition. The frightful epidemic of religious fundamentalism—Christian, Jewish, Islamic, Hindu—is a graphic manifestation of the impasse of society. As the new century beckons, we observe the most horrific throwbacks to the Dark Ages.

This phenomenon is not confined to Iran, India and Algeria. In the United States we saw the "Waco massacre", and after that, in Switzerland, the collective suicide of another group of religious fanatics. In other Western countries, we see the uncontrolled spread of religious sects, superstition, astrology and all kinds of irrational tendencies. In France, there are about 36,000 Catholic priests, and over 40,000 professional astrologers who declared their earnings to the taxman. Until recently, Japan appeared to be an exception to the rule. William Rees-Mogg, former editor of the London *Times*, and arch-Conservative, and James Dale Davidson in their recent book *The Great Reckoning: How the World Will Change in the Depression of the 1990s* state that: "The revival of religion is something that is happening throughout the world in varying degrees. Japan may be an exception, perhaps because social order has as yet shown no signs of breaking down there..." [3] Rees-Mogg and Davidson spoke too soon. A couple of years after these lines were written, the horrific gas attack on the Tokyo underground drew the world's attention to the existence of sizable groups of religious fanatics even in Japan, where the economic cri-

---

(2) The Economist, 9th January 1982.
(3) W. Rees-Mogg and J.D. Davidson, *The Great Reckoning: How the World Will Change in the Depression of the 1990s*, p. 445.

sis has put an end to the long period of full employment and social stability. All these phenomena bear a striking resemblance to what occurred in the period of the decline of the Roman Empire. Let no one object that such things are confined to the fringes of society. Ronald and Nancy Reagan regularly consulted astrologers about all their actions, big and small. Here are a couple of extracts from Donald Regan's book, *For the Record:*

"Virtually every major move and decision the Reagans made during my time as White House chief of staff was cleared in advance with a woman in San Francisco who drew up horoscopes to make certain that the planets were in a favourable alignment for the enterprise. Nancy Reagan seemed to have absolute faith in the clairvoyant powers of this woman, who had predicted that 'something' bad was going to happen to the president shortly before he was wounded in an assassination attempt in 1981.

"Although I had never met this seer—Mrs. Reagan passed along her prognostications to me after conferring with her on the telephone—she had become such a factor in my work, and in the highest affairs of the state at one point I kept a colour-coded calendar on my desk (numerals highlighted in green ink for 'good' days, red for 'bad' days, yellow for 'iffy' days) as an aid to remember when it was propitious to move the president of the United States from one place to another, or schedule him to speak in public, or commence negotiations with a foreign power.

"Before I came to the White House, Mike Deaver had been the man who integrated the horoscopes of Mrs. Reagan's into the presidential schedule... It is a measure of his discretion and loyalty that few in the White House knew that Mrs. Reagan was even part of the problem [waiting for schedules]—much less that an astrologer in San Francisco was approving the details of the presidential schedule. Deaver told me that Mrs. Reagan's dependence on the occult went back at least as far as her husband's governorship, when she had relied on the advice of the famous Jeane Dixon. Subsequently, she had lost confidence in Dixon's powers. But the First Lady seemed to have absolute faith in the clairvoyant talents of the woman in San Francisco. Apparently, Deaver had ceased to think there was anything remarkable about this long-established floating seance... To him it was simply one of the little problems in the life of a servant of the great. 'At least,' he said, 'this astrologer is not as kooky as the last one'."

Astrology was used in the planning of the summit between Ronald Reagan and Mikhail Gorbachev, according to the family soothsayer, but things didn't go smoothly between the two first ladies because Raisa Gorbachev's birth date was unknown! The movement in the direction of a "free market economy" in Russia has since bestowed the blessings of capitalist civilisation on that unfortunate country—mass unemployment, social disintegration, prostitution, the mafia, an unprecedented crime wave, drugs and religion. It has recently emerged that Yeltsin himself consults astrologers. In this respect also, the nascent capitalist class in Russia has shown itself to be an apt pupil of its Western role models.

The prevailing sense of disorientation and pessimism finds its reflection in all sorts of ways, not only directly in politics. This all-pervasive irrationality is not an accident. It is the psychological reflection of a world where the destiny of humanity is controlled by terrifying and seemingly invisible forces. Just look at the sudden panic on the stock exchange, with "respectable" men and women scurrying around like ants when their nest is broken open. These periodic spasms causing a herd-like panic are a graphic illustration of capitalist anarchy. And this is what determines the lives of millions of people. We live in the midst of a society in decline. The evidence of decay is present on all sides. Conservative reactionaries bemoan the breakdown of the family and the epidemic of drugs, crime, mindless violence, and the rest. Their only answer is to step up state repression—more police, more prisons, harsher punishments, even genetic investigation of alleged "criminal types". What they cannot or will not see is that these phenomena are the symptoms of the blind alley of the social system which they represent.

These are the defenders of "market forces", the same irrational forces that presently condemn millions of people to unemployment. They are the prophets of "supply-side" economics, which John Kenneth Galbraith shrewdly defined as the theory that the poor have too much money, and the rich too little. The prevailing "morality" is that of the market place, that is, the morality of the jungle. The wealth of society is concentrated into fewer and fewer hands, despite all the demagogic nonsense about a "property-owning democracy" and "small is beautiful". We are supposed to live in a democracy. Yet a handful of big banks, monopolies, and stock exchange speculators (generally the same people) decide the fate of millions. This tiny minority possesses powerful means of manipulating public opinion. They have a monopoly of the means of communication, the press, radio and television. Then there is the spiritual police—the church, which for generations has taught people to look for salvation in another world.

Science and the crisis of society

Until quite recently, it appeared that the world of science stood aloof from the general decay of capitalism. The marvels of modern technology conferred colossal prestige upon scientists, who appeared to be endowed with almost magical qualities. The respect enjoyed by the scientific community increased in the same proportion as their theories became increasingly incomprehensible to the majority of even educated people. However, scientists are ordinary mortals who live in the same world as the rest of us. As such, they can be influenced by prevailing ideas, philosophies, politics and prejudices, not to speak of sometimes very substantial material interests.

For a long time it was tacitly assumed that scientists—especially theoretical physicists—were a special sort of people, standing above the common run of humanity, and privy to the mysteries of the universe denied to ordinary mortals. This 20th century myth is well conveyed by the old science-fiction movies, where the earth was always threatened with annihilation by aliens from outer space (in reality, the threat to the future of humankind comes from a source much nearer to home, but that is another story). At the last moment, a man in a white coat always turns up, writes a complicated equation on the blackboard, and the problem is fixed in no time at all.

The truth is rather different. Scientists and other intellectuals are not immune to the general tendencies at work in society. The fact that most of them profess indifference to politics and philosophy only means that they fall prey more easily to the current prejudices that surround them. All too often their ideas can be used to support the most reactionary political positions. This is particularly clear in the field of genetics where a veritable counter-revolution has taken place, particularly in the United States. Allegedly scientific theories are being used to "prove" that criminality is caused, not by social conditions, but by a "criminal gene". Black people are alleged to be disadvantaged, not because of discrimination, but because of their genetic make-up. Similar arguments are used for poor people, single mothers, women, homosexuals, and so on. Of course, such "science" is highly convenient to the Republican dominated Congress intent on ruthlessly cutting welfare.

The present book is about philosophy—more precisely, the philosophy of Marxism, dialectical materialism. It is not the business of philosophy to tell scientists what to think and write, at least when they write about science. But scientists have a habit of expressing opinions about all kinds of things—philosophy, religion, politics. This they are perfectly entitled to do. But when they use what may well be perfectly sound scientific credentials in order to defend extremely unsound and reactionary philosophical views, it is time to put things in their context. These pronouncements do not remain among a handful of professors. They are seized upon by right wing politicians, racists and religious fanatics, who attempt to cover their backsides with pseudo-scientific arguments.

Scientists frequently complain that they are misunderstood. They do not mean to provide ammunition for mystical charlatans and political crooks. That may be so. But in that case, they are guilty of culpable negligence or, at the very least, astounding naïvety. On the other hand, those who make use of the erroneous philosophical views of scientists cannot be accused of naïvety. They know just where they stand. Rees-Mogg and Davidson argue that "as the religion of secular consumerism is left behind like a rusting tail fin, sterner religions that involve real moral principles and angry gods will make a comeback. *For the first time in centuries, the revelations of science will seem to enhance rather than undermine the spiritual dimension in life.*" For these authors religion is a useful weapon to keep the underprivileged in their place, alongside the police and prison service. They are commendably blunt about it:

"The lower the prospect of upward mobility, the more rational it is for the poor to adopt an anti-scientific, delusional world view. In place of technology, they employ magic. In place of independent investigation, they opt for orthodoxy. Instead of history, they prefer myths. In place of biography, they venerate heroes. And they generally substitute kin-based behavioural allegiances for the impersonal honesty required by the market." [4]

Let us leave aside the unconsciously humorous remark about the "impersonal honesty" of the marketplace, and concentrate on the core of their argument. At least Rees-Mogg and Davidson do not try to conceal their real intentions or their class standpoint. Here we have the utmost frankness from the defenders of the establishment. The creation of an under-class of poor, unemployed, mainly black people, living in slums, presents a potentially explosive threat to the existing social order. The poor, fortunately for us, are ignorant. They must be kept in ignorance and encouraged in their superstitious and religious delusions, which we of the "educated classes" naturally do not share! The message, of course, is not new. The same song has been sung by the rich and powerful for centuries. But what is significant is the reference to science, which, as Rees-Mogg and Davidson indicate, is now regarded for the first time as an important ally of religion.

Recently theoretical physicist Paul Davies was awarded £650,000 by the Templeton Prize for Progress in Religion, for showing "extraordinary originality" in advancing humankind's understanding of God or spirituality. Previous winners include Alexander Solzhenitsyn, Mother Teresa, evangelist Billy Graham, and the Watergate burglar-turned-preacher Charles Colson. Davies, author of such books as *God and the New Physics, The Mind of God* and *The Last Three Minutes*, insists that he is "not a religious person in the conventional sense" (whatever that might mean), but he maintains that "science offers a surer path to God than religion." [5]

Despite Davies' ifs and buts, it is clear that he represents a definite trend, which is attempting to inject mysticism and religion into science. This is not an isolated phenomenon. It is becoming all too common, especially in the field of theoretical physics and cosmology, both heavily dependent upon abstract mathematical models, which are increasingly seen as a substitute for empirical investigation of the real world. For every conscious peddler of mysticism in this field, there are a hundred conscientious scientists, who would be horrified to be identified with such obscurantism. The only real defence against idealist mysticism, however, is a consciously materialist philosophy—the philosophy of dialectical materialism.

It is the intention of this book to explain the basic ideas of dialectical materialism, first worked out by Marx and Engels, and show their relevance to the modern world, and to science in particular. We do not pretend to be neutral. Just as Rees-

(4) W. Rees-Mogg and J.D. Davidson, op. cit., p. 27, our emphasis.
(5) The Guardian, 9th March, 1995.

Mogg and Davidson defend the interests of the class they represent, and make no bones about it, so we openly declare ourselves as the opponents of the so-called market economy and all that it stands for. We are active participants in the fight to change society. But before we can change the world, one has to understand it. It is necessary to conduct an implacable struggle against all attempts to confuse the minds of men and women with mystical beliefs, which have their origin in the murky prehistory of human thought. Science grew and developed to the degree that it turned its back on the accumulated prejudices of the past. We must stand firm against this attempt to put the clock back four hundred years.

A growing number of scientists are becoming dissatisfied with the present situation, not only in science and education, but in society at large. They see the contradiction between the colossal potential of technology and a world where millions of people live on the borderline of starvation. They see the systematic misuse of science in the interest of profit for the big monopolies. And they must be profoundly disturbed by the continuous attempts to dragoon the scientists into the service of religious obscurantism and reactionary social policies. Many of them were repelled by the bureaucratic and totalitarian nature of Stalinism. But the collapse of the Soviet Union has shown that the capitalist alternative is even worse. By their own experience, many scientists will come to the conclusion that the only way out of the social, economic, and cultural impasse is by means of some kind of rational planned society, in which science and technology is put at the disposal of humanity, not private profit. Such a society must be democratic, in the real sense of the word, involving the conscious control and participation of the entire population. Socialism is democratic by its very nature. As Leon Trotsky pointed out "a nationalised planned economy needs democracy, as the human body needs oxygen."

It is not enough to contemplate the problems of the world. It is necessary to change it. First, however, it is necessary to understand the reason why things are as they are. Only the body of ideas worked out by Marx and Engels, and subsequently developed by Lenin and Trotsky can provide us with the adequate means of achieving this understanding. We believe that the most conscious members of the scientific community, through their own work and experience, will come to realise the need for a consistently materialist world outlook. That is offered by dialectical materialism. The recent advances of the theories of chaos and complexity show that an increasing number of scientists are moving in the direction of dialectical thinking. This is an enormously significant development. There is no doubt that new discoveries will deepen and strengthen this trend. We are firmly convinced that dialectical materialism is the philosophy of the future.

2. Philosophy and religion

Do we need philosophy?

Before we start, you may be tempted to ask, "Well, what of it?" Is it really necessary for us to bother about complicated questions of science and philosophy? To such a question, two replies are possible. If what is meant is: do we need to know about such things in order to go about our daily life, then the answer is evidently no. But if we wish to gain a rational understanding of the world in which we live, and the fundamental processes at work in nature, society and our own way of thinking, then matters appear in quite a different light.

Strangely enough, *everyone* has a "philosophy". A philosophy is a way of looking at the world. We all believe we know how to distinguish right from wrong, good from bad. These are, however, very complicated issues, which have occupied the attention of the greatest minds in history. When confronted with the terrible fact of the existence of events like the fratricidal war in the former Yugoslavia, the re-emergence of mass unemployment, the slaughter in Rwanda, many people will confess that they do not comprehend such things, and will frequently resort to vague references to "human nature". But what is this mysterious human nature that is seen as the source of all our ills and is alleged to be eternally unchangeable? This is a profoundly philosophical question, to which not many would venture a reply, unless they were of a religious cast of mind, in which case they would say that God, in His wisdom, made us like that. Why anyone should worship a Being that played such tricks on His creations is another matter.

Those who stubbornly maintain that they have no philosophy are mistaken. Nature abhors a vacuum. People who lack a coherently worked-out philosophical standpoint will inevitably reflect the ideas and prejudices of the society and the milieu in which they live. That means, in the given context, that their heads will be full of the ideas they imbibe from the newspapers, television, pulpit and schoolroom, which faithfully reflect the interests and morality of existing society.

Most people usually succeed in muddling through life, until some great upheaval compels them to reconsider the kind of ideas and values they grew up with. The crisis of society forces them to question many things they took for granted. At such times, ideas that seemed remote suddenly become strikingly relevant. Anyone who wishes to understand life, not as a meaningless series of accidents or an unthinking routine, must occupy themselves with philosophy, that is, with thought at a higher level than the immediate problems of everyday existence. Only by this means do we raise ourselves to a height where we begin to fulfil our potential as conscious human beings, willing and able to take control of our own destinies.

It is generally understood that anything worthwhile in life requires some effort. The study of philosophy, by its very nature, involves certain difficulties, because it deals with matters far removed from the world of ordinary experience. Even the terminology used presents difficulties because words are used in a way that does not necessarily correspond to the common usage. But the same is true for any specialised subject, from psychoanalysis to engineering.

The second obstacle is more serious. In the 19th century, when Marx and Engels first published their writings on dialectical materialism, they could assume that many of their readers had at least a working knowledge of classical philosophy, including Hegel. Nowadays it is not possible to make such an assumption. Philosophy no longer occupies the place it had before, since the role of speculation about the nature of the universe and life has long since been occupied by the sciences. The possession of powerful radio telescopes and spacecraft renders guesses about the nature and extent of our solar system unnecessary. Even the mysteries of the human soul are being gradually laid bare by the progress of neurobiology and psychology.

The situation is far less satisfactory in the realm of the social sciences, mainly because the desire for accurate knowledge often decreases to the degree that science impinges on the powerful material interests that govern the lives of people. The great advances made by Marx and Engels in the sphere of social and historical analysis and economics fall outside the scope of the present work. Suffice it to point out that, despite the sustained and frequently malicious attacks to which they were subjected from the beginning, the theories of Marxism in the social sphere have been the decisive factor in the development of modern social sciences. As for their vitality, this is testified to by the fact that the attacks not only continue, but tend to increase in intensity as time goes by.

In past ages, the development of science, which has always been closely linked to that of the productive forces, had not reached a sufficiently high level to permit men and women to understand the world in which they lived. In the absence of scientific knowledge, or the material means of obtaining it, they were compelled to rely upon the one instrument they possessed that could help them to make sense of the world, and thus gain power over it—the human mind. The struggle to understand the world was closely identified with humankind's struggle to tear itself away from a merely animal level of existence, to gain mastery over the blind forces of nature, and to become free in the real, not legalistic, sense of the word. This struggle is a red thread running through the whole of human history.

Role of religion

> "Man is quite insane. He wouldn't know how to create a maggot, and he creates Gods by the dozen." (Montaigne.)

> "All mythology overcomes and dominates and shapes the force of nature in the imagination and by the imagination; it therefore vanishes with the advent of real mastery over them." (Marx)

Animals have no religion, and in the past it was said that this constituted the main difference between humans and "brutes". But that is just another way of saying that only humans possess consciousness in the full sense of the word. In recent years, there has been a reaction against the idea of Man as a special and unique Creation. This is undoubtedly correct, in the sense that humans developed from animals, and, in many important respects, remain animals. Not only do we share many of the bodily functions with other animals, but the genetic difference between humans and chimpanzees is less than two per cent. That is a crushing answer to the nonsense of the Creationists.

Recent research with bonobo chimpanzees has proven beyond doubt that the primates closest to humans are capable of a level of mental activity similar in some respects to that of a human child. That is striking proof of the kinship between humans and the highest primates, but here the analogy begins to break down. Despite all the efforts of experimenters, captive bonobos have not been able to speak or fashion a stone tool remotely similar to the simplest implements created by early hominids. The two per cent genetic difference between humans and chimpanzees marks the qualitative leap from the animal to the human. This was accomplished, not by a Creator, but by the development of the brain through manual labour.

The skill to make even the simplest stone tools involves a very high level of mental ability and abstract thought. The ability to select the right sort of stone and reject others; the choice of the correct angle to strike a blow, and the use of precisely the right amount of force—these are highly complicated intellectual actions. They imply a degree of planning and foresight not found in even the most advanced primates. However, the use and manufacture of stone tools was not the result of conscious planning, but was something forced upon man's remote ancestors by necessity. It was not consciousness that created humanity, but the necessary conditions of human existence which led to an enlarged brain, speech and culture, including religion.

The need to understand the world was closely linked to the need to survive. Those early hominids that discovered the use of stone scrapers in butchering dead animals with thick hides obtained a considerable advantage over those who were denied access to this rich supply of fats and proteins. Those who perfected their stone implements and worked out where to find the best materials stood a better chance of survival than those who did not. With the development of technique came the expansion of the mind, and the need to explain the phenomena of nature that governed their lives. Over millions of years, through trial and error, our ancestors began to establish certain relations between things. They began to make *abstractions*, that is, to generalise from experience and practice.

For centuries, the central question of philosophy has been the relation of thinking to being. Most people live their lives quite happily without even considering this problem. They think and act, talk and work, with not the slightest difficulty. Moreover, it would not occur to them to regard as incompatible the two most basic human activities, which are in practice inseparably linked. Even the most elementary action, if we exclude simple biologically determined reactions, demands some thought. To a degree, this is true not only of humans but also of animals, such as a cat lying in wait for a mouse. In man, however, the kind of thought and planning has a qualitatively higher character than any of the mental activities of even the most advanced of the apes.

This fact is inseparably linked to the capacity for abstract thought, which enables humans to go far beyond the immediate situation given to us by our senses. We can envisage situations, not just in the past (animals also have memory, as a dog which cowers at the sight of a stick) but also the future. We can anticipate complex situations, plan and thereby determine the outcome, and to some extent determine our own destinies. Although we do not normally think about it, this represents a colossal conquest, which sets humankind apart from the rest of nature. "What is distinctive of human reasoning," says Professor Gordon Childe, "is that it can go immensely farther from the actual present situation than any other animal's reasoning ever seems to get it." [6] From this capacity springs all the manifold creations of civilisation, culture, art, music, literature, science, philosophy, religion. We also take for granted that all this does not drop from the skies, but is the product of millions of years of development.

The Greek philosopher Anaxagoras (500-428 B.C.), in a brilliant deduction, said that man's mental development depended upon the freeing of the hands. In his important article, *The Part Played by Labour in the Transition from Ape to Man*, Engels showed the exact way in which this transition was achieved. He proved that

---

(6) Gordon Childe, *What Happened in History*, p. 19.

the upright stance, freeing of the hands for labour, the form of the hands, with the opposition of the thumb to the fingers, which allowed for clutching, were the physiological preconditions for tool making, which, in turn, was the main stimulus to the development of the brain. Speech itself, which is inseparable from thought, arose out of the demands of social production, the need to realise complicated functions by means of co-operation. These theories of Engels have been strikingly confirmed by the most recent discoveries of palaeontology, which show that hominid apes appeared in Africa far earlier than previously thought, and that they had brains no bigger than those of a modern chimpanzee. That is to say, the development of the brain came after the production of tools, and as a result of it. Thus, it is not true that "In the beginning was the Word," but as the German poet Goethe proclaimed—*"In the beginning was the Deed."*

The ability to engage in abstract thought is inseparable from language. The celebrated prehistorian Gordon Childe observes: "Reasoning, and all that we call thinking, including the chimpanzee's, must involve mental operations with what psychologists call *images*. A visual image, a mental picture of, say, a banana, is always liable to be a picture of a particular banana in a particular setting. A word on the contrary is, as explained, more general and abstract, having eliminated just those accidental features that give individuality to any real banana. Mental images of words (pictures of the sound or of the muscular movements entailed in uttering it) form very convenient counters for thinking with. Thinking with their aid necessarily possesses just that quality of abstractness and generality that animal thinking seems to lack. Men can think, as well as talk, about the class of objects called 'bananas'; the chimpanzee never gets further than 'that banana in that tube'. In this way the social instrument termed language has contributed to what is grandiloquently described as 'man's emancipation from bondage to the concrete'." [7]

Early humans, after a long period of time, formed the general idea of, say, a plant or an animal. This arose out of the concrete observation of many particular plants and animals. But when we arrive at the general concept "plant", we no longer see before us this or that flower or bush, but that which is common to all of them. We grasp the essence of a plant, its innermost being. Compared with this, the peculiar features of individual plants seem secondary and unstable. What is permanent and universal is contained in the general conception. We can never actually see a plant as such, as opposed to particular flowers and bushes. It is an abstraction of the mind. Yet it is a deeper and truer expression of what is essential to the plant's nature when stripped of all secondary features.

However, the abstractions of early humans were far from having a scientific character. They were tentative explorations, like the impressions of a child—guesses and hypotheses, sometimes incorrect, but always bold and imaginative. To our

(7) Gordon Childe, *What Happened in History*, pp. 19-20.

remote ancestors, the sun was a great being that sometimes warmed them, and sometimes burnt them. The earth was a sleeping giant. Fire was a fierce animal that bit them when they touched it. Early humans experienced thunder and lightning. This must have frightened them, as it still frightens animals and people today. But, unlike animals, humans looked for a general explanation of the phenomenon. Given the lack of any scientific knowledge, the explanation was invariably a supernatural one—some god, hitting an anvil with his hammer. To our eyes, such explanations seem merely amusing, like the naïve explanations of children. Nevertheless, at this period they were extremely important hypotheses—an attempt to find a rational cause for the phenomenon, in which men began to generalise from the immediate experience, and saw something entirely separate from it.

The most characteristic form of early religion is *animism*—the notion that everything, animate or inanimate, has a spirit. We see the same kind of reaction in a child when it smacks a table against which it has banged its head. In the same way, early humans, and certain tribes today, will ask the spirit of a tree to forgive them before cutting it down. Animism belongs to a period when humankind has not yet fully separated itself from the animal world and nature in general. The closeness of humans to the world of animals is attested to by the freshness and beauty of cave art, where horses, deer and bison are depicted with a naturalness which can no longer be captured by the modern artist. It is the childhood of the human race, which has gone beyond recall. We can only imagine the psychology of these distant ancestors of ours. But by combining the discoveries of palaeontology with anthropology, it is possible to reconstruct, at least in outline, the world from which we have emerged.

In his classic anthropological study of the origins of magic and religion, Sir James Frazer writes:

"A savage hardly conceives the distinction commonly drawn by more advanced peoples between the natural and the supernatural. To him the world is to a great extent worked by supernatural agents, that is, by personal beings acting on impulses and motives like his own, liable like him to be moved by appeals to their pity, their hope, and their fears. In a world so conceived he sees no limit to this power of influencing the course of nature to his own advantage. Prayers, promises, or threats may secure him fine weather and an abundant crop from the gods; and if a god should happen, as he sometimes believes, to become incarnate in his own person, then he need appeal to no higher being; he, the savage, possesses in himself all the powers necessary to further his own well-being and that of his fellow men." [8]

The notion that the soul exists separate and apart from the body comes down from the most remote period of savagery. The basis of it is quite clear. When we are asleep, the soul appears to leave the body and roam about in dreams. By extension, the similarity between death and sleep ("death's second self", Shakespeare called it) suggested the idea that the soul could continue to exist after death. Early humans thus concluded that there is something inside them that is separate from their bodies. This is the soul, which commands the body, and can do all kinds of incredible things, even when the body is asleep. They also noticed how words of wisdom issued from the mouths of old people, and concluded that, whereas the body perishes, the soul lives on. To people used to the idea of migration, death was seen as the migration of the soul, which needed food and implements for the journey.

At first these spirits had no fixed abode. They merely wandered about, usually making trouble, which obliged the living to go to extraordinary lengths to appease them. Here we have the origin of religious ceremonies. Eventually, the idea arose that the assistance of these spirits could be enlisted by means of prayer. At this stage, religion (magic), art and science were not differentiated. Lacking the means to gain real power over their environment, early humans attempted to obtain their ends by means of magical intercourse with nature, and thus subject it to their will. The attitude of early humans to their spirit-gods and fetishes was quite practical. Prayers were intended to get results. A man would make an image with his own hands, and prostrate himself before it. But if the desired result were not forthcoming, he would curse it and beat it, in order to extract by violence what he failed to do by entreaty. In this strange world of dreams and ghosts, *this world of religion*, the primitive mind saw every happening as the work of unseen spirits. Every bush and stream was a living creature, friendly or hostile. Every chance event, every dream, pain or sensation, was caused by a spirit. Religious explanations filled the gap left by lack of knowledge of the laws of nature. Even death was not seen as a natural occurrence, but a result of some offence caused to the gods.

For the great majority of the existence of the human race, the minds of men and women have been full of this kind of thing. And not only in what people like to regard as primitive societies. The same kind of superstitious beliefs continue to exist in slightly different guises today. Beneath the thin veneer of civilisation lurk primitive irrational tendencies and ideas which have their roots in a remote past which has been half-forgotten, but is not yet overcome. Nor will they be finally rooted out of human consciousness until men and women establish firm control over their conditions of existence.

Division of labour

Frazer points out that the division between manual and mental labour in primitive society is invariably linked to the formation of a caste of priests, shamans or magicians:

"Social progress, as we know, consists mainly in a successive differentiation of functions, or, in simpler language, a division of labour. The work which in primitive society is done by all alike and by all equally ill, or nearly so, is gradually distributed among different classes of workers and executed more and more perfectly; and so far as the products, material or immaterial, of his specialised labour are shared by all, the whole community benefits by the increasing specialisation. Now magicians or medicine men appear to constitute the oldest artificial or professional class in the evolution of society. For sorcerers are found in every savage tribe known to us; and among the lowest savages, such as the Australian aborigines, they are the only professional class that exists." [9]

The *dualism* which separates soul from body, mind from matter, thinking from doing, received a powerful impulse from the development of the division of labour at a given stage of social evolution. The separation between mental and manual labour is a phenomenon which coincides with the division of society into classes. It marked a great advance in human development. For the first time, a minority of society was freed from the necessity to work to obtain the essentials of existence. The possession of that most precious commodity, leisure, meant that men could devote their lives to the study of the stars. As the German materialist philosopher Ludwig Feuerbach (1804-72) explains, real theoretical science begins with cosmology:

"The animal is sensible only of the beam which immediately affects life; while man perceives the ray, to him physically indifferent, of the remotest star. Man alone has purely intellectual, disinterested joys and passions; the eye of man alone keeps theoretic festivals. The eye which looks into the starry heavens, which gazes at that light, alike useless and harmless, having nothing in common with the earth and its necessities—this eye sees in that light its own nature, its own origin. The eye is heavenly in its nature. Hence man elevates himself above the earth only with the eye; hence theory begins with the contemplation of the heavens. The first philosophers were astronomers." [10]

Although at this early stage this was still mixed up with religion, and the requirements and interests of a priest caste, it also signified the birth of human civilisation. This was already understood by Aristotle, who wrote:

"These theoretical arts, moreover, were evolved in places where men had plenty of free time: mathematics, for example, originated in Egypt, where a priestly caste enjoyed the necessary leisure." [11]

Knowledge is a source of power. In any society in which art, science and government is the monopoly of a few, that minority will use and abuse its power in its own interests. The annual flooding of the Nile was a matter of life and death to the people of Egypt, whose crops depended on it. The ability of the priests in Egypt to predict, on the basis of astronomical observations, when the Nile would flood its banks must have greatly increased their prestige and power over society. The art of

(9) Sir James Frazer, *The Golden Bough*, p. 105.
(10) Ludwig Feuerbach, *The Essence of Christianity*, p. 5.
(11) Aristotle, *Metaphysics*, p. 53.

writing, a most powerful invention, was the jealously guarded secret of the priest caste. As Ilya Prigogine and Isabelle Stengers comment:

"Sumer discovered writing; the Sumerian priests speculated that the future might be written in some hidden way in the events taking place around us in the present. They even systematised this belief, mixing magical and rational elements." [12]

The further development of the division of labour gave rise to an unbridgeable gulf between the intellectual elite and the majority of humankind, condemned to labour with their hands. The intellectual, whether Babylonian priest or modern theoretical physicist, knows only one kind of labour, mental labour. Over the course of millennia, the superiority of the latter over "crude" manual labour becomes deeply ingrained and acquires the force of a prejudice. Language, words and thoughts become endowed with mystical powers. Culture becomes the monopoly of a privileged elite, which jealously guards its secrets, and uses and abuses its position in its own interests.

In ancient times, the intellectual aristocracy made no attempt to conceal its contempt for physical labour. The following extract from an Egyptian text known as *The Satire on the Trades*, written about 2000 B.C. is supposed to consist of a father's exhortation to his son, whom he is sending to the Writing School to train as a scribe:

"I have seen how the belaboured man is belaboured—thou shouldst set thy heart in pursuit of writing. And I have observed how one may be rescued from his duties [sic!]—behold, there is nothing which surpasses writing...

"I have seen the metalworker at his work at the mouth of his furnace. His fingers were somewhat like crocodiles; he stank more than fish-roe...

"The small building contractor carries mud...He is dirtier than vines or pigs from treading under his mud. His clothes are stiff with clay...

"The arrow-maker, he is very miserable as he goes out into the desert [to get flint points]. Greater is that which he gives to his donkey than its work thereafter [is worth]...

"The laundry man launders on the [river] bank, a neighbour of the crocodile...

"Behold, there is no profession free of a boss—except for the scribe: he is the boss...

"Behold, there is no scribe who lacks food from the property of the House of the King—life, prosperity, health!... His father and his mother praise god, he being set upon the way of the living. Behold these things—I [have set them] before thee and thy children's children." [13]

The same attitude was prevalent among the Greeks:

"What are called the mechanical arts," says Xenophon, "carry a social stigma and are rightly dishonoured in our cities, for these arts damage the bodies of those who work in them or who act as overseers, by compelling them to a sedentary life

---

(12) I. Prigogine and I. Stengers, *Order Out of Chaos, Man's New Dialogue with Nature*, p. 4.
(13) Quoted in Margaret Donaldson, *Children's Minds*, p. 84.

and to an indoor life, and, in some cases, to spend the whole day by the fire. This physical degeneration results also in deterioration of the soul. Furthermore, the workers at these trades simply have not got the time to perform the offices of friendship or citizenship. Consequently they are looked upon as bad friends and bad patriots, and in some cities, especially the warlike ones, it is not legal for a citizen to ply a mechanical trade." [14]

The radical divorce between mental and manual labour deepens the illusion that ideas, thoughts and words have an independent existence. This misconception lies at the heart of all religion and philosophical idealism.

It was not god who created man after his own image, but, on the contrary, men and women who created gods in their own image and likeness. Ludwig Feuerbach said that if birds had a religion, their god would have wings. "Religion is a dream, in which our own conceptions and emotions appear to us as separate existences, beings out of ourselves. The religious mind does not distinguish between subjective and objective—it has no doubts; it has the faculty, not of discerning other things than itself, but of seeing its own conceptions out of itself as distinct beings." [15] This was already understood by men like Xenophanes of Colophon (565-c.470 B.C.), who wrote: "Homer and Hesiod have ascribed to the gods every deed that is shameful and dishonourable among men: stealing and adultery and deceiving each other...The Ethiopians make their gods black and snub-nosed, and the Thracians theirs grey-eyed and red-haired...If animals could paint and make things, like men, horses and oxen too would fashion the gods in their own image." [16]

The creation myths, which exist in almost all religions invariably, take their images from real life, for example, the image of the potter who gives form to formless clay. In the opinion of Gordon Childe, the story of the Creation in the first book of *Genesis* reflects the fact that in Mesopotamia the land was indeed separated from the waters "in the Beginning", but not by divine intervention:

"The land on which the great cities of Babylonia were to rise had literally to be created; the prehistoric forerunner of the biblical Erech was built on a sort of platform of reeds, laid criss-cross upon the alluvial mud. The Hebrew book of *Genesis* has familiarised us with much older traditions of the pristine condition of Sumer— a 'chaos' in which the boundaries between water and dry land were still fluid. An essential incident in 'The Creation' is the separation of these elements. Yet it was no god, but the proto-Sumerian themselves who created the land; they dug channels to water the fields and drain the marsh; they built dykes and mounded platforms to protect men and cattle from the waters and raise them above the flood; they made the first clearings in the reed brakes and explored the channels between them. The tenacity with which the memory of this struggle persisted in tradition is some meas-

(14) Occonomicus, iv, 203, quoted in B. Farrington, *Greek Science*, pp. 28-9.
(15) Feuerbach, op. cit., pp. 204-5.
(16) Quoted in A. R. Burn, *Pelican History of Greece*, p. 132.

ure of the exertion imposed upon the ancient Sumerians. Their reward was an assured supply of nourishing dates, a bounteous harvest from the fields they had drained, and permanent pastures for flocks and herds." [17]

Man's earliest attempts to explain the world and his place in it were mixed up with mythology. The Babylonians believed that the god Marduk created Order out of Chaos, separating the land from the water, heaven from earth. The biblical creation myth was taken from the Babylonians by the Jews, and later passed into the culture of Christianity. The true history of scientific thought commences when men and women learn to dispense with mythology, and attempt to obtain a rational understanding of nature, without the intervention of the gods. From that moment, the real struggle for the emancipation of humanity from material and spiritual bondage begins.

The advent of philosophy represents a genuine revolution in human thought. Like so much of modern civilisation, we owe it to the ancient Greeks. Although important advances were also made by the Indians and Chinese, and later the Arabs, it was the Greeks who developed philosophy and science to its highest point prior to the Renaissance. The history of Greek thought in the four hundred year period, from the middle of the 7th century B.C., constitutes one of the most imposing pages in the annals of human history.

Materialism and idealism

The whole history of philosophy from the Greeks down to the present day consists of a struggle between two diametrically opposed schools of thought—materialism and idealism. Here we come across a perfect example of how the terms used in philosophy differ fundamentally from everyday language.

When we refer to someone as an "idealist" we normally have in mind a person of high ideals and spotless morality. A materialist, on the contrary, is viewed as an unprincipled so-and-so, a money-grubbing, self-centred individual with gross appetites for food and other things—in short, a thoroughly undesirable character.

This has nothing whatever to do with philosophical materialism and idealism. In a philosophical sense, idealism sets out from the view that the world is only a reflection of ideas, mind, spirit, or more correctly the Idea, which existed before the physical world. The crude material things we know through our senses are, according to this school, only imperfect *copies* of this perfect Idea. The most consistent proponent of this philosophy in Antiquity was Plato. However, he did not invent idealism, which existed earlier.

The Pythagoreans believed that the essence of all things was Number (a view apparently shared by some modern mathematicians). The Pythagoreans displayed

(17) G. Childe, *Man Makes Himself*, pp. 107-8.

contempt towards the material world in general and the human body in particular which they saw as a prison where the soul was trapped. This is strikingly reminiscent of the outlook of mediaeval monks. Indeed, it is probable that the Church took many of its ideas from the Pythagoreans, Platonists and Neo-Platonists. This is not surprising. All religions necessarily set out from an idealist view of the world. The difference is that religion appeals to the emotions, and claims to provide a mystical, intuitive understanding of the world ("Revelation"), while most idealist philosophers try to present logical arguments for their theories.

At bottom, however, the roots of all forms of idealism are religious and mystical. The disdain for the "crude material world" and the elevation of the "Ideal" flow directly from the phenomena we have just considered in relation to religion. It is no accident that Platonist idealism developed in Athens when the system of slavery was at its height. Manual labour at that time was seen, in a very literal sense, as a *mark of slavery*. The only labour worthy of respect was intellectual labour. Essentially, philosophical idealism is a product of the extreme division between mental and manual labour, which has existed from the dawn of written history down to the present day.

The history of Western philosophy, however, begins not with idealism but with materialism. This asserts precisely the opposite: that the material world, known to us and explored by science, is real; that the only real world is the material one; that thoughts, ideas and sensations are the product of matter organised in a certain way (a nervous system and a brain); that thought cannot derive its categories from itself, but only from the objective world which makes itself known to us through our senses.

The earliest Greek philosophers were known as "hylozoists" (from the Greek, meaning "those who believe that matter is alive"). Here we have a long line of heroes who pioneered the development of thought. The Greeks discovered that the world was round, long before Christopher Columbus. They explained that humans had evolved from fishes long before Charles Darwin. They made extraordinary discoveries in mathematics, especially geometry, which were not greatly improved upon for one and a half millennia. They invented mechanics and even built a steam engine. What was startlingly new about this way of looking at the world was that it was *not religious*. In complete contrast to the Egyptians and Babylonians, from whom they had learnt a lot, the Greek thinkers did not resort to gods and goddesses to explain natural phenomena. For the first time, men and women sought to explain the workings of nature purely in terms of nature. This was one of the greatest turning points in the entire history of human thought. True science starts here.

Aristotle, the greatest of the Ancient philosophers, can be considered a materialist, although he was not so consistent as the early hylozoists. He made a series of important scientific discoveries, which laid the basis for the great achievements of the Alexandrine period of Greek science.

The Middle Ages, which followed the collapse of Antiquity, were a desert in which scientific thought languished for centuries. Not accidentally, this was a period dominated by the Church. Idealism was the only philosophy permitted, either as a caricature of Plato or an even worse distortion of Aristotle.

Science re-emerged triumphantly in the period of the Renaissance. It was forced to wage a fierce battle against the influence of religion (not only Catholic, but also Protestant, by the way). Many martyrs paid the price of scientific freedom with their lives. Giordano Bruno (1548-1600) was burnt at the stake. Galileo Galilei (1564-1642) was twice put on trial by the Inquisition, and forced to renounce his views under threat of torture.

The predominant philosophical trend of the Renaissance was materialism. In England, this took the form of *empiricism*, the school of thought that states that all knowledge is derived from the senses. The pioneers of this school were Francis Bacon (1561-1626), Thomas Hobbes (1588-1679) and John Locke (1632-1704). The materialist school passed from England to France where it acquired a revolutionary content. In the hands of Diderot, Rousseau, Holbach and Helvetius, philosophy became an instrument for criticising all existing society. These great thinkers prepared the way for the revolutionary overthrow of the feudal monarchy in 1789-93.

The new philosophical views stimulated the development of science, encouraging experiment and observation. The 18th century saw a great advance in science, especially mechanics. But this fact had a negative as well as a positive side. The old materialism of the 18th century was narrow and rigid, reflecting the limited development of science itself. Newton expressed the limitations of empiricism with his celebrated phrase "I make no hypotheses". This one-sided mechanical outlook ultimately proved fatal to the old materialism. Paradoxically, the great advances in philosophy after 1700 were made by idealist philosophers.

Under the impact of the French revolution, the German idealist Immanuel Kant (1724-1804) subjected all previous philosophy to a thorough criticism. Kant made important discoveries not only in philosophy and logic but in science. His nebular hypothesis of the origins of the solar system (later given a mathematical basis by Laplace) is now generally accepted as correct. In the field of philosophy, Kant's masterpiece *The Critique of Pure Reason* was the first work to analyse the forms of logic which had remained virtually unchanged since they were first developed by Aristotle. Kant showed the contradictions implicit in many of the most fundamental propositions of philosophy. However, he failed to resolve these contradictions ("Antinomies"), and finally drew the conclusion that real knowledge of the world was impossible. While we can know appearances, we can never know how things are "in themselves".

This idea was not new. It is a theme that has recurred many times in philosophy, and is generally identified with what we call *subjective idealism*. This was put forward before Kant by the Irish bishop and philosopher George Berkeley and the last of the classical English empiricists, David Hume. The basic argument can be summed up as follows: "I interpret the world through my senses. Therefore, all that I know to exist are my sense-impressions. Can I, for example, assert that this apple exists? No. All I can say is that I see it, I feel it, I smell it, I taste it. Therefore, I cannot really say that the material world exists at all." The logic of subjective idealism is that, if I close my eyes, the world ceases to exist. Ultimately, it leads to solipsism (from the Latin "solo ipsus"—"I alone"), the idea that only I exist.

These ideas may seem nonsensical to us, but they have proved strangely persistent. In one way or another, the prejudices of subjective idealism have penetrated not only philosophy but also science for a great part of the 20th century. We shall deal more specifically with this trend later on.

The greatest breakthrough came in the first decades of the 19th century with Georg Wilhelm Friedrich Hegel (1770-1831). Hegel was a German idealist, a man of towering intellect, who effectively summed up in his writings the whole history of philosophy.

Hegel showed that the only way to overcome the "Antinomies" of Kant was to accept that contradictions actually existed, not only in thought, but in the real world. As an objective idealist, Hegel had no time for the subjective idealist argument that the human mind cannot know the real world. The forms of thought must reflect the objective world as closely as possible. The process of knowledge consists of penetrating ever more deeply into this reality, proceeding from the abstract to the concrete, from the known to the unknown, from the particular to the universal.

The dialectical method of thinking had played a great role in Antiquity, particularly in the naïve but brilliant aphorisms of Heraclitus (c.500 B.C.), but also in Aristotle and others. It was abandoned in the Middle Ages, when the Church turned Aristotle's formal logic into a lifeless and rigid dogma, and did not re-appear until Kant returned it to a place of honour. However, in Kant the dialectic did not receive an adequate development. It fell to Hegel to bring the science of dialectical thinking to its highest point of development.

Hegel's greatness is shown by the fact that he alone was prepared to challenge the dominant philosophy of mechanism. The dialectical philosophy of Hegel deals with processes, not isolated events. It deals with things in their life, not their death, in their inter-relations, not isolated, one after the other. This is a startlingly modern and scientific way of looking at the world. Indeed, in many aspects Hegel was far in advance of his time. Yet, despite its many brilliant insights, Hegel's philosophy was ultimately unsatisfactory. Its principal defect was precisely Hegel's idealist standpoint, which prevented him from applying the dialectical method to the real world in a consistently scientific way. Instead of the material world we have the world of the Absolute Idea, where real things, processes and people are replaced by insubstantial shadows. In the words of Frederick Engels, the Hegelian dialectic was the most colossal miscarriage in the whole history of philosophy. Correct ideas are here seen standing on their head. In order to put dialectics on a sound foundation, it was necessary to turn Hegel upside down, to transform idealist dialectics into dialectical materialism. This was the great achievement of Karl Marx and Frederick Engels. Our study begins with a brief account of the basic laws of materialist dialectics worked out by them.

3. Dialectical materialism

"Παντα χωρει, ουδει μενει."
"Everything flows and nothing stays."
(Heraclitus)

What is dialectics?

Dialectics is a method of thinking and interpreting the world of both nature and society. It is a way of looking at the universe, which sets out from the axiom that everything is in a constant state of change and flux. But not only that. Dialectics explains that change and motion involve contradiction and can only take place through contradictions. So instead of a smooth, uninterrupted line of progress, we have a line that is interrupted by sudden and explosive periods in which slow, accumulated changes (quantitative change) undergo a rapid acceleration, in which quantity is transformed into quality. Dialectics is the *logic of contradiction.*

The laws of dialectics were already worked out in detail by Hegel, in whose writings, however, they appear in a mystified, idealist form. It was Marx and Engels who first gave dialectics a scientific, that is to say, materialist basis. "Hegel wrote before Darwin and before Marx," wrote Trotsky. "Thanks to the powerful impulse given to thought by the French Revolution, Hegel anticipated the general movement of science. But because it was only an *anticipation*, although by a genius, it received from Hegel an idealistic character. Hegel operated with ideological shadows as the ultimate reality. Marx demonstrated that the movement of these ideological shadows reflected nothing but the movement of material bodies." [18]

In the writings of Hegel there are many striking examples of the law of dialectics drawn from history and nature. But Hegel's idealism necessarily gave his dialectics a highly abstract, and arbitrary character. In order to make dialectics serve the "Absolute Idea", Hegel was forced to impose a schema upon nature and society, in flat contradiction to the dialectical method itself, which demands that we derive the laws of a given phenomenon from a scrupulously objective study of the

(18) Trotsky, *In Defence of Marxism*, p. 66.

subject matter as Marx did in his *Capital*. Thus, far from being a mere regurgitation of Hegel's idealist dialectic arbitrarily foisted on history and society as his critics often assert, Marx's method was precisely the opposite. As he himself explains:

"My dialectic method," wrote Marx, "is not only different from the Hegelian, but is its direct opposite. To Hegel, the life-process of the human brain, i.e., the process of thinking, which, under the name of 'the Idea', he even transforms into an independent subject, is the demiurgos of the real world, and the real world is only the external, phenomenal form of 'the Idea'. With me, on the contrary, the ideal is nothing else than the material world reflected by the human mind, and translated into forms of thought." [19]

When we first contemplate the world around us, we see an immense and amazingly complex series of phenomena, an intricate web of seemingly endless change, cause and effect, action and reaction. The motive force of scientific investigation is the desire to obtain a rational insight into this bewildering labyrinth, to understand it in order to conquer it. We look for laws that can separate the general from the particular, the accidental from the necessary, and enable us to understand the forces that give rise to the phenomena which confront us.

In the words of the English physicist and philosopher David Bohm:

"In nature nothing remains constant. Everything is in a perpetual state of transformation, motion, and change. However, we discover that nothing simply surges up out of nothing without having antecedents that existed before. Likewise, nothing ever disappears without a trace, in the sense that it gives rise to absolutely nothing existing at later times. This general characteristic of the world can be expressed in terms of a principle which summarises an enormous domain of different kinds of experience and which has never yet been contradicted in any observation or experiment, scientific or otherwise; namely, everything comes from other things and gives rise to other things." [20]

The fundamental proposition of dialectics is that everything is in a constant process of change, motion and development. Even when it appears to us that nothing is happening, in reality, matter is always changing. Molecules, atoms and sub-atomic particles are constantly changing place, always on the move. Dialectics is thus an essentially dynamic interpretation of the phenomena and processes that occur at all levels of both organic and inorganic matter.

The American physicist Richard P. Feynman (1918-1988) notes: "To our eyes, our crude eyes, nothing is changing, but if we could see it a billion times magnified, we would see that from its own point of view it is always changing: molecules are leaving the surface, molecules are coming back." [21]

---

(19) Marx, *Capital*, Vol. 1, p. 19.
(20) David Bohm, *Causality and Chance in Modern Physics*, p. 1.
(21) R.P. Feynman, *Lectures on Physics*, chapter 1, p. 8.

So fundamental is this idea to dialectics that Marx and Engels considered motion to be the most basic characteristic of matter. As in so many cases, this dialectical notion was already anticipated by Aristotle, who wrote: "Therefore... the primary and proper meaning of 'nature' is the essence of things which have in themselves...the principle of motion." [22] This is not the mechanical conception of motion as something imparted to an inert mass by an external "force", but an entirely different notion of matter as self-moving. For them, matter and motion (energy) were one and the same thing, two ways of expressing the same idea. This idea was brilliantly confirmed by Albert Einstein's theory of the equivalence of mass and energy. This is how Engels expresses it:

"Motion in the most general sense, conceived as the mode of existence, the inherent attribute, of matter, comprehends all changes and processes occurring in the universe, from mere change of place right up to thinking. The investigation of the nature of motion had as a matter of course to start from the lowest, simplest forms of this motion and to learn to grasp these before it could achieve anything in the way of explanation of the higher and more complicated forms." [23]

'Everything flows'

Everything is in a constant state of motion, from neutrinos to super-clusters. The earth itself is constantly moving, rotating around the sun once a year, and rotating on its own axis once a day. The sun, in turn, revolves on its axis once in 26 days and, together with all the other stars in our galaxy, travels once around the galaxy in 230 million years. It is probable that still larger structures (clusters of galaxies) also have some kind of overall rotational motion. This seems to be a characteristic of matter right down to the atomic level, where the atoms that make up molecules rotate about each other at varying rates. Inside the atom, electrons rotate around the nucleus at enormous speeds.

The electron possesses a quality known as intrinsic spin. It is as if it rotates around its own axis at a fixed rate and cannot be stopped or changed except by destroying the electron as such. If the spin of the electron is increased, it so drastically alters its properties that it results in a qualitative change, producing a completely different particle. The quantity known as angular momentum—the combined measure of the mass, size and speed of the rotating system—is used to measure the spin of elementary particles. The principle of spin quantization is fundamental at the subatomic level but also exists in the macroscopic world. However, its effect is so infinitesimal that it can be taken for granted. The world of subatomic particles is in a state of constant movement and ferment, in which nothing is ever the same as itself. Particles are constantly changing into their opposites, so that it is

(22) Aristotle, *Metaphysics*, p. 9.
(23) Engels, *Dialectics of Nature*, p. 92.

impossible even to assert their identity at any given moment of time. Neutrons change into protons, and protons into neutrons in a ceaseless exchange of identity.

Engels defines dialectics as "the science of the general laws of motion and development of nature, human society and thought." In *Anti-Dühring* and *The Dialectics of Nature*, Engels gives an account of the laws of dialectics, beginning with the three most fundamental ones:

1) The law of the transformation of quantity into quality and vice versa;
2) The law of the interpenetration of opposites, and
3) The law of the negation of the negation.

At first sight, such a claim may seem excessively ambitious. Is it really possible to work out laws that have such a general application? Can there be an underlying pattern that repeats itself in the workings, not only of society and thought, but of nature itself? Despite all such objections, it is becoming increasingly clear that such patterns do indeed exist and constantly re-appear at all kinds of levels, in all kinds of ways. And there are an increasing number of examples, drawn from fields as diverse as subatomic particles to population studies, which lend increasing weight to the theory of dialectical materialism.

The essential point of dialectical thought is not that it is based on the idea of change and motion but that it views motion and change as phenomena based upon contradiction. Whereas traditional formal logic seeks to banish contradiction, dialectical thought embraces it. Contradiction is an essential feature of all being. It lies at the heart of matter itself. It is the source of all motion, change, life and development. The dialectical law that expresses this idea is the law of the unity and interpenetration of opposites. The third law of dialectics, the negation of the negation, expresses the notion of development. Instead of a closed circle, where processes continually repeat themselves, this law points out that movement through successive contradictions actually leads to development, from simple to complex, from lower to higher. Processes do not repeat themselves exactly in the same way, despite appearances to the contrary. These, in a very schematic outline, are the three most fundamental dialectical laws. Arising from them there are a whole series of additional propositions, involving the relation between whole and part, form and content, finite and infinite, attraction and repulsion and so on. These we shall attempt to deal with. Let us begin with quantity and quality.

Quantity and quality

The law of the transformation of quantity into quality has an extremely wide range of applications, from the smallest particles of matter at the subatomic level to the largest phenomena known to man. It can be seen in all kinds of manifestations, and at many levels. Yet this very important law has yet to receive the recognition it deserves. This dialectical law forces itself to our attention at every turn. The transformation of quantity into quality was already known to the Megaran Greeks, who used it to demonstrate certain paradoxes, sometimes in the form of jokes. For example, the "bald head" and the "heap of grain"—does one hair less mean a bald head, or one grain of corn a heap? The answer is no. Nor one more? The answer is still no. The question is then repeated until there is a heap of corn and a bald head. We are faced with the contradiction that the individual small changes, which are powerless to effect a qualitative change, at a certain point do exactly that: quantity changes into quality.

The idea that, under certain conditions, even small things can cause big changes finds its expression in all kinds of sayings and proverbs. For instance: "The straw that broke the camel's back", "many hands make light work", "constant dripping wears away the stone", and so on. In many ways, the law of the transformation of quantity into quality has penetrated the popular consciousness, as Trotsky wittily pointed out:

"Every individual is a dialectician to some extent or other, in most cases, unconsciously. A housewife knows that a certain amount of salt flavours soup agreeably, but that added salt makes the soup unpalatable. Consequently, an illiterate peasant woman guides herself in cooking soup by the Hegelian law of the transformation of quantity into quality. Similar examples from daily life could be cited without end. Even animals arrive at their practical conclusions not only on the basis of the Aristotelian syllogism but also on the basis of the Hegelian dialectic. Thus a fox is aware that quadrupeds and birds are nutritious and tasty. On sighting a hare, a rabbit, or a hen, a fox concludes: this particular creature belongs to the tasty and nutritive type, and—chases after the prey. We have here a complete syllogism, although the fox, we may suppose, never read Aristotle. When the same fox, however, encounters the first animal that exceeds it in size, for example, a wolf, it quickly concludes that quantity passes into quality, and turns to flee. Clearly, the legs of a fox are equipped with Hegelian tendencies, even if not fully conscious ones.

"All this demonstrates, in passing, that our methods of thought, both formal logic and the dialectic, are not arbitrary constructions of our reason but rather expressions of the actual inter-relationships in nature itself. In this sense, the universe throughout is permeated with 'unconscious' dialectics. But nature did not stop there. No little development occurred before nature's inner relationships were converted into the language of the consciousness of foxes and men, and man was then enabled to generalise these forms of consciousness and transform them into logical (dialectical) categories, thus creating the possibility for probing more deeply into the world about us." [24]

Despite the apparently trivial character of these examples, they do reveal a profound truth about the way the world works. Take the example of the heap of corn.

24 Trotsky, *In Defence of Marxism*, pp. 106-7.

Some of the most recent investigations related to chaos theory have centred on the critical point where a series of small variations produces a massive change of state. (In the modern terminology, this is called "the edge of chaos".) The work of the Danish-born physicist Per Bak (1947-2003) and others on "self-organised criticality" used precisely the example of a sand-heap to illustrate profound processes which occur at many levels of nature and which correspond precisely to the law of the transformation of quantity into quality.

One of the examples of this is that of a pile of sand—a precise analogy with the heap of grain of the Megarans. We drop grains of sand one by one on a flat surface. The experiment has been conducted many times, both with real sand heaped on tables, and in computer simulations. For a time they will just pile up on top of each other until they make a little pyramid. Once this point is reached, any additional grains will either find a resting place on the pile, or will unbalance one side of it just enough to cause some of the other grains to fall in an avalanche. Depending on how the other grains are poised, the avalanche could be very small, or devastating, dragging a large number of grains with it. When the pile reaches this critical point, even a single grain would be capable of dramatically affecting all around it. This seemingly trivial example provides an excellent "edge-of-chaos model", with a wide range of applications, from earthquakes to evolution; from stock exchange crises to wars.

The pile of sand grows bigger, with excess sand slipping from the sides. When all the excess sand has fallen off, the resulting sand-pile is said to be "self-organised." In other words, no one has consciously shaped it in this way. It "organises itself", according to its own inherent laws, until it reaches a state of *criticality*, in which the sand grains on its surface are barely stable. In this critical condition, even the addition of a single grain of sand can cause unpredictable results. It may just cause a further tiny shift, or it may trigger a chain reaction resulting in a catastrophic landslide and the destruction of the pile.

According to Per Bak, the phenomenon can be given a mathematical expression, according to which the average frequency of a given size of avalanche is inversely proportional to some power of its size. He also points out that this "power-law" behaviour is extremely common in nature, as in the critical mass of plutonium, at which the chain reaction is on the point of running away into a nuclear explosion. At the sub-critical level, the chain reaction within the plutonium mass will die out, whereas a supercritical mass will explode. A similar phenomenon can be seen in earthquakes, where the rocks on two sides of a fault in the earth's crust reach a point where they are ready to slip past each other. The fault experiences a series of little slips and bigger slips, which maintain the tension at the critical point for some time until it finally collapses into an earthquake.

Although the proponents of chaos theory seem unaware of it, these examples are all cases of the law of the transformation of quantity into quality. Hegel invented the nodal line of measure relations, in which small quantitative changes at a certain point give rise to a qualitative leap. The example is often given of water, which boils at 100°C at normal atmospheric pressure. As the temperature nears boiling point, the increase in heat does not immediately cause the water molecules to fly apart. Until it reaches boiling point, the water keeps its volume. It remains water, because of the attraction of the molecules for each other. However, the steady change in temperature has the effect of increasing the motion of the molecules. The volume between the atoms is gradually increased, to the point where the force of attraction is insufficient to hold the molecules together. At precisely 100°C, any increase in heat energy will cause the molecules to fly apart, producing steam.

The same process can be seen in reverse. When water is cooled from 100°C to 0°C, it does not gradually congeal, passing from a paste, through a jelly, to a solid state. The motion of the atoms is gradually slowed as heat energy is removed until, at 0°C, a critical point is reached, at which the molecules will lock into a certain pattern, which is ice. The qualitative difference between a solid and a liquid can be readily understood by anyone. Water can be used for certain purposes, like washing and quenching one's thirst, which ice cannot. Technically speaking, the difference is that, in a solid, the atoms are arranged in a crystalline array. They do not have a random position at long distances, so that the position of the atoms on one side of the crystal is determined by the atoms on the other side. That is why we can move our hand freely through water, whereas ice is rigid and offers resistance. Here we are describing a qualitative change, a change of state, which arises from an accumulation of quantitative changes. A water molecule is a relatively simple affair, one oxygen atom attached to two hydrogen atoms governed by well-understood equations of atomic physics. However, when a very large number of these molecules are combined, they acquire a property which none of them possesses in isolation—liquidity. Such a property is not implied in the equations. In the language of complexity, liquidity is an "emergent" phenomenon.

As Mitchell Waldrop says: "Cool those liquid water molecules down a bit, for example, and at 32°F they will suddenly quit tumbling over one another at random. Instead they will undergo a 'phase transition', locking themselves into the orderly crystalline array known as ice. Or if you were to go the other direction and heat the liquid, those same tumbling water molecules will suddenly fly apart and undergo a phase transition into water vapour. Neither phase transition would have any meaning for one molecule alone." [25]

The phrase "phase transition" is neither more nor less than a qualitative leap. Similar processes can be seen in phenomena as varied as the weather, DNA molecules, and the mind itself. This quality of liquidity is well known on the basis of our daily experience. In physics, too, the behaviour of liquids is well understood and

(25) M. Mitchell Waldrop, *Complexity, The Emerging Science at the Edge of Order and Chaos*, p. 82.

perfectly predictable—up to a point. The laws of motion of fluids (gases and liquids) clearly distinguish between smooth *laminar* flow, which is well defined and predictable, and *turbulent* flow, which can be expressed, at best, approximately. The movement of water around a pier in a river can be accurately predicted from the normal equations for fluids, provided it is moving slowly. Even if we increase the speed of the flow, causing eddies and vortices, we can still predict their behaviour. But if the speed is increased beyond a certain point, it becomes impossible to predict where the eddies will form, or, indeed, to say anything about the behaviour of the water at all. It has become *chaotic*.

Mendeleyev's periodic table

The existence of qualitative changes in matter was known long before human beings began to think about science, but it was not really understood until the advent of atomic theory. Earlier, physics took the changes of state from solid to liquid to gas as something that occurred, without knowing exactly why. Only now are these phenomena being properly understood.

The science of chemistry made great strides forward in the 19th century. A large number of elements were discovered. But, rather like the confused situation that exists in particle physics today, chaos reigned. Order was established by the great Russian scientist Dimitri Ivanovich Mendeleyev (1834-1907) who, in 1869, in collaboration with the German chemist Julius Lothar Meyer (1830-95), worked out *the periodic table of the elements*, so called because it showed the periodic recurrence of similar chemical properties.

The existence of atomic weight was discovered in 1862 by Stanislao Cannizzaro (1826-1910). But Mendeleyev's genius consisted in the fact that he did not approach the elements from a purely quantitative standpoint, that is, he did not see the relation between the different atoms just in terms of weight. Had he done so, he would never have made the breakthrough he did. From the purely quantitative standpoint, for instance, the element tellurium (atomic weight = 127.61) ought to have come after iodine (atomic weight = 126.91) in the periodic table, yet Mendeleyev placed it before iodine, under selenium, to which it is more similar, and placed iodine under the related element, bromine. Mendeleyev's method was vindicated in the 20th century, when the investigation of X-rays proved that his arrangement was the correct one. The new atomic number for tellurium was put at 52, while that of iodine is 53.

The whole of Mendeleyev's periodic table is based on the law of quantity and quality, deducing qualitative differences in the elements from quantitative differences in atomic weights. This was recognised by Engels at the time:

"Finally, the Hegelian law is valid not only for compound substances but also for the chemical elements themselves. We now know that 'the chemical properties of the elements are a periodic function of their atomic weights,' … and that, therefore, their quality is determined by the quantity of their atomic weight. And the test of this has been brilliantly carried out. Mendeleyev proved that various gaps occur in the series of related elements arranged according to atomic weights indicating that here new elements remain to be discovered. He described in advance the general chemical properties of one of these unknown elements, which he termed eka-aluminium, because it follows after aluminium in the series beginning with the latter, and he predicted its approximate specific and atomic weight as well as its atomic volume. A few years later, Lecoq de Boisbaudran actually discovered this element, and Mendeleyev's predictions fitted with only very slight discrepancies. Eka-aluminium was realised in gallium... By means of the—unconscious—application of Hegel's law of the transformation of quantity into quality, Mendeleyev achieved a scientific feat which it is not too bold to put on a par with that of Leverrier in calculating the orbit of the until then unknown planet Neptune." [26]

Chemistry involves changes of both a quantitative and qualitative character, both changes of degree and of state. This can clearly be seen in the change of state from gas to liquid or solid, which is usually related to variations of temperature and pressure. In *Anti-Dühring*, Engels gives a series of examples of how, in chemistry, the simple quantitative addition of elements creates qualitatively different bodies. Since Engels' time the naming system used in chemistry has been changed. However, the change of quantity into quality is accurately expressed in the following example:

"CH_2O_2 — formic acid   boiling point $100°$ melting point $1°$
$C_2H_4O_2$ — acetic acid   "   " $118°$ "   " $17°$
$C_3H_6O_2$ — propionic acid   "   " $140°$ "   "   —
$C_4H_8O_2$ — butyric acid   "   " $162°$ "   "   —
$C_5H_{10}O_2$ — valerianic acid   "   " $175°$ "   "   —

and so on to $C_{30}H_{60}O_2$, melissic acid, which melts only at $80°$ and has no boiling point at all, because it does not evaporate without disintegrating." [27]

The study of gases and vapours constitutes a special branch of chemistry. The great British pioneer of chemistry, Michael Faraday (1791-1867), thought that it was impossible to liquefy six gases, which he called permanent gases—hydrogen, oxygen, nitrogen, carbon monoxide, nitric oxide and methane. But in 1877, the Swiss chemist Raoul Pierre Pictet (1846-1929) managed to liquefy oxygen at a temperature of $-140°C$ under a pressure of 500 atmospheres. Later, nitrogen, oxygen and carbon monoxide were all liquefied at still lower temperatures. In 1900, hydrogen was liquefied at $-240°$ and, at a lower temperature, it even solidified. Finally, the most difficult challenge of all, the liquefaction of helium, was achieved at $-255°$. These discoveries had important practical applications. Liquid hydrogen and oxy-

(26) Engels, *Dialectics of Nature*, pp. 90-1.
(27) Engels, *Anti-Dühring*, p. 162.

gen are now used in large amounts in rockets. The transformation of quantity into quality is shown by the fact that changes of temperature bring about important changes of properties. This is the key to the phenomenon of superconductivity. Through super-cooling, certain substances, beginning with mercury, were shown to offer no resistance to electric currents.

The study of extremely low temperatures was developed in the mid-19th century by the mathematician and physicist William Thomson (later Lord Kelvin) (1824-1907), who established the concept of absolute zero (the lowest possible temperature), which he calculated to be –273°C. At this temperature, he thought, the energy of molecules would sink to zero. This temperature is sometimes referred to as zero Kelvin, and used as the basis for a scale to measure very low temperatures. However, even at absolute zero, motion is not done away with altogether. There is still some energy, which cannot be removed. For practical purposes, energy is said to be zero, but that is not actually the case. Matter and motion, as Engels pointed out, are absolutely inseparable—even at "absolute zero".

Nowadays, incredibly low temperatures are routinely achieved, and play an important role in the production of superconductors. Mercury becomes superconductive at exactly 4.12° Kelvin (K); lead at 7.22°K; tin at 3.73°K; aluminium at 1.20°K; uranium at 0.8°K, titanium at 0.53°K. Some 1,400 elements and alloys display this quality. Liquid hydrogen boils at 20.4°K. Helium is the only known substance which cannot be frozen even at absolute zero. It is the only substance that possesses the phenomenon known as superfluidity. Here too changes of temperature produce qualitative leaps. At 2.2°K, the behaviour of helium undergoes so fundamental a change that it is known as helium-2 to distinguish it from liquid helium above this temperature (helium-1). Using new techniques, temperatures as low as 0.000001°K have been reached, though it is thought that absolute zero is unattainable.

So far, we have concentrated on chemical changes in the laboratory and in industry. But it should not be forgotten that these changes take place on a much vaster scale in nature. The chemical composition of coal and diamonds, barring impurities, is the same—carbon. The difference is the result of colossal pressure, which, at a certain point transforms the contents of the coal-sack into a duchess' necklace. To convert common graphite into diamonds would require the pressure of at least 10,000 atmospheres over a very long period of time. This process occurs naturally beneath the earth's surface. In 1955, the big monopoly GEC succeeded in changing graphite into diamonds with a temperature of 2,500°C, and a pressure of 100,000 atmospheres. The same result was obtained in 1962, with a temperature of 5,000°C, and a pressure of 200,000 atmospheres, which turned graphite into diamond directly, without the aid of a catalyst. These are synthetic diamonds, which are not used to adorn the necks of duchesses, but for far more productive purposes—as cutting tools in industry.

Phase transitions

A most important field of investigation concerns what are known as *phase transitions*—the critical point where matter changes from solid to liquid or from liquid to vapour; or the change from nonmagnet to magnet; or from conductor to superconductor. All these processes are different, yet it has now been established beyond doubt that they are similar, so much so that the mathematics applied to one of these experiments can be applied to many others. This is a very clear example of a qualitative leap, as the following passage from James Gleick (1954-) shows:

"Like so much of chaos itself, phase transitions involve a kind of macroscopic behaviour that seems hard to predict by looking at the microscopic details. When a solid is heated, its molecules vibrate with the added energy. They push outward against their bonds and force the substance to expand. The more heat, the more expansion. Yet at a certain temperature and pressure, the change becomes sudden and discontinuous. A rope has been stretching; now it breaks. Crystalline form dissolves, and the molecules slide away from one another. They obey fluid laws that could not have been inferred from any aspect of the solid. The average atomic energy has barely changed, but the material—now a liquid, or a magnet, or a superconductor—has entered a new realm." [28]

Newton's dynamics were quite sufficient to explain large-scale phenomena but broke down for systems of atomic dimensions. Indeed, classical mechanics are still valid for most operations that do not involve very high speeds or the processes that take place at the subatomic level. Quantum mechanics will be dealt with in detail in another section. It represented a qualitative leap in science. Its relation to classical mechanics is similar to that between higher and lower mathematics and that between dialectics and formal logic. It can explain facts which classical mechanics could not, such as radioactive transformation, the transformation of matter into energy. It gave rise to new branches of science—theoretical chemistry, capable of solving previously insoluble problems. The theory of metallic magnetism underwent a fundamental change, making possible brilliant discoveries in the flow of electricity through metals. A whole series of theoretical difficulties were eliminated, once the new standpoint was accepted. But for a long time it met with a stubborn resistance, precisely because its results clashed head-on with the traditional mode of thinking and the laws of formal logic.

Modern physics furnishes a wealth of examples of the laws of dialectics, starting with quantity and quality. Take, for instance, the relation between the different kinds of electromagnetic wave and their frequencies, that is, the speed with which they pulsate. The work of Scottish physicist James Clerk Maxwell (1831-79), which Engels was very interested in, showed that electromagnetic waves and light waves were of the same kind. Quantum mechanics later showed that the situation is much

(28) J. Gleick, *Chaos, Making a New Science*, p. 127.

more complex and contradictory, but at lower frequencies, the wave theory holds good.

The properties of different waves are determined by the number of oscillations per second. The difference is in the frequency of the waves, the speed with which they pulsate, the number of vibrations per second. That is to say, quantitative changes give rise to different kinds of wave signals. Translated into colours, red light indicates light waves of low frequency. An increased rate of vibration turns the colour to orange-yellow, then to violet, then to the invisible ultraviolet and X-rays and finally to gamma rays. If we reverse the process, at the lower end, we go from infrared and heat rays to radio waves. Thus, the same phenomenon manifests itself differently, in accordance with a higher or lower frequency. Quantity changes into quality.

The Electromagnetic Spectrum

Frequency in oscillations/sec	Name	Rough behaviour
10^2	Electrical disturbance	Field
$5 \times 10^5 - 10^6$	Radio Broadcast	
10^8	FM-TV	Waves
10^{10}	Radar	
$5 \times 10^{14} - 10^{15}$	Light	
1018	X-rays	
1021	γ-rays, nuclear	Particle
1024	γ-rays, "artificial"	
1027	γ-rays, in cosmic rays	

Source: R. P. Feynman, *Lectures on Physics*, chapter 2, p. 7, Table 2-1.

Organic and inorganic

The law of quantity and quality also serves to shed light on one of the most controversial aspects of modern physics, the so-called uncertainty principle, which we will examine in greater detail in another section. Whereas it is impossible to know the exact position and velocity of an individual subatomic particle, it is possible to predict with great accuracy the behaviour of large numbers of particles. A further example: radioactive atoms decay in a way that makes a detailed prediction impossible. Yet large numbers of atoms decay at a rate so statistically reliable that they are used by scientists as natural "clocks" with which they calculate the age of the earth, the sun and the stars. The very fact that the laws governing the behaviour of subatomic particles are different to those which function at the "normal" level is itself an example of the transformation of quantity into quality. The precise point at which the laws of the small-scale phenomena cease to apply was defined by the *quantum of action* laid down by Max Planck (1858-1947) in 1900.

At a certain point, the concatenation of circumstances causes a qualitative leap whereby inorganic matter gives rise to organic matter. The difference between inorganic and organic matter is only relative. Modern science is well on the way to discovering exactly how the latter arises from the former. Life itself consists of atoms organised in a certain way. We are all a collection of atoms but not "merely" a collection of atoms. In the astonishingly complex arrangement of our genes, we have an infinite number of possibilities. The task of allowing each individual to develop these possibilities to the fullest extent is the real task of socialism.

Molecular biologists now know the complete DNA sequence of an organism, but cannot deduce from this how the organism assembles itself during its development, any more than knowledge of the structure of H_2O provides an understanding of the quality of liquidity. An analysis of the chemicals and cells of the body does not add up to a formula for life. The same is true of the mind itself. Neuroscientists have a great deal of data about what the brain does. The human brain consists of ten billion neurons, each of which has an average of a thousand links with other neurons. The fastest computer is capable of performing around a billion operations a second. The brain of a fly sitting on a wall carries out 100 billion operations in the same time. This comparison gives an idea of the vast difference between the human brain and even the most advanced computer.

The enormous complexity of the human brain is one of the reasons why idealists have attempted to surround the phenomenon of mind with a mystical aura. Knowledge of the details of individual neurons, axons and synapses, is not sufficient to explain the phenomenon of thought and emotion. However, there is nothing mystical about it. In the language of complexity theory, both mind and life are *emergent phenomena*. In the language of dialectics, the leap from quantity to quality means that the whole possesses qualities that cannot be deduced from the sum of the parts or reduced to it. None of the neurons is conscious. Yet the sum total of neurons and their connections are. Neural networks are non-linear dynamical systems. It is the complex activity and interactions between the neurons that produce the phenomenon we call consciousness.

The same kind of thing can be seen in large numbers of multi-component systems in the most varied spheres. Studies of ant colonies at Bath University have shown how behaviour not witnessed in individual ants appears in a colony. A single ant, left to itself, will wander around at random, foraging and resting at irregular intervals. However, when the observation shifts to a whole colony of ants it immediately becomes evident that they become active at perfectly regular intervals. It is thought that this maximises the effectiveness of their labours: if they all work together, one ant is unlikely to repeat a task just performed by another. The degree of coordination at the level of an ant colony is such that some people have thought of it as a single animal, rather than a colony. This too is a mystical presentation of a phenomenon which exists on many levels in nature and in animal and human society, and which can only be understood in terms of the dialectical relation between whole and part.

We can see the law of the transformation of quantity into quality at work when we consider the evolution of the species. In biological terms a specific "breed" or "race" of animal is defined by its capacity to inter-breed. But as evolutionary modifications take one group further away from another a point is reached where they can no longer inter-breed. At this point a new species has been formed. Palaeontologists Stephen Jay Gould (1941-2002) and Niles Eldredge (1944-) have demonstrated that these processes are some times slow and protracted and at other times extremely rapid. Either way, they show how a gradual accumulation of small changes at a certain point provokes a qualitative change. Punctuated equilibria is the term used by these biologists to describe long periods of stability, interrupted by sudden bursts of change. When this idea was proposed by Gould and Eldredge of the American Museum to Natural History in 1972, it provoked an acrimonious debate among biologists, for whom, until then, Darwinian evolution was synonymous with gradualism.

For a long time, it was thought that evolution precluded such drastic changes. It was pictured as a slow, gradual change. However, the fossil record, although incomplete, presents a very different picture, with long periods of gradual evolution punctuated by violent upheavals, accompanied by the mass extinction of some species and the rapid rise of others. Whether or not the dinosaurs became extinct as a consequence of a meteorite colliding with the earth, it seems highly improbable that most of the great extinctions were caused in this way. While external phenomena, including meteorite or comet impacts, can play a role as "accidents" in the evolutionary process, it is necessary to seek an explanation of evolution as a result of its internal laws. The theory of "punctuated equilibria", which is now supported by most palaeontologists, represents a decisive break with the old gradualist interpretation of Darwinism, and presents a truly dialectical picture of evolution, in which long periods of stasis are interrupted by sudden leaps and catastrophic changes of all kinds.

There is an endless number of examples of this law covering a very wide field. Is it possible now to continue to doubt the validity of this extremely important law? Is it really justified to continue to ignore it or to write it off as a subjective invention, which has been arbitrarily applied to diverse phenomena that bear no relation to one another? We see how in physics the study of phase transitions has led to the conclusion that apparently unrelated changes—of the boiling of liquids and the magnetising of metals—all follow the same rules. It is only a matter of time before similar connections will be established which will reveal beyond a shadow of doubt that the law of the transformation of quantity into quality is indeed one of the most fundamental laws of nature.

Whole and part

According to formal logic, the whole is equal to the sum of its parts. On closer examination, however, this is seen not to be true. In the case of living organisms it is manifestly not the case. A rabbit cut up in a laboratory, and reduced to its constituent parts is no longer a rabbit. This fact has been grasped by the advocates of chaos theory and complexity. Whereas classical physics, with its linear systems, accepted that the whole was precisely the sum of its parts, the non-linear logic of complexity maintains the opposite proposition, in complete agreement with dialectics:

"The whole is almost always equal to a great deal more than a sum of its parts," says Waldrop. "And the mathematical expression of that property—to the extent that such systems can be described by mathematics at all—is a *non-linear* equation: one whose graph is curvy." [29]

We have already quoted the examples of the qualitative changes in chemistry used by Engels in *Anti-Dühring*. While these examples remain valid, they by no means tell the whole story. Engels was limited, of course, by the scientific knowledge of his time. Today it is possible to go much further. The classical atomic theory of chemistry sets out from the idea that any combination of atoms into a greater unity can only be an aggregate of these atoms, that is, a purely quantitative relation. The union of atoms into molecules was seen as a simple juxtaposition. Chemical formulae such as H_2O, H_2SO_4, etc. presuppose that each of the atoms remains basically unchanged even when it enters a new combination to form a molecule.

This reflected precisely the mode of thinking of formal logic, which states that the whole is only the sum of the parts. Thus, since the molecular weight equals the sum of the weights of the respective atoms, it was assumed that the atoms themselves had remained unchanged, having entered into a purely quantitative relationship. However, many of the properties of the compounds could not be determined in this way. Indeed, most chemical properties of compounds differ considerably from those of the elements of which they are made up. The so-called principle of juxtaposition does not explain these changes. It is one-sided, inadequate and, in a word, wrong.

Modern atomic theory has shown the incorrectness of this idea. While accepting that complex structures must be explained in terms of aggregates of more elementary factors, it has shown that the relations between these elements are not merely indifferent and quantitative, but dynamic and dialectical. The elementary particles which make up the atoms interact constantly, passing into each other. They are not

(29) M.M. Waldrop, op. cit., p. 65.

fixed constants but are at every moment both themselves and something else at the same time. It is precisely this dynamic relationship that gives the resulting molecules their particular nature, properties and specific identity.

In this new combination the atoms are and are not themselves. They combine in a dynamic way to produce an entirely different entity, a different relationship, which, in turn, determines the behaviour of its component parts. Thus, we are not dealing merely with a lifeless "juxtaposition", a mechanical aggregate, but with a process. In order to understand the nature of an entity it is therefore entirely insufficient to reduce it to its individual atomic components. It is necessary to understand its dynamic interrelations, that is, to arrive at a dialectical, not a formal, analysis.

David Bohm was one of the few to provide a worked out theoretical alternative to the subjectivist "Copenhagen interpretation" of quantum mechanics. Bohm's analysis, which is clearly influenced by the dialectical method, advocates a radical rethinking of quantum mechanics and a new way of looking at the relationship between whole and parts. He points out that the usual interpretation of quantum theory does not give an adequate idea of just how far reaching was the revolution affected by modern physics.

"Indeed," says Bohm, "when this interpretation is extended to field theories, not only the inter-relationships of the parts, but also their very existence is seen to flow out of the law of the whole. There is therefore nothing left of the classical scheme, in which the whole is derived from pre-existent parts related in predetermined ways. Rather, what we have is reminiscent of the relationship of whole and parts in an organism, in which each organ grows and sustains itself in a way that depends crucially on the whole." [30]

A molecule of sugar can be broken down into its constituent parts of single atoms but then it is no longer sugar. A molecule cannot be reduced to its component parts without losing its identity. This is precisely the problem when we try to treat complex phenomena from a purely quantitative point of view. The resulting oversimplification leads to a distorted and one-sided picture of the natural world since the *qualitative* aspect is entirely left out of account. It is precisely through *quality* that we are able to distinguish one thing from another. Quality lies at the basis of all our knowledge of the world because it expresses the fundamental reality of all things, showing the critical boundaries that exist at all levels of material reality. The exact point at which small changes of degree give rise to a change of state is one of the most fundamental problems of science. It is a question that occupies a central place in dialectical materialism.

Complex organisms

Life itself arises from a qualitative leap from inorganic to organic matter. The explanation of the processes by which this occurred constitutes one of the most important

(30) D. Bohm, *Causality and Chance in Modern Physics*, p. x.

and exciting problems of present-day science. The advances of chemistry, analysing in great detail the structures of complex molecules, predicting their behaviour with great accuracy and identifying the role of particular molecules in living systems, paved the way for the emergence of new sciences, *biochemistry* and *biophysics*, dealing respectively with the chemical reactions that take place in living organisms and the physical phenomena involved in living processes. These, in turn, have been merged together in *molecular biology*, which has registered the most amazing advances in recent years.

In this way, the old fixed divisions separating organic and inorganic matter have been entirely abolished. The early chemists drew a rigid distinction between the two. Gradually, it was understood that the same chemical laws applied to organic as to inorganic molecules. All substances containing carbon (with the possible exception of a few simple compounds like carbon dioxide) are characterised as organic. The rest are inorganic. Only carbon atoms are capable of forming very long chains, thus giving rise to the possibility of an infinite variety of complex molecules.

In the 19th century chemists analysed the properties of "albuminous" substances (from the Latin word for egg-white). From this, it was discovered that life was dependent upon *proteins*, large molecules made up of amino acids. At the beginning of the 20th century, when Planck was making his breakthrough in physics, Emil Fischer was attempting to join up amino acids in chains in such a manner that the carboxyl group of one amino acid was always linked to the amino group of the next. By 1907, he had succeeded in synthesising a chain of eighteen amino acids. Fischer called these chains *peptides*, from the Greek word "to digest", because he thought that proteins would break down into such chains in the process of digestion. This theory was finally proven by Max Bergmann in 1932.

These chains were still too simple to produce the complex polypeptide chains needed to create proteins. Moreover, the task of deciphering the structure of a protein molecule itself was incredibly difficult. *The properties of each protein depend on its exact relation to each amino acid on the molecular chain. Here too, quantity determines quality.* This posed a seemingly insurmountable problem for biochemists, since the number of possible arrangements in which nineteen amino acids can appear on a chain comes to nearly 120 million billion. A protein the size of serum albumen, made up of more than 500 amino acids, therefore has a number of possible arrangements of about 10^{600}, that is, 1 followed by 600 zeros. The complete structure of a key protein molecule—insulin—was established for the first time by the British Nobel Prize winner biochemist Frederick Sanger in 1953. Using the same method, other scientists succeeded in deciphering the structure of a whole series of other protein molecules. Later, they succeeded in synthesising protein in the laboratory. It is now possible to synthesise many proteins, including one as complex as the human growth hormone which involves a chain of 188 amino acids.

Life is a complex system of interactions involving an immense number of chemical reactions which proceed continuously and rapidly. Every reaction in the heart, blood, nervous system, bones and brain interacts with every other part of the body. The workings of the simplest living body are far more complicated than the most advanced computer, permitting rapid movement, swift reactions to the slightest change in the environment, constant adjustments to changing conditions, internal and external. Here, most emphatically, the whole is more than the sum of the parts. Every part of the body, every muscular and nervous reaction, depends upon all the rest. Here we have a dynamic and complex, in other words dialectical, interrelationship, which alone is capable of creating and sustaining the phenomenon we know as life.

The process of metabolism means that, at any given moment, the living organism is constantly changing, taking in oxygen, water, and food (carbohydrates, fats, proteins, minerals and other raw materials), negating these by transforming them into the materials needed to sustain and develop life and excreting waste products. The dialectical relationship between whole and part manifests itself in the different levels of complexity in nature, reflected in the different branches of science:

a) Atomic interactions and the laws of chemistry determine the laws of biochemistry, but life itself is qualitatively different.

b) The laws of biochemistry "explain" all the processes of human interaction with the environment. And yet human activity and thought are qualitatively different to the biological processes that constitute them.

c) Each individual person, in turn, is a product of his or her physical and environmental development. Yet the complex interactions of the sum total of individuals who make up a society are also qualitatively different. In each of these cases the whole is greater than the sum of the parts and obeys different laws.

In the last analysis, all human existence and activity is based on the laws of motion of atoms. We are part of a material universe, which is a continuous whole, functioning according to its inherent laws. And yet, when we pass from a) to c), we make a series of qualitative leaps, and must operate with different laws at different "levels"; c) is based upon b) and b) is based upon a), but nobody in their right mind would seek to explain the complex movements in human society in terms of atomic forces. For the same reason, it is absolutely futile to reduce the problem of crime to the laws of genetics.

An army is not merely the sum total of individual soldiers. The very act of combining in a massive force, organised on military lines transforms the individual soldier both physically and morally. As long as the cohesiveness of the army is maintained, it represents a formidable force. This is not only a question of numbers. Napoleon was well aware of the importance of morale in war. As part of a disciplined numerous fighting force, the individual soldier is capable of achieving feats of bravery and self-sacrifice in situations of extreme danger, of which, under normal conditions, as an isolated individual, he would never imagine himself capable. Yet he remains the same person as before. The moment the cohesiveness of the army breaks down under the impact of defeat, the whole dissolves into its individual "atoms", and the army becomes a demoralised rabble.

Engels was very interested in military tactics, for which Marx's daughters nicknamed him "the General". He closely followed the progress of the American Civil War and the Crimean War, about which he wrote many articles. In *Anti-Dühring*, he shows how the law of quantity and quality relates to military tactics, for example, in the relative fighting capacity of the highly disciplined soldiers of Napoleon and the Egyptian (Mameluke) cavalry:

"In conclusion, we shall call one more witness for the transformation of quantity into quality, namely Napoleon. He describes the combat between the French cavalry, who were bad riders but disciplined, and the Mamelukes, who were undoubtedly the best horsemen of their time for single combat but who lacked discipline, as follows:

"'Two Mamelukes were undoubtedly more than a match for three Frenchmen; 100 Mamelukes were equal to 100 Frenchmen; 300 Frenchmen could generally beat 300 Mamelukes, and 1,000 Frenchmen invariably defeated 1,500 Mamelukes.' Just as with Marx a definite, though varying, minimum sum of exchange-value was necessary to make possible its transformation into capital, so with Napoleon a detachment of cavalry had to be of a definite minimum number in order to permit the force of discipline, embodied in close order and planned utilisation, to manifest itself and even rise superior to greater numbers of irregular cavalry, who were better mounted, more dextrous horsemen and fighters, and at least as brave as the former." [31]

The molecular process of revolution

The process of chemical reaction involves crossing a decisive barrier known as a *transition state*. At this point, before the reactants become products, they are neither one thing nor the other. Some of the old bonds are breaking and other new ones are being formed. The energy needed to pass this critical point is known as *Gibbs energy*. Before a molecule can react, it requires a quantity of energy, which, at a certain point, brings it to the transition state. At normal temperatures only a minute fraction of the reactant molecules possess sufficient energy. At a greater temperature, a higher proportion of the molecules will have this energy. That is why heating is one way to speed up a chemical reaction. The process can be assisted by the use of catalysts, which are widely used in industry. Without catalysts, many processes, though they would still take place, would be so slow that they would be uneconomic. The catalyst cannot change the composition of the substances involved nor can it alter the Gibbs energy of the reactants, but it can provide an easier pathway between them.

There are certain analogies between this phenomenon and the role of the indi-

(31) Engels, *Anti-Dühring*, p. 163.

vidual in history. It is a common misconception that Marxism has no place for the role of individuals in shaping their own destiny. According to this caricature, the materialist conception of history reduces everything to "the productive forces". Human beings are seen as mere blind agents of economic forces or marionettes dancing on the strings of historical inevitability. This mechanistic view of the historic process (economic determinism) has nothing in common with the dialectical philosophy of Marxism.

Historical materialism sets out from the elementary proposition that men and women make their own history. But, contrary to the idealist notion of human beings as *absolutely* free agents, Marxism explains that they are limited by the actual material conditions of the society into which they are born. These conditions are shaped in a fundamental way by the level of development of the productive forces, which is the ultimate ground upon which all human culture, politics and religion rest. However, these things are not directly shaped by economic development but can and do take on a life of their own. The extremely complex relation between all these factors has a dialectical character, not a mechanical one. Individuals do not choose the conditions into which they are born. They are "given". Nor is it possible, as idealists imagine, for individuals to impose their will upon society, simply because of the greatness of their intellect or the strength of their character. The theory that history is made by "great individuals" is a fairy story fit to amuse five-year olds. It has approximately the same scientific value as the "conspiracy theory" of history, which attributes revolutions to the malign influence of "agitators".

Every worker knows that strikes are not caused by agitators but by bad wages and conditions. Contrary to the impression sometimes given by certain sensationalist newspapers, strikes are not common occurrences. For many years, a factory or workplace can remain apparently peaceful. The workforce may not react, even when their wages and conditions are attacked. This is especially true in conditions of mass unemployment or when there is no lead from the tops of the trade unions. This apparent indifference of the majority often leads the minority of activists to despair. They draw the mistaken conclusion that the rest of the workers are "backward", and will never do anything. But, in fact, beneath the surface of apparent tranquillity, changes are taking place. A thousand small incidents, pinpricks, injustices, injuries, gradually leave their mark on the consciousness of the workers. This process was aptly described by Trotsky as "the molecular process of revolution". It is the equivalent of the Gibbs energy in a chemical reaction.

In real life, as in chemistry, molecular processes take their time. No chemist would ever complain because the anticipated reaction was taking a long time, especially if the conditions for a speedy reaction (high temperature, etc.) were absent. But eventually, the chemical transition state is reached. At this point, the presence of a catalyst is of great assistance in bringing the process to a successful conclusion, in the speediest and most economical manner. In the same way, at a given point, the accumulated mood of discontent in the workplace boils over. The whole situation is transformed in the space of 24 hours. If the activists are not prepared, if they have allowed themselves to be deceived by the surface calm of the previous period, they will be taken completely off guard.

In dialectics, sooner or later, things change into their opposite. In the words of the Bible, "the first shall be last and the last shall be first." We have seen this many times, not least in the history of great revolutions. Formerly backward and inert layers can catch up with a bang. Consciousness develops in sudden leaps. This can be seen in any strike. And in any strike we can see the elements of a revolution in an undeveloped, embryonic form. In such situations, the presence of a conscious and audacious minority can play a role quite similar to that of a catalyst in a chemical reaction. In certain instances, even a single individual can play an absolutely decisive role.

In November 1917 the fate of the Russian Revolution was ultimately determined by two men—Lenin and Trotsky. Without them, there is no doubt that the revolution would have been defeated. The other leaders, Kamenev, Zinoviev and Stalin, came under the pressure of other classes and capitulated. The question here is not one of abstract "historical forces" but the concrete one of the degree of preparation, foresight, personal courage and ability of leaders. After all, we are talking about a struggle of living forces not a simple mathematical equation.

Does this mean then that the idealist interpretation of history is correct? Is it all decided by great individuals? Let the facts speak for themselves. For a quarter of a century before 1917, Lenin and Trotsky had spent most of their lives more or less isolated from the masses, often working with very small groups of people. Why were they unable to have the same decisive effect, for example, in 1916? Or in 1890? Because the objective conditions were absent. In the same way, a union activist who continually called for a strike when there was no mood for action would soon end up a laughing stock. Similarly, when the revolution was isolated in conditions of unspeakable backwardness and the class balance of forces changed, neither Lenin nor Trotsky could prevent the rise of the bureaucratic counterrevolution headed by a man in every way their inferior, Stalin. Here, in a nutshell, we have the dialectical relation between the subjective and objective factor in human history.

The unity and interpenetration of opposites

Everywhere we look in nature, we see the dynamic co-existence of opposing tendencies. This creative tension is what gives life and motion. That was already understood by Heraclitus 2,500 years ago. It is even present in embryo in certain Oriental religions, as in the idea of the *ying* and *yang* in China, and in Buddhism. Dialectics appears here in a mystified form, which nonetheless reflects an intuition of the workings of nature. The Hindu religion contains the germ of a dialectical idea, when it poses the three phases of creation (Brahma), maintenance or order (Vishnu) and destruction or disorder (Shiva). In his interesting book on the mathematics of chaos, Ian Stewart points out that the difference between the gods Shiva, "the Untamed", and Vishnu is not the antagonism between good and evil, *but that the two principles of harmony and discord together underlie the whole of existence.*

"In the same way," he writes, "mathematicians are beginning to view order and chaos as two distinct manifestations of an underlying determinism. And neither exists in isolation. The typical system can exist in a variety of states, some ordered, some chaotic. Instead of two opposed polarities, there is a continuous spectrum. As harmony and discord combine in musical beauty, so order and chaos combine in mathematical beauty." [32]

In Heraclitus, all this was in the nature of an inspired guess. Now this hypothesis has been confirmed by a huge amount of examples. The unity of opposites lies at the heart of the atom, and the entire universe is made up of molecules, atoms, and subatomic particles. The matter was very well put by R.P. Feynman: "All things, even ourselves, are made of fine-grained, enormously strongly interacting plus and minus parts, all neatly balanced out." [33]

The question is: how does it happen that a plus and a minus are "neatly balanced out?" This is a contradictory idea! In elementary mathematics, a plus and a minus do not "balance out". They negate each other. Modern physics has uncovered the tremendous forces which lie at the heart of the atom. Why do the contradictory forces of electrons and protons not cancel each other out? Why do atoms not merely fly apart? The current explanation refers to the "strong force" which holds the atom together. But the fact remains that the unity of opposites lies at the basis of all reality.

Within the nucleus of an atom, there are two opposing forces, attraction and repulsion. On the one hand, there are electrical repulsions which, if unrestrained, would violently tear the nucleus apart. On the other hand, there are powerful forces of attraction which bind the nuclear particles to each other. This force of attraction, however, has its limits, beyond which it is unable to hold things together. The forces of attraction, unlike repulsion, have a very short reach. In a small nucleus they can keep the forces of disruption in check. But in a large nucleus, the forces of repulsion cannot be easily dominated.

Beyond a certain critical point, the bond is broken and a qualitative leap occurs. Like an enlarged drop of water, it is on the verge of breaking apart. When an extra neutron is added to the nucleus, the disruptive tendency increases rapidly. The nucleus breaks up, forming two smaller nuclei, which fly apart violently, releasing a vast amount of energy. This is what occurs in nuclear fission. However, analogous processes may be seen at many different levels of nature. Water falling on a polished surface will break up into a complex pattern of droplets. This is because

(32) I. Stewart, *Does God Play Dice?* p. 22.
(33) R.P. Feynman, op. cit., chapter 2, p. 5.

two opposing forces are at work: gravity, which tries to spread out the water in a flat film spread over the whole surface, and surface tension, the attraction of one water molecule to another, which tries to pull the liquid together, forming compact globules.

Nature seems to work in pairs. We have the "strong" and the "weak" forces at the subatomic level; attraction and repulsion; north and south in magnetism; positive and negative in electricity; matter and anti-matter; male and female in biology; odd and even in mathematics; even the concept of "left and right handedness" in relation to the spin of subatomic particles. There is a certain symmetry, in which contradictory tendencies, to quote Feynman, "balance themselves out", or, to use the more poetical expression of Heraclitus, "agree with each other by differing like the opposing tensions of the strings and bow of a musical instrument". There are two kinds of matter, which can be called positive and negative. Like kinds repel and unlike attract.

Positive and negative

Positive is meaningless without negative. They are necessarily inseparable. Hegel long ago explained that "pure being" (devoid of all contradiction) is the same as pure nothing, that is, an empty abstraction. In the same way, if everything were white, it would be the same for us as if everything were black. Everything in the real world contains positive and negative, being and not being, because everything is in a state of constant movement and change. Incidentally, mathematics shows that zero itself is not equal to nothing.

"*Zero*," writes Engels, "because it is the negation of any definite quantity, is not therefore devoid of content. On the contrary, zero has a very definite content. As the borderline between all positive and negative magnitudes, as the sole really neutral number, which can be neither positive nor negative, it is not only a very definite number, but also in itself more important than all other numbers bounded by it. In fact, zero is richer in content than any other number. Put on the right of any other number, it gives to the latter, in our system of numbers, the tenfold value. Instead of zero one could use here any other sign, but only on the condition that this sign taken by itself signifies zero = 0. Hence it is part of the nature of zero itself that it finds this application and that it alone can be applied in this way. Zero annihilates every other number with which it is multiplied; united with any other number as divisor or dividend, in the former case it makes this infinitely large, in the latter infinitely small; it is the only number that stands in a relation of infinity to every other number. $0/0$ can express every number between $-\infty$ and $+\infty$ and in each case represents a real magnitude." [34]

The negative magnitudes of algebra only have meaning in relation to the positive magnitudes, without which they have no reality whatsoever. In the differential

(34) Engels, *Dialectics of Nature*, pp. 345-6.

calculus, the dialectical relation between being and not being is particularly clear. This was extensively dealt with by Hegel in his *Science of Logic*. He was greatly amused by the perplexity of the traditional mathematicians, who were shocked by the use of a method which makes use of the infinitesimally small, and "cannot do without the suggestion that a certain quantity is not equal to nil but is so inconsiderable that it may be neglected," [35] and yet always obtains an exact result.

Moreover, everything is in a permanent relation with other things. Even over vast distances, we are affected by light, radiation, gravity. Undetected by our senses, there is a process of interaction, which causes a continual series of changes. Ultraviolet light is able to "evaporate" electrons from metal surfaces in much the same way as the sun's rays evaporate water from the ocean. Mathematician and physicist Banesh Hoffmann states: "It is still a strange and awe-inspiring thought, that you and I are thus rhythmically exchanging particles with one another, and with the earth and the beasts of the earth, and the sun and the moon and the stars, to the uttermost galaxy." [36]

The Dirac equation for the energy of an individual electron involves two answers—one positive and one negative. It is similar to the square root of a number, which can either be positive or negative. Here, however, the negative answer implies a contradictory idea—negative energy. This appears to be an absurd concept from the standpoint of formal logic. Since energy and mass are equivalent, negative energy, in turn, means negative mass. Paul A.M. Dirac (1902-84) himself was disturbed by the implications of his own theory. He was compelled to predict the existence of particles which would be identical to the electron, but with a positive electric charge, a previously unheard of matter.

On August 2nd, 1932, Robert A. Millikan (1868-1953) and Carl David Anderson (1905-91) of the California Institute of Technology discovered a particle the mass of which was clearly that of an electron, but moving in the opposite direction. This was not an electron, proton or neutron. Anderson described it as a "positive electron" or positron. This was a new kind of matter—antimatter—predicted by Dirac's equations. Subsequently, it was discovered that electrons and positrons, when they meet, annihilate each other, producing two photons (two flashes of light). In the same way, a photon passing through matter could split to form a virtual electron and a positron.

The phenomenon of *oppositeness* exists in physics, where, for example, every particle has its anti-particle (electron and positron, proton and anti-proton, etc.). These are not merely different, but opposites in the most literal sense of the word, being identical in every respect, except one: they have opposite electrical charges—positive and negative. Incidentally, it is a matter of indifference which one is characterised as negative and which positive. The important thing is the relationship between them.

(35) Hegel, *Science of Logic*, Vol. 1, p. 258.
(36) B. Hoffmann, *The Strange Story of the Quantum*, p. 159.

Every particle possesses the quality known as spin, expressed as a plus or a minus, depending on its direction. Strange as it may seem, the opposite phenomena of left and right-handedness, which is known to play a fundamental role in biology, also has its equivalent at the subatomic level. Particles and waves stand in contradiction to each other. The Danish physicist Niels H.D. Bohr (1885-1962) referred to them, rather confusingly, as "complementary concepts", by which he meant precisely that they exclude one another.

The most recent investigations of particle physics are casting light on the deepest level of matter so far discovered—*quarks*. These particles also have opposing "qualities" which are not comparable to ordinary forms, so physicists are obliged to make up new, artificial qualities to describe them. Thus we have up quarks, down quarks, charm quarks, strange quarks, and so on. Although the qualities of quarks have still to be thoroughly explored, one thing is clear: that the property of oppositeness exists at the most fundamental levels of matter yet known to science.

This universal phenomenon of the unity of opposites is, in reality, the motor-force of all motion and development in nature. It is the reason why it is not necessary to introduce the concept of external impulse to explain movement and change—the fundamental weakness of all mechanistic theories. Movement, which itself involves a contradiction, is only possible as a result of the conflicting tendencies and inner tensions which lie at the heart of all forms of matter.

The opposing tendencies can exist in a state of uneasy equilibrium for long periods of time, until some change, even a small quantitative change, destroys the equilibrium and gives rise to a critical state which can produce a qualitative transformation. In 1936, Bohr compared the structure of the nucleus to a drop of liquid, for example, a raindrop hanging from a leaf. Here the force of gravity struggles with that of surface tension striving to keep the water molecules together. The addition of just a few more molecules to the liquid renders it unstable. The enlarged droplet begins to shudder, the surface tension is no longer able to hold the mass to the leaf and the whole thing falls.

Nuclear fission

This apparently simple example, of which many equivalents can be observed a hundred times in daily experience, is a fairly close analogy to the processes at work in nuclear fission. The nucleus itself is not at rest, but in a constant state of change. In one quadrillionth of a second, there have already been billions of random collisions of particles. Particles are constantly entering and leaving the nucleus. Nevertheless, the nucleus is held together by what is often described as the strong force. It remains in a state of unstable equilibrium, "on the edge of chaos", as chaos theory would put it.

As in a drop of liquid which quivers as the molecules move around inside it, the particles are constantly moving, transforming themselves, exchanging energy. Like an enlarged raindrop, the bond between the particles in a large nucleus is less stable, and more likely to break up. The steady release of alpha particles from the surface of the nucleus makes it smaller and steadier. As a result, it may become stable. But it was discovered that by bombarding a large nucleus with neutrons they can be made to break up, releasing part of the colossal amounts of energy locked up in the atom. This is the process of nuclear fission. This process can occur even without the introduction of particles from without. The process of *spontaneous fission* (radio active decay) is going on all the time in nature. In one second, a pound of uranium experiences four spontaneous fissions, and alpha particles are emitted from around eight million nuclei. The heavier the nucleus, the more likely the process of fission becomes.

The unity of opposites lies at the root of life itself. When spermatozoa were first discovered, they were believed to be "homunculae", perfectly formed miniature human beings, which—like Topsy in *Uncle Tom's Cabin*—"just grow'd". In reality, the process is far more complex and dialectical. Sexual reproduction depends on the combination of a single sperm and egg, in a process in which both are destroyed and preserved at the same time, passing on all the genetic information necessary for the creation of an embryo. After undergoing a whole series of transformations, bearing a striking resemblance to the evolution of all life from the division of a single cell, eventually results in an entirely new individual. Moreover, the result of this union contains the genes of both parents, but in such a way as to be different from either. So what we have is not simple reproduction, but a real development. The increased diversity made possible by this is one of the great evolutionary advantages of sexual reproduction.

Contradictions are found at all levels of nature, and woe betide the logic that denies it. Not only can an electron be in two or more places at the same time, but it can move simultaneously in different directions. We are sadly left with no alternative but to agree with Hegel: they are and are not. Things change into their opposite. Negatively charged electrons become transformed into positively charged positrons. An electron that unites with a proton is not destroyed, as one might expect, but produces a new particle, a neutron, with a neutral charge.

The laws of formal logic have received a humiliating drubbing in the field of modern physics, where they have shown themselves to be hopelessly inadequate to deal with the contradictory processes that occur at the subatomic level. Particles which disintegrate so rapidly that it is difficult to say whether they exist or not, pose insurmountable problems for a system which attempts to ban all contradiction from nature and thought. This immediately leads to new contradictions of an insoluble character. Thought finds itself in opposition to the facts established and repeatedly confirmed by experiment and observation. The unity of the proton and the electron is a neutron. But if a positron should unite with a neutron, the result would be the shedding of an electron and the neutron would change into a proton. By means of this ceaseless process, the universe makes and re-makes itself over and over again. No need then for any external force, no "first impulse", as in classical physics. No need for anything whatsoever, except the infinite, restless movement of matter in accordance with its own objective laws.

Polar opposites?

Polarity is an all-pervasive feature in nature. It does not only exist as the North and South Poles of the earth. Polarity is to be found in the sun and moon and other planets. It also exists at the subatomic level, where nuclei behave precisely as if they possess not one but two pairs of magnetic poles.

"Dialectics," wrote Engels, "has proved from the result of our experience of nature so far that all polar opposites in general are determined by the mutual action of the two opposite poles on each other, that the separation and opposition of these poles exist only within their mutual connection and union, and, conversely, that their union exists only in their separation and their mutual connection only in their opposition. This once established, there can be no question of a final cancelling out of repulsion and attraction, or of a final partition between the one form of motion in one half of matter and the other form in the other half, consequently there can be no question of mutual penetration or of absolute separation of the two poles. It would be equivalent to demanding in the first case that the north and south poles of a magnet should mutually cancel themselves out or, in the second case, that dividing a magnet in the middle between the two poles should produce on one side a north half without a south pole, and on the other side a south half without a north pole." [37]

There are some things which people consider to be absolute and immutable opposites. For instance, when we wish to convey the notion of extreme incompatibility, we use the term "polar opposites"—north and south are taken to be absolutely fixed and opposed phenomena. For over a thousand years, sailors have placed their faith in the compass, which guided them through unknown oceans, always pointing to this mysterious thing called the North Pole. Yet closer analysis shows that the North Pole is neither fixed nor stable. The earth is surrounded by a strong magnetic field (a geocentric axis dipole), as if a gigantic magnet were present at the centre of the earth, aligned parallel to the earth's axis. This is related to the metallic composition of the earth's core, which is mainly made up of iron. In the 4.6 billion years since the solar system was formed, the rocks on earth have formed and reformed many times. And not only the rocks but everything else. Detailed measurements and investigation has now proved beyond doubt that the location of the magnetic poles is continually shifting. At the present time, they are moving very slowly—0.3 degrees every million years. This phenomenon is a reflection of complex changes taking place in the earth, the atmosphere and the sun's magnetic field.

(37) Engels, *Dialectics of Nature*, p. 96.

So small is the shift that for centuries it remained undetected. However, even this apparently imperceptible process of change gives rise to a sudden and spectacular leap, in which north becomes south and south becomes north. The changes in the location of the poles are accompanied by fluctuations in the strength of the magnetic field itself. This gradual process, characterised by a weakening of the magnetic field, culminates in a sudden leap. They change place, literally turning into their opposite. After this, the field starts to recover and gather strength again.

This revolutionary change has occurred many times during the history of the earth. It has been estimated that more than 200 such polar reverses have taken place in the last 65 million years; at least four have occurred in the last four million years. About 700,000 years ago, the north magnetic pole was located somewhere in Antarctica, the present south geographical pole. At this moment, we are in a process of weakening of the earth's magnetic field, which will inevitably culminate in a new reversal. The study of the earth's magnetic history is the special field of an entirely new branch of science—*palaeomagnetism*—which is attempting to construct maps of all the reversals of the poles throughout the history of our planet. The discoveries of palaeomagnetism, in turn, have provided conclusive evidence for the correctness of the theory of continental drift. When rocks (especially volcanic rocks) create iron-rich minerals, these respond to the earth's magnetic field, as it exists at that moment, in the same way that pieces of iron react to a magnet, their atoms orienting in line with the field axis. In effect, they behave like a compass. By comparing the orientations of minerals in rocks of the same age in different continents, it is possible to trace the movements of the continents, including those which no longer exist, or only exist as tiny remnants.

In the reversal of the poles we see a most graphic example of the dialectical law of the unity and interpenetration of opposites. North and south—polar opposites in the most literal sense of these words—are not only inseparably united but determine each other by means of a complex and dynamic process, which culminates in a sudden leap in which supposedly fixed and immutable phenomena change into their opposites. And this dialectical process is not the arbitrary and fanciful invention of Hegel or Engels, but is conclusively demonstrated by the most recent discoveries of palaeomagnetism. Truly it has been said, "when men are silent, the stones cry out!"

Attraction and repulsion is an extension of the law of the unity and interpenetration of opposites. It is a law that permeates the whole of nature, from the smallest phenomena to the largest. At the base of the atom are immense forces of attraction and repulsion. The hydrogen atom, for example, is made up of a proton and an electron held together by electrical attraction. The charge carried by a particle may be positive or negative. Similar charges repel each other, whereas opposite kinds attract. Thus, within the nucleus, protons repel each other, but the nucleus is held together by tremendous nuclear force. In very heavy nuclei, however, the force of electrical repulsion can reach a point where the nuclear force is overcome and the nucleus flies apart.

Engels points out the universal role of attraction and repulsion:

"All motion consists in the interplay of attraction and repulsion. Motion, however, is only possible when each individual attraction is compensated by a corresponding repulsion somewhere else. Otherwise in time one side would get the preponderance over the other and then motion would finally cease. Hence all attractions and all repulsions in the universe must mutually balance one another. Thus the law of the indestructibility and uncreatability of motion is expressed in the form that each movement of attraction in the universe must have as its complement an equivalent movement of repulsion and vice versa; or, as ancient philosophy—long before the natural-scientific formulation of the law of conservation of force or energy—expressed it: the sum of all attractions in the universe is equal to the sum of all repulsions."

In Engels' day, the prevailing idea of motion was derived from classical mechanics, where motion is imparted from an external force that overcomes the force of inertia. Engels was quite scathing about the very expression "force", which he considered one-sided and insufficient to describe the real processes of nature. "All natural processes," he wrote, "are two-sided, they are based on the relation of at least two operative parts, action and reaction. The notion of force, however, owing to its origin from the action of the human organism on the external world, and further from terrestrial mechanics, implies that only one part is active, operative, the other part being passive, receptive." [38]

Engels was far in advance of his time in being highly critical of this notion, which had already been attacked by Hegel. In his *History of Philosophy*, Hegel remarks that "It is better (to say) that a magnet has a *soul* (as Thales expresses it) than that it has an attractive force; force is a kind of property that, *separate from matter*, is put forward as a kind of predicate—while soul, on the other hand, *is this movement itself, identical with the nature of matter*." This remark of Hegel, approvingly quoted by Engels, contains a profound idea—that motion and energy are inherent to matter. Matter is self-moving and self-organising.

Even the word "energy" was not, in Engels' opinion, entirely adequate, although greatly to be preferred to "force". His objection was that "It still makes it appear as if 'energy' was something external to matter, something implanted in it. But in all circumstances it is to be preferred to the expression 'force'." [39] The real relation has been demonstrated by Einstein's theory of the equivalence of mass and energy, which shows that matter and energy are one and the same thing. This was precisely the standpoint of dialectical materialism, as expressed by Engels, and even anticipated by Hegel, as the above quotation shows.

Every science has its own vocabulary, the terms of which frequently do not coincide with everyday usage. This can lead to difficulties and misunderstandings. The

(38) Engels, *Dialectics of Nature*, pp. 95-6 and p. 110.
(39) Engels, *Dialectics of Nature*, p. 108 and p. 107.

word "negation" is commonly understood to signify simple destruction, or annihilation. It is important to understand that in dialectics negation has an entirely different content. It means *to negate and to preserve at the same time*. One can negate a seed by crushing it underfoot. The seed is "negated" but not in the dialectical sense! If, however, the same seed is left to itself, under favourable conditions, it will germinate. It has thus negated itself as a seed and develops into a plant, which at a later stage will die producing new seeds.

Apparently, this represents a return to the starting point. However, as professional gardeners know, identical seeds vary from generation to generation, giving rise to new species. Gardeners also know that certain strains can be artificially induced by selective breeding. It was precisely this *artificial selection* which gave Charles Darwin a vital clue to the process of *natural selection* which takes place spontaneously throughout nature, and is the key to understanding the development of all plants and animals. What we have is not only change but *actual development*, generally proceeding from simpler to more complex forms, including the complex molecules of life itself, which, at a certain stage, arises from inorganic matter.

Consider the following example of negation from quantum mechanics. What occurs when an electron unites with a photon? The electron experiences a "quantum leap" and the photon disappears. The result is not some kind of mechanical unity or compound. It is the same electron as before but in a new state of energy. The same is true when the electron unites with a proton. The electron vanishes and there is a leap in the proton's state of energy and charge. The proton is the same as before but in a new state of energy and charge. It is now electrically neutral and becomes a neutron. Dialectically speaking, the electron has been negated and preserved at the same time. It has disappeared, but is not annihilated. It enters into the new particle and expresses itself as a change of energy and charge.

The ancient Greeks were well acquainted with the dialectic of discussion. In a properly conducted debate, an idea is put forward (the *Thesis*) and is then countered by the opposing view (the *Antithesis*) which negates it. Finally, through a thorough process of discussion, which explores the issue concerned from all points of view and discloses all the hidden contradictions, we arrive at a conclusion (the *Synthesis*). We may or may not arrive at agreement but by the very process of discussion, we have deepened our knowledge and understanding and raised the whole discussion onto a different plane.

It is quite evident that almost none of the critics of Marxism have taken the trouble to read Marx and Engels. It is frequently supposed, for example, that dialectics consists of "Thesis-Antithesis-Synthesis", which Marx is alleged to have copied from Hegel (who, in turn, was supposed to have copied it from the Holy Trinity) and applied to society. This childish caricature is still repeated by supposedly intelligent people today. As a matter of fact, not only is Marx's dialectical materialism the opposite of Hegel's idealist dialectic, but the dialectic of Hegel is itself very different from that of classical Greek philosophy.

George Plekhanov rightly ridiculed the attempt to reduce the imposing edifice of Hegelian dialectic to the "wooden Triad" of Thesis-Antithesis-Synthesis. The advanced dialectics of Hegel bears approximately the same relation to that of the Greeks as modern chemistry to the primitive investigations of the alchemists. It is quite correct that the latter prepared the ground for the former, but to assert that they are "basically the same" is simply ludicrous. Hegel returned to Heraclitus, but on a qualitatively higher level, enriched by 2,500 years of philosophical and scientific advances. The development of dialectics is itself a dialectical process.

Nowadays the word "alchemy" is used as a synonym for quackery. It conjures up all kinds of images of spells and black magic. Such elements were not absent from the history of alchemy, but its activities were by no means limited to this. In the history of science, alchemy played a most important role. Alchemy is an Arabic word, used for any science of materials. Charlatans there were, but not a few good scientists too! And chemistry is the Western word for the same thing. Many chemical words are, in fact, Arab in origin—acid, alkali, alcohol, and so on.

The alchemists set out from the proposition that it was possible to transmute one element into another. They tried for centuries to discover the "philosopher's stone", which they believed would enable them to turn base metal (lead) into gold. Had they succeeded, it would not have done them a lot of good, since the value of gold would have quickly sunk to that of lead! But that is another story. Given the actual level of technique at that time, the alchemists were attempting the impossible. In the end, they were forced to come to the conclusion that the transmutation of the elements was impossible. However, the endeavours of the alchemists were not in vain. In their pursuit of an unscientific hypothesis, the philosopher's stone, they actually did valuable pioneering work, developing the art of experiment, inventing equipment still used in laboratories today and describing and analysing a wide range of chemical reactions. In this way, alchemy prepared the ground for the development of chemistry.

Modern chemistry was able to progress only by repudiating the alchemists' basic hypothesis—the transmutation of the elements. From the late 18th century onwards, chemistry developed on a scientific basis. By setting aside the grandiose aims of the past, it made giant steps forward. Then, in 1919, the New Zealand nuclear physicist Ernest Rutherford (1871-1937) carried out an experiment involving the bombardment of nitrogen nuclei with alpha particles. This led to the breaching of the atomic nucleus for the first time. In so doing, he succeeded in transmuting one element (nitrogen) into another element (oxygen). The age-old quest of the alchemists had been resolved but not at all in a way they could have foreseen!

Now look at this process a bit more closely. We start with the thesis: a) the transmutation of the elements; this is then negated by its antithesis b) impossibility of transmuting the elements; this, in turn, is overturned by a second negation c) the transmutation of the elements. Here we must note three things. Firstly, each negation marks a definite advance, indeed, a qualitative leap forward. Secondly, each successive advance both negates the earlier stage, reacts against it, whilst preserving all that is useful and necessary in it. Lastly, the final stage—the negation of the negation—does not at all signify a return to the original idea (in this case, alchemy), but the reappearance of earlier forms on a qualitatively higher level. Incidentally, it is now possible to convert lead into gold, but would be too expensive to be worth the trouble!

Dialectics envisages the fundamental processes at work in the universe, in society and in the history of ideas, not as a closed circle, where the same processes merely repeat themselves in an endless mechanical cycle, but as a kind of open-ended spiral of development in which nothing is ever repeated exactly in the same way. This process can be clearly seen in the history of philosophy and science. The entire history of thought consists of an endless process of development through contradiction.

A theory is put forward which explains certain phenomena. This gradually gains acceptance, both through the accumulation of evidence which bears it out, and because of the absence of a satisfactory alternative. At a certain point, discrepancies appear, which are initially shrugged off as unimportant exceptions. Then a new theory emerges which contradicts the old one and seems to explain the observed facts better. Eventually, after a struggle, the new theory overthrows the existing orthodoxy. But new questions arise from this, which in turn have to be resolved. Frequently, it appears that we return again to ideas which were earlier thought to be discredited. But this does not mean a return to the starting point. What we have is a dialectical process, involving a deeper and deeper understanding of the workings of nature, society, and ourselves. This is the dialectic of the history of philosophy and science.

Joseph Dietzgen (1828-1888), a companion of Marx and Engels, once said that an old man who looks back on his life may see it as an endless series of mistakes which, if he could only have his time back again, he would doubtless choose to eliminate. But then he is left with the dialectical contradiction that it was only by means of these mistakes that he arrived at the wisdom to be able to judge them to be such. As Hegel profoundly observed, the selfsame maxims on the lips of a youth do not carry the same weight as when spoken by a man whose life's experience has filled them with meaning and content. They are the same and yet not the same. What was initially an abstract thought, with little or no real content, now becomes the product of mature reflection.

It was Hegel's genius to understand that the history of different philosophical schools was itself a dialectical process. He compares it to the life of a plant, going through different stages, that negate each other, but which, in their totality, represent the life of the plant itself:

"The more the ordinary mind takes the opposition between true and false to be fixed, the more is it accustomed to expect either agreement or contradiction with a given philosophical system, and only to see reason for the one or the other in any explanatory statement concerning such a system. It does not conceive the diversity of philosophical systems as the progressive evolution of truth; rather, it sees only contradiction in that variety. The bud disappears when the blossom breaks through, and we might say that the former is refuted by the latter; in the same way, when the fruit comes, the blossom may be explained to be a false form of the plant's existence, for the fruit appears as its true nature in place of the blossom. These stages are not merely differentiated; they supplant one another as being incompatible with one another. But the ceaseless activity of their own inherent nature makes them at the same time moments of an organic unity, where they not merely do not contradict one another, but where one is as necessary as the other; and this equal necessity of all moments constitutes alone and thereby the life of the whole." [40]

The dialectics of *Capital*

In the three volumes of *Capital*, Marx provides a brilliant example of how the dialectical method can be used to analyse the most fundamental processes in society. By so doing he revolutionised the science of political economy, a fact that is not denied even by those economists whose views sharply conflict with those of Marx. So fundamental is the dialectical method to Marx's work, that Lenin went so far as to say that it was not possible to understand *Capital*, and especially its first chapter, without having read the whole of Hegel's *Logic*! This was undoubtedly an exaggeration. But what Lenin was driving at was the fact that Marx's *Capital* is itself a monumental object lesson on how dialectics ought to be applied.

"If Marx did not leave behind him a *'Logic'* (with a capital letter), he did leave the *logic* of Capital, and this ought to be utilised to the full in this question. In *Capital*, Marx applied to a single science logic, dialectics and the theory of knowledge of materialism [three words are not needed: it is one and the same thing] which has taken everything valuable in Hegel and developed it further." [41]

What method did Marx use in *Capital*? He did not impose the laws of dialectics upon economics but derived them from a long and painstaking study of all aspects of the economic process. He did not put forward an arbitrary schema and then proceed to make the facts fit into it but set out to uncover the laws of motion of capitalist production through a careful examination of the phenomenon itself. In his *Preface to the Critique of Political Economy*, Marx explains his method:

"I am omitting a general introduction which I had jotted down because on closer reflection any anticipation of results still to be proved appears to me to be objec-

---

(40) Hegel, *The Phenomenology of Mind*, p. 68.
(41) Lenin, *Collected Works*, Vol. 38, p. 319; henceforth referred to as LCW.

tionable, and the reader who on the whole desires to follow me must be resolved to ascend from the particular to the general." [42]

Capital represented a breakthrough, not only in the field of economics, but for social science in general. It has a direct relevance to the kind of discussions which are taking place among scientists at the present time. When Marx was alive, this discussion had already begun. At that time, scientists were obsessed with the idea of taking things apart and examining them in detail. This method is now referred to as "reductionism", although Marx and Engels, who were highly critical of it, called it the "metaphysical method". The mechanicists dominated physics for 150 years. Only now is the reaction against reductionism gathering steam. A new generation of scientists is setting itself the task of overcoming this heritage, and moving on to the formulation of new principles, in place of the old approximations.

It was thanks to Marx that the reductionist tendency in economics was routed in the middle of the 19th century. After *Capital*, such an approach was unthinkable. The "Robinson Crusoe" method of explaining political economy ("imagine two people on a desert island...") occasionally resurfaces in bad school textbooks and vulgar attempts at popularisation, but cannot be taken seriously. Economic crises and revolutions do not take place between two individuals on a desert island! Marx analyses the capitalist economy, not as the sum total of individual acts of exchange, but as a complex system, dominated by laws of its own which are as powerful as the laws of nature. In the same way, physicists are now discussing the idea of complexity, in the sense of a system in which the whole is not just a collection of elementary parts. Of course, it is useful to know where possible the laws that govern each individual part, but the complex system will be governed by new laws which are not merely extensions of the previous ones. This is precisely the method of Marx's *Capital*—the method of dialectical materialism.

Marx begins his work with an analysis of the *basic cell* of capitalist economy—the commodity. From this he explains how all the contradictions of capitalist society arise. Reductionism treats things like whole and part, particular and universal as mutually incompatible and exclusive, whereas they are completely inseparable, and interpenetrate and determine each other. In the first volume of *Capital*, Marx explains the twofold nature of commodities, as *use-values and exchange-values*. Most people see commodities exclusively as use-values, concrete, useful objects for the satisfaction of human wants. Use-values have always been produced in every type of human society.

However, capitalist society does strange things to use-values. It converts them into exchange-values—goods that are produced not directly for consumption, but for sale. Every commodity thus has two faces—the homely, familiar face of a use-value, and the mysterious, hidden face of an exchange-value. The former is directly linked to the physical properties of a particular commodity (we wear a shirt, drink

(42) Marx and Engels, *Selected Works*, Vol. 1, p. 502; henceforth referred to as MESW.

coffee, drive a car, etc.). But exchange value cannot be seen, worn or eaten. It has no material being whatsoever. Yet it is the essential nature of a commodity under capitalism. The ultimate expression of exchange-value is money, the universal equivalent, through which all commodities express their value. These little pieces of green paper have no relation whatever to shirts, coffee or cars as such. They cannot be eaten, worn or driven. Yet such is the power they contain, and so universally is this recognised, that people will kill for them.

The dual nature of the commodity expresses the central contradiction of capitalist society—the conflict between wage-labour and capital. The worker thinks he sells his labour to the employer, but in fact what he sells is his *labour power*, which the capitalist uses as he sees fit. The surplus value thus extracted is the unpaid labour of the working class, the source of the accumulation of capital. It is this unpaid labour which maintains all the non-working members of society, through rent, interest, profits and taxation. The class struggle is really the struggle for the division of this surplus value.

Marx did not invent the idea of surplus value, which was known to previous economists like Adam Smith and Ricardo. But, by disclosing the central contradiction involved in it, he completely revolutionised political economy. This discovery can be compared to a similar process in the history of chemistry. Until the late 18th century, it was assumed that the essence of all combustion consisted in the separation from burning substances of a hypothetical thing called *phlogiston*. This theory served to explain most of the known chemical phenomena at the time. Then in 1774, the English scientist Joseph Priestley (1733-1804) discovered something which he called "dephlogisticated air", which was later found to disappear whenever a substance was burned in it.

Priestley had, in fact, discovered oxygen. But he and other scientists were unable to grasp the revolutionary implications of this discovery. For a long time afterwards they continued to think in the old way. Later, the French chemist Antoine Lavoisier (1743-1794) discovered that the new kind of air was really a chemical element, which did not disappear in the process of burning, but combined with the burnt substance. Although others had discovered oxygen, they did not know *what* they had discovered. This was the great discovery of Lavoisier. Marx played a similar role in political economy.

Marx's predecessors had discovered the existence of surplus value, but its real character remained shrouded in obscurity. By subjecting all previous theories, beginning with Ricardo, to a searching analysis, Marx discovered the real, contradictory nature of value. He examined all the relations of capitalist society, starting with the simplest form of commodity production and exchange, and following the process through all its manifold transformations, pursuing a strictly dialectical method.

Marx showed the relation between commodities and money, and was the first one to provide an exhaustive analysis of money. He showed how money is transformed into capital, demonstrating how this change is brought about through the buying and selling of labour power. This fundamental distinction between labour and labour power was the key that unlocked the mysteries of surplus value, a problem that Ricardo had been unable to solve. By establishing the difference between constant and variable capital, Marx was able to trace the entire process of the formation of capital in detail, and thus explain it, which none of his predecessors were able to do.

Marx's method throughout is rigorously dialectical, and follows quite closely the main lines traced by Hegel's *Logic*. This is explicitly stated in the Afterword to the Second German edition, where Marx pays a handsome tribute to Hegel:

"Whilst the writer pictures what he takes to be actually my method, in this striking and [as far as concerns my own application of it] generous way, what else is he picturing but the dialectic method?

"Of course the method of presentation must differ in form from that of inquiry. The latter has to appropriate the material in detail, to analyse its different forms of development, to trace out their inner connection. Only after this work is done, can the actual movement be adequately described. If this is done successfully, if the life of the subject matter is ideally reflected as in a mirror, then it may appear as if we had before us a mere a priori construction...

"The mystifying side of Hegelian dialectic I criticised nearly thirty years ago, at a time when it was still the fashion. But just as I was working at the first volume of *Das Kapital*, it was the good pleasure of the peevish, arrogant, mediocre 'Epigonoi' who now talk large in cultured Germany, to treat Hegel in the same way as the brave Moses Mendelssohn in Lessing's time treated Spinoza, i.e., a 'dead dog'. I therefore openly avowed myself the pupil of that mighty thinker, and even here and there, in the chapter on the theory of value, coquetted with the modes of expression peculiar to him. The mystification which dialectic suffers in Hegel's hands, by no means prevents him from being the first to present its general form of working in a comprehensive and conscious manner. With him it is standing on its head. It must be turned right side up again, if you would discover the rational kernel within the mystical shell.

"In its mystified form, dialectic became the fashion in Germany, because it seemed to transfigure and to glorify the existing state of things. In its rational form it is a scandal and abomination to bourgeoisdom and its doctrinaire professors, because it includes in its comprehension and affirmative recognition of the existing state of things, at the same time also, the recognition of the negation of that state, of its inevitable breaking up; because it regards every historically developed social form as in fluid movement, and therefore takes into account its transient nature not less than its momentary existence; because it lets nothing impose upon it, and is in its essence critical and revolutionary." [43]

(43) Marx, *Capital*, Vol. 1, pp. 19-20.

4. Formal logic and dialectics

The ability of men and women to think logically is the product of a lengthy process of social evolution. It antedates the invention of formal logic, not by thousands, but by millions of years. Locke already expressed this thought in the 17th century, when he wrote: "God has not been so sparing to men as to make them barely two-legged creatures, and left it to Aristotle to make them rational." Behind Logic, according to Locke, stands "a naïve faculty to perceive the coherence or incoherence of its ideas." [44]

The categories of logic did not drop from the clouds. These forms have taken shape in the course of the socio-historical development of humankind. They are elementary generalisations of reality, reflected in the minds of men and women. They are drawn from the fact that every object has certain qualities which distinguish it from other objects; that everything exists in certain relations to other things; that objects form larger classes, with which they share specific properties; that certain phenomena cause other phenomena, and so on.

To some extent, as Trotsky remarked, even animals possess the ability to reason and draw certain conclusions from a given situation. In higher mammals, and in particular the apes, this capacity is quite advanced, as the most recent research into bonobo chimpanzees strikingly reveal. However, while the capacity to reason may not be a monopoly of the human species, there is no doubt that, at least in our small corner of the universe, the ability to think rationally has reached its highest point so far in the development of the human intellect.

Abstraction is absolutely necessary. Without it, thought in general would be impossible. The question is: what sort of abstraction? When I abstract from reality, I concentrate on some aspects of a given phenomenon, and leave the others out of account. A good mapmaker, for instance, is not someone who reproduces every detail of every house and paving stone, and every parked car. Such an amount of detail would destroy the very purpose of the map, which is to make available a con-

(44) Quoted in A.A. Luce, *Logic*, p. 8.

venient scheme of a town or other geographical area. Similarly, the brain early on learns to ignore certain sounds and concentrate on others. If we were not able to do this, the amount of information reaching our ears from all sides would overwhelm the mind completely. Language itself presupposes a high level of abstraction.

The ability to make correct abstractions, which adequately reflect the reality we wish to understand and describe, is the essential prerequisite for scientific thought. The abstractions of formal logic are adequate to express the real world only within quite narrow limits. But they are one-sided and static, and are hopelessly inadequate to deal with complex processes, particularly movement, change and contradictions. The concreteness of an object consists of the sum total of its aspects and interrelationships, determined by its underlying laws. It is the task of science to uncover these laws, and to get as close as possible to this concrete reality. The whole purpose of cognition is to reflect the objective world and its underlying lawfulness and necessary relationships as faithfully as possible. As Hegel pointed out, "the truth is always concrete."

But here we have a contradiction. It is not possible to arrive at an understanding of the concrete world of nature without first resorting to abstraction. The word abstract comes from the Latin "to take from". By a process of abstraction, we take from the object under consideration certain aspects that we consider important, leaving others to one side. Abstract knowledge is necessarily one-sided because it expresses only one particular side of the phenomenon under consideration, isolated from that which determines the specific nature of the whole. Thus, mathematics deals exclusively with quantitative relations. Since quantity is an extremely important aspect of nature, the abstractions of mathematics have provided us with a powerful instrument for probing her secrets. For this reason, it is tempting to forget their real nature and limitations. Yet they remain one-sided, like all abstractions. We forget this at our peril.

Nature knows quality as well as quantity. To determine the precise relation between the two, and to show how, at a critical point, one turns into the other is absolutely necessary if we wish to understand one of the most fundamental processes in nature. This is one of the most basic concepts of dialectical as opposed to merely formal thought, and one of its most important contributions to science. The deep insights provided by this method, which was long decried as "mysticism", are only now beginning to be understood and appreciated. One-sided abstract thought, as manifested in formal logic, did a colossal disservice to science by *excommunicating* dialectics. But the actual results of science show that, in the last analysis, dialectical thinking is far closer to the real processes of nature than the linear abstractions of formal logic.

It is necessary to acquire a concrete understanding of the object as an integral system, not as isolated fragments; with all its necessary interconnections, not torn out of context, like a butterfly pinned to a collector's board; in its life and movement, not as something lifeless and static. Such an approach is in open conflict with the so-called laws of formal logic, the most absolute expression of dogmatic thought ever conceived, representing a kind of mental rigor mortis. But nature lives and breathes, and stubbornly resists the embraces of formalistic thinking. "A" is not equal to "A". Subatomic particles are and are not. Linear processes end in chaos. The whole is greater than the sum of its parts. Quantity changes into quality. Evolution itself is not a gradual process, but interrupted by sudden leaps and catastrophes. What can we do about it? Facts are stubborn things.

Without abstraction it is impossible to penetrate the object in "depth", to understand its essential nature and laws of motion. Through the mental work of abstraction, we are able to get beyond the immediate information provided by our senses (sense-perception), and probe deeper. We can break the object down into its constituent parts, isolate them, and study them in detail. We can arrive at an idealised, general conception of the object as a "pure" form, stripped of all secondary features. This is the work of abstraction, an absolutely necessary stage of the process of cognition.

"Thought proceeding from the concrete to the abstract," wrote Lenin, "—provided it is *correct* (and Kant, like all philosophers, speaks of correct thought)—does not get away *from* the truth but comes closer to it. The abstraction of *matter*, of a *law* of nature, the abstraction of *value*, etc., in short *all* scientific (correct, serious, not absurd) abstractions reflect nature more deeply, truly and *completely*. From living perception to abstract thought, *and from this to practice*—such is the dialectical path of the cognition of *truth*, of the cognition of objective reality." [45]

One of the main features of human thought is that it is not limited to what is, but also deals with what must be. We are constantly making all kinds of logical assumptions about the world we live in. This logic is not learned from books, but is the product of a long period of evolution. Detailed experiments have shown that the rudiments of this logic are acquired by a baby at a very young age, from experience. We reason that if something is true, then something else, for which we have no immediate evidence, must also be true. Such logical thought-processes take place millions of times all our waking hours, without us even being aware of them. They acquire the force of habit, and even the simplest actions in life would not be possible without them.

The elementary rules of thought are taken for granted by most people. They are a familiar part of life, and are reflected in many proverbs, such as "you can't have your cake and eat it"—a most important lesson for any child to learn! At a certain point, these rules were written down and systematised. This is the origin of formal logic, for which Aristotle must take the credit, along with so many other things. This was most valuable, since without a knowledge of the elementary rules of logic, thought runs the risk of becoming incoherent. It is necessary to distinguish black from white, and know the difference between a true statement and one that is false. The value of formal logic is, therefore, not in question. The problem is that the categories of formal logic, drawn from quite a limited range of experience and observation, are really valid only within these limits. They do, in fact, cover a great deal of everyday phenomena, but are quite inadequate to deal with more complex processes, involving movement, turbulence, contradiction, and the change from quantity to quality.

In an interesting article entitled *The Origins of Inference*, which appeared in the anthology *Making Sense*, on the child's construction of the world, Margaret Donaldson draws attention to one of the problems of ordinary logic—its static character:

"Verbal reasoning commonly appears to be about 'states of affairs'—the world seen as static, in a cross-section of time. And considered in this way the universe appears to contain no incompatibility: things just are as they are. That object over there is a tree; that cup is blue; that man is taller than that man. Of course these states of affairs preclude infinitely many others, but how do we come to be aware of this? How does the idea of incompatibility arise in our minds? Certainly not directly from our impressions of things-as-they-are."

The same book makes the valid point that the process of knowing is not passive, but active:

"We do not sit around passively waiting for the world to impress its 'reality' on us. Instead, as is now widely recognised, we get much of our most basic knowledge through taking action." [46]

Human thought is essentially concrete. The mind does not readily assimilate abstract concepts. We feel most at home with what is immediately before our eyes, or at least with things that can be represented in a concrete way. It is as if the mind requires a crutch in the shape of images. On this, Margaret Donaldson remarks: "even preschool children can frequently reason well about the events in the stories they hear. However, when we move beyond the bounds of human sense there is a dramatic difference. Thinking which does move beyond these bounds, so that it no longer operates within the supportive context of meaningful events, is often called 'formal' or 'abstract'." [47]

The initial process thus goes from the concrete to the abstract. The object is dismembered, analysed, in order to obtain a detailed knowledge of its parts. But there are dangers in this. The parts cannot be correctly understood apart from their relationship with the whole. It is necessary to return to the object as an integral system, and to grasp the underlying dynamics that condition it as a whole. In this way, the process of cognition moves from the abstract back to the concrete. This is the

(46) M. Donaldson, *Making Sense*, pp. 98-9.
(47) M. Donaldson, *Children's Minds*, p. 76.

essence of the dialectical method, which combines analysis with synthesis, induction and deduction.

The whole swindle of idealism is derived from an incorrect understanding of the nature of abstraction. Lenin pointed out that the possibility of idealism is inherent in any abstraction. The abstract concept of a thing is counterpoised artificially to the thing itself. It is supposed not only to have an existence of its own, but is said to be superior to crude material reality. The concrete is portrayed as somehow defective, imperfect and impure, as opposed to the Idea, which is perfect, absolute and pure. Thus reality is stood on its head.

The ability to think in abstractions marks a colossal conquest of the human intellect. Not only "pure" science, but also engineering would be impossible without abstract thought, which lifts us above the immediate, finite reality of the concrete example, and gives thought a universal character. The unthinking rejection of abstract thought and theory indicates the kind of narrow, Philistine mentality, which imagines itself to be "practical", but, in reality, is impotent. Ultimately, great advances in theory lead to great advances in practice. Nevertheless, all ideas are derived one way or another from the physical world, and, ultimately, must be applied back to it. The validity of any theory must be demonstrated, sooner or later, in practice.

In recent years there has been a healthy reaction against the mechanical *reductionism*, counterpoising the need for a *holistic* approach to science. The term holistic is unfortunate, because of its mystical associations. Nevertheless, in attempting to see things in their movement and interconnections, chaos theory undoubtedly comes close to dialectics. The real relationship between formal logic and dialectics is that between the type of thinking that takes things apart, and looks at them separately, and that which is also able to put them together again and make them work. If thought is to correspond to reality, it must be capable of grasping it as a living whole, with all its contradictions.

What is a syllogism?

"Logical thinking, formal thinking in general," says Trotsky, "is constructed on the basis of the deductive method, proceeding from a more general syllogism through a number of premises to the necessary conclusion. Such a chain of syllogisms is called a sorites." [48]

Aristotle was the first one to write a systematic account of both dialectics and formal logic, as methods of reasoning. The purpose of formal logic was to provide a framework to distinguish valid from invalid arguments. This he did in the form of syllogisms. There are different forms of syllogism, which are really variations on the same theme.

(48) Trotsky, *Writings, 1939-40*, p. 400.

Aristotle in his *Organon*, names ten categories—substance, quantity, quality, relation, place, time, position, state, action, passion—which form the basis of the *dialectical logic*, later given its full expression in the writings of Hegel. This side of Aristotle's work on logic is frequently ignored. The British philosopher Bertrand A.W. Russell (1872-1970), for example, considered these categories to be meaningless. But since logical positivists like Russell have written off practically the whole history of philosophy (except the bits and pieces that coincide with their dogmas) as "meaningless", this should neither surprise nor trouble us too much.

The syllogism is a method of logical reasoning, which may be variously described. The definition given by Aristotle himself was as follows: "A discourse in which, certain things being stated, something other than what is stated follows of necessity from their being so." The simplest definition is given by A.A. Luce: *"A syllogism is a triad of connected propositions, so related that one of them, called the Conclusion, necessarily follows from the other two, which are called the Premises."* [49]

The mediaeval Schoolmen focused their attention on this kind of formal logic, which Aristotle developed in *The Prior and Posterior Analytics*. It is in this form that Aristotle's logic came down from the Middle Ages. In practice, the syllogism consists of two premises and a conclusion. The subject and the predicate of the conclusion each occur in one of the premises, together with a third term (the *middle*) that is found in both premises, but not in the conclusion. The predicate of the conclusion is *the major term*; the premise in which it is contained is the *major premise*; the subject of the conclusion is *the minor term*; and the premise in which it is contained is *the minor premise*. For example,

a) All men are mortal. (*Major premise*)
b) Caesar is a man. (*Minor premise*)
c) Therefore, Caesar is mortal. (*Conclusion*)

This is called an *affirmative categorical statement*. It gives the impression of being a logical chain of argument, in which each stage is derived inexorably from the previous one. But actually, this is not the case, because "Caesar" is already included in "all men". Kant, like Hegel, regarded the syllogism (that "tedious doctrine", as he called it) with contempt. For him, it was "nothing more than an artifice" in which the conclusions were already surreptitiously introduced into the premises to give a false appearance of reasoning. [50]

Another type of syllogism is conditional in form (if...then), for example: "If an animal is a tiger, it is a carnivore." This is just another way of saying the same thing as the affirmative categorical statement, i.e., all tigers are carnivores. The same in relation to the negative form—"If it's a fish, it's not a mammal" is just another way of saying "No fishes are mammals". The formal difference conceals the fact that we have not really advanced a single step.

(49) A.A. Luce, op. cit., p. 83 (our emphasis).
(50) Kant, *Critique of Pure Reason*, p. 99, footnote.

What this really reveals is the inner connections between things, not just in thought, but in the real world. "A" and "B" are related in certain ways to "C" (*the middle*) and the premise, therefore, they are related to each other in the conclusion. With great profundity and insight, Hegel showed that what the syllogism showed was the relation of the particular to the universal. In other words, the syllogism itself is an example of the unity of opposites, the contradiction *par excellence*, and that, in reality, all things are a "syllogism".

The heyday of the syllogism was in the Middle Ages, when the Schoolmen devoted their entire lives to endless disputations on all manner of obscure theological questions, like the sex of angels. The labyrinthine constructions of formal logic made it appear that they were really involved in a profound discussion, when, in fact, they were arguing about *nothing at all*. The reason for this lies in the nature of formal logic itself. As the name suggests, it is all about form. The question of the content does not enter into it. This is precisely the chief defect of formal logic, and its Achilles' heel.

By the time of the Renaissance, that great re-awakening of the human spirit, dissatisfaction with Aristotelian logic was widespread. There was a growing reaction against Aristotle, which was not really fair to this great thinker, but stemmed from the fact that the Church had suppressed all that was worthwhile in his philosophy, and preserved only a lifeless caricature. For Aristotle, the syllogism was only part of the process of reasoning, and not necessarily the most important part. Aristotle also wrote on the dialectic, but this aspect was forgotten. Logic was deprived of all life, and turned, in Hegel's phrase, into "the lifeless bones of a skeleton".

The revulsion against this lifeless formalism was reflected in the movement towards empiricism, which gave a tremendous impetus to scientific investigation and experiment. However, it is not possible to dispense altogether with forms of thought, and empiricism from the beginning carried the seeds of its own destruction. The only viable alternative to inadequate and incorrect methods of reasoning is to develop adequate and correct ones.

By the end of the Middle Ages the syllogism was discredited everywhere, and subjected to ridicule and abuse. Rabelais, Petrarch and Montaigne all denounced it. But it continued to trundle along, especially in those Catholic lands, untouched by the fresh winds of the Reformation. By the end of the 18th century, logic was in such a bad state that Kant felt obliged to launch a general criticism of the old thought forms in his *Critique of Pure Reason*.

Hegel was the first one to subject the laws of formal logic to a thoroughgoing critical analysis. In this, he was completing the work commenced by Kant. But whereas Kant only showed the inherent deficiencies and contradictions of traditional logic, Hegel went much further, working out a completely different approach to logic, a dynamic approach, which would include movement and contradiction, which formal logic is powerless to deal with.

Does logic teach how to think?

Dialectics does not pretend to teach people to think. That is the pretentious claim of formal logic, to which Hegel ironically replied that logic no more teaches you to think than physiology teaches you to digest! Men and women thought, and even thought logically, long before they ever heard of logic. The categories of logic, and also dialectics, are derived from actual experience. For all their pretensions, the categories of formal logic do not stand above the crude world of material reality, but are only empty abstractions taken from reality comprehended in a one-sided and static manner, and then arbitrarily applied back to it.

By contrast, the first law of the dialectical method is *absolute objectivity*. In every case, it is necessary to discover the laws of motion of a given phenomenon by studying it from every point of view. The dialectical method is of great value in approaching things correctly, avoiding elementary philosophical blunders, and making sound scientific hypotheses. In view of the astonishing amount of mysticism that has emerged from arbitrary hypotheses, above all in theoretical physics, this is no mean advantage! But the dialectical method always seeks to derive its categories from a careful study of the facts and processes, not to force the facts into a rigid preconceived straitjacket:

"We all agree," wrote Engels, "that in every field of science, in natural as in historical science, one must proceed from the given facts, in natural science therefore from the various material forms and the various forms of motion of matter; that therefore in theoretical natural science too the inter-connections are not to be built into the facts but to be discovered in them, and when discovered to be verified as far as possible by experiment." [51]

Science is founded on the search for general laws which can explain the workings of nature. Taking its starting point as experience, it does not confine itself to the mere collection of facts, but seeks to generalise on the basis of experience, going from the particular to the universal. The history of science is characterised by an ever-deepening process of approximation. We get closer and closer to the truth, without ever knowing the *"whole truth"*. Ultimately, the test of scientific truth is experiment. "Experiment," says Feynman, "is the *sole judge* of scientific 'truth'." [52]

The validity of forms of thought must, in the last analysis, depend on whether they correspond to the reality of the physical world. This cannot be established a priori, but must be demonstrated through observation and experiment. Formal logic, in contrast to all the natural sciences, is not empirical. Science derives its data from observation of the real world. Logic is supposed to be a priori, unlike all the subject matter with which it deals. There is a glaring contradiction here between form and content. Logic is not supposed to be derived from the real world, yet it is constantly applied to the facts of the real world. What is the relationship between the two sides?

(51) Engels, *The Dialectics of Nature*, pp. 64-5.
(52) Feynman, op. cit., chapter 1, p. 2.

Kant long ago explained that the forms of logic must reflect objective reality, or they would be entirely meaningless:

"When we have reason to consider a judgment necessarily universal...we must consider it objective also, that is, that it expresses not merely a reference of our perception to a subject, but a quality of the object. For there would be no reason for the judgments of other men necessarily agreeing with mine, if it were not the unity of the object to which they all refer, and with which they accord; hence they must all agree with one another." [53]

This idea was developed further by Hegel, who removed the ambiguities present in Kant's theory of knowledge and logic, and finally put on a sound basis by Marx and Engels:

"Logical schemata," Engels explains, "can only relate to *forms of thought*; but what we are dealing with here are only forms of *being*, of the external world, and these forms can never be created and derived by thought out of itself, but only from the external world. But with this the whole relationship is inverted: the principles are not the starting point of the investigation, but its final result; they are not applied to nature and human history, but abstracted from them; it is not nature and the realm of humanity which conform to these principles, but the principles are only valid in so far as they are in conformity with nature and history." [54]

Limits of the Law of Identity

It is an astonishing fact that the basic laws of formal logic worked out by Aristotle have remained fundamentally unchanged for over two thousand years. In this period, we have witnessed a continuous process of change in all spheres of science, technology and human thought. And yet scientists have been content to continue to use essentially the same methodological tools that were used by the mediaeval Schoolmen in the days when science was still on the level of alchemy.

Given the central role played by formal logic in Western thought, it is surprising how little attention is paid to its real content, meaning and history. It is normally taken as something given, self-evident, and fixed for all time. Or it is presented as a convenient convention which reasonable people agree upon, in order to facilitate thought and discourse, rather as people in polite social circles agree upon good table manners. The idea is put forward that the laws of logic are entirely artificial constructions, made up by logicians, in the belief that they will have some application in some field of thought, where they will reveal some truth or other. But why should the laws of logic have any bearing upon anything, if they are only abstract constructions, the arbitrary imaginings of the brain?

(53) Kant, *Prolegomena zu einer jeden künftigen Metaphysik*, quoted in E.V. Ilyenkov, *Dialectical Logic*, p. 90.
(54) Engels, *Anti-Dühring*, p. 43.

On this idea, Trotsky commented ironically:

"To say that people have come to an agreement about the syllogism is almost like saying, or more correctly it is exactly the same as saying, that people came to an agreement to have nostrils in their noses. The syllogism is no less an objective product of organic development, i.e., the biological, anthropological, and social development of humanity than are our various organs, among them our organ of smell." In reality, formal logic is ultimately derived from experience, just as any other way of thinking. From their experience, humans draw certain conclusions, which they apply in their daily life. This applies even to animals, though at a different level.

"The chicken knows that grain is in general useful, necessary, and tasty. It recognises a given piece of grain as that grain—of the wheat—with which it is acquainted and hence draws a logical conclusion by means of its beak. The syllogism of Aristotle is only an articulated expression of those elementary mental conclusions which we observe at every step among animals." [55]

Trotsky once said that the relationship between formal logic and dialectics was similar to the relationship between lower and higher mathematics. The one does not deny the other and continues to be valid within certain limits. Likewise, Newton's laws, which were dominant for a hundred years, were shown to be false in the world of subatomic particles. More correctly, the old mechanistic physics, which was criticised by Engels, was shown to be one-sided and of limited application.

"The dialectic," writes Trotsky, "is neither fiction nor mysticism, but a science of the forms of our thinking *insofar as it is not limited to the daily problems of life but attempts to arrive at an understanding of more complicated and drawn-out processes.*" [56]

The most common method of formal logic is that of deduction, which attempts to establish the truth of its conclusions by meeting two distinct conditions: a) the conclusion must really flow from the premises; and b) the premises themselves must be true. If both conditions are met, the argument is said to be valid. This is all very comforting. We are here in the familiar and reassuring realm of common sense. "True or false?" "Yes or no?" Our feet are firmly on the ground. We appear to be in possession of "the truth, the whole truth, and nothing but the truth". There is not a lot more to be said. Or is there?

Strictly speaking, from the standpoint of formal logic, it is a matter of indifference whether the premises are true or false. As long as the conclusions can be correctly drawn from its premises, the inference is said to be deductively valid. The important thing is to distinguish between valid and invalid inferences. Thus, from the standpoint of formal logic, the following assertion is *deductively valid*: All sci-

(55) Trotsky, *Writings, 1939-40*, pp. 399 and 400.
(56) Trotsky, *In Defence of Marxism*, p. 65, our emphasis.

entists have two heads. Einstein was a scientist. Therefore, Einstein had two heads. The validity of the inference does not depend upon the subject matter in the slightest. In this way, the form is elevated above the content.

In practice, of course, any mode of reasoning that did not demonstrate the truth of its premises would be worse than useless. The premises must be shown to be true. But this leads us into a contradiction. The process of validating one set of premises automatically raises a new set of questions, which in turn need to be validated. As Hegel points out, every premise gives rise to a new syllogism, and so on ad infinitum. So that what appeared to be very simple turns out to be extremely complex, and contradictory.

The biggest contradiction of all lies in the fundamental premises of formal logic itself. While demanding that everything else under the sun must justify itself in the High Court of the Syllogism, logic becomes utterly confused when asked to justify its own presuppositions. It suddenly loses all its critical faculties, and resorts to appeals to belief, common sense, the "obvious", or, the final philosophical get-out clause—a priori. The fact is that the so-called *axioms* of logic are unproved formulas. These are taken as the starting point, from which all further formulae (*theorems*) are deduced, exactly as in classical geometry, where the starting point is provided by Euclid's principles. They are assumed to be correct, without any proof whatsoever, i.e., *we just have to take them on trust.*

But what if the basic axioms of formal logic turn out to be false? Then we would be in just the same position as when we gave poor Mr. Einstein an additional head. Is it conceivable that the eternal laws of logic might be flawed? Let us examine the matter more closely. The basic laws of formal logic are:

1) The law of identity ("A" = "A").
2) The law of contradiction ("A" does not equal "not-A").
3) The law of the excluded middle ("A" does not equal "B").

These laws, at first sight, seem eminently sensible. How could anyone quarrel with them? Yet closer analysis shows that these laws are full of problems and contradictions of a philosophical nature. In his *Science of Logic*, Hegel provides an exhaustive analysis of the Law of Identity, showing it to be one-sided and, therefore, incorrect.

Firstly, let us note that the appearance of a necessary chain of reasoning, in which one step follows from another, is entirely illusory. The law of contradiction merely restates the law of identity in a negative form. The same is true of the law of the excluded middle. All we have is a repetition of the first line in different ways. The whole thing stands or falls on the basis of the law of identity ("A" = "A"). At first sight this is incontrovertible, and, indeed, the source of all rational thought. It is the Holy of Holies of Logic, and not to be called into question. Yet called into question it was, and by one of the greatest minds of all time.

There is a story by Hans-Christian Andersen called *The Emperor's New Suit of Clothes*, in which a rather foolish emperor is sold a new suit by a swindler, which is supposed to be very beautiful, but invisible. The gullible emperor goes about in his fine new suit, which everyone agrees is exquisite, until one day a little boy points out that the emperor is, in fact, stark naked. Hegel performed a comparable service to philosophy in his critique of formal logic. Its defenders have never forgiven him for it.

The so-called law of identity is, in fact, a tautology. Paradoxically, in traditional logic, this was always regarded as one of the most glaring mistakes that can be committed in defining a concept. It is a logically untenable definition which merely repeats in other words what is already contained in the part to be defined. Let us put this more concretely. A teacher asks his pupil what a cat is, and the pupil proudly informs him that a cat is—a cat. Such an answer would not be considered very intelligent. After all, a sentence is generally intended to say something, and this sentence tells us nothing at all. Yet this not very bright scholar's definition of a feline quadruped is a perfect expression of the law of identity in all its glory. The young person concerned would immediately be sent to the bottom of the class. Yet for over two thousand years, the most learned professors have been content to treat it as the most profound philosophical truth.

All that the law of identity tells us about something is that it is. We do not get a single step further. We remain on the level of the most general and empty abstraction. For we learn nothing about the concrete reality of the object under consideration, its properties and relationships. A cat is a cat; I am myself; you are you; human nature is human nature; things are as they are. The emptiness of such assertions stands out in all its uncouthness. It is the consummate expression of one-sided, formalistic, dogmatic thinking.

Is the law of identity invalid, then? Not entirely. It has its applications, but these are far more limited in scope than what one might think. The laws of formal logic can be useful in clarifying certain concepts, analysing, labelling, cataloguing, defining. It has the merit of neatness and tidiness. This has its place. For normal, simple, everyday phenomena, it holds good. But when dealing with more complex phenomena, involving movement, sudden leaps, qualitative changes, it becomes wholly inadequate, and, in fact, breaks down completely.

The following extract by Trotsky brilliantly sums up Hegel's line of argument in relation to the law of identity:

"I will here attempt to sketch the substance of the problem in a very concise form. The Aristotelian logic of the simple syllogism starts from the proposition that 'A' is equal to 'A'. This postulate is accepted as an axiom for a multitude of practical human actions and elementary generalisations. But in reality 'A' is not equal to 'A'. This is easy to prove if we observe these two letters under a lens—they are quite different from each other. But, one can object, the question is not of the size or the form of the letters, since they are only symbols for equal quantities, for instance, a pound of sugar. The objection is beside the point; in reality a pound of sugar is never equal to a pound of sugar—a more delicate scale always discloses a difference. Again one can object: but a pound of sugar is equal to itself. Neither is this true—all bodies change uninterruptedly in size, weight, colour, etc. They are never equal to themselves. A sophist will respond that a pound of sugar is equal to itself 'at any given moment'. Aside from the extremely dubious practical value of this 'axiom', it does not withstand theoretical criticism either. How should we really conceive the word 'moment'? If it is an infinitesimal interval of time, then a pound of sugar is subjected during the course of that 'moment' to inevitable changes. Or is the 'moment' a purely mathematical abstraction, that is, a zero of time? But everything exists in time; and existence itself is an uninterrupted process of transformation; time is consequently a fundamental element of existence. Thus the axiom 'A' is equal to 'A' signifies that a thing is equal to itself if it does not change, that is, if it does not exist.

"At first glance it could seem that these 'subtleties' are useless. In reality they are of decisive significance. The axiom 'A' is equal to 'A' appears on one hand to be the point of departure for all the errors in our knowledge. To make use of the axiom 'A' is equal to 'A' with impunity is possible only within certain limits. When quantitative changes in 'A' are negligible for the task at hand then we can presume that 'A' is equal to 'A'. This is, for example, the manner in which a buyer and a seller consider a pound of sugar. We consider the temperature of the sun likewise. Until recently we considered the buying power of the dollar in the same way. But quantitative changes beyond certain limits become converted into qualitative. A pound of sugar subjected to the action of water or kerosene ceases to be a pound of sugar. A dollar in the embrace of a president ceases to be a dollar. To determine at the right moment the critical point where quantity changes into quality is one of the most important and difficult tasks in all the spheres of knowledge including sociology...

"Dialectical thinking is related to vulgar thinking in the same way that a motion picture is related to a still photograph. The motion picture does not outlaw the still photograph but combines a series of them according to the laws of motion. Dialectics does not deny the syllogism, but teaches us to combine syllogisms in such a way as to bring our understanding closer to the eternally changing reality. Hegel in his *Logic* established a series of laws: change of quantity into quality, development through contradictions, conflict of content and form, interruption of continuity, change of possibility into inevitability, etc., which are just as important for theoretical thought as is the simple syllogism for more elementary tasks." [57]

Similarly with the law of the excluded middle, which asserts that it is necessary either to assert or deny, that a thing must be either black or white, either alive or

---

(57) Trotsky, *In Defence of Marxism*, pp. 63-6.

dead, either "A" or "B". It cannot be both at the same time. For normal everyday purposes, we can take this to be true. Indeed, without such assumptions, clear and consistent thought would be impossible. Moreover, what appear to be insignificant errors in theory sooner or later make themselves felt in practice, often with disastrous results. In the same way, a hairline crack in the wing of a jumbo jet may seem insignificant, and, indeed, at low speeds may pass unnoticed. At very high speeds, however, this tiny error can provoke a catastrophe. In *Anti-Dühring*, Engels explains the deficiencies of the so-called law of the excluded middle:

"To the metaphysician," wrote Engels, "things and their mental images, ideas, are isolated, to be considered one after the other and apart from each other, fixed, rigid objects of investigation given once for all. He thinks in absolutely unmediated antitheses. 'His communication is "yea, yea; nay, nay"; for whatsoever is more than these cometh of evil.' For him a thing either exists or does not exist; a thing cannot at the same time be itself and something else. Positive and negative absolutely exclude one another; cause and effect stand in a rigid antithesis one to the other.

"At first sight this way of thinking seems to us most plausible because it is that of so-called sound common sense. Yet sound common sense, respectable fellow that he is in the homely realm of his own four walls, has very wonderful adventures directly he ventures out into the wide world of research. The metaphysical mode of thought, justifiable and even necessary as it is in a number of domains whose extent varies according to the nature of the object, invariably bumps into a limit sooner or later, beyond which it becomes one-sided, restricted, abstract, lost in insoluble contradictions, because in the presence of individual things it forgets their connections; because in the presence of their existence it forgets their coming into being and passing away; because in their state of rest it forgets their motion. It cannot see the wood for the trees...

"In like manner, every organic being is every moment the same and not the same; every moment it assimilates matter supplied from without and gets rid of other matter; every moment some cells of its body die and others build themselves anew; in a longer or shorter time the matter of its body is completely renewed and is replaced by other molecules of matter, so that every organic being is always itself, and yet something other than itself." [58]

The relationship between dialectics and formal logic can be compared to the relationship between quantum mechanics and classical mechanics. They do not contradict but complement each other. The laws of classical mechanics still hold good for an immense number of operations. However, they cannot be adequately applied to the world of subatomic particles, involving infinitesimally small quantities and tremendous velocities. Similarly, Einstein did not replace Newton, but merely exposed the limits beyond which Newton's system did not work.

(58) Engels, *Anti-Dühring*, pp. 26-7.

Formal logic (which has acquired the force of popular prejudice in the form of "common sense") equally holds good for a whole series of everyday experiences. However, the laws of formal logic, which set out from an essentially static view of things, inevitably break down when dealing with more complex, changing and contradictory phenomena. To use the language of chaos theory, the "linear" equations of formal logic cannot cope with the turbulent processes which can be observed throughout nature, society and history. Only the dialectical method will suffice for this purpose.

Logic and the subatomic world

The deficiencies of traditional logic have been grasped by other philosophers, who are very far from the dialectical standpoint. In general, in the Anglo-Saxon world, there has traditionally been a greater inclination towards empiricism, and inductive reasoning. Nevertheless, science still requires a philosophical framework that will enable it to assess its results and guide its steps through the confused mass of facts and statistics, like Ariadne's thread in the labyrinth. Mere appeals to "common sense", or the "facts", will not suffice.

Syllogistic thinking, the abstract deductive method, is very much in the French tradition, especially since Descartes. The English tradition was altogether different, being heavily influenced by empiricism. From Britain, this school of thought was early on imported to the United States, where it sunk deep roots. Thus, the formal-deductive mode of thought was not at all characteristic of the Anglo-Saxon intellectual tradition. "On the contrary," wrote Trotsky, "it is possible to say that this [school of] thought is distinguished by a sovereign-empirical contempt for the pure syllogism, which did not prevent the English from making colossal conquests in many spheres of scientific investigation. If one really thinks this through as one should, then it is impossible not to arrive at the conclusion that the empirical disregard for the syllogism is a primitive form of dialectical thinking."

Empiricism historically played both a progressive role (in the struggle against religion and mediaeval dogmatism) and a negative one (an excessively narrow interpretation of materialism, resistance to broad theoretical generalisations). Locke's famous assertion that there is nothing in the intellect which is not derived from the senses contains the germ of a profoundly correct idea, but presented in a one-sided way, which could, and did, have the most harmful consequences on the future development of philosophy. In relation to this, Trotsky wrote shortly before his assassination:

"'We do not know anything about the world except what is provided through experience.' This is correct if one does not understand experience in the sense of the direct testimony of our individual five senses. If we reduce the matter to experience in the narrow empirical sense, then it is impossible for us to arrive at any judgment concerning either the origin of the species or, still less, the formation of the earth's crust. To say that the basis for everything is experience is to say too much or to say nothing at all. Experience is the active interrelationship between subject and object. To analyse experience outside this category, i.e., outside the objective material milieu of the investigator who is counterposed to it and who from another stand-point is a part of this milieu—to do this is to dissolve experience in a formless unity where there is neither object nor subject but only the mystical formula of experi-ence. 'Experiment' or 'experience' of this kind is peculiar only to a baby in its moth-er's womb, but unfortunately the baby is deprived of the opportunity to share the scientific conclusions of its experiment." [59]

The uncertainty principle of quantum mechanics cannot be applied to ordinary objects, but only to atoms and subatomic particles. Subatomic particles obey differ-ent laws to those of the "ordinary" world. They move at incredible speeds, close to the speed of light. They can move in different directions at the same time. Given this situation, the forms of thought which apply to everyday experience are no longer valid. Formal logic is useless. Its black and white, yes-or-no, take it or leave it cat-egories have no point of contact with this fluid, unstable and contradictory reality. All we can do is to say that it is probably such and such a motion, with an infinite number of possibilities. Far from proceeding from the premises of formal logic, quantum mechanics violates the law of identity by asserting the "non-individuality" of individual particles. The law of identity cannot apply at this level, because the "identity" of individual particles cannot be fixed. Hence the lengthy controversy over "wave" or "particle". It could not be both! Here "A" turns out to be "not-A", and "A" can indeed be also "B". Hence, the impossibility of "fixing" an electron's position and velocity in the neat and absolute manner of formal logic. That is a seri-ous problem for formal logic and "common sense", but not for dialectics or for quantum mechanics. An electron has both the qualities of a wave and a particle, and this has been experimentally demonstrated.

In 1932, Werner Heisenberg (1901-76), a German physicist, suggested that the protons inside the nucleus were held together by something he called *exchange force*. This implied that protons and neutrons were *constantly exchanging identity*. Any given particle is in a constant state of flux, changing from a proton into a neu-tron and back again. Only in this way is the nucleus held together. Before a proton can be repelled by another proton, it changes into a neutron, and vice versa. This process in which particles are changed into their opposites takes place uninterrupt-edly, so that it is impossible to say at any given moment whether a particle is a pro-ton or a neutron. In fact it is *both*—it is and is *not*.

The exchange of identities between electrons does not mean a simple change of position, but a complicated process where electron "A" interpenetrates with electron "B" to produce a "mix" of, say, 60 per cent "A" and 40 per cent "B" and vice versa. Later, they may have completely exchanged identities, with all "A" here and all "B"

(59) Trotsky, *Writings, 1939-40*, pp. 401 and 403.

there. The flow would then be reversed in a permanent oscillation, involving a rhythmic interchange of the electrons' identities, which goes on indefinitely. The old rigid, fixed Law of Identity vanishes altogether in this kind of pulsating identity-in-difference, which underlies all being, and received its scientific expression in Pauli's principle of exclusion.

Thus, two and a half millennia later, Heraclitus' principle "everything flows" turns out to be true—literally. Here we have, not only a state of unceasing change and motion, but also a process of universal interconnection, and the unity and inter-penetration of opposites. Not only do electrons condition each other, but they actually pass into each other and become transformed into each other. How far removed from the static, unchanging idealist universe of Plato! How does one fix the position of an electron? By looking at it. And how to determine its momentum? By looking at it twice. But in that time, even in an infinitesimally small space of time, the electron has changed, and is no longer what it was. It is something else. It is *both* a particle (a "thing", a "point") *and* a wave (a "process", movement, becoming). *It is and is not.* The old black and white method of formal logic used in classical mechanics cannot give results here because of the very nature of the phenomenon.

In 1963, it was suggested by Japanese physicists that the extremely small particle known as the neutrino changed its identity as it travelled through space at very high speeds. At one point it was an *electron-neutrino*, at another, a *muon-neutrino*, at another, a *tauon-neutrino*, and so on. If this is true, the law of identity, which has already been thoroughly battered, can be said to have received the final *coup de grace*. Such a rigid, black-and-white conception is clearly out of its depth when confronted with any one of the complex and contradictory phenomena of nature described by modern science.

Modern logic

In the 19th century, there were a number of attempts to bring logic up to date (George Boyle, Ernst Schröder, Gotlob Frege, Bertrand Russell and Alfred N. Whitehead). But, apart from the introduction of symbols, and a certain tidying up, there is no real change here. Great claims are made, for example by the linguistic philosophers, but there are not many grounds for them. Semantics (which deals with the validity of an argument) was separated from syntax (which deals with the deductibility of the conclusions from axioms and premises). This is supposed to be something new, when, in reality, it is merely a re-hash of the old division, well known to the ancient Greeks, between *logic* and *rhetoric*. Modern logic is based on the logical relations among whole sentences. The centre of attention has moved away from the syllogism towards hypothetical and disjunctive arguments. This is hardly a breathtaking leap. One can begin with sentences (judgments) instead of syllogisms. Hegel did this in his *Logic*. Rather than a great revolution in thought, it is like re-shuffling cards in a pack.

Using a superficial and inexact analogy with physics, the so-called atomic method developed by Russell and Wittgenstein (and later repudiated by the latter) tried to divide language into its "atoms". The basic atom of language is supposed to be the simple sentence, out of which compound sentences are constructed. Wittgenstein dreamed of developing a "formal language" for every science—physics, biology, even psychology. Sentences are subjected to a "truth test" based on the old laws of identity, contradiction and the excluded middle. In reality, the basic method remains exactly the same. The "truth value" is a question of "either...or", "yes or no", "true or false". The new logic is referred to as the *propositional calculus*. But the fact is that this system cannot even deal with arguments formerly handled by the most basic (categorical) syllogism. The mountain has laboured, and brought forth a mouse.

The fact is that not even the simple sentence is really understood, although it is supposed to be the linguistic equivalent of the "building-blocks of matter". Even the simplest judgment, as Hegel points out, contains a contradiction. "Caesar is a man", "Fido is a dog", "the tree is green", all state that *the particular is the universal*. Such sentences seem simple, but in fact are not. This is a closed book for formal logic, which remains determined to banish all contradictions, not only from nature and society, but from thought and language as well. Propositional calculus sets out from exactly the same basic postulates as those worked out by Aristotle in the 4th century B.C., namely, the law of identity, the law of (non-)contradiction, the law of the excluded middle, to which is added the law of double negation. Instead of being written with normal letters, they are expressed in symbols. This makes not the slightest difference to the content of the syllogism. Moreover, symbolic logic itself is not a new idea. In the 1680s, the ever-fertile brain of the German philosopher Gottfried Wilhelm Leibniz (1646-1716) created a symbolic logic, although he never published it.

The introduction of symbols into logic does not carry us a single step further, for the very simple reason that they, in turn, must sooner or later be translated into words and concepts. They have the advantage of being a kind of shorthand, more convenient for some technical operations, computers and so on, but the content remains exactly as before. The bewildering array of mathematical symbols is accompanied by a truly Byzantine jargon, which seems deliberately designed to make logic inaccessible to ordinary mortals, just as the priest-castes of Egypt and Babylon used secret words and occult symbols to keep their knowledge to themselves. The only difference is that they actually did know things that were worth knowing, like the movements of the heavenly bodies, something that cannot be said of modern logicians.

Terms such as *"monadic predicates"*, *"quantifiers"*, *"individual variables"*, and so on and so forth, are designed to give the impression that formal logic is a science to be reckoned with, since it is quite unintelligible to most people. Sad to say, the scientific value of a body of beliefs is not directly proportionate to the obscurity of its language. If that were the case, every religious mystic in history would be as great a scientist as Newton, Darwin and Einstein, all rolled into one.

In Moliere's comedy, *Le Bourgeois Gentilhomme*, M. Jourdain was surprised to be told that he had been talking *prose* all his life, without realising it. Modern logic merely repeats all the old categories, but throws in a few symbols and fancy-sounding terms, in order to hide the fact that absolutely nothing new is being said. Aristotle used monadic predicates (expressions that attribute a property to an individual) a long time ago. No doubt, like M. Jourdain, he would have been delighted to discover that he had been using monadic predicates all the time, without knowing it. But it would not have made a scrap of difference to what he was actually doing. The use of new labels does not alter the contents of a jar of jam. Nor does the use of jargon enhance the validity of outworn forms of thought.

The sad truth is that, in the 20th century formal logic has reached its limits. Every new advance of science deals it yet another blow. Despite all the formal changes, the basic laws remain the same. One thing is clear. The developments of formal logic over the past hundred years, first by propositional calculus (p.c.), then by lower predicate calculus (l.p.c.) has carried the subject to such a point of refinement that no further development is possible. We have reached the most comprehensive system of formal logic, so that any other additions will certainly not add anything new. Formal logic has said all that it has to say. If the truth were to be told, it reached this stage quite some time ago.

Recently, the ground has shifted from argument to deducing conclusions. How are the "theorems of logic derived"? This is quite shaky ground. The basis of formal logic has always been taken for granted in the past. A thorough investigation of the theoretical grounds of formal logic would inevitably result in transforming them into their opposite. Arend Heyting, the founder of the Intuitionist School of mathematics, denies the validity of some of the proofs used in classical mathematics. However, most logicians cling desperately to the old laws of formal logic, like a drowning man clutching at a straw:

"We do not believe that there is any non-Aristotelian logic in the sense in which there is a non-Euclidean geometry," remark Morris R. Cohen and Ernest Nagel, "that is, a system of logic in which the contraries of the Aristotelian principles of contradiction and the excluded middle are assumed to be true, and valid inferences drawn from them." [60]

There are two main branches of formal logic today—propositional calculus and predicate calculus. They all proceed from axioms, which are assumed to be true "in all possible worlds", under all circumstances. The fundamental test remains freedom from contradiction. Anything contradictory is deemed to be "not valid". This

---

(60) Morris R. Cohen and Ernest Nagel, *An Introduction to Logic and the Scientific Method*, p. vii.

has a certain application, for example, in computers, which are geared to a simple *yes* or *no* procedure. In reality, however, all such axioms are *tautologies*. These empty forms can be filled with almost any content. They are applied in a mechanical and external fashion to any subject. When it comes to simple linear processes, they do their work tolerably well. This is important, because a great many of the processes in nature and society do, in fact, work in this way. But when we come to more complex, contradictory, non-linear phenomena, the laws of formal logic break down. It immediately becomes evident that, far from being universal truths valid "in all possible worlds", they are, as Engels explained, quite limited in their application, and quickly find themselves out of their depth in a whole range of circumstances. Moreover, these are precisely the kind of circumstances that have occupied the attention of science, especially the most innovative parts of it, for most of the 20th century.

Part two:
Time, space and motion

5. Revolution in physics

Two thousand years ago, it was thought that the laws of the universe were completely covered by Euclid's geometry. There was nothing more to be said. This is the illusion of every period. For a long time after Newton's death, scientists thought that he had said the last word about the laws of nature. Laplace lamented that there was only one universe, and that Newton had had the good fortune to discover all its laws. For two hundred years, Newton's particle theory of light was generally accepted, as against the theory, advocated by the Dutch physicist Christiaan Huygens (1629-95), that light was a wave. Then the particle theory was negated by the Frenchman, Augustin Jean Fresnel (1788-27), whose wave theory was experimentally confirmed by Jean.B.L. Foucault (1819-68). Newton had predicted that light, which travels at 186,000 miles per second (around 300,000 km) in empty space, should travel faster in water. The supporters of the wave theory predicted a lower speed, and were shown to be correct.

The great breakthrough for wave theory, however, was accomplished by the outstanding Scottish scientist James Clerk Maxwell, in the latter half of the 19th century. Maxwell based himself in the first instance on the experimental work of Michael Faraday, who discovered electromagnetic induction, and investigated the properties of the magnet, with its two poles, north and south, involving invisible forces stretching to the ends of the earth. Maxwell gave these empirical discoveries a universal form by translating them into mathematics. His work led to the discovery of the *field*, on which Einstein later based his general theory of relativity. One generation stands on the shoulders of its predecessors, both negating and preserving earlier discoveries, continually deepening them, and giving them a more general form and content.

Seven years after Maxwell's death, Heinrich Rudolf Hertz (1857-94) first detected the electromagnetic waves predicted by Maxwell. The particle theory, which had held sway ever since Newton, appeared to be annihilated by Maxwell's electromagnetics. Once again, scientists believed themselves in possession of a theory that could explain everything. There were just a few questions to be cleared up, and we would really know all there was to know about the workings of the universe. Of course, there were a few discrepancies that were troublesome, but they appeared to be small details which could safely be ignored. However, within a few decades, these "minor" discrepancies proved sufficient to overthrow the entire edifice and effect a veritable scientific revolution.

Waves or particles?

Everyone knows what a wave is. It is a common feature associated with water. Just as waves can be caused by a duck moving over the surface of a pond, so a charged particle, an electron for example, can cause an *electromagnetic wave*, when it moves through space. The oscillatory motion of the electron disturbs the electric and magnetic fields, causing waves to spread out continuously, like the ripples on the pond. Of course, the analogy is only approximate. There is a fundamental difference between a wave on water and an electromagnetic wave. The latter does not require a continuous medium through which to travel, like water. An electromagnetic oscillation is a periodical disturbance that propagates itself through the electrical structure of matter. However, the comparison may help to make the idea clearer.

The fact that we cannot see these waves does not mean that their presence cannot be detected even in everyday life. We have direct experience of light waves and radio waves, and even X-rays. The only differences between them are their frequency. We know that a wave on water will cause a floating object to bob up and down faster or slower, depending on the intensity of the wave—the ripples caused by the duck, as compared to those provoked by a speedboat. Similarly, the oscillations of the electrons will be proportionate to the intensity of the light wave.

The equations of Maxwell, backed up by the experiments of Hertz and others, provided powerful evidence to support the theory that light consisted of waves, which were electromagnetic in character. However, at the turn of the century, evidence was accumulating which suggested that this theory was wrong. In 1900 Max Planck had shown that the classical wave theory made predictions that were not verified in practice. He suggested that light came in discrete particles or "packets" (*quanta*). The situation was complicated by the fact that different experiments proved different things. It could be shown that an electron was a particle by letting it strike a fluorescent screen and observing the resulting scintillations; or by watching the tracks made by electrons in a cloud chamber; or by the tiny spot that appeared on a developed photographer's plate. On the other hand, if two holes are made in a screen, and electrons were allowed to flood in from a single source, they caused an interference pattern, which indicated the presence of a wave.

The most peculiar result of all, however, was obtained in the celebrated two-slot experiment, in which a single electron is fired at a screen containing two slots and a photographer's plate behind it. Which of the two holes did the electron pass through? The interference pattern on the plate is quite clearly a two-hole pattern.

This proves that the electron must have gone through *both* holes, and then set up an interference pattern. This is against all the laws of common sense, but it has been shown to be irrefutable. The electron behaves both like a particle and a wave. It is in two (or more than two) places at once, and in several states of motion at once!

"Let us not imagine," comments Banesh Hoffmann, "that scientists accepted these new ideas with cries of joy. They fought them and resisted them as much as they could, inventing all sorts of traps and alternative hypotheses in vain attempts to escape them. But the glaring paradoxes were there as early as 1905 in the case of light, and even earlier, and no one had the courage or wit to resolve them until the advent of the new quantum mechanics. The new ideas are so difficult to accept because we still instinctively strive to picture them in terms of the old-fashioned particle, despite Heisenberg's indeterminacy principle. We still shrink from visual-ising an electron as something which, having motion, may have no position, and having position, may have no such thing as motion or rest." [1]

Here we see the negation of the negation at work. At first sight, we seem to have come full circle. Newton's particle theory of light was negated by Maxwell's wave theory. This, in turn, was negated by the new particle theory, advocated by Planck and Einstein. Yet this does not mean going back to the old Newtonian theory, but a qualitative leap forward, involving a genuine revolution in science. All of science had to be overhauled, including Newton's law of gravitation.

This revolution did not invalidate Maxwell's equations, which still remain valid for a vast field of operations. It merely showed that, beyond certain limits, the ideas of classical physics no longer apply. The phenomena of the world of subatomic par-ticles cannot be understood by the methods of classical mechanics. Here the ideas of quantum mechanics and relativity come into play. For most of the present centu-ry, physics has been dominated by the theory of relativity and quantum mechanics that in the beginning were rejected out of hand by the scientific establishment, which clung tenaciously to the old views. There is an important lesson here. Any attempt to impose a "final solution" to our view of the universe is doomed to fail.

Quantum mechanics

The development of quantum physics represented a giant step forward in science, a decisive break with the old stultifying mechanical determinism of "classical" physics. (The "metaphysical" method, as Engels would have called it.) Instead, we have a much more flexible, dynamic—in a word dialectical—view of nature. Beginning with Planck's discovery of the existence of the quantum, which at first appeared to be a tiny detail, almost an anecdote, the face of physics was trans-formed. Here was a new science which could explain the phenomenon of radioac-tive transformation and analyse in great detail the complex data of spectroscopy. It

(1) B. Hoffmann, *The Strange Story of the Quantum*, p. 147.

directly led to the establishment of a new science—theoretical chemistry, capable of solving previously insoluble questions. In general, a whole series of theoretical difficulties were eliminated, once the new standpoint was accepted. The new physics revealed the staggering forces locked up within the atomic nucleus. This led directly to the exploitation of nuclear energy—the path to the potential destruction of life on earth—or the vista of undreamed of and limitless abundance and social progress through the peaceful use of nuclear fusion. Einstein's theory of relativity explains that mass and energy are equivalents. If the mass of an object is known, by multiplying it by the square of the speed of light, it becomes energy.

Einstein (1879-1955) showed that light, hitherto thought of as a wave, behaved like a particle. Light, in other words, is just another form of matter. This was proved in 1919, when it was shown that light bends under the force of gravity. Louis de Broglie later pointed out that matter, which was thought to consist of particles, partakes of the nature of waves. The division between matter and energy was abolished once and for all. Matter and energy are…the same. Here was a mighty advance for science. And from the standpoint of dialectical materialism matter and energy are the same. Engels described energy ("motion") as "the mode of existence, the inherent attribute, of matter." [2]

The argument that dominated particle physics for many years, whether subatomic particles like photons and electrons were particles or waves was finally resolved by quantum mechanics, which asserts that subatomic particles can and do behave both like a particle and like a wave. Like a wave, light produces interferences, yet a photon of light also bounces off all electrons, like a particle. This goes against the laws of formal logic. How can "common sense" accept that an electron can be in two places at the same time? Or even move, at incredible speeds, simultaneously, in different directions? For light to behave both as a wave and as a particle was seen as an intolerable contradiction. The attempts to explain the contradictory phenomena of the subatomic world in terms of formal logic leads to the abandonment of rational thinking all together. In his conclusion to a work dealing with the quantum revolution, Banesh Hoffmann is capable of writing:

"How much more, then, shall we marvel at the wondrous powers of God who created the heaven and the earth from a primal essence of such exquisite subtlety that with it he could fashion brains and minds afire with the divine gift of clairvoyance to penetrate his mysteries. If the mind of a mere Bohr or Einstein astound us with its power, how may we begin to extol the glory of God who created them?" [3]

Unfortunately, this is not an isolated example. A great part of modern literature about science, including a lot written by scientists themselves, is thoroughly impregnated with such mystical, religious or quasi-religious notions. This is a direct result of the idealist philosophy, which a great many scientists, consciously or unconsciously, have adopted.

(2) Engels, *Dialectics of Nature*, p. 92.
(3) B. Hoffmann, op. cit., pp. 194-5.

The laws of quantum mechanics fly in the face of "common sense" (i.e., formal logic), but are in perfect consonance with dialectical materialism. Take, for example, the conception of a point. All traditional geometry is derived from a point, which subsequently becomes a line, a plane, a cube, etc. Yet close observation reveals that the point does not exist.

The point is conceived as the smallest expression of space, something that has no dimension. In reality, such a point consists of atoms—electrons, nuclei, photons, and even smaller particles. Ultimately, it disappears in a restless flux of swirling quantum waves. And there is no end to this process. No fixed "point" at all. That is the final answer to the idealists who seek to find perfect "forms" which allegedly lie "beyond" observable material reality. The only "ultimate reality" is the infinite, eternal, ever-changing material universe, which is far more wonderful in its endless variety of form and processes than the most fabulous adventures of science fiction. Instead of a fixed location—a "point"—we have a process, a never-ending flux. All attempts to impose a limit on this, in the form of a beginning or an end, will inevitably fail.

Disappearance of matter?

Long before the discovery of relativity, science had discovered two fundamental principles—the conservation of energy and the conservation of mass. The first of these was worked out by Leibniz in the 17th century, and subsequently developed in the 19th century as a corollary of a principle of mechanics. Long before that, early man discovered in practice the principle of the equivalence of work and heat, when he made fire by means of friction, thus translating a given amount of energy (work) into heat. At the beginning of this century, it was discovered that mass is merely one of the forms of energy. A particle of matter is nothing more than energy, highly concentrated and localised. The amount of energy concentrated in a particle is proportional to its mass, and the total amount of energy always remains the same. The loss of one kind of energy is compensated for by the gain of another kind of energy. While constantly changing its form, nevertheless, energy always remains the same.

The revolution effected by Einstein was to show that mass itself contains a staggering amount of energy. The equivalence of mass and energy is expressed by the formula $E = mc^2$ in which c represents the velocity of light (about 186,000 miles per second), E is the energy that is contained in the stationary body, and m is its mass. The energy contained in the mass m is equal to this mass, multiplied by the square of the tremendous speed of light. Mass is therefore an immensely concentrated form of energy, the power of which may be conveyed by the fact that the energy released by an atomic explosion is less than one tenth of one per cent of the mass converted into energy. Normally this vast amount of energy locked up in matter is not manifested, and therefore passes unnoticed. But if the processes within the nucleus reach a critical point, part of the energy is released, as kinetic energy.

Since mass is only one of the forms of energy, matter and energy can neither be created nor destroyed. The forms of energy, on the other hand, are extremely diverse. For example, when protons in the sun unite to form helium nuclei, nuclear energy is released. This may first appear as the kinetic energy of motion of nuclei, contributing to the heat energy from the sun. Part of this energy is emitted from the sun in the form of photons, containing particles of electromagnetic energy. The latter, in turn, is transformed by the process of photosynthesis into the stored chemical energy in plants, which, in turn, is acquired by man by eating the plants, or animals which have fed upon the plants, to provide the warmth and energy for muscles, blood circulation, brain, etc.

The laws of classical physics in general cannot be applied to processes at the subatomic level. However, there is one law that knows no exception in nature—the law of the conservation of energy. Physicists know that neither a positive nor a negative charge can be created out of nothing. This fact is expressed by the law of the conservation of electric charge. Thus, in the process of producing a beta particle, the disappearance of the neutron (which has no charge) gives rise to a pair of particles with opposed charges—a positively charged proton and a negatively charged electron. Taken together, the two new particles have a combined electrical charge equal to zero.

If we take the opposite process, when a proton emits a positron and changes into a neutron, the charge of the original particle (the proton) is positive, and the resulting pair of particles (the neutron and positron), taken together, are positively charged. In all these myriad changes, the law of the conservation of electrical charge is strictly maintained, as are all the other conservation laws. Not even the tiniest fraction of energy is created or destroyed. Nor will such a phenomenon ever occur.

When an electron and its anti-particle, the positron, destroy themselves, their mass "disappears", that is to say, it is transformed into two light-particles (photons) which fly apart in opposite directions. However, these have the same total energy as the particles from which they emerged. Mass-energy, linear momentum and electric charge are all preserved. This phenomenon has nothing in common with disappearance in the sense of annihilation. Dialectically, the electron and positron are negated and preserved at the same time. Matter and energy (which is merely two ways of saying the same thing) can neither be created nor destroyed, only transformed.

From the standpoint of dialectical materialism, matter is the objective reality given to us in sense perception. That includes not just "solid" objects, but also light. Photons are just as much matter as electrons or positrons. Mass is constantly being changed into energy (including light—photons) and energy into mass. The "annihilation" of a positron and an electron produces a pair of photons, but we also see the opposite process: when two photons meet, an electron and a positron can be produced, provided that the photons possess sufficient energy. This is sometimes presented as the creation of matter "from nothing". It is no such thing. What we see here is neither the destruction nor the creation of anything, but the continuous transformation of matter into energy, and vice versa. When a photon hits an atom, it ceases to exist as a photon. It vanishes, but causes a change in the atom—an electron jumps from one orbit to another of higher energy. Here too, the opposite process occurs. When an electron jumps to an orbit of lower energy, a photon emerges.

The process of continual change that characterises the world at the subatomic level is a striking confirmation of the fact that dialectics is not just a subjective invention of the mind, but actually corresponds to objective processes taking place in nature. This process has gone on uninterruptedly for all eternity. It is a concrete demonstration of the indestructibility of matter—precisely the opposite of what it was meant to prove.

'Bricks of matter'?

For centuries, scientists have tried in vain to find the "bricks of matter"—the ultimate, smallest particle. A hundred years ago, they thought they had found it in the atom (which, in Greek, signifies "that which cannot be divided"). The discovery of subatomic particles led physics to probe deeper into the structure of matter. By 1928 scientists imagined that they had discovered the smallest particles—protons, electrons and photons. All the material world was supposed to be made up of these three. Subsequently, this was shattered by the discovery of the neutron, the positron, the deuteron, then a host of other particles, ever smaller, with an increasingly fleeting existence—neutrinos, pi-mesons, mu-mesons, k-mesons, and many others. The life span of some of these particles is so evanescent—maybe a billionth of a second—that they have been described as "virtual particles"—something utterly unthinkable in the pre-quantum era.

The *tauon* lasts only for a trillionth of a second, before breaking down into a *muon*, and then to an electron. The neutral *pion* is even more fleeting, breaking down in less than one quadrillionth of a second to form a pair of gamma rays. However, these gammas live to a ripe old age compared to others, which have a life of only one hundredth of a microsecond. Other particles, like the neutral *sigma* particle, break down after a hundred trillionth of a second. In the 1960s, even this was overtaken by the discovery of particles so evanescent that their existence could only be determined from the necessity of explaining their breakdown products. The half-lives of these particles are in the region of a few trillionths of a second. These are known as *resonance particles*. And even this was not the end of the story.

Over a hundred and fifty new particles were later discovered, which have been called *hadrons*. The situation was becoming extremely confused. An American physicist, Dr. Murray Gell-Mann, in an attempt to explain the structure of subatomic particles, postulated still other, more basic particles, the quarks, which were yet again heralded as the "ultimate building-blocks of matter". Gell-Mann theorised that there were six different kinds of quarks and that the quark family was parallel to a six-member family of lighter particles known as *leptons*. All matter was now supposed to consist of these twelve particles. Even these, the most basic forms of matter so far known to science, still possess the same contradictory qualities we observe throughout nature, in accordance with the dialectical law of the unity of opposites. Quarks also exist in pairs, and possess a positive and negative charge, although it is, unusually, expressed in fractions.

Despite the fact that experience has demonstrated that there is no limit to matter, scientists still persist in the vain search for the "bricks of matter". It is true that such expressions are the sensational inventions of journalists and some scientists with an over-developed flare for self-promotion, and that the search for ever smaller and fundamental particles is undoubtedly a bona fide scientific activity, which serves to deepen our knowledge of the workings of nature. Nevertheless, one certainly gets the impression that at least some of them really do believe that it is possible to reach a kind of ultimate level of reality, beyond which there is nothing left to discover, at least at the subatomic level.

The quark is supposed to be the last of twelve subatomic "building blocks" which are said to make up all matter. "The exciting thing is that this is *the final piece of matter* as we know it, as predicted by cosmology and the Standard Model of particle physics, Dr. David Schramm was reported as saying, 'It is the final piece of that puzzle'." [4] So the quark is the "ultimate particle". It is said to be fundamental and structureless. But similar claims were made in the past for the atom, then the proton, and so on and so forth. And in the same way, we can confidently predict the discovery of still more "fundamental" forms of matter in the future. The fact that the present state of our knowledge and technology does not permit us to determine the properties of the quark does not entitle us to affirm that it has no structure. The properties of the quark still await analysis, and there is no reason to suppose that this will not be achieved, pointing the way to a still deeper probing of the endless properties of matter. This is the way science has always advanced. The supposedly unbreachable barriers to knowledge erected by one generation are overturned by the next, and so on down the ages. The whole of previous experience gives us every reason to believe that this dialectical process of the advance of human knowledge is as endless as the infinite universe itself.

(4) Financial Times, 1/4/94, our emphasis.

6. Uncertainty
and idealism

The uncertainty principle

The real death knell for Newtonian mechanics as an universal theory was sounded by Albert Einstein, Erwin Schrödinger, Werner Heisenberg and other scientists that stood at the cradle of quantum mechanics in the early 20th century. The behaviour of "elementary particles" could not be explained by classical mechanics. A new mathematics had to be developed.

In this mathematics there are concepts like a "phase-space" wherein a system is defined as a point which has its degrees of freedom as coordinates, and "operators", magnitudes that are incompatible with algebraic magnitudes in the sense that they are more similar to operations than to magnitudes themselves (in fact they express relations instead of fixed properties) play a significant role. Probability also plays an important role, but in the sense of "intrinsic probability": it is one of the essential characteristics of quantum mechanics. In fact quantum mechanic systems must be interpreted as the superposition of all the possible pathways they can follow.

Quantum particles can only be defined as a set of internal relationships between their "actual" and its "virtual" state. In that sense they are purely dialectical. Measuring those particles in one way or another leads only to the revealing of the "actual" state, which is only one aspect of the whole (this paradox is popularly explained by the tale of "Schrödinger's cat"). It is called the "collapse of the wave function", and is expressed by the uncertainty principle of Heisenberg. This entirely new way of looking toward physical reality, which is expressed by quantum mechanics, was kept "in quarantine" for long time by the rest of the scientific disciplines. It was seen as an exceptional kind of mechanics, only to be used in describing the behaviour of elementary particles, the exception to the rule of classic mechanics, without any importance whatsoever.

In place of the old certainties, uncertainty now reigned. The apparently random movements of subatomic particles, with their unimaginable velocities, could not be expressed in terms of the old mechanics. When a science reaches a blind alley, when it is no longer able to explain the facts, the ground is prepared for a revolution, and the emergence of a new science. However, the new science, in its initial form, is not yet completely developed. Only over a period does it emerge in its final and complete form. A degree of improvisation, of uncertainty, of varying and often contradictory interpretations, is virtually inevitable at first.

In recent decades a debate has opened up between the so-called stochastic ("random") interpretation of nature and determinism. The fundamental problem is that necessity and chance are here treated as absolute opposites, mutually exclusive contraries. In this way, we arrive at two opposing views, neither of which is adequate to explain the contradictory and complex workings of nature.

Werner Heisenberg, a German physicist, developed his own peculiar version of quantum mechanics. In 1932, he received the Nobel Prize for physics for his system of *matrix mechanics*, which described the energy levels of orbits of electrons purely in terms of numbers, without any recourse to pictures. In this way, he hoped to get round the problems caused by the contradiction between "particles" and "waves" by abandoning any attempt to visualise the phenomenon, and treating it in a purely mathematical abstraction. Erwin Schrödinger's wave mechanics covered exactly the same ground as Heisenberg's matrix mechanics without any need to retreat into the realms of absolute mathematical abstraction. Most physicists preferred Schrödinger's approach, which seemed far less abstract, and they were not wrong. In 1944, John von Neumann, the Hungarian-American mathematician, demonstrated that wave mechanics and matrix mechanics were mathematically equivalent, and could achieve exactly the same results.

Heisenberg achieved some important advances in quantum mechanics. However, permeating his whole approach was the determination to inflict his peculiar brand of philosophical idealism upon the new science. From this arose the so-called Copenhagen interpretation of quantum mechanics. This was really a variety of subjective idealism, thinly disguised as a school of scientific thought. "Werner Heisenberg," wrote Isaac Asimov, "proceeded to raise a profound question that projected particles, and physics itself, almost into a realm of the unknowable." [5] That is the correct word to use. We are not dealing here with the *unknown*. That is always present in science. The whole history of science is the advance from the unknown to the known, from ignorance to knowledge. But a serious difficulty arises when people confuse the unknown with the *unknowable*. There is a fundamental difference between the words "we do not know" and "we cannot know". Science sets out from the basic notion that the objective world exists and can be known to us.

However, in the whole history of philosophy there have been repeated attempts to place a limit upon human cognition, to assert that there are certain things which "we cannot know", for this reason or that. Thus Kant claimed that we could only

(5) I. Asimov, *New Guide to Science*, p. 375.

know appearances, but not Things-in-Themselves. In this, he was following in the footsteps of the scepticism of David Hume, the subjective idealism of Berkeley and the sophists: that we cannot know the world.

In 1927, Werner Heisenberg advanced his celebrated "uncertainty principle", according to which it is impossible to determine, with the desired accuracy, both the position and velocity of a particle simultaneously. The more certain a particle's position, the more uncertain its momentum, and vice versa. (This also applies to other specified pairs of properties.) The difficulty in establishing precisely the position and velocity of a particle that is moving at 5,000 miles per second in different directions is self-evident. However, to deduce from this that cause and effect (causality) in general does not exist is an entirely false proposition.

How can we decide on the position of an electron? he asked. By looking at it. But if we use a powerful microscope, it would mean striking it with a particle of light, a photon. Because light behaves like a particle, it will inevitably disturb the momentum of the observed particle. Therefore, we change it by the very act of observation. The disturbance will be unpredictable and uncontrollable, since (at least from the existing quantum theory) there is no way of knowing or controlling beforehand the precise angle with which the light quantum will be scattered into the lens. Because an accurate determination of the position requires the use of light of short wavelength, a large but unpredictable and uncontrollable momentum is transferred to the electron. On the other hand, an accurate determination of the momentum requires the use of light quanta of very low momentum (and therefore of long wave-length), which means a large angle of diffraction, and hence a poor definition of the position. The more accurately the position is defined, the less accurate the momentum can be defined, and vice versa.

So can we get round this problem if we develop new kinds of electron microscopes? Not according to Heisenberg's theory. Since all energy comes in quanta, and all matter has the property of acting both as a wave and a particle, any type of apparatus we use will be governed by this principle of uncertainty (or indeterminacy). Indeed, the term uncertainty principle is inexact, because what is asserted here is not just that we cannot be certain, because of problems of measurement. The theory implies that *all forms of matter are indeterminate by their very nature*. As David Bohm says in his book *Causality and Chance in Modern Physics*:

"Thus the renunciation of causality in the usual interpretation of the quantum theory is not to be regarded as merely the result of our inability to *measure* the precise values of the variables that would enter into the expression of causal laws at the atomic level, but, rather, it should be regarded as a reflection of the fact that no such laws exist."

Instead of seeing it as a special aspect of quantum theory at a particular stage in its development, Heisenberg postulated indeterminacy as a fundamental and universal law of nature, and assumed that all other laws of nature would have to be consistent with it. This is completely different to the approach of science in the past when it was confronted with problems related to irregular fluctuations and random movement. No-one imagines it is possible to determine the exact motion of an individual molecule in a gas, or predict all the details of a specific car accident. But never before has a serious attempt been made to derive from such facts the *non-existence of causality in general.*

Yet this is precisely the conclusion we are invited to draw from the *principle of indeterminacy.* Scientists and idealist philosophers have gone on to argue that causality in general does not exist. That is to say, that there is no cause and effect. Nature thus appears as an entirely causeless, random affair. The entire universe is unpredictable. "We cannot be certain" of anything. "Instead, it is assumed that in any particular experiment, the *precise* result that will be obtained is *completely arbitrary* in the sense that it has no relationship whatever to anything else that exists in the world or that ever has existed." [6]

This position is the complete negation, not only of science, but of rational thought in general. If there is no cause and effect, not only is it impossible to predict anything; it is impossible to explain anything. We can only limit ourselves to describe what is. In fact, not even that, since we cannot even be certain that anything exists outside ourselves and our own senses. This brings us right back to the philosophy of subjective idealism. It reminds us of the argument of the sophist philosophers of ancient Greece: "I cannot know anything about the world. If I can know something, I cannot understand it. If I can understand it, I cannot express it."

What the "indeterminacy principle" really represents is the highly elusive character of the movement of subatomic particles, which are not susceptible to the kind of simplistic equations and measurements of classical mechanics. There is no doubt about Heisenberg's contribution to physics. What is in question is the philosophical conclusions which he drew from quantum mechanics. The fact that we cannot measure exactly the position and momentum of an electron does not imply in the slightest that there is a lack of objectivity here. The subjective way of thinking permeates the so-called Copenhagen school of quantum mechanics. Niels Bohr went so far as to state that "it is wrong to think that the task of physics is to find out how nature *is.* Physics concerns what we can say about nature."

The physicist John Wheeler maintains that "no phenomenon is a real phenomenon until it is an observed phenomenon." And Max Born spells out the same subjectivist philosophy with absolute clarity: "The generation to which Einstein, Bohr, and I belong was taught that there exists an objective physical world, which unfolds itself according to immutable laws independent of us; we are watching this process as the audience watches a play in a theatre. Einstein still believes that this should be the relation between the scientific observer and his subject." [7]

(6) D. Bohm, *Causality and Chance in Modern Physics*, pp. 86 and 87.
(7) T. Ferris, *The World Treasury of Physics, Astronomy, and Mathematics*, pp. 103 and 106.

What we have here is not a scientific evaluation, but a philosophical opinion reflecting a definite world outlook—that of subjective idealism, which permeates the entire Copenhagen interpretation of quantum theory. A number of eminent scientists, to their credit, made a stand against this subjectivism, which runs contrary to the whole outlook and method of science. Among these were Albert Einstein, Max Planck, Louis de Broglie and Erwin Schrödinger, all of whom played a role in developing the new physics at the very least as important as Heisenberg.

Objectivity versus subjectivism

There is not the slightest doubt that Heisenberg's interpretation of quantum physics was heavily influenced by his philosophical views. Even as a student, Heisenberg was a conscious idealist, who admits being greatly impressed by Plato's *Timaeus* (where Plato's idealism is expressed in the most obscurantist way), while fighting in the ranks of the reactionary *Freikorps* against the German workers in 1919. Subsequently he stated that he was "much more interested in the underlying philosophical ideas than in the rest", and that it was necessary "to get away from the idea of objective processes in time and space". In other words, Heisenberg's philosophical interpretation of quantum physics was very far from being the objective result of scientific experiment. It was clearly linked to idealist philosophy, which he consciously applied to physics, and which determined his outlook.

Such a philosophy is at odds not only with science, but the whole of human experience. Not only does it lack any scientific content, but it turns out to be perfectly useless in practice. Scientists who, as a rule, like to steer clear of philosophical speculation, make a polite nod in the direction of Heisenberg, and simply get on with the job of investigating the laws of nature, taking for granted not only that it exists, but that it functions according to definite laws, including those of cause and effect, and that, with a bit of effort, can be perfectly well understood, and even predicted by men and women. The reactionary consequences of this subjective idealism are shown by Heisenberg's own evolution. He justified his active collaboration with the Nazis on the grounds that "There are no general guidelines to which we can cling. We have to decide for ourselves, and cannot tell in advance if we are doing right or wrong." [8]

Erwin Schrödinger did not deny the existence of random phenomena in nature in general or in quantum mechanics. He specifically mentions the example of the random combining of DNA molecules at the moment of conception of a child, in which the quantum features of the chemical bond play a role. However, he objected to the standard Copenhagen interpretation about the implications of the "two-hole" experiment; that Max Born's waves of probability meant that we had to renounce the objectivity of the world, the idea that the world exists independently of our observing it.

(8) E.J. Lerner, *The Big Bang Never Happened*, pp. 362-3.

Schrödinger ridiculed the assertion of Heisenberg and Bohr that, when an electron or photon is not being observed, it has "no position" and only materialises at a given point as a result of the observation. To counter it, he devised a famous "thought experiment". Take a cat and put it in a box with a vial of cyanide, he said. When a Geiger counter detects the decay of an atom, the vial is broken. According to Heisenberg, the atom does not "know" it has decayed until someone measures it. In this case, therefore, until someone opens the box and looks in, according to the idealists, the cat is neither dead nor alive! By this anecdote, Schrödinger meant to highlight the absurd contradictions caused by the acceptance of Heisenberg's subjective idealist interpretation of quantum physics. The processes of nature take place objectively, irrespective of whether human beings are around to observe them or not.

According to the Copenhagen interpretation, reality only comes into being when we observe it. Otherwise, it exists in a kind of limbo, or "probability wave superposition state", like our live-and-dead cat. The Copenhagen interpretation draws a sharp line of distinction between the observer and the observed. Some physicists take the view, following the Copenhagen interpretation, that consciousness must exist, but the idea of material reality without consciousness is unthinkable. This is precisely the standpoint of subjective idealism, which Lenin comprehensively answered in his book *Materialism and Empirio-criticism.*

Dialectical materialism sets out from the objectivity of the material universe, which is given to us through sense perception. "I interpret the world through my senses." That is self-evident. But the world exists independently of my senses. That is also self-evident, one might think, but not for modern bourgeois philosophy! One of the main strands of 20th century philosophy is logical positivism, which precisely denies the objectivity of the material world. More correctly, it considers that the very question of whether the world exists or not to be irrelevant and "metaphysical". The standpoint of subjective idealism has been completely undermined by the discoveries of 20th century science. The act of observation means that our eyes are receiving energy from an external source in the form of light waves (photons). This was clearly explained by Lenin in 1908-09:

"If colour is a sensation only depending upon the retina (as natural science compels you to admit), then light rays, falling upon the retina, produce the sensation of colour. This means that outside us, independently of us and of our minds, there exists a movement of matter, let us say of ether waves of a definite length and of a definite velocity, which, acting upon the retina, produce the sensation of colour. This is precisely how natural science regards it. It explains the sensations of various colours by the various lengths of light waves existing outside the human retina, outside man and independently of him. This is materialism: matter acting upon our sense organs produces sensation. Sensation depends on the brain, nerves, retina, etc., i.e., on matter organised in a definite way. The existence of matter does not depend on sensation. Matter is primary. Sensation, thought, consciousness are the supreme product of matter organised in a particular way. Such are the views of materialism in general, and of Marx and Engels in particular." [9]

The subjective idealist nature of Heisenberg's method is quite explicit:

"Our actual situation in research work in atomic physics is usually this: we wish to understand a certain phenomenon, we wish to recognise how this phenomenon follows from the general laws of nature. Therefore, that part of matter or radiation that takes part in the phenomenon is the natural 'object' in the theoretical treatment and should be separated in this respect from the tools used to study the phenomenon. This again emphasises a subjective element in the description of atomic events, since the measuring device has been constructed by the observer, and we have to remember that what we observe is not nature in itself but nature exposed to our method of questioning. Our scientific work in physics consists in asking questions about nature in the language that we possess and trying to get an answer from experiment by the means that are at our disposal." [10]

Kant erected an impenetrable barrier between the world of appearances and reality "in itself". Here Heisenberg goes one better. He not only speaks about "nature in itself", but even maintains that we cannot really know that part of nature which can be observed, since we change it by the very act of observing it. In this way, Heisenberg seeks to abolish the criterion of scientific objectivity altogether. Unfortunately, many scientists who would indignantly deny the charge of mysticism have uncritically assimilated Heisenberg's philosophical ideas, merely because they are unwilling to accept the necessity for a consistently materialist philosophical approach to nature.

The whole point is that the laws of formal logic break down beyond certain limits. This most certainly applies to the phenomena of the subatomic world, where the laws of identity, contradiction and the excluded middle cannot be applied. Heisenberg defends the standpoint of formal logic and idealism, and therefore, inevitably arrives at the conclusion that the contradictory phenomena at the subatomic level cannot be comprehended by human thought at all. The contradiction, however, is not in the observed phenomena at the subatomic level, but in the hopelessly antiquated and inadequate mental schema of formal logic. The so-called paradoxes of quantum mechanics are precisely this. Heisenberg cannot accept the existence of dialectical contradictions, and therefore prefers to revert to philosophical mysticism—"we cannot know", and all the rest of it.

We find ourselves here in the presence of a kind of philosophical conjuring trick. The first step is to confuse the concept of causality with the old mechanical determinism represented by people like Laplace. These limitations were explained and criticised by Engels in the *Dialectics of Nature*. The discoveries of quantum mechanics finally destroyed the old mechanical determinism. The kind of predic-

(9) LCW, Vol. 14, p. 55.
(10) T. Ferris, op. cit., pp. 95-6.

tions made by quantum mechanics is somewhat different from those of classical mechanics. Yet quantum mechanics still makes predictions, and obtains precise results from them.

Causality and chance

One of the problems faced by the student of philosophy or science is when a particular terminology is used that is frequently at variance with everyday language. One of the fundamental problems in the history of philosophy is the relationship between freedom and necessity, a complex question, which is not made any easier when it emerges in different disguises—causality and chance, necessity and accident, determinism and indeterminism, etc.

We all know from everyday experience what we mean by necessity. When we need to do something, it means that we have no choice. We cannot do otherwise. The dictionary defines necessity as a set of circumstances compelling something to be, or to be done, especially relating to a law of the universe, inseparable from, and directing, human life and action. The idea of physical necessity involves the notion of compulsion and constraint. It is conveyed by expressions like "to bow to necessity". It occurs in proverbs like "necessity knows no law".

In the philosophical sense, necessity is closely related to *causality*, the relation between *cause and effect*—a given action or event necessarily gives rise to a particular result. For example, if I stop breathing for an hour, I will die, or if I rub two sticks together, I will produce heat. This relation between cause and effect, which is confirmed by an infinite number of observations and practical experiences, plays a central role in science. By contrast, *accident* is regarded as an unexpected event, which occurs without apparent cause, as when we trip over a loose paving stone, or drop a cup in the kitchen. In philosophy, however, accident is a property of a thing which is a merely *contingent* attribute, that is, something which is not part of its essential nature. An accident is something that does not exist of necessity, and which equally well could not have happened. Let us consider an example.

If I let this piece of paper go, it will normally fall to the floor, because of the law of gravity. That is an example of causation, of *necessity*. But if a sudden draught should cause the paper to blow away unexpectedly, that would be generally seen as *chance*. Necessity is therefore governed by law, and can be scientifically expressed and predicted. Things which happen of necessity are things which could not have happened otherwise. On the other hand, random events, contingencies, are events that might, or might not, happen; they are governed by no law that can be clearly expressed and are by their very nature, unpredictable.

Experience of life convinces us that both necessity and accident exist and play a role. The history of science and society shows exactly the same thing. The whole essence of the history of science is the search for the underlying patterns of nature. We learn early in life to distinguish between the essential and non-essential, the necessary and contingent. Even when we come across exceptional conditions that may seem "irregular" to us at a given stage of our knowledge, it often turns out that subsequent experience reveals a different kind of regularity, and still deeper causal relations, which were not immediately obvious.

The search for a rational insight and understanding of the world in which we live is intimately connected with the need to discover causality. A small child, in the process of learning about the world, will always ask "why?"—to the distraction of its parents, who are frequently at a loss for an answer. On the basis of observation and experience, we formulate a hypothesis as to what causes a given phenomenon. This is the basis of all rational understanding. As a rule these hypotheses in turn give rise to predictions concerning things that have not yet been experienced. These may then be tested, either by observation or practice. This is not only a description of the history of science, but also of an important part of the mental development of every human being from early childhood on. It therefore covers intellectual development in the very broadest sense of the word, from the most basic learning processes of a child up to the most advanced study of the universe.

The existence of causality is shown by an immense number of observations. These enable us to make important predictions, not only in science, but in everyday life. Everyone knows that if water is heated to 100°C, it turns into steam. This is the basis not only for making a cup of tea, but for the industrial revolution, upon which the whole of modern society rests. Yet there are philosophers and scientists who seriously maintain that steam cannot be said to be caused by heating water. The fact that we can make predictions about a vast number of events is itself proof that causality is not merely a convenient way of describing events, but, as David Bohm points out, an inherent and essential aspect of things. Indeed, it is impossible even to define the properties of things without resorting to causality. For example, when we say that something is red, we imply that it will react in a certain way when subjected to specified conditions—i.e., a red object is defined as one which when exposed to white light will reflect mostly red light. Similarly, the fact that water becomes steam when heated, and ice when cooled, is the expression of a qualitative causal relationship which is part of the essential properties of this liquid, without which it could not be water. The general mathematical laws of motion of moving bodies are likewise essential properties of these bodies, without which they could not be what they are. Such examples may be multiplied without limit. In order to understand why and how causality is so closely bound up with the essential properties of things, it is not enough to consider things statically and in isolation. It is necessary to consider things as they are, as they have been, and as they will necessarily become in the future—that is to say, to analyse things as *processes*.

In order to understand particular events, it is not necessary to specify *all* the causes. Indeed, this is not possible. The kind of absolute determinism put forward by Laplace was answered in advance by Spinoza in the following witty passage:

"For example, if a stone falls from a roof on the head of a passer-by and kills him, they will show by their method of argument that the stone was sent to fall and kill the man; for if it had not fallen on him for that end, by God's will, how could so many circumstances (for often very many circumstances concur at the same time) concur by chance? You will reply, perhaps: 'The wind was blowing and the man had to pass that way, and hence it happened.' But they will retort: 'Why was the wind blowing at that time? And why was the man going that way at that time?' If again you reply: 'The wind had then arisen on account of the agitation of the sea the day before, the previous weather having been calm, and the man was going that way at the invitation of a friend,' they will again retort, for there is no end to their questioning: 'Why was the sea agitated, and why was the man invited at that time?'

"And thus they will pursue you from cause to cause until you are glad to take refuge in the will of God, that is, the asylum of ignorance. Thus again, when they see the human body they are amazed, and as they know not the cause of so much art, they conclude that it was not by mechanical art, but divine or supernatural art, and constructed in such a manner that one part does not injure another. And hence it comes about that someone who wishes to seek out the true causes of miracles, and to understand the things of nature like a man of learning, and not to stare at them in amazement like a fool, is widely deemed heretical and impious, and proclaimed such by those whom the mob adore as interpreters of nature and the Gods. For these know that once ignorance is laid aside, that wonderment which is their only means of arguing and of preserving their authority would be taken away." [11]

Mechanism

The attempt to eliminate all contingency from nature leads necessarily to a mechanistic viewpoint. In the mechanistic philosophy of the 18th century—represented in science by Isaac Newton, the bare idea of necessity was elevated to an absolute principle. It was seen as perfectly simple, free from all contradiction, and with no irregularities or crosscurrents.

The idea of the universal lawfulness of nature is profoundly true, but a bare statement of lawfulness is insufficient. What is necessary is a concrete understanding of how the laws of nature actually operate. The mechanistic outlook necessarily developed a one-sided view of the phenomena of nature, reflecting the actual level of scientific development at the time. The highest achievement of this view was classical mechanics, which deals with relatively simple processes, cause and effect, understood as the simple external action of one solid body upon another, levers, equilibrium, mass, inertia, pushing, pressing, and the like. Important as these discoveries were, they were clearly insufficient to arrive at an accurate idea of the complex workings of nature. Later on, the discoveries of biology, particularly after

(11) Spinoza, *Ethics*, p. 8.

the Darwinian revolution, made possible a different approach to scientific phenomena, in line with the more flexible and subtle processes of organic matter.

In classical Newtonian mechanics motion is treated as something simple. If we know at any given moment what different forces apply to a specific moving object, we can predict exactly how it will behave in the future. This leads to mechanistic determinism, the most prominent exponent of which was Pierre Simon de Laplace, the French 18th century mathematician, whose theory of the universe really is identical to the idea of predestination present in several religions, notably Calvinism.

In his *Philosophical Essays on Probabilities*, Laplace wrote:

"An intellect which at any given moment knew all the forces that animate Nature and the mutual positions of the being that comprise it, if this intellect were vast enough to submit its data to analysis, could condense into a single formula the movement of the greatest bodies of the universe and that of the lightest atom: for such an intellect nothing could be uncertain; and the future just like the past would be present before our eyes." [12]

The difficulty arises from the mechanistic method inherited by 19th century physics from the 18th century. Here necessity and chance were regarded as fixed opposites, the one excluding the other. A thing or process was either accidental or necessary, but not both. This method was subjected to a searching analysis by Engels in *The Dialectics of Nature*, where he explains that the mechanistic determinism of Laplace inevitably led to fatalism and a mystical concept of nature:

"And then it is declared that the necessary is the sole thing of scientific interest and that the accidental is a matter of indifference to science. That is to say: what can be brought under laws, hence what one *knows*, is interesting; what cannot be brought under laws, and therefore what one does not know, is a matter of indifference and can be ignored. Thereby all science comes to an end, for it has to investigate precisely that which we do *not* know. It means to say: what can be brought under general laws is regarded as necessary, and what cannot be so brought as accidental. Anyone can see that this is the same sort of science as that which proclaims natural what it can explain, and ascribes what it cannot explain to supernatural causes; whether I term the cause of the inexplicable chance, or whether I term it God, is a matter of complete indifference as far as the thing itself is concerned. Both are only equivalents for: I do not know, and therefore do not belong to science. The latter ceases where the requisite connection is wanting."

Engels points out that such mechanical determinism effectively reduces necessity to the level of chance. If every trifling occurrence is of the same order of importance and necessity as the universal law of gravity, then all fundamental laws are on the same level of triviality:

"According to this conception only simple, direct necessity prevails in nature. That a particular pea-pod contains five peas and not four or six, that a particular

dog's tail is five inches long and not a whit longer or shorter, that this year a particular clover flower was fertilised by a bee and another not, and indeed by precisely
one particular bee and at a particular time, that a particular windblown dandelion
seed has sprouted and another not, that last night I was bitten by a flea at four
o'clock in the morning, and not at three or five o'clock, and on the right shoulder
and not on the left calf—these are all facts which have been produced by an irrev-
ocable concatenation of cause and effect, by an unshatterable necessity of such a
nature indeed that the gaseous sphere, from which the solar system was derived, was
already so constituted that these events had to happen thus and not otherwise. With
this kind of necessity we likewise do not get away from the theological conception
of nature. Whether with Augustine and Calvin we call it the eternal decree of God,
or Kismet as the Turks do, or whether we call it necessity, is all pretty much the
same for science. There is no question of tracing the chain of causation in any of
these cases; so we are just as wise in one as in another, the so-called necessity
remains an empty phrase, and with it—chance also remains what it was before." [13]

Laplace thought that if he could trace the causes of everything in the universe he
could abolish contingency altogether. For a long time, it appeared that the workings
of the entire universe could be reduced to a few relatively simple equations. One of
the limitations of the classical mechanistic theory is that it assumes that there are no
outside influences on the motion of particular bodies. In reality, however, everybody
is influenced and determined by every other body. Nothing can be taken in isolation.

Nowadays the claims of Laplace seem extravagant and unreasonable. But then,
similar extravagances are to be seen at every stage in the history of science, where
each generation firmly believes itself to be in possession of the "ultimate truth". Nor
is this entirely mistaken. The ideas of each generation are indeed the ultimate truth,
for that period. But all that we are saying when we make such assertions is: "This
is as far as we have got in understanding Nature, with the information and technological capabilities we currently possess." Therefore, it is not incorrect to claim that
these truths are absolute for us at this moment in time since we can base ourselves
on no others.

The 19th century

Newton's classical mechanics in their time represented an enormous step forward in
science. For the first time, Newton's laws of motion made possible precise quantitative predictions, which could be checked against the observed phenomena.
However, precisely this precision leads to new problems when Laplace and others
attempted to apply them to the universe as a whole. Laplace was convinced that
Newton's laws were absolutely and universally valid. This was doubly incorrect.
First of all, Newton's laws were not seen as approximations applicable in certain

(13) Engels, *The Dialectics of Nature*, pp. 289-90.

circumstances. Secondly Laplace did not consider the possibility that under different circumstances, in areas not yet studied in physics, these laws might need to be modified or extended. The mechanistic determinism of Laplace supposed that once the positions and velocities were known at any instant of time the future behaviour of the whole universe would be determined for all time. According to this theory, all the rich diversity of things can be reduced to an absolute set of quantitative laws based on a few variables.

Classical mechanics as expressed in Newton's laws of motion deal with simple cause and effect, for example the isolated action of one body upon another. However, in practice, this is impossible, since no mechanical system is ever completely isolated. Outside influences inevitably destroy the isolated one-to-one character of the connection. Even if we could isolate the system, there will still be disturbances arisen from motions at the molecular level, and other disturbances at the even deeper level of quantum mechanics. As Bohm remarks: "Thus, there is no real case known of a set of *perfect* one-to-one causal relationships that could in principle make possible predictions of *unlimited* precision, without the need to take into account qualitatively new sets of causal factors existing outside the system of interest or at other levels." [14]

Does this mean that prediction is impossible? Not at all. When we aim a gun at a certain point, the individual bullet will not land precisely at the point predicted by Newton's law of motion. However, a large number of shots fired will form a cluster in a small region near the point predicted. Thus, within a given range of error, which always exists, very precise predictions are possible. If we wanted to obtain unlimited precision in this instance, we would discover an ever increasing number of factors which influence the result—irregularities in the structure of the gun and bullet, tiny variations of temperature, pressure, humidity, air currents, and even the molecular motions of all these factors.

Some degree of approximation is necessary, which does not take into account the infinity of factors required for a perfectly precise prediction of a given result. This involves a necessary abstraction from reality, as in Newtonian mechanics. However, science continually proceeds, step by step, to discover ever deeper and more precise laws that enable us to gain a deeper understanding of the processes of nature, and thus make more accurate predictions. The abandonment of the old mechanical determinism of Newton and Laplace does not mean the abolition of causality, but a deeper understanding of the way in which causality actually works.

The first breaches in the wall of Newtonian science appeared in the second half of the 19th century, especially with Darwin's theory of evolution and the work of the Austrian physicist Ludwig Boltzmann on a statistical interpretation of thermodynamic processes. Physicists endeavoured to describe many-particle systems like

(14) D. Bohm, op. cit., p. 20.

gases or fluids with statistical methods. Those statistics however, were seen as an auxiliary in situations where it was impossible for practical reasons to collect detailed information about all the properties of the system (for example all the positions and velocities of the particles of gas at a given moment in time).

The 19th century saw the development of statistics, first in the social sciences, then in physics, for example in the theory of gases, where randomness and determinacy can both be seen in the movement of molecules. On the one hand, individual molecules seem to move in an entirely random manner. On the other hand, very large numbers of the molecules that make up a gas are seen to behave in a way that obeys precise dynamical laws. How to explain this contradiction? If the movement of its constituent molecules is random and therefore cannot be predicted, surely the behaviour of a gas ought to be similarly unpredictable? Yet this is far from the case.

The answer to the problem is supplied by the law of the transformation of quantity into quality. Out of the apparently random movement of a large number of molecules, there arises a regularity and a pattern which can be expressed as a scientific law. Out of chaos arises order. This dialectical relation between freedom and necessity, between chaos and order, between randomness and determinacy was a closed book to the science of the 19th century, which regarded the laws governing random phenomena (statistics) to be entirely separate and apart from the precise equations of classical mechanics.

"Any liquid or gas," writes Gleick, "is a collection of individual bits, so many that they may as well be infinite. If each piece moved independently, then the fluid would have infinitely many possibilities, infinitely many 'degrees of freedom' in the jargon, and the equations describing the motion would have to deal with infinitely many variables. But each particle does not move independently—its motion depends very much on the motion of its neighbours—and in a smooth flow, the degrees of freedom can be few." [15]

Classical mechanics worked very well for a long time, making important technological advances possible. Even down to the present time, it has a vast amount of applications. However, eventually it was found that certain areas could not adequately be dealt with by these methods. They had reached their limit. The neatly ordered, logical world of classical mechanics describes part of nature. But only part. In nature we see order, but also disorder. Alongside organisation and stability there are equally powerful forces tending in the opposite direction. Here we have to resort to dialectics, to determine the relation between necessity and chance, to show at what point the accumulation of tiny, apparently insignificant changes of quantity became transformed into sudden qualitative leaps.

Bohm proposed a radical re-thinking of quantum mechanics, and a new way of looking at the relation between whole and parts.

(15) J. Gleick, *Chaos, Making a New Science*, p. 124.

"In these studies…it became clear that even the one-body system has a basically non-mechanical feature, in the sense that it and its environment have to be understood as an *undivided whole*, in which the usual classical analysis into system plus environment, considered as separately external, is no longer applicable." The relationship of the parts "depends crucially on the state of the whole, in a way that is not expressible in terms of properties of the parts alone. Indeed, the parts are organised in ways that flow out of the whole." [16]

The dialectical law of transformation of quantity into quality expresses the idea that matter behaves differently at different levels. Thus, we have the molecular level, the laws of which are studied mainly in chemistry but partly in physics; we have the level of living matter, studied mainly in biology; the subatomic level, studied in quantum mechanics; and also another level still deeper than that of elementary particles, which is presently being explored in particle physics. Each of these levels has many subdivisions.

It has been shown that the laws governing the behaviour of matter at each level are not the same. This was already shown in the 19th century by the kinetic theory of gases. If we take a box of gas containing billions of molecules, moving in irregular paths and in constant collision with other molecules, it is clearly impossible to determine the precise motions of each individual molecule. In the first place, it is ruled out on purely mathematical grounds. However, even if it were possible to solve the mathematical problems involved, it would be impossible in practice to measure the initial position and velocity of each molecule which would be needed to make precise predictions concerning it. Even a slight change in the initial angle of motion of any molecule would alter its direction, in turn leading to a still bigger change in the next collision, and so on, leading to huge errors in any prediction concerning the movement of an individual molecule.

If we try to apply the same kind of reasoning to the behaviour of gases at the macroscopic ("normal") level, one would assume that it is also impossible to predict their behaviour. But this is not the case; the behaviour of gases at a large-scale level can be perfectly predicted. As Bohm points out:

"It is clear that one is justified in speaking of *a macroscopic level* possessing a set of *relatively autonomous qualities* and satisfying a set of *relatively autonomous relations* which effectively constitute a set of *macroscopic casual laws*. For example, if we consider a mass of water, we know by direct large-scale experience that it acts in its own characteristic way as a *liquid*. By this we mean that it shows all the macroscopic qualities that we associate with liquidity. For example, it flows, it 'wets' things, it tends to maintain a certain volume, etc. In its motion it satisfies a set of basic hydrodynamic equations which are expressed in terms of the large-scale properties alone, such as pressure, temperature, local density, local stream velocity,

(16) D. Bohm, op. cit., pp. x and xi.

etc. Thus, if one wishes to understand the properties of the mass of water, one does not treat it as an aggregate of molecules, but rather as an entity existing at the macroscopic level, following laws appropriate to that level."

This is not to say that the molecular constitution has nothing to do with the behaviour of water. On the contrary. The relation between the molecules determines, for example, whether it manifests itself as a liquid, a solid or vapour. But, as Bohm points out, there is a relative autonomy, which means that matter behaves differently at different levels; there exists "a certain *stability* of the characteristic modes of macroscopic behaviour, which tend to maintain themselves not only more or less independently of what the individual molecules are doing, but also of the various disturbances to which the system may be subjected from outside." [17]

Is prediction possible?

When we toss a coin in the air, the chance that it will land "heads or tails" may be put at 50:50. That is a truly random phenomenon, which cannot be predicted. (Incidentally, when spinning, the coin is neither "heads" nor "tails"; dialectics—and the new physics—would say that it is both heads and tails.) As there are only two possible results, chance predominates. But matters change radically when very large numbers are involved. The owners of casinos, which are supposedly based on a game of "chance", know that, in the long run, zero or double zero will come up as frequently as any other number, and therefore they can make a handsome and predictable profit. The same is true of insurance companies, which make a lot of money out of precise probabilities, which, in the last analysis, turn out to be practical certainties, even though the precise fate of individual clients cannot be predicted.

What are known as "mass random events" can be applied to a very wide field in physical, chemical, biological and social phenomena, from the sex of babies to the frequency of defects on a factory production line. The laws of probability have a very long history and have been used in the past in different spheres: the theory of errors (Gauss), the theory of accuracy in shooting (Poisson, Laplace), and above all, in statistics. For example, the "law of great numbers" establishes the general principle that the combined effect of a large number of accidental factors produces, for a very large class of such factors, results that are almost independent of chance. This idea was expressed in the beginning of the 18th century by Daniel Bernoulli, whose theory was generalised by Siméon Denis Poisson in 1837, and given its final form by Pafnuty Lvovich Chebyshev in 1867. All Heisenberg did was to apply the already known mathematics of mass-scale random events to the movements of sub-

(17) D. Bohm, op. cit., pp. 50-1.

atomic particles, where, predictably, the element of randomness was quickly over-come.

"Quantum mechanics having discovered precise and wonderful laws governing the probabilities, it is with numbers such as these that science overcomes its handicap of basic indeterminacy. It is by these means that science boldly predicts. Though now humbly confessing itself powerless to foretell the exact behaviour of individual electrons or photons or other fundamental entities, it can yet tell you with enormous confidence how such great multitudes of them must behave precisely." [18]

Out of apparent randomness, a pattern emerges. It is the search for such patterns, that is, for underlying laws, which forms the basis of the whole history of science. Of course, if we were to accept that everything is just random, that there is no causality, and that, anyway, we cannot know anything because there are objective limitations to our knowledge, then all will have been a complete waste of time. Fortunately, the whole history of science demonstrates that such fears are without the slightest basis. In the great majority of scientific observations, the degree of indeterminacy is so small that, for practical purposes, it may be ignored. At the level of everyday objects, the uncertainty principle proves to be absolutely useless. Thus, all the attempts to draw general philosophical conclusions from it, and apply it to knowledge and science in general, is simply a dishonest trick. Even at the subatomic level, it does not at all mean that we cannot make definite predictions. On the contrary, quantum mechanics makes very exact predictions. It is impossible to achieve a high level of certainty about the coordinates of individual particles, which may thus be said to be random. Yet, at the end of the day, out of randomness arises order and uniformity.

Accident, chance, contingencies, etc., are phenomena that cannot be defined solely in terms of the known properties of the objects under consideration. However, this does not mean that they cannot be understood. Let us consider a typical example of a chance event—a car accident. An individual accident is determined by an infinite number of chance events: if the driver had left home one minute later, if he had not turned his head for a split second, if he had been travelling ten miles an hour slower, if the old lady had not stepped into the road, etc., etc. We have all heard this kind of thing many times. The number of causes here is literally infinite. Precisely for that reason, the event is entirely unpredictable. It is accidental, and not necessary, because it might or might not have occurred. Such events, contrary to the theory of Laplace, are determined by so many independent factors that they cannot be determined at all.

However, when we consider a very large number of such accidents, the picture changes radically. There are regular trends, which can be precisely calculated and

(18) B. Hoffmann, op. cit., p. 152.

predicted by what are called *statistical laws*. We cannot predict an individual accident, but we can predict with great accuracy the number of accidents that will occur in a city over a period of time. Not only that, but we can introduce laws and regulations which have a definite impact on the number of accidents. Thus, there are laws that govern chance, which are just as necessary as the laws of causality themselves.

The real relationship between causality and chance was worked out by Hegel, who explained that necessity expresses itself through chance. A good example of this is the origin of life itself. The Russian biologist and biochemist Aleksandr Ivanovich Oparin (1894-1980) explains how in the complex conditions of the early period of the earth's history, the random movements of molecules would tend to form ever more complex molecules with all sorts of chance combinations. At a certain point, this huge number of accidental combinations gave rise to a qualitative leap, the emergence of living matter. At this point, the process would no longer be a matter of pure chance. Living matter would begin to evolve in accordance with certain laws, reflecting changing conditions. This relationship between the necessity and accident in science has been explored by David Bohm:

"We see, then, the important role of chance. For given enough time, it makes possible, and indeed even inevitable, all kinds of combinations of things. One of those combinations which set in motion irreversible processes or lines of development that remove the system from the influence of the chance fluctuations is then eventually certain to occur. Thus, one of the effects of chance is to help 'stir things up' in such a way as to permit the initiation of qualitatively new lines of development."

Polemicising against the subjective idealist interpretation of quantum mechanics, Bohm shows conclusively the dialectal relationship between causality and chance. The existence of causality has been demonstrated by the whole history of human thought. This is not a question of philosophical speculation, but of practice and the never-ending process of human cognition:

"The causal laws in a specific problem cannot be known *a priori*; they must be *found* in nature. However, in response to scientific experience over many generations along with the general background of common human experience over countless centuries, there have evolved fairly well defined methods for finding the causal laws. The first thing that suggests causal laws is, of course, the existence of a regular relationship that holds within a wide range of variations of conditions. When we find such regularities, we do not suppose that they have arisen in an arbitrary, capricious, or coincidental fashion, but, … we assume, at least provisionally, that they are the result of necessary causal relationships. And even with regard to the irregularities, which always exist along with the regularities, one is led on the basis of general scientific experience to expect that phenomena that may seem completely irregular to us in the context of a particular stage of development of our understanding will later be seen to contain more subtle types of regularity, which will in turn suggest the existence of deeper causal relationships." [19]

Hegel on necessity and accident

In analysing the nature of being in all its different manifestations, Hegel deals with the relation between *potential* and *actual*, and also between *necessity* and *accident* ("contingency"). In relation to this question, it is important to clarify one of Hegel's most famous (or notorious) sayings: "What is rational is actual, and what is actual is rational." [20] At first sight, this statement seems mystifying, and also reactionary, since it seems to imply that all that exists is rational, and therefore justified. This, however, was not at all what Hegel meant, as Engels explains:

"Now, according to Hegel, reality is, however, in no way an attribute predicable of any given state of affairs, social or political, in all circumstances and at all times. On the contrary. The Roman Republic was real, but so was the Roman Empire, which superseded it. In 1789 the French monarchy had become so unreal, that is to say, so robbed of all necessity, so irrational, that it had to be destroyed by the Great Revolution, of which Hegel always speaks with the greatest enthusiasm. In this case, therefore, the monarchy was the unreal and the revolution the real. And so, in the course of development, all that was previously real becomes unreal, loses its necessity, its right of existence, its rationality. And in the place of moribund reality comes a new, viable reality—peacefully if the old has enough intelligence to go to its death without a struggle; forcibly if it resists this necessity. Thus the Hegelian proposition turns into its opposite through Hegelian dialectics itself: All that is real in the sphere of human history becomes irrational in the process of time, is therefore irrational by its very destination, is tainted beforehand with irrationality; and everything which is rational in the minds of men is destined to become real, however much it may contradict existing apparent reality. In accordance with all the rules of the Hegelian method of thought, the proposition of the rationality of everything which is real resolves itself into the other proposition: All that exists deserves to perish." [21]

A given form of society is "rational" to the degree that it achieves its purpose, that is, that it develops the productive forces, raises the cultural level, and thus advances human progress. Once it fails to do this, it enters into contradiction with itself, that is, it becomes irrational and unreal, and no longer has any right to exist. Thus, even in the most apparently reactionary utterances of Hegel, there is hidden a revolutionary idea.

All that exists evidently does so of necessity. But not everything can exist. Potential existence is not yet actual existence. In *Science of Logic*, Hegel carefully

(19) D. Bohm, op. cit., pp. 25 and 4.

(20) Hegel, *Philosophy of Right*, p. 10.

(21) MESW, Vol. 3, pp. 338-9.

traces the process whereby something passes from a state of being merely possible to the point where *possibility* becomes *probability*, and the latter becomes *inevitable* ("necessity"). In view of the colossal confusion that has arisen in modern science around the issue of "probability", a study of Hegel's thorough and profound treatment of this subject is highly instructive.

Possibility and actuality denote the dialectical development of the real world and the various stages in the emergence and development of objects. A thing which exists *in potential* contains within itself the objective tendency of development, or at least the absence of conditions which would preclude its coming into being. However, there is a difference between abstract possibility and real potential, and the two things are frequently confused. Abstract or formal possibility merely expresses the absence of any conditions that might exclude a particular phenomenon, but it does not assume the presence of conditions which would make its appearance inevitable.

This leads to endless confusion, and is actually a kind of trick that serves to justify all kinds of absurd and arbitrary ideas. For example, it is said that if a monkey were allowed to hammer away at a typewriter for long enough, it would eventually produce one of Shakespeare's sonnets. This objective seems too modest. Why only one sonnet? Why not the collected works of Shakespeare? Indeed, why not the whole of world literature, with the theory of relativity and Beethoven's symphonies thrown in for good measure? The bare assertion that it is "statistically possible" does not take us a single step further. The complex processes of nature, society and human thought are not all susceptible to simple statistical treatment, nor will great works of literature emerge out of mere accident, no matter how long we wait for our monkey to deliver the goods.

In order for potential to become actual, a particular concatenation of circumstances is required. Moreover, this is not a simple, linear process, but a dialectical one, in which an accumulation of small quantitative changes eventually produces a qualitative leap. Real, as opposed to abstract, possibility implies the presence of all the necessary factors out of which the potential will lose its character of provisionality, and become actual. And, as Hegel explains, it will remain actual only for as long as these conditions exist, and no longer. This is true whether we are referring to the life of an individual, a given socioeconomic form, a scientific theory, or any natural phenomenon. The point at which a change becomes inevitable can be determined by the method invented by Hegel and known as the "nodal line of measurement". If we regard any process as a line, it will be seen that there are specific points ("nodal points") on the line of development, where the process experiences a sudden acceleration, or qualitative leap.

It is easy to identify cause and effect in isolated cases, as when one hits a ball with a bat. But in a wider sense, the notion of causality becomes far more complicated. Individual causes and effects become lost in a vast ocean of *interaction*, where cause becomes transformed into effect and vice versa. Just try tracing back even the simplest event to its "ultimate causes" and you will see that eternity will not be long enough to do it. There will always be some new cause, and that in turn will have to be explained and so on ad infinitum. This paradox has entered the popular consciousness in such sayings as this one:

For the want of a nail, a shoe was lost;
For the want of a shoe, a horse was lost;
For the want of a horse, a rider was lost;
For the want of a rider, a battle was lost;
For the want of a battle, a kingdom was lost;
…And all for the want of a nail.

The impossibility of establishing a "final cause" has led some people to abandon the idea of cause altogether. Everything is considered to be random and accidental. In the 20th century this position has been adopted, at least in theory, by a large number of scientists on the basis of an incorrect interpretation of the results of quantum physics, particularly the philosophical positions of Heisenberg. Hegel answered these arguments in advance, when he explained the dialectical relation between accident and necessity.

Hegel explains that there is no such thing as causality *in the sense of an isolated cause and effect*. Every effect has a counter-effect, and every action has a counter-action. The idea of an isolated cause and effect is an abstraction taken from classical Newtonian physics, which Hegel was highly critical of, although it enjoyed tremendous prestige at that time. Here again, Hegel was in advance of his time. Instead of the action-reaction of mechanics, he advanced the notion of *Reciprocity*, of universal interaction. Everything influences everything else, and is in turn, influenced and determined by everything. Hegel thus re-introduced the concept of accident, which had been rigorously banned from science by the mechanist philosophy of Newton and Laplace.

At first sight, we seem to be lost in a vast number of accidents. But this confusion is only apparent. The accidental phenomena which constantly flash in and out of existence, like the waves on the face of an ocean, express a deeper process, which is not accidental but necessary. At a decisive point, this necessity *reveals itself through accident*. This idea of the dialectical unity of necessity and accident may seem strange, but it is strikingly confirmed by a whole series of observations from the most varied fields of science and society. The mechanism of natural selection in the theory of evolution is the best known example. But there are many others. In the last few years, there have been many discoveries in the field of chaos and complexity theory which precisely detail how "order arises out of chaos", which is exactly what Hegel worked out one and a half centuries earlier.

We must remember that Hegel was writing at the beginning of the 19th century, when science was completely dominated by classical mechanical physics, and half a century before Darwin developed the idea of natural selection through the medium of random mutations. He had no scientific evidence to back up his theory that necessity expresses itself through accident. But that is the central idea behind the most recent innovative thinking in science.

This profound law is equally fundamental to an understanding of history. As Marx wrote to Ludwig Kugelmann in 1871:

"World history would indeed be easy to make if the struggle were to be taken up only on condition of infallibly favourable chances. It would on the other hand be of a very mystical nature, if 'accidents' played no part. These accidents naturally form part of the general course of development and are compensated by other accidents. But acceleration and delay are very much dependent upon such 'accidents', including the 'accident' of the character of the people who head the movement." [22]

Engels made the same point a few years later in relation to the role of "great men" in history:

"Men make their history themselves, but not as yet with a collective will according to a collective plan or even in a definite delimited given society. Their aspirations clash, and for that very reason all such societies are governed by *necessity*, the complement and form of appearance of which is *accident*. The necessity which here asserts itself athwart all accident is again ultimately economic necessity. This is where the so-called great men come in for treatment. That such and such a man and precisely that man arises at a particular time in a particular country is, of course, pure chance. But cut him out and there will be a demand for a substitute, and this substitute will be found, good or bad, but in the long run he will be found." [23]

Determinism and chaos

Chaos theory deals with processes in nature that are apparently chaotic or random. A dictionary definition of chaos might suggest disorder, confusion, randomness, or chance: haphazard movement without aim, purpose or principle. But the intervention of pure "chance" into material processes invites the entry of non-physical, that is, metaphysical factors: whim, spirit or divine intervention. Because it deals with "chance" events, therefore, the new science of chaos has profound philosophical implications.

Natural processes that were previously considered to be random and chaotic have now proved to be lawful in a scientific sense, implying a basis in deterministic causes. Moreover, this discovery has such a widespread, not to say universal application, that it has engendered a whole new science—the study of chaos. It has created a new outlook and methodology, some would say a revolution, applicable to

---

(22) MESC, *Marx to Kigelmann, 17th April 1871*, p. 264.
(23) MESC., *Engels to Starkenburg, 25th January 1894*, p. 467.

all established sciences. When a block of metal becomes magnetised, it goes into an "ordered state", in which all of its particles point the same way. It can be oriented one way or the other. Theoretically, it is "free" to orient in any direction. In practice, every little piece of metal makes the same "decision".

A chaos scientist has worked out the basic mathematical rules that describe the "fractal geometry" of a leaf of the black spleenwort fern. He has fed the information into his computer that also has a random number generator. It is programmed to build up a picture using dots put at random on the screen. As the experiment progresses, it is impossible to anticipate where each dot will appear. But unerringly, the image of the fern leaf is built up. The superficial similarity between these two experiments is obvious. But it suggests a deeper parallel. Just as the computer was basing its apparently random selection of dots (and to the observer "outside" the computer, for all practical purposes it was random) on well-defined mathematical rules, so also it would suggest that the behaviour of photons (and by implication all quantum events) are subject to underlying mathematical rules which, however, are well beyond human understanding at the present time.

The Marxist view holds that the entire universe is based upon material forces and processes. Human consciousness is in the final analysis only a reflection of the real world that exists outside it, a reflection based on the physical interaction between the human body and the material world. In the material world there is no discontinuity, no interruption in the physical interconnection of events and processes. There is no room, in other words, for the intervention of metaphysical or spiritual forces. Materialist dialectics, Engels said, is the "science of universal interconnection". Moreover, the interconnectedness of the physical world is based upon the principle of causality, in the sense that processes and events are *determined* by their conditions and the *lawfulness* of their interconnections:

"The first thing that strikes us in considering matter in motion is the interconnection of the individual motions of separate bodies, their *being determined* by one another. But not only do we find that a particular motion is followed by another, we find also that we can evoke a particular motion by setting up the conditions in which it takes place in nature, that we can even produce motions which do not occur at all in nature (industry), at least not in this way, and that we can give these motions a predetermined direction and extent. *In this way*, by the *activity of human beings*, the idea of *causality* becomes established, the idea that one motion is the *cause* of another." [24]

The complexity of the world may disguise the processes of cause and effect and make the one indistinguishable from the other, but that does not alter the underlying logic. As Engels explained, "cause and effect are conceptions which only hold good their application to individual cases; but as soon as we consider the individual

(24) Engels, *The Dialectics of Nature*, pp. 17 and 304.

cases in their general interconnection with the universe as a whole, they run into each other, and they become confounded when we contemplate that universal action and reaction in which causes and effects are eternally changing places, so that what is effect here and now will be cause there and then, and vice versa." [25]

Chaos theory undoubtedly represents a big advance, but here also there are some questionable formulations. The celebrated *butterfly effect*, according to which a butterfly flaps its wings in Tokyo, and causes a storm the following week in Chicago is no doubt a sensational example, intended to provoke controversy. However, it is incorrect in this form. Qualitative changes can only occur as the result of an accumulation of quantitative changes. A small accidental change (a butterfly flapping its wings) could only produce a dramatic result if all the conditions for a storm were already in existence. In this case, necessity could express itself through an accident. But only in this case.

The dialectical relationship between necessity and chance can be seen in the process of natural selection. The number of random mutations within the organism is infinitely large. However, in a particular environment, one of these mutations is found to be useful to the organism and retained, while all the others perish. Necessity once again manifests itself through the agency of chance. In a sense, the appearance of life on earth can be seen as an "accident". It was not preordained that the earth should be exactly at the right distance from the sun, with the right kind of gravity and atmosphere, for this to happen. But, given this concatenation of circumstances, over a period of time, out of a vast number of chemical reactions, life would inevitably arise. This applies not only to our own planet, but to a vast number of other planets where similar conditions exist, although not in our solar system. However, once life had arisen, it ceases to be a question of accident, and develops according to its own inherent laws.

Consciousness itself did not arise out of any Divine plan, but, in one sense also arose from the "accident" of bipedalism (upright stance), which freed the hands, and thus made it possible for early hominids to evolve as a tool-making animal. It is probable that this evolutionary quirk was the result of a climatic change in East Africa, which partly destroyed the forest habitat of our simian ancestors. This was an accident. As Engels explains in *The Part Played by Labour in the Transition of Ape to Man*, this was the basis upon which human consciousness developed. But in a broader sense, the emergence of consciousness—of *matter aware of itself*—cannot be regarded as an accident, but a necessary product of the evolution of matter, which proceeds from the simplest forms to more complex forms, and which, where the conditions exist, will inevitably give rise to intelligent life, and higher forms of consciousness, complex societies, and what we know as civilisation.

In his *Metaphysics*, Aristotle devotes a lot of space to a discussion of the nature of necessity and accident. He gives us an example, the accidental words that lead to

(25) Engels, *Anti-Dühring*, p. 32.

a quarrel. In a tense situation, for example a marriage in difficulties, even the most innocuous comment can lead to a row. But it is clear that the words spoken are not the real cause of the dispute. It is the product of an accumulation of stresses and strains, which sooner or later reaches a breaking point. When this point is reached, the slightest thing can provoke an outburst. We can see the same phenomenon in the workplace. For years, an apparently docile workforce, fearful of unemployment, is prepared to accept all manner of impositions—wage reductions, sackings of colleagues, worsening conditions, etc. On the surface, nothing is happening. But in reality, there is a steady increase in discontent, which, at a certain point, must find an expression. One day, the workers decide that "enough is enough". At this precise point, even the most trivial incident can provoke a walkout. The whole situation changes into its opposite.

There is a broad analogy between the class struggle and the conflicts between nations. In August 1914, the Crown Prince of Austro-Hungary was assassinated in Sarajevo. This was alleged to have caused the First World War. As a matter of fact, this was an historical accident, which might or might not have occurred. Prior to 1914 there were several other incidents (the Morocco incident, the Agadir incident), which could equally have led to war. The real cause of World War One was the accumulation of unbearable contradictions between the main imperialist powers— Britain, France, Germany, Austro-Hungary and Russia. This reached a critical stage, where the whole explosive mixture could be ignited by a single spark in the Balkans.

Finally, we see the same phenomenon in the world of economics. At the moment when we write these lines the City of London has been shaken by the collapse of the Barings Bank. This was instantly blamed on the fraudulent activities of one of the bank's employees in Singapore. But the Barings collapse was merely the latest symptom of a far deeper malaise in the world financial system. The headlines in *The Independent* newspaper read "an accident waiting to happen". On a world scale, there are at present US \$25 trillion invested in derivatives. This shows that capitalism is no longer based on production, but to a greater and greater extent upon speculative activities. The fact that Mr. Leeson lost a large amount of money in the Japanese stock markets may be connected with the accident of the Kobe earthquake. But serious economic analysts understand that this was an expression of the fundamental unsoundness of the international financial system. With or without Mr. Leeson, future collapses are inevitable. The big international corporations and financial institutions, all of whom are involved in this reckless gambling, are playing with fire. A major financial collapse is implicit in the whole situation.

It may be that there are many phenomena whose underlying processes and causative relationships are not fully understood so that they appear to be random. For all practical purposes, therefore, these can only be treated statistically, like the roulette wheel to the punter. But underlying these "chance" events there are still forces and processes that determine the end results. We live in a universe governed by dialectical determinism.

Marxism and freedom

The problem of the relation between "freedom and necessity" was known to Aristotle and endlessly discussed by the mediaeval Schoolmen. Kant uses it as one of his celebrated "antinomies", where it is presented as an insoluble contradiction. In the 17th and 18th centuries it cropped up in mathematics as the theory of chance, related to gambling.

The dialectical relationship between freedom and necessity has resurfaced in chaos theory. Doyne Farmer, an American physicist investigating complicated dynamics, comments:

"On a philosophical level, it struck me as an operational way to define free will, in a way that allowed you to reconcile free will with determinism. The system is deterministic, but you can't say what it's going to do next. At the same time, I'd always felt that the important problems out there in the world had to do with the creation of organisation, in life or intelligence. But how did you study that? What biologists were doing seemed so applied and specific; chemists certainly weren't doing it; mathematicians weren't doing it at all, and it was something that physicists just didn't do. I always felt that the spontaneous emergence of self-organisation ought to be part of physics. Here was one coin with two sides. Here was order, with randomness emerging, and then one step further away was randomness with it own underlying order." [26]

Dialectical determinism has nothing in common with the mechanical approach, still less with fatalism. In the same way that there are laws that govern inorganic and organic matter, so there are laws that govern the evolution of human society. The patterns that can be observed through history are not at all fortuitous. Marx and Engels explained that the transition from one social system to another is determined by the development of the productive forces, in the last analysis. When a given socioeconomic system is no longer able to develop the productive forces, it enters into crisis, preparing the ground for a revolutionary overturn.

This is not at all to deny the role of the individual in history. As we have already said, men and women make their own history. However, it would be foolish to imagine that human beings are "free agents" who can determine their future purely on the basis of their own will. They have to base themselves on conditions which have been created independent of their will—economic, social, political, religious, and cultural. In this sense, the idea of free will is nonsense. The real attitude of Marx and Engels towards the role of the individual in history is shown by the following quotation from *The Holy Family*:

(26) Quoted in Gleick, op. cit., pp. 251-2.

"*History* does *nothing*, it 'possesses *no* immense wealth', it 'wages *no* battles'. It is *man*, real, living man who does all that, who possesses and fights; 'history' is not, as it were, a person apart, using man as a means to achieve *its own* aims; history is *nothing but* the activity of man pursuing its aims." [27]

There is no question of men and women being merely blind puppets of fate, powerless to change their own destiny. However, the *real* men and women living in the real world of which Marx and Engels write, do not and cannot stand above the society in which they live. Hegel once wrote that "interests move the life of the peoples". Consciously or otherwise, the individual actors on the historical stage ultimately reflect the interests, opinions, prejudices, morality and aspirations of a specific class or group within society. This is really self-evident from even the most superficial reading of history.

Nevertheless, the illusion of "free will" is persistent. The German philosopher Leibniz remarked that a magnetic needle, if it could think, would doubtless imagine that it pointed North because it choose to do so. In the 20th century, Sigmund Freud utterly demolished the prejudice that men and women are in complete control even of their own thoughts. The phenomenon of *Freudian slips* is a perfect example of the dialectical relationship between accident and necessity. Freud gives numerous examples of mistakes in speech, "forgetfulness", and other "accidents", which, in many cases, undoubtedly reveal deeper psychological processes. In the words of Freud:

"Certain inadequacies of our psychic capacities...and certain performances which are unintentional prove to be well motivated when subjected to the psychoanalytic investigation, and are determined through the consciousness of unknown motives." [28]

It was a fundamental tenet of Freud's approach that none of human behaviour is accidental. The small mistakes of everyday life, dreams, and the apparently inexplicable symptoms of mentally ill people are not "accidental". By definition, the human mind is not aware of unconscious processes. The more deeply unconscious the motivation, from the standpoint of psychoanalysis, the more obvious it is that a person will *not* be aware of it. Freud grasped early on the general principle that these unconscious processes reveal themselves (and therefore can be studied) in those fragments of behaviour which the conscious mind dismisses as silly mistakes or accidents.

Is it possible to attain freedom? If what is meant by a "free" action is one that is not caused or determined, we must say quite frankly that such an action has never existed, and never will exist. Such imaginary "freedom" is pure metaphysics. Hegel explained that real freedom is the recognition of necessity. To the degree that men and women understand the laws that govern nature and society, they will be in a

(27) Marx and Engels, *Collected Works*, Vol. 4, p. 93, henceforth referred to as MECW.
(28) Freud, *The Psychopathology of Everyday Life*, p. 193.

position to master these laws and turn them to their own advantage. The real material basis upon which humankind can become free has been established by the development of industry, science and technology. In a rational system of society—one in which the means of production are harmoniously planned and consciously controlled—we will really be able to speak about free human development. In the words of Engels, this is "mankind's leap from the realm of necessity to the realm of freedom."

7. Relativity theory

What is time?

Few ideas have penetrated the human consciousness as profoundly as that of time. The idea of time and space has occupied human thought for thousands of years. These things at first sight seem simple and easy to grasp, because they are close to everyday experience. Everything exists in time and space, so they appear as familiar conceptions. However, what is familiar is not necessarily understood. On closer examination, time and space are not so easily grasped. In the 5th century, St. Augustine remarked: "What, then, is time? If no one asks me, I know what time is. If I wish to explain it to him who asks me, I do not know." The dictionary is not much help here. Time is defined as "a period", and a period is defined as "time". This does not get us very far! In reality, the nature of time and space is quite a complex philosophical problem.

Men and women clearly distinguish between past and future. A sense of time is, however, not unique to humans or even animals. Organisms often have a kind of "internal clock", like plants which turn one way during the day and another at night. Time is an objective expression of the changing state of matter. This is revealed even by the way we talk about it. It is common to say that time "flows". In fact, only material fluids can flow. The very choice of metaphor shows that time is inseparable from matter. It is not only a subjective thing. It is the way we express an actual process that exists in the physical world. Time is thus just an expression of the fact that all matter exists in a state of *constant change*. It is the destiny and necessity of all material things to change into something other than what they are. "Everything that exists deserves to perish."

A sense of rhythm underlies everything: the heart-beat of a human, the rhythms of speech, the movement of the stars and planets, the rise and fall of the tides, the alternations of the seasons. These are deeply engraved upon the human consciousness, not as arbitrary imaginings, but as real phenomena expressing a profound truth about the universe. Here human intuition is not in error. Time is a way of expressing change of state and motion, which are inseparable features of matter in all its forms. In language we have tense, future, present and past. This colossal conquest of the mind enabled humankind to free itself from the slavery of the moment, to rise above the concrete situation and be "present", not just in the here and now, but in the past and the future, at least in the mind.

Time and movement are inseparable concepts. They are essential to all life and all knowledge of the world, including every manifestation of thought and imagination. Measurement, the cornerstone of all science, would be impossible without time and space. Music and dance are based upon time. Art itself attempts to convey a sense of time and movement, which are present not just in representations of physical energy, but in design. The colours, shapes and lines of a painting guide the eye across the surface in a particular rhythm and tempo. This is what gives rise to the particular mood, idea and emotion conveyed by the work of art. Timelessness is a word that is often used to describe works of art, but really expresses the opposite of what is intended. We cannot conceive of the absence of time, since time is present in everything.

There is a difference between time and space. Space can also express change, as change of position. Matter exists and moves through space. But the number of ways that this can occur is infinite: forward, backward, up or down, to any degree. Movement in space is *reversible*. Movement in time is *irreversible*. They are two different (and indeed contradictory) ways of expressing the same fundamental property of matter—change. This is the only Absolute that exists.

Space is the "otherness" of matter, to use Hegel's terminology, whereas time is the process whereby matter (and energy, which is the same thing) constantly changes into something other than what it is. Time—"the fire in which we are all consumed"—is commonly seen as a destructive agent. But it is equally the expression of a permanent process of self-creation, whereby matter is constantly transformed into an endless number of forms. This process can be seen quite clearly in non-organic matter, above all at the subatomic level.

The notion of change, as expressed in the passing of time, deeply permeates human consciousness. It is the basis of the tragic element in literature, the feeling of sadness at the passing of life, which reaches its most beautiful expression in the sonnets of Shakespeare, like this one which vividly conveys a sense of the restless movement of time:

"Like as the waves make toward the pebbled shore,
So do our minutes hasten to their end;
Each changing place with that which goes before,
In sequent toil all forward do contend."
(Sonnet 60)

The irreversibility of time does not only exist for living beings. Not only humans, but stars and galaxies are born and perish. Change affects all, but not only in a negative way. Alongside death there is life, and order arises spontaneously out of chaos. The two sides of the contradiction are inseparable. Without death, life itself would be impossible. Every man and woman is not only aware of themselves, but also the negation of themselves, their limit. We come from nature and will return to nature.

Mortals understand that as finite beings their lives must end in death. As the *Book of Job* reminds us: "Man that is born of woman is of a few days, and full of trouble. He cometh forth like a flower, and is cut down; he fleeth also as a shadow, and continueth not." [29] Animals do not fear death in the same way because they have no knowledge of it. Human beings have attempted to escape their destiny by establishing a privileged communion with an imaginary supernatural existence after death. The idea of everlasting life is present in almost all religions in one form or another. It is the motive-force behind the egotistical thirsting for an imaginary immortality in a non-existent Heaven, which is supposed to provide a consolation for the "Vale of Tears" on this sinful earth. Thus, for countless centuries men and women have been taught to submit meekly to suffering and privation on earth in expectation of a life of happiness—once they are dead.

That every *individual* must pass away is well known. In the future, human life will be prolonged far beyond its "natural" span; nevertheless the end must come. But what is true for particular men and women is not true of the species. We live on through our children, through the memories of our friends, and through the contribution we make to the good of humanity. This is the only immortality to which we are entitled to aspire. Generations pass away, but are replaced by new generations, which develop and enrich the scope of human activity and knowledge. Humanity can conquer the earth and reach out its hands to the heavens. The real search for immortality is realised in this endless process of human development and perfection, as men and women make themselves anew on a higher basis than before. The highest goal we can set ourselves is thus not to long for an imaginary paradise in the beyond, but to fight to attain the real social conditions for the building of a paradise in this world.

From our earliest experiences, we come to an understanding of the importance of time. So it is surprising that some have thought time to be an illusion, a mere invention of the mind. This idea has persisted down to the present In fact, the idea that time and change are mere illusions is not new. It is present in ancient religions like Buddhism, and also in idealist philosophies like that of Pythagoras, Plato and Plotinus. The aspiration of Buddhism was to reach *Nirvana*, a state where time ceased to exist. It was Heraclitus, the father of dialectics, who understood correctly

(29) Job 14: 1

the nature of time and change, when he wrote: "everything is and is not because everything is in flux" and "we step and do not step in the same stream, we are and are not".

The idea of change as cyclical is the product of an agricultural society utterly dependent upon the change of seasons. The static way of life rooted in the mode of production of former societies found its expression in static philosophies. The Catholic Church could not stomach the cosmology of Copernicus and Galileo because it challenged the existing view of the world and society. Only in capitalist society has the development of industry disrupted the old, slow rhythms of peasant life. Not only is the difference between the seasons abolished in production, but even the difference between night and day, as machines run for 24 hours a day, seven days a week, fifty two weeks a year, under the glare of artificial lights. Capitalism has revolutionised the means of production, and with it the minds of men and women. However, the progress of the latter has proved to be far slower than the former. The conservatism of the mind is revealed in the constant attempt to cling to outworn ideas, old certainties whose time has long past, and, ultimately, the age-old hope for a life after death.

The idea that the universe must have a beginning and an end has been revived in recent decades by the cosmological theories of the big bang. This inevitably involves a supernatural being who creates the world according to some unfathomable plan from nothing, and keeps it going for as long as He considers it necessary. The old religious cosmology of Moses, Isaiah, Tertullian and Plato's *Timaeus*, incredibly resurfaces in the writings of some modern cosmologists and theoretical physicists. There is nothing new in this. Every social system that enters into a phase of irreversible decline always presents its own demise as the end of the world, or, better still, the universe. Yet the universe still carries on, indifferent to the destiny of this or that temporary social formation on earth. Humankind continues to live, to fight and, despite all reverses, to develop and progress. So that every period sets out on a higher level than before. And there is, in principle, no limit to this process.

Time and philosophy

The Ancient Greeks actually had a far deeper insight into the meaning of time, space and motion than the moderns. Not only Heraclitus, the greatest dialectician of Antiquity, but also the Eleatic philosophers (Parmenides, Zeno) arrived at a very scientific conception of these phenomena. The Greek atomists already put forward the picture of a universe which required no Creator, no beginning and no end. Space and matter are generally seen as opposites, as conveyed by the idea of "full" and "empty". In practice, however, the one cannot exist without the other. They presuppose each other, determine, limit and define each other. The unity of space and matter is the most fundamental unity of opposites of all. This was already understood by the Greek atomists who visualised the universe as being composed of only two things—the "atoms" and the "void". In essence, this view of the universe is correct.

Relativism has been observed many times in the history of philosophy. The sophists held that "man is the measure of all things". They were relativists *par excellence*. Denying the possibility of absolute truth, they inclined towards extreme *subjectivism*. The sophists nowadays have a bad name, but in fact they represented a step forward in the history of philosophy. While there were many charlatans in their ranks, they also had a number of talented dialecticians like Protagoras. The dialectic of sophism was based on the correct idea that *truth is many sided*. A thing can be shown to have many properties. It is necessary to have the ability to see a given phenomenon from different sides. For the undialectical thinker, the world is a very simple place, made up of things existing separately, one after the other. Every "thing" enjoys a solid existence in time and space. It is before me "here" and "now". However, closer observation reveals these simple and familiar words to be one-sided abstractions.

Aristotle as in so many other fields, dealt with space, time and motion with great rigour and profundity. He wrote that only two things are imperishable: time and change, which he rightly considers *identical*:

"It is impossible, however, that motion should be generable or perishable; it must always have existed. Nor can time come into being or cease to be; for there cannot be a 'before' or 'after' where there is no time. Movement, then, is also continuous in the sense in which time is, for time is either the same thing as motion or an attribute of it; so than motion must be continuous as time is, and if so it must be local and circular." Elsewhere he says that "Movement can neither come into being nor cease to be: nor can time come into being, or cease to be." [30] How much wiser were the great thinkers of the Ancient World than those who now write about "the beginning of time", and without even smiling!

The German idealist philosopher Emmanuel Kant was the man who, after Aristotle, investigated the question of the nature of time and space most fully, although his solutions were ultimately unsatisfactory. Every material thing is an assemblage of many properties. If we take away all these concrete properties, we are left with only two abstractions: time and space. The idea of time and space as really existing metaphysical entities was given a philosophical basis by Kant, who claimed that space and time were "phenomenally real", but could not be known "in themselves".

Time and space are properties of matter, and cannot be conceived separately from matter. In his book *The Critique of Pure Reason*, Kant claimed that time and space were not objective concepts drawn from observation of the real world, but were somehow inborn. In point of fact, all the concepts of geometry are derived

(30) Aristotle, op cit., pp. 342 and 1b.

from observations of material objects. One of the achievements of Einstein's general theory of relativity was precisely to develop geometry as an empirical science, the axioms of which are inferred from actual measurements, and which differ from the axioms of classical Euclidean geometry, which were (incorrectly) supposed to have been the products of pure reason, deduced from logic alone.

Kant attempted to justify his claims in the famous section in his *Critique of Pure Reason* known as the *Antinomies*, which deal with the contradictory phenomena of the natural world, including space and time. The first four of Kant's (cosmological) antinomies deal with this question. Kant had the merit of posing the existence of such contradictions, but his explanation was at best incomplete. It fell to the great dialectician Hegel to resolve the contradiction in *Science of Logic*.

Throughout the 18th century, science was dominated by the theories of classical mechanics, and one man set his stamp on the whole epoch. The poet Alexander Pope sums up the adulatory attitude of contemporaries to Newton in his verse:

"Nature and Nature's laws lay hid in night:
God said 'Let Newton be!' and all was light."

Newton envisaged time as flowing in a straight line everywhere. Even if there was no matter, there would be a fixed frame of space and time would still flow "through" it. Newton's absolute spatial frame was supposed to be filled with a hypothetical "ether" through which light waves flowed. Newton thought that time was like a gigantic "container" inside which everything exists and changes. In this idea, time is conceived as having an existence separate and apart from the natural universe. Time would exist, even if the universe did not. This is characteristic of the mechanical (and idealist) method in which time, space, matter and motion are regarded as absolutely separate. In reality, it is impossible to separate them.

Newtonian physics was conditioned by mechanics which In the 18th century was the most advanced of the sciences. It was also convenient for the new ruling class because it presented an essentially static, timeless, unchanging view of the universe, in which all contradiction were smoothed out—no sudden leaps, no revolutions, but a perfect harmony, in which everything sooner or later returned to equilibrium, just as the British parliament had reached a satisfactory equilibrium with the Monarchy under William of Orange. The 20th century has pitilessly destroyed this view of the world. One after the other, the old rigid, static mechanism has been displaced. The new science has been characterised by restless change, fantastic speed, contradictions and paradoxes at all levels.

Newton distinguished between absolute time and "relative, apparent and common time", as it appears in earthly clocks. He advanced the notion of *absolute time*, an ideal time scale which simplified the laws of mechanics. These abstractions of time and space proved to be powerful ideas that have greatly advanced our understanding of the universe. They were held to be absolute for a long time. However, upon closer examination, the "absolute truths" of classical Newtonian mechanics proved to be—*relative*. They were true *only within certain limits*.

Newton and Hegel

The mechanistic theories that dominated science for two centuries after Newton were first seriously challenged in the field of biology by the revolutionary discoveries of Charles Darwin. Darwin's theory of evolution showed that life could originate and develop without the need for Divine intervention, on the basis of the laws of nature. At the end of the 19th century the idea of the "arrow of time" was put forward by Ludwig Boltzmann in the second law of thermodynamics. This striking image no longer presents time as a never-ending cycle, but as an *arrow* moving in a single direction. These theories assume that time is real and that the universe is in a continual process of change, as old Heraclitus had foreseen.

Almost half a century before Darwin's epoch-making work, Hegel had anticipated not only him, but many other discoveries of modern science. Boldly challenging the assumption of the prevailing Newtonian mechanics, Hegel advanced a dynamic view of the world, based on processes and *change through contradiction*. The brilliant anticipations of Heraclitus were transformed by Hegel into a completely elaborated system of dialectical thought. There is no doubt that, had Hegel been taken more seriously, the process of science would have advanced far more rapidly than it did.

The greatness of Einstein was to get beyond these abstractions and reveal their relative character. The relative aspect of time was, however, not new. It was thoroughly analysed by Hegel. In his early work *The Phenomenology of Mind*, he explains the relative content of words like "here" and "now". These ideas which seem quite simple and straightforward turn out to be very complex and contradictory. "To the question, what is the Now? we reply, for example, the Now is night-time. To test the truth of this certainty of sense, a simple experiment is all we need: write that truth down. A truth cannot lose anything by being written down, and just as little by our preserving and keeping it. If we look again at the truth we have written down, look at it *now, at his noon-time*, we shall have to say it has turned stale and become out of date." [31]

It is a very simple matter to dismiss Hegel (or Engels) because their writings on science were necessarily limited by the actual state of science of the day. What is remarkable, however, is how advanced Hegel's views on science actually were. In their book *Order out of Chaos*, Prigogine and Stengers point out that Hegel rejected the mechanistic method of classical Newtonian physics, at a time when Newton's ideas were universally sacrosanct:

"The Hegelian philosophy of nature systematically incorporates all that is denied by Newtonian science. In particular, it rests on the qualitative difference

(31) Hegel, *The Phenomenology of Mind*, p. 151.

between the simple behaviour described by mechanics and the behaviour of more complex entities such as living beings. It denies the possibility of reducing those levels, rejecting the idea that differences are merely apparent and that nature is basically homogeneous and simple. It affirms the existence of a hierarchy, each level of which presupposes the preceding ones." [32]

Hegel wrote scornfully about the allegedly absolute truths of Newtonian mechanics. He was the first one to subject the mechanistic approach of the 18th century to a thorough criticism, although the limitations of the science of his day did not allow him to put forward a worked-out alternative. For Hegel, every finite thing was *mediated*, that is, relative to something else. Moreover, this relationship was not merely a formal juxtaposition, but a living process: everything was *limited, conditioned and determined by everything else*. Thus, cause and effect only hold good in relation to isolated relations (such as we find in classical mechanics), but not if we regard things as processes, in which everything is the result of *universal interrelations and interactions*.

Time is the form of existence of matter. Mathematics and formal logic cannot really deal with time, but treat it merely as a *quantitative relation*. Now there is no doubt about the importance of quantitative relations for understanding reality, since every finite thing can be approached from a quantitative point of view. Without a grasp of quantitative relationships, science would be impossible. But in and of themselves they cannot adequately express the complexity of life and movement, the restless process of change in which gradual, smooth developments suddenly give rise to chaotic transformations.

Purely quantitative relations, to use Hegel's terminology, present the real processes of nature "only in an arrested paralysed form." [33] The universe is an infinite, self-moving whole, which is self-establishing and contains life within itself. Movement is a contradictory phenomenon, containing both positive and negative. This is one of the fundamental propositions of dialectics, which are closer to the real nature of things than the axioms of classical mathematics.

Only in classical geometry is it possible to conceive of completely empty space. It is yet another mathematical abstraction, which plays an important role, but only approximately represents reality. Geometry essentially compares *different spatial magnitudes*. Contrary to what Kant believed, the abstractions of mathematics are not "a priori" and inborn, but derived from observations of the material world. Hegel shows that the Greeks had already understood the limitedness of purely quantitative descriptions of nature, and comments:

"How much further had they progressed in thought than those who in our day, when some put in the place of determinations of thought number and determinations of numbers (like powers), next the infinitely great and the infinitely small, one

(32) Prigogine and Stengers, op. cit., p. 89.
(33) Hegel, *The Phenomenology of Mind*, p. 104.

divided by infinity, and other such determinations, which often are a perverted mathematical formalism, take the return to this impotent childishness for something praiseworthy and even for something thorough and profound." [34]

These lines are even more appropriate today than when they were written. It really is incredible when certain cosmologists and mathematicians make the most preposterous claims about the nature of the universe without the slightest attempt to prove them on the basis of observed facts, and then appeal to the alleged beauty and simplicity of their equations as the final authority. The cult of mathematics is greater today than at any time since Pythagoras who thought that "all things are Number". And, as with Pythagoras, there are similarly mystical overtones. Mathematics leaves aside all *qualitative* determinations except *number*. It ignores the real content, and applies its rules externally to things. None of these abstractions have real existence. Only the material world exists. This fact is all too frequently overlooked with disastrous results.

Relativity

Albert Einstein was undoubtedly one of the great geniuses of our time. Between his twenty-first and thirty-eighth birthdays he completed a revolution in science, with profound repercussions at many levels. The two great breakthroughs were the Special Theory of Relativity (1905) and the General Theory of Relativity (1915). Special relativity deals with high speeds, general relativity with gravity.

Despite their extremely abstract character, Einstein's theories were ultimately derived from experiments, and were successfully given practical applications, which confirmed their correctness time and again. Einstein set out from the famous Michelson-Morley experiment, "the greatest negative experiment of the history of science" (John D. Bernal), which exposed an inner contradiction in 19th century physics. This experiment attempted to generalise the electromagnetic theory of light by demonstrating that the apparent velocity of light was dependent upon the rate at which the observer travelled through the supposedly fixed "ether". In the end, no difference was found in the velocity of light, in whatever direction the observer was travelling.

Joseph John Thomson later showed that the velocity of electrons in high electrical fields was slower than predicted by the classical Newtonian physics. These contradictions in 19th century physics were resolved by the special theory of relativity. The old physics was unable to explain the phenomenon of radioactivity. Einstein explained this as the release of a tiny part of the enormous amount of energy trapped in "inert" matter.

In 1905, Einstein developed his special theory of relativity in his spare time, while working as a clerk in a Swiss patent office. Setting out from the discoveries

(34) Hegel, *Science of Logic*, Vol. 1, p. 229.

of the new quantum mechanics, he showed that light travels through space in a quantum form (as bundles of energy). This was clearly in contradiction to the previously accepted theory of light as a wave. In effect, Einstein revived the old corpuscular theory of light, but in an entirely different way. Here light was shown as a new kind of particle, with a contradictory character, simultaneously displaying the properties of a particle and a wave. This startling theory made possible the retention of all the great discoveries of 19th century optics, including spectroscopes, as well as Maxwell's equation. But it killed stone dead the old idea that light requires a special vehicle, the "ether", to travel through space.

Special relativity starts from the assumption that the speed of light in a vacuum will always be measured at the same constant value, irrespective of the speed of the light source relative to the observer. From this it is deduced that the speed of light represents the limiting speed for anything in the universe. In addition, special relativity states that energy and mass are in reality equivalents. This is a striking confirmation of the fundamental philosophical postulate of dialectical materialism—the inseparable character of matter and energy the idea that motion ("energy") is the mode of existence of matter.

Einstein's discovery of the law of equivalence of mass and energy is expressed in his famous equation $E = mc^2$, which expresses the colossal energies locked up in the atom. This is the source of all the concentrated energy in the universe. The symbol e represents energy (in ergs), m stands for mass (in grams) and c is the speed of light (in centimetres per second). The actual value of c^2 is 900 billion billion. That is to say, the conversion of one gram of energy locked up in matter will produce a staggering 900 billion billion ergs. To give a concrete example of what this means, the energy contained in a single gram of matter is equivalent to the energy produced by burning 2,000 tons of petrol.

Mass and energy are not just "interchangeable", as dollars are interchangeable with euros; they are one and the same substance, which Einstein characterised as "mass-energy". This idea goes far deeper and is more precise than the old mechanical concept whereby, for example, friction is transformed into heat. Here, matter is just a particular form of "frozen" energy, while every other form of energy (including light), has mass associated with it. For this reason, it is quite wrong to say that matter "disappears" when it is changed into energy.

Einstein's law displaced the old law of the conservation of mass, worked out by Lavoisier, which says that matter, understood as mass, can neither be created nor destroyed. In fact, every chemical reaction that releases energy converts a small amount of mass into energy. This could not be measured in the kind of chemical reaction known to the 19th century, such as the burning of coal. But nuclear reaction releases sufficient energy to reveal a measurable loss of mass. All matter, even when at "rest", contains staggering amounts of energy. However, as this cannot be observed, it was not understood until Einstein explained it.

Far from overthrowing materialism, Einstein's theory establishes it on a firmer basis. In place of the old mechanical law of the "conservation of mass", we have the far more scientific and more general laws of the *conservation of mass-energy*, which expresses the first law of thermodynamics in a universal and unassailable form. The mass does not "disappear" at all, but is converted into energy. The total amount of mass-energy remains the same. Not a single particle of matter can be created or destroyed. The second idea is the special limiting character of the speed of light: the assertion that no particle can travel faster than the speed of light, since as it approaches this critical velocity, its mass approaches infinity, so that it becomes harder and harder to go faster. These ideas seem abstract and difficult to grasp. They challenge the assumptions of "sound common sense". The relationship between "common sense" and science was summed up by the Soviet scientist Professor Lev D. Landau in the following lines:

"So-called common sense represents nothing but a simple generalisation of the notions and habits that have grown up in our daily life. It is a definite level of understanding reflecting a particular level of experiment." And he adds: "Science is not afraid of clashes with so-called common sense. It is only afraid of disagreement between existing ideas and new experimental facts and if such disagreement occurs science relentlessly smashes the ideas it has previously built up and raises our knowledge to a higher level." [35] How can a moving object increase its mass? Such a notion contradicts our everyday experience. A spinning top does not visibly gain in mass while revolving. In point of fact, it does, but the increase is so infinitesimal that it may be discounted for all practical purposes. The effects of special relativity cannot be observed on the level of everyday phenomena. However, under extreme conditions, for example, at very high speeds approaching the speed of light, relativistic effects begin to come into play.

Einstein predicted that the mass of a moving object would increase at very high speeds. This law can be ignored when dealing with normal speeds. Nevertheless, subatomic particles move at speeds of nearly 10,000 miles per second or more, and at such speeds as these relativistic effects appear. The discoveries of quantum mechanics demonstrated the correctness of the special theory of relativity, not only qualitatively, but quantitatively. An electron gains in mass as it moves at 9/10th the speed of light; moreover, the gain in mass is 3 1/6th times, precisely as Einstein's theory predicted. Since then, special relativity has been tested many times, and so far it has always given correct results. Electrons emerge from a powerful particle accelerator about 40,000 times heavier than when they started, the extra mass representing energy of motion.

At far higher velocities the increase in mass becomes noticeable. And modern physics deals precisely with extremely high velocities, such as the speed of sum-

(35) Landau, L.D. and Rumer, G.B, *What is Relativity?* pp. 36 and 37.

atomic particles, which approach the speed of light. Here the classical laws of mechanics, which adequately describe everyday phenomena, cannot be applied. To common sense the mass of an object never changes. Therefore a spinning-top has the same weight as a still one. In this way a law was invented which states that mass is constant irrespective of speed.

Later, this law was shown to be incorrect. It was found that mass increases with velocity. Yet, since the increase only becomes appreciable near the speed of light, we take it as constant. The correct law would be: "If an object moves with a speed of less than 100 miles per second, the mass is consistent to within one part in a million." For everyday purposes, we can assume that mass is constant irrespective of speed. But for high speeds, this is false, and the higher the speed, the falser is the assertion. Like thinking based on formal logic, it is accepted as valid for practical purposes. Feynman points out:

"...*Philosophically, we are completely wrong* with the approximate law. Our entire picture of the world has to be altered even though the mass changes only by a little bit. This is a very peculiar thing about the philosophy, or the ideas, behind the laws. Even a very small effect sometimes requires profound changes in our ideas." [36]

The predictions of special relativity have been shown to correspond to the observed facts. Scientists discovered by experiment that gamma rays could produce atomic particles, transforming the energy of light into matter. They also found that the minimum energy required to create a particle depended on its rest energy, as predicted by Einstein. In point of fact not one, but *two* particles were produced: a particle and its opposite, the "anti-particle". In the gamma-ray experiment, we get an electron and an anti-electron (positron). The reverse process also takes place: when a positron meets an electron, they annihilate each other, producing gamma rays. Thus, energy is transformed into matter, and matter into energy. Einstein's discovery provided the basis for a far more profound understanding of the workings of the universe. It provided an explanation of the source of the sun's energy, which had been a mystery throughout the ages. The immense storehouse of energy turned out to be—matter itself. The awesome power of the energy locked up in matter was revealed to the world in August 1945 at Hiroshima and Nagasaki. All this is contained in the deceptively simple formula $E = mc^2$.

The general theory of relativity

Special relativity is quite adequate when dealing with an object moving at constant speed and direction in relation to the observer. However, in practice motion is never constant. There are always forces which cause variations in the speed and direction of moving objects. Since subatomic particles move at immense speeds over short

(36) Feynman, op. cit., Vol. 1, 1-2.

distances, they do not have time to accelerate much, and special relativity can be applied. Nevertheless, in the motion of planets and stars, special relativity proved insufficient. Here we are dealing with large accelerations caused by huge gravitational fields. It is once again a case of quantity and quality. At the subatomic level, gravitation is insignificant in comparison with other forces, and can be ignored. In the everyday world, on the contrary, all other forces except gravity can be ignored.

Einstein attempted to apply relativity to motion in general, not just to constant motion. Thus we arrive at the general theory of relativity, which deals with gravity. It marks a break, not only with the classical physics of Newton, with its absolute mechanical universe, but with the equally absolute classical geometry of Euclid. Einstein showed that Euclidean geometry only applied to "empty space", an ideally conceived abstraction. In reality, space is not "empty". Space is inseparable from matter. Einstein maintained that space itself is conditioned by the presence of material bodies. In his general theory, this idea is conveyed by the seemingly paradoxical assertion that, near heavy bodies, "space is curved".

The real, i.e., material, universe is not at all like the world of Euclidean geometry, with the perfect circles, absolutely straight lines, and so on. The real world is full of irregularities. It is not straight, but precisely "warped". On the other hand, space is not something that exists separate and apart from matter. The curvature of space is just another way of expressing the curvature of matter that "fills" space. For example, it has been proved that light rays bend under the influence of the gravitational fields of bodies in space.

The general theory of relativity is essentially of a geometrical character, but this geometry is completely different to the classical Euclidean kind. In Euclidean geometry, for instance, parallel lines never meet or diverge, and the angles of a triangle always add up to 180°. Einstein's *space-time* (actually first developed by the Russian-German mathematician, Hermann Minkowski, one of Einstein's teachers, in 1907) represents a synthesis of three-dimensional space (height, breadth and length) with time. This four dimensional geometry deals with curved surfaces ("curved space-time"). Here the angles of a triangle may not add up to 180°, and parallel lines can cross or diverge.

In Euclidean geometry, as Engels points out, we meet a whole series of abstractions which do not at all correspond to the real world: a dimensionless point which becomes a straight line, which, in turn, becomes a perfectly flat surface, and so on and so forth. Among all these abstractions we have the emptiest abstraction of all, that of "empty space". Space, in spite of what Kant believed, cannot exist without something to fill it, and that something is precisely matter (and energy, which is the same thing). *The geometry of space is determined by the matter which it contains.* That is the real meaning of "curved space". It is merely a way of expressing the real properties of matter. The issue is only confused by inappropriate metaphors contained in popularisations of Einstein: "Think of space as a rubber sheet", or "Think of space as glass", and so on. In reality, the idea that must be kept in mind at all times is *the indissoluble unity of time, space, matter and motion*. The moment this unity is forgotten, we instantly slide into idealist mystification.

If we conceive space as a Thing-in-Itself, empty space, as in Euclid, clearly it cannot be curved. It is "nothing". However, as Hegel put it, there is nothing in the universe that does not contain both being and not-being. Space and matter are not two diametrically opposed, mutually exclusive phenomena. Space contains matter, and matter contains space. They are completely inseparable. The dialectical unity of matter and space is precisely what the universe is. In a most profound way, the general theory of relativity conveys this dialectical idea of the unity of space and matter. In the same way in mathematics zero itself is not "nothing", but expresses a real quantity, and plays a determining role.

Einstein presents gravitation as a property of space rather than a "force" acting upon bodies. According to this view space itself curves as a result of the presence of matter. This is a rather singular way of expressing the unity of space and matter, and one that is open to serious misinterpretations. Space itself, of course, cannot curve if it is understood as "empty space". The point is that it is impossible to conceive of space without matter. It is an inseparable unity. What we are considering is a definite relationship of space to matter. The Greek atomists long ago pointed out that atoms existed in the "void". The two things cannot exist without each other. Matter without space is the same as space without matter. A totally empty void is just nothing. But so is matter without any boundaries. Space and matter are opposites that presuppose each other, define each other, limit each other, and cannot exist without each other.

The general theory served to explain at least one phenomenon which could not be explained by Newton's classical theory. As the planet Mercury approaches its closest point to the sun, its revolutions display a peculiar irregularity, which had been previously attributed to the perturbations caused by the gravity of other planets. However, even when these were taken into account, it did not explain the phenomenon. The deviation of Mercury's orbit around the sun ("perihelion") was very small, but enough to upset the astronomers' calculations. Einstein's general theory predicted that the perihelion of any revolving body should have a motion beyond that prescribed by Newton's law. This was shown to be correct for Mercury, and later also for Venus.

He also predicted that a gravitational field would bend light-rays. Thus, he claimed, a light ray passing close to the surface of the sun would be bent out of a straight line by 1.75 seconds of arc. In 1919 an astronomic observation of an eclipse of the sun showed this to be correct. Einstein's brilliant theory was demonstrated in practice. It was able to explain the apparent shift in the position of stars near the sun by the bending of their rays, and also the irregular motion of the planet Mercury, which could not be accounted for by Newton's theories.

Newton worked out the laws governing the movement of objects, according to which the strength of gravitational pull depends upon mass. He also maintained that any force exerted upon an object produces acceleration in inverse proportion to the mass of the object. Resistance to acceleration is called inertia. All masses are measured either through gravitational effects or inertial effects. Direct observation has shown that inertial mass and gravitational mass are, in fact, identical to within one part in one trillion. Einstein began his theory of general relativity by assuming that inertial mass and gravitational mass are exactly equal, because they are essentially the same thing.

The apparently motionless stars are moving at colossal speeds. Einstein's cosmic equations of 1917 implied that the universe itself was not fixed for all time, but could be expanding. The galaxies are moving away from us at speeds of about 700 miles a second. The stars and galaxies are constantly changing, coming into being and passing away. The whole universe is a vast arena where the drama of birth and death of stars and galaxies is played out across eternity. These are truly revolutionary events! Exploding galaxies, supernovas, catastrophic collisions between stars, black holes with a density billions of times greater than our sun greedily devouring entire clusters of stars. These things put in the shade the imaginings of the poets.

Relations between things

Many notions are purely relative in character. For example, if one is asked to say whether a road is on the right or left side of a house, it is impossible to answer. It depends on which direction one is moving relative to the house. On the other hand, it is possible to speak of the right bank of a river, because the current determines the direction of the river. Similarly, we can say that cars keep to the left (at least in Britain!) because the movement of a car singles out one of the two possible directions along the road. In all these examples, however, the notions "left" and "right" are shown to be *relative*, since they only acquire meaning after the direction by which they are defined as indicated.

In the same way, if we ask, "Is it night or day?" the answer will depend on where we are. In London it is day, but in Australia it is night. Day and night are relative notions, determined by our position on the globe. An object will appear bigger or smaller depending upon its distance from a given point of observation. "Up" and "down" are also relative notions, which changed when it was discovered that the world is round, not flat. Even to this day, it is hard for "common sense" to accept that people in Australia can walk "upside down". Yet there is no contradiction if we understand that the notion of the vertical is not absolute but relative. For all practical purposes, we can take the earth's surface to be "flat" and therefore all verticals to be parallel, when dealing for instance, with two houses in one town. But when dealing with far larger distances, involving the whole earth's surface, we find that the attempt to make use of an absolute vertical leads to absurdities and contradictions.

By extension, the position of a planetary body is necessarily relative to the position of others. It is impossible to fix the position of an object without reference to other objects. The notion of "displacement" of a body in space means no more than that it changed its position relative to other bodies. A number of important laws of nature have a relativistic character, for example the principle of the relativity of motion and the law of inertia. The latter states that an object on which no external force acts can be not only in a state of rest but also in a state of uniform straight-line motion. This fundamental law of physics was discovered by Galileo.

In practice, we know that objects upon which no external force is applied tend to come to rest, at least in everyday life. In the real world, the conditions for the law of inertia to apply, namely the total absence of external forces acting on the body, cannot exist. Forces such as friction act on the body to bring it to a halt. However, by constantly improving the condition of the experiment, it is possible to get closer and closer to the ideal conditions envisaged by the law of inertia, and thus show that it is valid even for the motions observed in everyday life. The *relative* (quantitative) aspect of time was perfectly expressed in Einstein's theories, which conveyed it far more profoundly than the classical theories of Newton.

Gravity is not a "force", but a *relation* between real objects. To a man falling off a high building, it seems that the ground is "rushing towards him". From the standpoint of relativity, that observation is not wrong. Only if we adopt the mechanistic and one-sided concept of "force" do we view this process as the earth's gravity pulling the man downwards, instead of seeing that it is precisely the interaction of two bodies upon each other. For "normal" conditions, Newton's theory of gravity agrees with Einstein's. But in extreme conditions, they completely disagree. In effect, Newton's theory is contradicted by the general theory of relativity in the same way as formal logic is contradicted by dialectics. And, to date, the evidence shows that both relativity and dialectics are correct.

As Hegel explained, every measurement is really the statement of a ratio. However, since every measurement is really a comparison, there must be one standard, which cannot be compared with anything but itself. In general, we can only understand things by comparing them to other things. This expresses the dialectical concept of universal interconnections. To analyse things in their movement, development and relationships is precisely the essence of the dialectical method. It is the exact antithesis of the mechanical mode of thought (the "metaphysical" method in the sense of the word used by Marx and Engels) which views things as static and absolute. This was precisely the defect of the old classical Newtonian view of the universe, which, for all its achievements, never escaped from the one-sidedness that characterised the mechanistic world outlook.

The properties of a thing are not the result of relations to other things, but can only manifest themselves in relations to other things. Hegel refers to these relations in general as "reflex-categories". The concept of relativity is an important one, and was already fully developed by Hegel in the first volume of his masterpiece *Science of Logic*.

We see this, for example, in social institutions such as *kingship*.

"Naïve minds," Trotsky observed, "think that the office of kingship lodges in the king himself, in his ermine cloak and his crown, in his flesh and bones. As a matter of fact, the office of kingship is an interrelation between people. The king is king only because the interests and prejudices of millions of people are refracted through his person. When the flood of development sweeps away these interrelations, then the king appears to be only a washed-out man with a flabby lower lip. He who was once called Alfonso XIII could discourse upon this from fresh impressions.

"The leader by will of the people differs from the leader by will of God in that the former is compelled to clear the road for himself or, at any rate, to assist the conjuncture of events in discovering him. Nevertheless, the leader is always a relation between people, the individual supply to meet the collective demand. The controversy over Hitler's personality becomes the sharper the more the secret of his success is sought in himself. In the meantime, another political figure would be difficult to find that is in the same measure the focus of anonymous historic forces. Not every exasperated petty bourgeois could have become Hitler, but a particle of Hitler is lodged in every exasperated petty bourgeois." [37]

In *Capital*, Marx showed how concrete human labour becomes the medium for expressing abstract human labour. It is the form under which its opposite, abstract human labour, manifests itself. Value is not a material thing which can be derived from the physical properties of a commodity. In fact, it is an abstraction of the mind. But it is not on that account an arbitrary invention. In fact, it is an expression of an objective process, and is determined by the amount of socially necessary labour power expended in production. In the same way, time is an abstraction which, although it cannot be seen, heard or touched, and can only be *expressed* in relative terms as measurement, nevertheless denotes an objective physical process.

Space and time are abstractions, which enable us to measure and understand the material world. All measurement is related to space and time. Gravity, chemical properties, sound, light, are all analysed from these two points of view. Thus, the speed of light is 186,000 miles per second, while sound is determined by the number of vibrations per second. The sound of a stringed instrument, for instance, is determined by the time in which a certain number of vibrations occur and the spatial elements (length and thickness) of the vibrating body. That harmony which appeals to the aesthetic feelings of the mind is also another manifestation of ratio, measurement and therefore time.

Time cannot be *expressed* except in a relative way. In the same way, the magnitude value of a commodity can only be expressed relative to other commodities. Yet

(37) Trotsky, *The Struggle Against Fascism in Germany*, p. 399.

value is intrinsic to commodities, and time is an objective feature of matter in general. The idea that time itself is merely subjective, that is to say an illusion of the human mind, is reminiscent of the prejudice that money is merely a *symbol*, with no objective significance. The attempt to "demonetise" gold, which flowed from this false premise, led to inflation every time it was attempted. In the Roman Empire, the value of money was fixed by imperial decree, and it was forbidden to treat money as a commodity. The result was a continuous debasement of the currency. A similar phenomenon has taken place in modern capitalism, particularly since the Second World War. In economics, as in cosmology, the confusion of *measurement* with the nature of the thing itself leads to disaster in practice.

The measurement of time

While defining what time is presents a difficulty, measuring it does not. Scientists themselves do not explain what time is, but confine themselves to the *measurement* of time. From the mixing up of these two concepts endless confusion arises. Thus, Feynman:

"Maybe it is just as well if we face the fact that time is one of the things we cannot define (in the dictionary sense), and just say that it is what we already know it to be: it is how long we wait! What really matters anyway is not how we *define* time, but how we measure it." [38]

The *measurement* of time necessarily involves a frame of reference, and any phenomenon that entails change with time—e.g., the rotation of the earth or the swing of a pendulum. The earth's daily rotation on its axis provides a time scale. The decay of radioactive elements can be used for measuring long time intervals. The measurement of time involves a subjective element. The Egyptians divided day and night into twelfths. The Sumerians had a numerical system based on 60, and thus divided the hour into 60 minutes and the minute into 60 seconds. The metre was defined as one 10 millionth of the distance from the earth's pole to the equator (although this is not strictly accurate). The centimetre is 100th of a metre, and so on. At the beginning of this century, the investigation of the subatomic world led to the discovery of two natural units of measurement: the speed of light, c, and Planck's constant, h. These are not directly mass, length, or time, but the unity of all three.

There is an international agreement that the metre is defined as the distance between two scratches on a bar kept in a laboratory in France. More recently, it has been realised that this definition is neither as precise as would be useful, nor as permanent or universal as one would like. It is currently being considered that a new definition be adopted, an agreed-upon (arbitrary) number of wavelengths of a chosen spectral line. On the other hand, the measurement of time varies according to the scale and life span of the objects under consideration.

---

(38) Feynman, op. cit., chapter 5, p. 2.

It is clear that the concept of time will vary according to the frame of reference. A year on earth is not the same as a year on Jupiter. Nor is the idea of time and space the same for a human being as for a mosquito with a life span of a few days, or a subatomic particle with a life span of a trillionth of a second (assuming, of course, that such entities could possess a concept of anything at all). What we are referring to here is the way time is perceived in different contexts. If we accept the given frame of references the way in which time would be seen would be different. Even in practice this can be seen, to some extent. For example, normal methods of measuring time cannot be applied to the measurement of the life span of subatomic particles, and different standards must also be used for measuring "geological time".

From this point of view, time can be said to be relative. Measurement necessarily involves relationships. Human thought contains many concepts that are essentially relative, for example relative magnitudes, such as "big" and "small". A man is small compared to an elephant, but big in comparison to an ant. Smallness and bigness, in themselves, have no meaning. A millionth of a second, in ordinary terms, seems a very short length of time, yet at the subatomic level it is an extremely long time. At the other extreme, a million years is an extremely short time on the cosmological level.

All ideas of space, time and motion depend on our observations of the relations and changes in the material world. However, the measurement of time varies considerably when we consider different kinds of matter. The measurement of space and time is inevitably relative to some frame of reference—the earth, the sun, or any other static point—to which events of the universe can relate. Now it is clear that matter undergoes all kinds of different change: change of position, which, in turn, involves different velocities, change of state, involving different energy states, birth, decay and death, organisation and disorganisation, and many other transformations, all of which can be expressed and measured in terms of time.

In Einstein, time and space are not regarded as isolated phenomena, and indeed it is impossible to regard them as "things in themselves". Einstein advanced the view that time depends on the movement of a system and that the intervals of time change in such a way that the speed of light in the given system does not vary according to the movement. Spatial scales are also subject to change. The old classical Newtonian theories are still valid for everyday purposes, and even as a good approximation of the general workings of the universe. Newtonian mechanics still applies in a very wide branch of sciences, not only astronomy, but also practical sciences such as engineering. At low speeds, the effects of special relativity can be ignored. For example, the error involved in considering the behaviour of a plane moving at 250 miles an hour would be about ten billionth of one per cent. However, beyond certain limits it breaks down. At the kind of speeds that we find in particle acceleration, for example, it is necessary to take into account Einstein's prediction that mass is not constant, but increases with velocity.

From the point of view of our normal everyday notion of the measurement of time, the extremely short life span of certain subatomic particles cannot be adequately expressed. A pi-meson, for instance, has a life span of only about 10^{-16} of a second, before it disintegrates. Likewise, the period of a nuclear vibration, or the lifetime of a strange resonance particle, is 10^{-24} second, approximately the time needed for light to cross the nucleus of a hydrogen atom. Another scale of measurement is necessary. Very short times, say 10^{-12} second, are measured by an electron beam oscilloscope. Even shorter times can be calibrated by means of laser techniques. At the other end of the scale, very long periods can be measured by a radioactive "clock".

In a sense, every atom in the universe is a clock, because it absorbs light (that is, electromagnetic rays) and emits it at precisely defined frequencies. Since 1967, the official internationally recognised standard of time is based on the atomic (caesium) clock. One second is defined as 9,192,631,770 vibrations of the microwave radiation from caesium-133 atoms during a specified atomic rearrangement. Even this highly accurate clock is not absolutely perfect. Different readings are taken from atomic clocks in about 80 different countries, and agreement is reached, "weighting" the time in favour of the steadiest clocks. By such means it is possible to arrive at accurate time-measurement to one millionth of a second per day, or even less.

For everyday purposes, "normal" time keeping, based on the rotation of the earth and the apparent movements of the sun and stars, is sufficient. But for a whole series of operations in the field of modern advanced technology, such as certain radio navigational aids in ships and aeroplanes, it becomes inadequate, leading to serious errors. It is at these kinds of levels that the effects of relativity begin to make themselves felt. Experiments have shown that atomic clocks run slower at ground level than at high altitudes, where the gravitational effect is weaker. Atomic clocks, flown at an altitude of 30,000 feet, gained about three billionth of a second an hour. This conforms to Einstein's prediction to within one per cent.

Problem not resolved

The special theory of relativity was one of the greatest achievements of science. It has revolutionised the way we look at the universe to such an extent that it has been compared with the discovery that the earth is round. Gigantic strides forward have been made possible by the fact that relativity established a far more accurate method of measurement than the old Newtonian laws it partially displaced. The philosophical question of time has, however, not been removed by Einstein's theory of relativity. If anything, it is more acute than ever. That there is something subjective and even arbitrary in the *measurement* of time is evident, as we have already commented. But this does not lead to the conclusion that time is purely a subjective thing. Einstein's entire life was spent in the pursuit of the objective laws of nature. The question is whether the laws of nature, including time, are the same for everyone, regardless of the place in which they are and the speed at which they are moving. On this question, Einstein vacillated. At times, he seemed to accept it, but elsewhere he rejected it.

The objective processes of nature are not determined by whether they are observed or not. They exist in and for themselves. The universe, and therefore time, existed before there were human beings to observe it, and will continue to exist long after there are no humans to concern themselves about it. The material universe is eternal, infinite, and constantly changing. However, in order that human minds may grasp the infinite universe, it is necessary to translate it into finite terms, to analyse and quantify it, so that it can become a reality *for us*. The way we observe the universe does not change it (unless it involves physical processes which interfere with what is being observed). But the way it appears to us can indeed change. From our standpoint, the earth appears to be at rest. But to an astronaut flying past our planet, it seems to be hurtling past him at a great speed. Einstein, who seems to have had a very dry sense of humour, apparently once asked an astonished ticket inspector: "What time does Oxford stop at this train?"

Einstein was determined to re-write the laws of physics in such a way that the predictions would always be correct, irrespective of the motions of different bodies, or the "points of view" which derive from them. From the standpoint of relativity, steady motion on a straight line is indistinguishable from being at rest. When two objects pass each other at a constant speed, it is equally possible to say that A is passing B, or that B is passing A. Thus, we arrive at the apparent contradiction that the earth is both at rest and moving at the same time. In the example of the astronaut, "it has to be simultaneously correct to say that the earth has great energy of motion and no energy and motion; the astronaut's point of view is just as valid as the view of learned men on earth." [39]

Although it seems straightforward, the measurement of time nevertheless presents a problem, because the rate of change of time must be compared to something else. If there is some absolute time, then this in turn must flow, and therefore must be measured against some other time, and so on ad infinitum. It is important to realise, however, that this problem presents itself only in relation to the *measurement* of time. The philosophical question of the *nature* of time itself does not enter into it. For the practical purposes of calculation and measurement, it is essential that a specific frame of reference be defined. We must know the position of the observer relative to the observed phenomena. Relativity theory shows that such statement as "at one and the same place" and "at one and the same time" are, in fact, meaningless.

The theory of relativity involves a contradiction. It implies that simultaneity is relative to a frame of axes. If one frame of axes is moving relative to another, then

(39) N. Calder, *Einstein's Universe*, p. 22.

events that are simultaneous relative to the first are not simultaneous relative to the second, and vice versa. This fact, which flies in the face of common sense, has been experimentally demonstrated. Unfortunately, it can lend itself to an idealist interpretation of time, for instance, the assertion that there can be a variety of "presents". Moreover, the future can be portrayed as things and processes "that come into being" as four-dimensional solids that have as earliest temporal cross section or "time slice".

Unless this question is settled, all kinds of mistakes can be made: for example, the idea that the future already exists, and suddenly materialises in the "now", as a submerged rock suddenly appears when a wave breaks over it. In point of fact, both the past and the future are combined in the present. The future is being-in-potential. The past is what has already been. The "now" is the unity of both. It is *actual* being as opposed to potential being. Precisely for this reason, it is usual to feel regret for the past and fear for the future, not vice versa. The feeling of regret flows from the realisation, corroborated by all human experience, that the past is lost forever, whereas the future is uncertain, consisting in a great number of potential states.

Benjamin Franklin (1706-90) once observed that there are only two things certain in this life—death and taxes, and the Germans have a proverb: "Man muss nur sterben"— "one only has to die," meaning that everything else is optional. Of course, this is not actually true. Many more things are inevitable than death, or even taxes. Out of an infinitely large number of potential states, in practice we know that only a certain number are really possible. Out of these, fewer still are probable at a given moment. And of the latter, in the end, only one will actually arise. The exact way in which this process unfolds is precisely the task of the different sciences to uncover. But this task will prove to be impossible if we do not accept that events and processes unfold in time, and that time is an objective phenomenon which expresses the most fundamental fact of all forms of matter and energy—change.

The material world is in a constant state of change, and therefore it "is and is not". This is the fundamental proposition of dialectics. Philosophers like the Anglo-American Alfred North Whitehead and the French intuitionist Henry Begson believed that the flow of time was a metaphysical fact, which could only be grasped by non-scientific intuition. "Process philosophers" like these, despite their mystical overtones, at least are correct in saying that the future is open or indeterminate whereas the past is unchangeable, fixed and determinate. It is "congealed time". On the other hand we have the "philosophers of the manifold" who maintain that future events may exist but not be connected in a sufficiently lawlike way with past events. Pursuing a philosophically incorrect view of time, we end up with sheer mysticism, as in the notion of the "multiverse"—an infinite number of "parallel" universes (if that is the right word, since they do not exist in space "as we know it") existing simultaneously (if that is the right word, since they do not exist in time "as we know it"). Such is the confusion that arises from the idealist interpretation of relativity.

Idealist interpretations

> "There was a young lady named Bright
> Whose speed was faster than light;
> She set out one day
> In a relative way
> And returned home the previous night."
> (A. Buller, *Punch*, 19th December 1923)

As with quantum mechanics, relativity has been seized upon by those who wish to introduce mysticism into science. "Relativity" is taken to mean that we cannot really know the world. As John Desmond Bernal explains:

"It is, however, equally true that the effect of Einstein's work, outside the narrow specialist fields where it can be applied, was one of general mystification. It was eagerly seized on by the disillusioned intellectuals after the First World War to help them in refusing to face realities. They only needed to use the word 'relativity' and say 'Everything is relative', or 'It depends on what you mean'." [40]

This is a complete misinterpretation of Einstein's ideas. In point of fact, the very word "relativity" is a misnomer. Einstein himself preferred the name *invariance theory* which gives a far better idea of what he intended—the exact opposite of the vulgar idea of relativity theory. It is quite untrue that for Einstein, "everything is relative". To begin with, rest energy (that is, the unity of matter and energy) is one of the *absolutes* of the theory of relativity. The limiting speed of light is another. Far from an arbitrary, subjective interpretation of reality, in which one opinion is as good as another, and "it all depends how you look at it," Einstein "discovered what was 'absolute' and reliable *despite* the apparent confusions, illusions and contradictions produced by relative motions or the action of gravity." [41]

The universe exists in a constant state of change. In that sense, nothing is "absolute" or eternal. *The only absolute is motion and change, the basic mode of existence of matter*—something that Einstein demonstrated conclusively in 1905. Time and space, as the mode of existence of matter are objective phenomena. They are not merely abstractions or arbitrary notions invented by humans (or gods) for their own convenience, but fundamental properties of matter, expressing the universality of matter.

Space is three dimensional, but time has only one dimension. With apologies to the makers of films in which it is possible to "go back to the future", it is only possible to travel in one direction in time, from the past to the future. There is no more danger of a spaceman returning to earth before he was born, or of a man marrying his great grandmother, than there is of any of the other amusing but idiotic fantasies of Hollywood. Time is *irreversible*, which is to say, every material process devel-

(40) J.D Bernal, *Science in History*, pp. 527-8.
(41) N. Calder, op. cit., p. 13.

ops in only one direction—from the past to the future. Time is merely a way of expressing the real movement and changing state of matter. Matter, motion, time and space are inseparable.

The shortcoming of Newton's theory was to regard space and time as separate entities, one alongside the other, independent of matter and motion. Up till the 20th century, scientists identified space with a vacuum (a "nothing"), which was seen as something absolute, that is, always and everywhere the same, changeless "thing". These empty abstractions have been discredited by modern physics, which has demonstrated the profound relation between time, space, matter and motion. Einstein's relativity theory firmly establishes that time and space do *not* exist in and of themselves, in isolation from matter, but are part of a universal interrelation of phenomena. This is conveyed by the concept of the integral and indivisible space-time, of which time and space are seen as relative aspects. A controversial idea here is the prediction that a clock in motion will keep time more slowly than one that is stationary. However, it is important to understand that this effect only becomes noticeable at extraordinarily high speeds, approaching the speed of light.

If Einstein's general theory of relativity is correct, then the theoretical possibility would exist in the future of travelling unimaginable distances through space. Theoretically, it would be possible for a human being to survive thousands of years into the future. The whole question hinges upon whether the changes observed in rates of atomic clocks also apply to the rate of life itself. Under the effect of strong gravity, atomic clocks run slower than in empty space. The question is whether the complex interrelations of molecules that constitute life can behave in the same way. Isaac Asimov, who knew a thing or two about science fiction, wrote: "If time really slows down in motion, one might journey even to a distant star in one's own life-time. But of course one would have to say good-bye to one's own generation and return to the world of the future." [42]

The argument for this is that the rates of living processes are determined by the rates of atomic action. Thus, under strong gravity, the heart will beat more slowly, and the brain impulses will also slow down. In fact, all energy diminishes in the presence of gravity. If processes slow down, they also take longer in time. If a space-ship were able to travel close to the speed of light, the universe would be seen flashing past it, while for those inside, time would continue as "normal", i.e., at a much slower rate. The impression would be that time outside would be speeded up. Is that correct? Would he *in fact* be living in the future, relative to people on earth, or not? Einstein seems to answer in the affirmative.

All kinds of mystical notions arise from such speculation—for example about hopping into a black hole and entering another universe. If a black hole exists, and

(42) Asimov, op. cit., p. 359.

that is still not definitely proven,* all that would be at the centre would be the collapsed remains of a gigantic star, not another universe. Any real person who entered it would be instantly torn apart and converted into pure energy. If that is what is considered as passing into another universe, then those who advocate such ideas are most welcome to make the first excursion! In reality, this is pure speculation, however entertaining it may be. The whole idea of "time-travel" inevitably lands one in a mass of contradictions, not of dialectical but of the absurd variety. Einstein would have been shocked at the mystical interpretation of his theories which involve notions such as shuttling back and forth in time, altering the future, and nonsense of that sort. But he himself must bear some responsibility for this situation because of the idealist element in his outlook, particularly on the question of time.

Let us grant that an atomic clock at a high altitude runs faster at high altitudes than on the ground, because of the effect of gravitation. Let us also grant that, when this clock returns to earth, it is found to be, say, 50 billionths of a second older than equivalent clocks which had never left the ground. Does that mean that a man travelling in the same flight has equally aged? The process of ageing is dependent upon the rate of metabolism. This is partly influenced by gravitation, but also by many other factors. It is a complex biological process, and it is not easy to see how it could be fundamentally affected either by velocity or gravitation, except that extremes of either can cause material damage to living organisms.

If it were possible to slow down the rate of metabolism in the way predicted, so that, for example, the heart-beat would slow to one every twenty minutes, the process of ageing would presumably be correspondingly slower. It is, in fact, possible to slow down metabolism, for example, by freezing. Whether this would be the effect of travelling at very high speeds, without killing the organism, is open to doubt. According to the well-known theory, such a relativistic space-man, if he succeeded on returning to earth, would come back after, say 10,000 years, and to pursue the usual analogy, would presumably be in a position to marry his own remote descendants. But he would never be able to return to his "own" time.

Experiments conducted with subatomic particles (muons) indicate that particles travelling at 99.94 per cent of the speed of light extended their life by nearly thirty times, precisely as predicted by Einstein. However, whether these conclusions can be applied to matter on a larger scale, and living matter in particular, is an issue that remains to be seen. Many serious mistakes have been made by attempting to apply the results derived from one sphere to another, entirely different, area. In the future, space-travel at very high speeds—maybe one-tenth of the speed of light—may become possible. At such speed, a journey of five light-years would take fifty years

*Recent research suggests that black holes do exist, and are to be found at the center of galaxies. Their massive gravitational attraction appears to be what holds galaxies together. For obvious reasons, little is known about this phenomenon. However, it is clear that at the hart of black holes there is an enormous concentration of matter. See Alan Woods' author's preface to the English edition.

(though according to Einstein, it would take three months less for those travelling). Will it ever be possible to travel at the speed of light, thus enabling human beings to reach the stars? At this moment in time, such a prospect seems remote. But then, a hundred years ago—a mere blink in history—the idea of travelling to the moon was still confined to the novels of Jules Verne.

Mach and positivism

> "The object, however, is the real truth, is the essential reality; it is, quite indifferent to whether it is known or not; it remains and stands even though it is not known, while the knowledge does not exist if the object is not there." (Hegel) [43]

The existence of past, present and future is deeply engraved on the human consciousness. We live now, but we can remember past events, and, to some extent, foresee future ones. There is a "before" and an "after". Yet some philosophers and scientists dispute this. They regard time as a product of the mind, an illusion. In their view, in the absence of human observers, there is no time, no past, present or future. This is the standpoint of *subjective idealism*, an entirely irrational and anti-scientific outlook which nevertheless has attempted for the last hundred years to base itself in the discoveries of physics to lend respectability to what is essentially a mystical view of the world. It seems ironical that the school of philosophy that has had the biggest impact upon science in the 20th century, logical positivism, is precisely a branch of subjective idealism.

Positivism is a narrow view that holds that science should confine itself to the "observed facts". The founders of this school were reluctant to refer to theories as true or false, but preferred to describe them as more or less "useful". It is interesting to note that Ernst Mach, the real spiritual father of neo-positivism, opposed the atomist theory of physics and chemistry. This was the natural consequence of the narrow empiricism of the positivist outlook. Since the atom could not be seen, how could it exist? It was regarded by them at best as a convenient fiction, and at worst as an unacceptable ad hoc hypothesis. One of Mach's co-thinkers, Wilhelm Ostwald actually attempted to derive the basic laws of chemistry without the help of the atomic hypothesis!

Boltzmann sharply criticised Mach and the Positivists, as did Max Planck, the father of quantum physics. Lenin subjected the views of Mach and Richard Avenarius, the founder of the school of Empirio-criticism, to a devastating criticism in his book *Materialism and Empirio-criticism*, (1908). Nevertheless, the views of Mach had a big impact and, among others, impressed the young Albert Einstein. Setting out from the view of that all ideas must be derived from "the given", that is,

(43) Hegel, *The Phenomenology of Mind*, p. 151.

from the information provided immediately by our senses, they went on to deny the existence of the natural world, independent of human sense-perception. Mach and Avenarius referred to physical objects as "complexes of sensation". Thus, for example, this table is no more than a collection of sense-impressions such as hardness, colour, mass and so on. Without these, they maintained, nothing would be left. Therefore, the idea of matter (in the philosophical sense, that is, the objective world given to us in sense-perception) was declared to be *meaningless*.

As we have already pointed out, these ideas lead directly to solipsism—the idea that only "I" exist. If I close my eyes, the world ceases to exist. Mach attacked Newton's idea that space and time are absolute and real entities, but he did so from the standpoint of subjective idealism. Incredibly, the most influential school of modern philosophy (and the one that had the biggest influence on scientists) was derived from the subjective idealism of Mach and Avenarius.

The obsession with "the observer" which is a thread running through the whole of 20th century theoretical physics is derived from the subjective idealist philosophy of Ernst Mach. Taking his starting-point from the empiricist argument that "all our knowledge is derived from immediate sense-perception", Mach argued that objects cannot exist independently of our consciousness. Carried to its logical conclusion, this would mean that, for example, the world could not have existed before there were people present to observe it. As a matter of fact, it could not have existed before I was present, since I can only know my own sensations, and cannot therefore be sure that any other consciousness exists.

The important thing is that Einstein himself was initially impressed by these arguments, which left their mark on his early writings on relativity. This has, beyond doubt, exercised the most harmful influence upon modern science. Whereas Einstein was capable of realising his mistake, and attempted to correct it, those who have slavishly followed the master, have been incapable of sorting out the chaff from the grain. As often happens, over-eager disciples become dogmatic. They are more Papist than the Pope! In his autobiography, Karl Popper shows clearly that in his later years Einstein regretted his earlier subjective idealism, or "operationalism", which demanded the presence of an observer to determine natural processes:

"It is an interesting fact that Einstein himself was for years a dogmatic positivist and operationalist. He later rejected this interpretation: he told me in 1950 that he regretted no mistake he ever made as much as this mistake. The mistake assumed a really serious form in his popular book, *Relativity: The Special and the General Theory*. There he says 'I would ask the reader not to proceed farther until he is fully convinced on this point.' The point is, briefly, that 'simultaneity' must be *defined*— and defined in an *operational* way—since otherwise 'I allow myself to be deceived...when I imagine that I am able to attach a meaning to the statement of simultaneity.' Or in other words, a term has to be operationally defined or else it is *meaningless*. (Here in a nutshell is the positivism later developed by the Vienna

Circle under the influence of Wittgenstein's *Tractatus*, and in a very dogmatic form)."

This is important, because it shows that Einstein in the end rejected the subjectivist interpretation of relativity theory. All the nonsense about "the observer" as a determining factor was not an essential part of the theory, but merely the reflection of *a philosophical mistake*, as Einstein frankly confirmed. That, unfortunately, did not prevent the followers of Einstein from taking over the mistake, and blowing it up to the point where it appeared to be a fundamental cornerstone of relativity. It is here that we find the real origin of Heisenberg's subjective idealism:

"But many excellent physicists," Popper continues, "were greatly impressed by Einstein's operationalism, which they regarded (as did Einstein himself for a long time) as an integral part of relativity. And so it happened that operationalism became the inspiration of Heisenberg's paper of 1925, and of his widely accepted suggestion that the concept of the track of an electron, or of its classical position-*cum*-momentum, was *meaningless*." [44]

The fact that time is an objective phenomenon, reflecting real processes in nature was first demonstrated by the laws of thermodynamics, which were worked out in the 19th century and which still play a central role in modern physics. These laws, particularly as developed by Boltzmann, firmly establish the idea not only that time exists objectively, but that it flows in only one direction, from past to future. *Time cannot be reversed, nor is it dependent upon any "observer".*

Boltzmann and time

The fundamental question that has to be addressed is: Is time an objective feature of the physical universe? Or is it something purely subjective, an illusion of the mind, or merely a convenient way of describing things to which it has no real relationship? The latter position has been held, in one or other degree, by a number of different schools of thought, all of them closely related to the philosophy of subjective idealism. Mach, as we have seen, introduced this subjectivism into science. It was decisively answered towards the end of the 19th century by the pioneer of the science of thermodynamics, Ludwig Boltzmann.

Einstein, under the influence of Ernst Mach, treated time as something subjective, which depended on the observer, at least in the beginning before he realised the harmful consequences of this approach. In 1905, his paper on the special theory of relativity introduced the notion of a "local time" associated with each separate observer. The concept of time here contains an idea carried over from classical physics, namely that time is *reversible*. This is really quite an extraordinary notion, and one that flies in the face of all experience. Film directors often resort to a trick photography, in which the camera is put into reverse, whereupon the most peculiar

(44) K. Popper, *Unended Quest*, pp. 96-7 and 98.

events occur: milk flows from the glass back into the bottle, buses and cars run backwards, eggs return to their shells, and so on. Our reaction to all this is to laugh, which is what is intended. We laugh because we know that what we are seeing is not just impossible, but absurdly so. We know that the processes we are seeing *cannot* be reversed.

Boltzmann understood this, and the concept of irreversible time lies at the heart of his famous theory of the arrow of time. The laws of thermodynamics represented a major breakthrough in science, but were controversial. These laws could not be reconciled with the existing laws of physics at the end of the 19th century. The second law cannot be derived from the laws of mechanics or quantum mechanics, and, in effect, marks a sharp break with the theories of previous physical science. It says that entropy increases in the direction of the future, not the past. It denotes a change in state over time, which is irreversible. The notion of a tendency towards dissipation clashed with the accepted idea that the essential task of physics was to reduce the complexity of nature to simple laws of motion.

The idea of entropy, which is usually understood as a tendency of things towards greater disorganisation and decay with the passing of time, entirely bears out what people have always believed: that time exists objectively and that it is a one-way process. The two laws of thermodynamics imply the existence of the phenomenon known as entropy that is observed in all irreversible processes. Its definition is based on another property known as available energy. The entropy of an isolated system may remain constant or increase, but it cannot decrease. One of the results of this is the impossibility of a "perpetual motion machine".

Einstein considered the idea of irreversible time to be an illusion that had no place in physics. In Max Planck's words, the second law of thermodynamics expresses the idea that there exists in nature a quantity that changes always in the same sense in all natural processes. This does not depend on the observer, but is an objective process. But Planck's view was in a small minority. The great majority of scientists, like Einstein, attributed it to subjective factors. Einstein's position on this question shows up the central weakness of his standpoint in making objective processes depend upon a non-existent "observer". This was undoubtedly the weakest element in his entire outlook, and, for that very reason, is the part that has proved most popular with his successors, who do not seem aware of the fact that Einstein himself changed his mind on this towards the end of his life.

In physics and mathematics the expression of time is *reversible*. A "time-reversal invariant" implies that the same laws of physics apply equally well in both situations. The second event is indistinguishable from the first and the flow of time does not have any preferred direction in the case of fundamental interactions. For example, a film of two billiard balls colliding, in a near-perfect elastic collision, can be run forward or backward, without giving any idea of the true time sequence of the event. The same was assumed to be true of interactions at the sub atomic level, but evidence to the contrary was found in 1964 in weak nuclear interactions. For a long time it was believed that the fundamental laws of nature were "charge symmetrical". For example, an antiproton and a positron behave like a proton and an electron. Experiments have now shown that the laws of nature are symmetrical if three basic things are combined—time, charge and parity. This is known as a "CPT mirror".

In dynamics, the direction of a given trajectory was irrelevant. For example, a ball bouncing on the ground would return to its initial position. Any system can thus "go backwards in time", if all the points involved in it are reversed. All the states it previously went through would simply be retraced. In classical dynamics, changes such as time reversal ($t \rightarrow -t$) and velocity reversal ($v \rightarrow -v$) are treated as mathematically equivalent. This kind of calculation works well for simple closed systems, where there are no interactions. In reality, however, every system is subject to many interactions. One of the most important problems in physics is the "three-body" problem, for example, the moon's motion is influenced by the sun and the earth. In classical dynamics, a system changes according to a trajectory that is given once and for all, the starting point of which is never forgotten. Initial conditions determine the trajectory for all time. The trajectories of classical physics were simple and deterministic. But there are other trajectories that are not so easy to pin down, for example, a rigid pendulum, where an infinitesimal disturbance would be enough to set it rotating or oscillating.

The importance of Boltzmann's work was that he dealt with the physics of processes rather than the physics of *things*. His greatest achievement was to show how the properties of atoms (mass, charge, structure) determine the visible properties of matter (viscosity, thermal conductivity, diffusion, etc.). His ideas were viciously attacked during his lifetime, but vindicated by the discoveries of atomic physics shortly before 1900, and the realisation that the random movements of microscopic particles suspended in a fluid ("Brownian motion") could only be explained in terms of the statistical mechanics invented by Boltzmann.

The bell-shaped Gauss curve describes the random motion of molecules in a gas. An increased temperature leads to an increase in the average velocity of the molecules and the energy associated with their motion. Whereas Clausius and Maxwell approached this question from the standpoint of the trajectories of *individual* molecules, Boltzmann considered the *population* of molecules. His kinetic equations play an important role in the physics of gases. It was a major advance in the physics of processes. Boltzmann was a great pioneer, who was treated as a madman by the scientific establishment. He was finally driven to suicide in 1906, having previously been compelled to retreat from his attempt to establish the irreversible nature of time as an objective feature of nature.

Whereas in the theory of classical mechanics, the events in the film earlier described are perfectly possible, *in practice*, they are not. In the theory of dynamics, for example, we have an ideal world in which such things as friction and collision do not exist. In this ideal world, all the invariants involved in a given motion are fixed at the start. Nothing could happen to alter its course. By these means, we arrive at a completely static view of the universe, where everything is reduced to smooth, linear equations. Despite the revolutionary advances made possible by relativity theory, Einstein, at heart, remained wedded to the idea of a static, harmonious universe—just like Newton.

The equations of motion of Newtonian or for that matter quantum mechanics have no built-in irreversibility. It is possible to run a movie film forward or backwards. But this is not true of nature in general. The second law of thermodynamics predicts an irreversible tendency towards disorder. It states that randomness always increases in time. Until recently, it was thought that the fundamental laws of nature are symmetrical in time. Time is asymmetrical and moves only in one direction, from past to future. We see fossils, footprints and photographs and hear recordings of things from the past, but never from the future. It is easy to mix eggs to make an omelette or put milk and sugar into a cup of coffee, but not to reverse these processes. The water in the bath transfers its heat to the surrounding air, but not vice versa.

The second law of thermodynamics is the "arrow of time". The subjectivists objected that irreversible processes like chemical affinity, heat conduction, viscosity, etc., would depend on the "observer". In reality, they are *objective* processes that take place in nature, and this is clear to everyone in relation to life and death. A pendulum (at least in an ideal state) can swing back to its initial position. But everyone knows that the life of an individual moves in only one direction, from the cradle to the grave. It is an *irreversible* process. Ilya Prigogine, one of the leading theorists of chaos theory, has devoted a lot of attention to the question of time. When he first began to study physics as a student in Brussels, Prigogine recalls that he was "astonished by the fact that science had so little to say about time, especially since his earlier education had centred mainly around history and archaeology." In relation to the conflict between classical mechanics (dynamics) and thermodynamics, Prigogine and Stengers write:

"To a certain extent, there is an analogy between this conflict and the one that gave rise to dialectical materialism. We have described…a nature that might be called 'historical'—that is, capable of development and innovation. The idea of a history of nature as an integral part of materialism was asserted by Marx and, in greater detail, by Engels. Contemporary developments in physics, the discovery of the constructive role played by irreversibility, have thus raised within the natural sciences a question that has long been asked by materialists. For them, understanding nature meant understanding it as being capable of producing man and his societies.

"Moreover, at the time Engels wrote his *Dialectics of Nature*, the physical sciences seemed to have rejected the mechanistic world view and drawn close to the idea of an historical development of nature. Engels mentions three fundamental discoveries: energy and the laws governing its qualitative transformations, the cell as the basic constituent of life, and Darwin's discovery of the evolution of species. In view of these great discoveries, Engels came to the conclusion that the mechanistic world view was dead."

Against the subjective interpretation of time, the authors conclude: "Time flows in a single direction, from past to future. We cannot manipulate time, we cannot travel back to the past." [45]

Relativity and black holes

In Einstein's view, unlike that of Newton, gravity affects time because it affects light. If one could imagine a particle of light poised on the edge of a black hole, it would be suspended indefinitely, neither advancing nor retreating, neither losing energy, nor gaining it. In such a state, it is possible to argue that "time stands still". This is the argument of the relativist proponents of the black hole and its properties. What this boils down to is that if all motion were to cease, then there would be no change either of state or position, and therefore no time in any meaningful sense of the word. Such a situation is alleged to exist at the edge of a black hole. This, however, seems a highly speculative and mystical interpretation of this phenomenon.

All matter exists in a constant state of change and motion, and therefore, all that is being said here is that if matter and motion are eliminated, there is no time either, which is a complete tautology. It is like saying—if there is no matter, there is no matter, or if there is no time, there is no time. Because both statements mean just the same thing. Strangely enough, one would seek in vain in the theory of relativity for a definition of what time and space are. Einstein certainly found it difficult to explain. However, he came close to it when he explained the difference between his geometry and the classical geometry of Euclid. He said that one could imagine a universe in which space was not warped, but it would be completely devoid of matter. This points clearly in the right direction. After all the fuss about black holes, you may also be surprised to discover that this subject was not even mentioned by Einstein. He relied upon a rigorous approach, mainly based on very complicated mathematics, and made predictions that could be verified by observation and experiment. The physics of black holes, in the absence of clearly established empirical data, has an extremely speculative character.

Despite its successes, it is still possible that the general theory of relativity may be wrong. Unlike special relativity, the experimental tests that have been carried out on it are not very many. There is no conclusive proof, although up to the present time no conflict has been found between the theory and the observed facts. It is not even ruled out that the assertion of special relativity, that nothing can move faster than the speed of light, may be shown to be incorrect in the future.

(45) Prigogine and Stengers, op. cit., pp. 10, 252-3 and 277.

Alternative theories of relativity have been put forward, for example, by Robert Dicke. Dicke's theory predicted a deflection of the moon's orbit of several feet towards the sun. Using advanced laser technology, the McDonald observatory in Texas found no trace of this displacement. However, there is no reason to suppose that the last word has been spoken. So far, Einstein's theories have been borne out by repeated experiment. But the constant probing of extreme conditions must sooner or later reveal a set of circumstances that are not covered by the equations, preparing the way for new epoch-making discoveries. The theory of relativity cannot be the end of the line, any more than Newtonian mechanics, Maxwell's theory of electromagnetism, or any previous theory.

For two hundred years, the theories of Newton were held to be absolutely valid. His authority could not be challenged. After his death, Laplace and others carried his theories to an extreme where they became absurd. The radical break with the old mechanistic Absolutes was a necessary condition for the further advance of physics in the 20th century. It was the proud boast of the new physics that they had forever killed off the ogre of the Absolute. Suddenly thought was free to move into hitherto unheard of realms. These were heady times! Unfortunately, such happiness cannot last forever. In the words of Robert Burns:

"But pleasures are like poppies spread:
You seize the flow'r, its bloom is shed."

The new physics solved many problems, but only at the cost of creating new contradictions, which remain unresolved even at the present time. For most of the present century, physics has been dominated by two imposing theories: quantum mechanics and relativity. What is not generally realised is that the two theories are at variance. In fact, they are incompatible. The general theory of relativity takes no account whatever of the uncertainty principle. Einstein spent the last years of his life attempting to resolve this contradiction, but failed to do so.

Relativity theory was a great and revolutionary theory. So was Newtonian mechanics in its day. Yet it is the fate of all such theories to become transformed into orthodoxies, to suffer a kind of hardening of the arteries, until they are no longer able to answer the questions posed by the march of science. For a long time, theoretical physicists have been content to rest on the discoveries of Einstein, in the same way that an earlier generation were content to swear by Newton. And in just the same way, they are guilty of bringing general relativity into disrepute by reading into it the most absurd and fantastic notions, which its author never even dreamed of.

Singularities, black holes where time stands still, multiverses, a time before time began, about which no questions must be asked—one can imagine Einstein clutching his head! All this is supposed to flow inevitably from general relativity, and anyone who raised the slightest doubt about it is immediately confronted with the authority of the great Einstein. This is not one whit better than the situation before relativity, when the authority of Newton was similarly wielded in defence of the existing orthodoxy. The only difference is that the fantastic notions of Laplace seem extremely sensible alongside the mystical gobbledygook written by some physicists today. And even less than Newton can Einstein be made responsible for the outlandish flights of fancy of his successors, which represent the *reductio ad absurdum* of the original theory.

These senseless and arbitrary speculations are the best proof that the theoretical framework of modern physics is in need of a complete overhaul. For the problem here is one of method. It is not just that they provide no answers. The problem is that they do not even know how to ask the right questions. This is not so much a scientific as a philosophical question. If everything is possible, then one arbitrary theory (more correctly, guess) is as good as the next. The whole system has been pushed near to breaking point. And to cover up the fact, they resort to a mystical kind of language, in which the obscurity of expression does not disguise the complete lack of any real content.

This state of affairs is clearly intolerable, and has led a section of scientists to begin to question the basic assumptions on which science has been operating. David Bohm's investigations into the theory of quantum mechanics, Ilya Prigogine's new interpretation of the Second Law of Thermodynamics, Hannes Alfvén's attempt to work out an alternative to the orthodox cosmology of the big bang, above all, the spectacular rise of chaos and complexity theory—all this indicates the existence of a ferment in science. While it is too early to predict the exact outcome of this, it seems likely that we are entering into one of those exciting periods in the history of science, when an entirely new approach will emerge.

There is every reason to suppose that eventually the theories of Einstein will be surpassed by a new and broader-based theory, which, while preserving all that is viable in relativity, will correct and amplify it. In the process, we shall certainly arrive at a truer and more balanced understanding of the questions relating to the nature of time, space and causality. This does not signify a return to the old mechanical physics, any more than the fact that we can now achieve the transformation of the elements means a return to the ideas of the alchemists. As we have seen, the history of science frequently involves an apparent return to earlier positions, but on a qualitatively higher level.

One thing we can predict with absolute confidence: when the new physics finally emerges from the present chaos there will be no place in it for time-travel, multiverses, or singularities which compress the whole of the universe into a single point, about which no questions are allowed to be asked. This will sadly make it much more difficult to win big cash prizes for providing the Almighty with scientific credentials, a fact which some may regret, but which, in the long term, may not be a bad thing for the progress of science!

8. The arrow of time

The second law of thermodynamics

> "This is the way the world ends
> Not with a bang but a whimper."
> (Thomas Stearns Eliot)

Thermodynamics is the branch of theoretical physics that deals with the laws of heat motion, and the conversion of heat into other types of energy. The word is derived from the Greek words *therme* ("heat") and *dynamis* ("force"). It is based upon two fundamental principles originally derived from experiments, but which are now regarded as axioms. The first principle is the law of the conservation of energy, which assumes the form of the law of the equivalence of heat and work. The second principle states that heat cannot of itself pass from a cooler body to a hotter body without changes in any other bodies.

The science of thermodynamics was a product of the industrial revolution. At the beginning of the 19th century, it was discovered that energy could be transformed in different ways, but can never be created or destroyed. This is the first law of thermodynamics—one of the fundamental laws of physics. Then, in 1850, Robert Clausius discovered the second law of thermodynamics. This states that "entropy" (i.e., the ratio of a body's energy to its temperature) always increases in any transformation of energy, for example, in a steam engine.

Entropy is generally understood to signify an inherent tendency towards disorganisation. Every family is well aware that a house, without some conscious intervention, tends to pass from a state of order to disorder, especially when young children are around. Iron rusts, wood rots, dead flesh decays, the water in the bath gets cold. In other words, there appears to be a general tendency towards decay. According to the second law, atoms, when left to themselves, will mix and randomise themselves as much as possible. Rust occurs because the iron atoms tend to mingle with oxygen in the surrounding air to form iron oxide. The fast moving molecules on the surface of the bath water collide with the slower moving molecules in the cold air and transfer their energy to them.

This is a limited law, which has no bearing on systems consisting of a small number of particles (microsystems) or to systems with an infinitely large number of particles (the universe). However, there have been repeated attempts to extend its application well beyond the proper sphere, leading to all kinds of false philosophical conclusions. In the middle of the 19th century, Rudolf Clausius and William Thomson (Lord Kelvin), the authors of the second principle of thermodynamics, attempted to apply the second law to the universe as a whole, and arrived at a completely false theory, known as the "thermal death" theory of the end of the universe.

This law was redefined in 1877 by Ludwig Boltzmann, who attempted to derive the second law of thermodynamics from the atomic theory of matter, which was then gaining ground. In Boltzmann's version, entropy appears as a function of the probability of a given state of matter: the more probable the state, the higher its entropy. In this version, all systems tend towards a state of equilibrium (a state in which there is no net flow of energy). Thus, if a hot object is placed next to a cold one, energy (heat) will flow from the hot to the cold, until they reach equilibrium, i.e., they both have the same temperature.

Boltzmann was the first one to deal with the problems of the transition from the microscopic (small-scale) to the macroscopic (large-scale) level in physics. He attempted to reconcile the new theories of thermodynamics with the classical physics of trajectories. Following Maxwell's example, he tried to resolve the problems through the theory of probability. This represented a radical break with the old Newtonian methods of mechanistic determinism. Boltzmann realised that the irreversible increase in entropy could be seen as the expression of a growing molecular disorder. His principle of order implies that the more probable state available to a system is one in which a multiplicity of events taking place simultaneously within the system cancel each other out statistically. While molecules can move randomly, on average, at any given moment, the same number will be moving in one direction as in another.

There is a contradiction between energy and entropy. The unstable equilibrium between the two is determined by temperature. At low temperatures, energy dominates and we see the emergence of ordered (weak-entropy) and low energy states, as in crystals, where molecules are locked in a certain position relative to other molecules. However, at high temperature, entropy prevails, and is expressed in molecular disorder. The structure of the crystal is disrupted, and we get the transition, first to a liquid, then to a gaseous state.

The second law states that the entropy of an isolated system always increases, and that when two systems are joined together, the entropy of the combined system is greater than the sum of the entropies of the individual systems. However, the second law of thermodynamics is not like other laws of physics, such as Newton's law of gravity, precisely because it is not always applicable. Originally derived from a particular sphere of classical mechanics, the second law is limited by the fact that Boltzmann took no account of such forces as electromagnetism or even gravity, allowing only for atomic collisions. This gives such a restricted picture of physical processes, that it cannot be taken as generally applicable, although it does apply to limited systems, like boilers. The second law is not true of all circumstances. Brownian motion contradicts it, for example. As a general law of the universe in its classical form, it is simply not true.

It has been claimed that the second law means that the universe as a whole must tend inexorably towards a state of entropy. By an analogy with a closed system, the entire universe must eventually end up in a state of equilibrium, with the same temperature everywhere. The stars will run out of fuel. All life will cease. The universe will slowly peter out in a featureless expanse of nothingness. It will suffer a "heat death". This bleak view of the universe is in direct contradiction to everything we know about its past evolution, or see at present. The very notion that matter tends to some absolute state of equilibrium runs counter to nature itself. It is a lifeless, abstract view of the universe. At present, the universe is very far from being in any sort of equilibrium, and there is not the slightest indication either that such a state ever existed in the past, or will do so in the future. Moreover, if the tendency towards increasing entropy is permanent and linear, it is not clear why the universe has not long ago ended up in a tepid soup of undifferentiated particles.

This is yet another example of what happens when attempts are made to extend scientific theories beyond the limits where they have a clearly proven application. The limitations of the principles of thermodynamics were already shown in the 19th century in a polemic between Lord Kelvin, the celebrated British physicist, and geologists, concerning the age of the earth. The predictions made by Lord Kelvin on the basis of thermodynamics ran counter to all that was known by geological and biological evolution. The theory postulated that the earth must have been molten just 20 million years ago. A vast accumulation of evidence proved the geologists right, and Lord Kelvin wrong.

In 1928, Sir James Jean, the English scientist and idealist, revived the old arguments about the "heat death" of the universe, adding in elements taken from Einstein's relativity theory. Since matter and energy are equivalents, he claimed, the universe must finally end up in the complete conversion of matter into energy: "The second law of thermodynamics," he prophesied darkly, "compels materials in the universe (sic!) to move ever in the same direction along the same road which ends only in death and annihilation." [46]

Similar pessimistic scenarios have been put forward more recently. In the words of a book, published recently:

(46) Quoted in Lerner, op. cit., p. 134.

"The universe of the very far future would thus be an inconceivably dilute soup of photons, neutrinos, and a dwindling number of electrons and positrons, all slowly moving farther and farther apart. As far as we know, no further basic physical processes would ever happen. No significant event would occur to interrupt the bleak sterility of a universe that has run its course yet still faces eternal life—perhaps eternal death would be a better description.

"This dismal image of cold, dark, featureless near-nothingness is the closest that modern cosmology comes to the 'heat death' of nineteenth century physics." [47]

What conclusion must we draw from all this? If all life, indeed all matter, not just on earth, but throughout the universe, is doomed, then why bother about anything? The unwarranted extension of the second law beyond its actual scope of application has given rise to all manner of false and nihilistic philosophical conclusions. Thus, Bertrand Russell, the British philosopher, could write the following lines in his book *Why I Am Not a Christian*:

"All the labours of the ages, all the devotion, all the inspiration, all the noonday brightness of human genius, are destined to extinction in the vast death of the solar system, and…the whole temple of man's achievement must inevitably be buried beneath the debris of a universe in ruins—all these things, if not quite beyond dispute, are yet so nearly certain that no philosophy which rejects them can hope to stand. Only within the scaffolding of these truths, only on the firm foundation of unyielding despair, can the soul's habitation henceforth be safely built." [48]

Order out of chaos

In recent years, this pessimistic interpretation of the second law has been challenged by a startling new theory. The Belgian Nobel Prize winner Ilya Prigogine and his collaborators have pioneered an entirely different interpretation of the classical theories of thermodynamics. There are some parallels between Boltzmann's theories and those of Darwin. In both, a large number of *random fluctuations* lead to a point of *irreversible change*, one in the form of biological evolution, the other in that of the dissipation of energy, and evolution towards disorder. In thermodynamics, time implies degradation and death. The question arises, how does this fit in with the phenomenon of life, with its inherent tendency towards organisation and ever increasing complexity.

The law states that things, if left to themselves, tend towards increased entropy. In the 1960s, Ilya Prigogine and others realised that in the real world atoms and molecules are almost never "left to themselves". Everything affects everything else. Atoms and molecules are almost always exposed to the flow of energy and material from the outside, which, if it is strong enough, can partially reverse the apparently inexorable process of disorder posited in the second law of thermodynamics. In

(47) P. Davies, *The Last Three Minutes*, pp. 98-9.
(48) Quoted by P. Davies, op. cit., p. 13.

fact, nature shows numerous instances not only of disorganisation and decay, but also of the opposite processes—spontaneous self-organisation and growth. Wood rots, but trees grow. According to Prigogine, self-organising structures occur everywhere in nature. Likewise, M. Waldrop concluded:

"A laser is a self-organising system in which particles of light, photons, can spontaneously group themselves into a single powerful beam that has every photon moving in lockstep. A hurricane is a self-organising system powered by the steady stream of energy coming in from the sun, which drives the winds and draws rainwater from the oceans. A living cell—although much too complicated to analyse mathematically—is a self-organising system that survives by taking in energy in the form of food and excreting energy in the form of heat and waste." [49]

Everywhere in nature we see patterns. Some are orderly, some disorderly. There is decay, but there is also growth. There is life, but there is also death. And, in fact, these conflicting tendencies are bound up together. They are inseparable. The second law asserts that all of nature is on a one-way ticket to disorder and decay. Yet this does not square with the general patterns we observe in nature. The very concept of "entropy", outside the strict limits of thermodynamics, is a problematic one.

"Thoughtful physicists concerned with the workings of thermodynamics realise how disturbing is the question of, as one put it, 'how a purposeless flow of energy can wash life and consciousness into the world.' Compounding the trouble is the slippery notion of entropy, reasonably well defined for thermodynamic purposes in terms of heat and temperature, but devilishly hard to pin down as a measure of *disorder*. Physicists have trouble enough measuring the degree of order in water, forming crystalline structures in the transition to ice, energy bleeding away all the while. But thermodynamic entropy fails miserably as a measure of the changing degree of form and formlessness in the creation of amino acids, of microorganisms, of selfreproducing plants and animals, of complex information systems like the brain. Certainly these evolving islands of order must obey the second law. The important laws, the creative laws, lie elsewhere." [50]

The process of nuclear fusion is an example, not of decay, but of the buildingup of the universe. This was pointed out in 1931 by H.T. Poggio, who warned the prophets of thermodynamic gloom against the unwarranted attempts to extrapolate a law that applies in certain limited situations on earth to the whole universe. "Let us not be too sure that the universe is like a watch that is always running down. There may be a rewinding." [51]

The second law contains two fundamental elements—one negative and another positive. The first says that certain processes are impossible (e.g. that heat flows from a hot source to a cold one, never vice versa) and the second (which flows from

(49) M.M Waldrop, *Complexity, The Emerging Science at the Edge of Order and Chaos*, pp. 33-4.
(50) J. Gleick, op. cit., p. 308.
(51) Lerner, op. cit., p. 139.

the first) states that entropy is an inevitable feature of all isolated systems. In an isolated system all non-equilibrium situations produce evolution towards the same kind of equilibrium state. Traditional thermodynamics saw in entropy only a movement towards disorder. This, however, refers *only to simple, isolated systems* (e.g., a steam engine). Prigogine's new interpretation of Boltzmann's theories is far wider, and radically different.

Chemical reactions take place as a result of collisions between molecules. Normally, the collision does not bring about a change of state; the molecules merely exchange energy. Occasionally, however, a collision produces changes in the molecules involved (a "reactive collision"). These reactions can be speeded up by catalysts. In living organisms, these catalysts are specific proteins, called enzymes. There is every reason to believe that this process played a decisive role in the emergence of life on earth. What appear to be chaotic, merely random movements of molecules, at a certain point reach a critical stage where quantity suddenly becomes transformed into quality. And this is an essential property of all forms of matter, not only organic, but also inorganic.

"Remarkably, the perception of oriented time increases as the level of biological organisation increases and probably reaches its culminating point in human consciousness." [52]

Every living organism combines order and activity. By contrast, a crystal in a state of equilibrium is structured, but inert. In nature, equilibrium is not normal but, to quote Prigogine "a rare and precarious state". *Non-equilibrium* is the rule. In simple isolated systems like a crystal, equilibrium can be maintained for a long time, even indefinitely. But matters change when we deal with complex processes, like living things. A living cell cannot be kept in a state of equilibrium, or it would die. The processes governing the emergence of life are not simple and linear, but dialectical, involving sudden leaps, where quantity is transformed into quality.

"Classical" chemical reactions are seen as very random processes. The molecules involved are evenly distributed in space, and their spread is distributed "normally" i.e., in a Gauss curve. These kinds of reaction fit into the concept of Boltzmann, wherein all side-chains of the reaction will fade out and the reaction will end up in a stable reaction, an immobile equilibrium. However, in recent decades chemical reactions were discovered that deviate from this ideal and simplified concept. They are known under the common name of "chemical clocks". The most famous examples are the Belousov-Zhabotinsky reaction, and the Brussels model devised by Ilya Prigogine.

Linear thermodynamics describes a stable, predictable behaviour of systems that tend towards the minimum level of activity possible. However, when the thermodynamic forces acting on a system reach the point where the linear region is

(52) Prigogine and Stengers, op. cit., p. 298.

exceeded, stability can no longer be assumed. Turbulence arises. For a long time turbulence was regarded as a synonym for disorder or chaos. But now, it has been discovered that what appears to be merely chaotic disorder on the macroscopic (large-scale) level, is, in fact, highly organised on the microscopic (small-scale) level.

Today, the study of chemical instabilities has become common. Of special interest is the research done in Brussels under the guidance of Ilya Prigogine. The study of what happens beyond the critical point where chemical instability commences has enormous interest from the standpoint of dialectics. Of particular importance is the phenomenon of the "chemical clock". The Brussels model (nicknamed the "Brusselator" by American scientists) describes the behaviour of gas molecules. Suppose there are two types of molecules, "red" and "blue", in a state of chaotic, totally random motion. One would expect that, at a given moment, there would be an irregular distribution of molecules, producing a "violet" colour, with occasional flashes of red or blue. But in a chemical clock, this does not occur beyond the critical point. The system is all blue, then all red, and these changes occur at regular interval.

"Such a degree of order stemming from the activity of billions of molecules seems incredible," say Prigogine and Stengers, "and indeed, if chemical clocks had not been observed, no one would believe that such a process is possible. To change colour all at once, molecules must have a way to 'communicate'. The system has to act as a whole. We will return repeatedly to this key word, communicate, which is of obvious importance in so many fields, from chemistry to neurophysiology. Dissipative structures introduce probably one of the simplest physical mechanisms for communication."

The phenomena of the "chemical clock" shows how in nature order can *arise spontaneously out of chaos* at a certain point. This is an important observation, especial in relation to the way in which life arises from inorganic matter.

"'Order through fluctuations' models introduce an unstable world where small causes can have large effects, but this world is not arbitrary. On the contrary, the reasons for the amplification of a small event are a legitimate matter for rational inquiry."

In classical theory, chemical reactions take place in a statistically ordered manner. Normally, there is an average concentration of molecules, with an even distribution. In reality, however, local concentrations appear which can *organise themselves*. This result is entirely unexpected from the standpoint of the traditional theory. These focal points of what Prigogine calls "self-organisation" can consolidate themselves to the point where they affect the whole system. What was previously thought of as marginal phenomena turn out to be absolutely decisive. The traditional view was to regard irreversible processes as a nuisance, caused by friction and other sources of heat loss in engines. But the situation has changed. Without irreversible processes, life would not be possible. The old view of irreversibility as a *subjective* phenomenon (a result of ignorance) is being strongly challenged. According to Prigogine irreversibility exists on all levels, both microscopic and macroscopic. For him, the second law leads to a *new concept of matter*. In a state of non-equilibrium, *order emerges*. "Non-equilibrium brings order out of chaos." [53]

(53) Prigogine and Stengers, op. cit., pp. 148, 206 and 287.

9. The Big Bang

Cosmology

To many people, unaccustomed to dialectical thinking, the notion of infinity is difficult to accept. It is so far at variance with the finite world of everyday objects, where everything has a beginning and an end, that it seems strange and unaccountable. Moreover, it is at variance with the teachings of most of the main world religions. Most of the ancient religions had their creation myth. Medieval Jewish scholars put the date of Creation at 3760 B.C., and in fact, the Jewish calendar dates from then. In 1658, Bishop Ussher worked out that the universe was created in 4004 B.C. Throughout the 18th century, the universe was considered to be six or seven thousand years old at most.

But—you might object—20th century science has nothing in common with all these creation myths! With modern scientific methods we can get an exact picture of the size and origins of the universe. Unfortunately, things are not as simple as that. Firstly, despite colossal advances our knowledge of the observable universe is limited by the power of even the largest telescopes, radio signals and space probes, to provide information. Secondly, and more seriously, is the way in which these results and observations are interpreted in a highly speculative manner, frequently bordering on mere mysticism. All too often, one has the impression that we have indeed regressed to the world of the creation myth (the "Big Bang"), complete with its inseparable companion, the Day of the Final Judgement (the "Big Crunch").

Gradually, beginning with the invention of the telescope, the advance of technology has pushed the boundaries of the universe further and further away. The crystal spheres which ever since Aristotle and Ptolemy had hemmed in the minds of men, were finally shattered, along with all the other barriers that the religious prejudices of the Middle Ages had placed in the way of progress.

In 1755, Kant postulated the existence of distant collections of stars, which he called "island universes". Yet as late as 1924, the entire universe was estimated to be only 200,000 light years in diameter, and consisted of just three galaxies—our own and the two neighbouring ones. Then the American cosmologist, Edwin Powell Hubble (1889-1953), using the new 100-inch telescope at Mount Wilson, in Southern California, showed the Andromeda nebula to be far outside our own galaxy. Later, other galaxies were discovered still further away. Kant's "island universes" hypothesis was shown to be correct. Thus the universe was rapidly "expanded"—in the minds of men—and has continued to expand ever since, as more and more distant objects are discovered. Instead of 200,000 light years, it is now thought to measure tens of billions of light years across, and time will show that even the present calculations are nowhere near big enough. For the universe, as Nicolas of Cusa and others thought, is infinite. Before the Second World War, it was thought that the age of the universe was only two billion years. That is slightly better than Bishop Ussher's calculation. But it was still hopelessly wrong. At present there is a fierce dispute among the supporters of the big bang concerning the supposed age of the universe. We shall return to that later.

The big bang theory is really a creation myth (just like the first book of *Genesis*). It states that the universe came into being about 15 billion years ago. Before that, according to this theory, there was no universe, no matter, no space, and, if you please, no time. At that time, all the matter in the universe is alleged to have been concentrated at a single point. This invisible dot, known to big bang aficionados as a *singularity*, then exploded, with such a force that it instantly filled the entire universe, which is still expanding as a result. Oh, by the way, this was the moment when "time began". In case you are wondering whether this is some kind of joke, forget it. This is precisely what the big bang theory states. This is what the great majority of university professors with long strings of letters after their name actually believe. There is the clearest evidence of a drift towards mysticism in the writings of a section of the scientific community. In recent years, we have seen a flood of books about science, which, under the guise of popular accounts of the latest theories of the universe, attempt to smuggle in religious notions of all kinds, in particular, in connection with the so-called theory of the big bang.

The New Scientist (7th May 1994) published an article entitled *In the Beginning Was the Bang*. The author, Colin Price, trained and worked as a scientist, but is now a Congregationalist minister. He begins by asking: "Is the big bang theory disconcertingly biblical? Or to put it another way, is the *Genesis* story disconcertingly scientific?" And he ends with the confident assertion: "No one would have appreciated the big bang story more than the authors of the first two chapters of the book of *Genesis*." This is quite typical of the mystical philosophy that lies behind what Mr. Price, no doubt with tongue in cheek, but quite accurately describes as the big bang *story*.

The Doppler effect

In 1915, Albert Einstein put forward his general theory of relativity. Before this, the general view of the universe was derived from the classical mechanistic model worked out in the 18th century by Sir Isaac Newton. For Newton, the universe was like a vast clockwork mechanism, obeying a number of fixed laws of motion. It was infinite in extent, but essentially unchanging. This vision of the universe suffered from the defect of all mechanistic, non-dialectical theories. It was *static*.

In 1929, Edwin Hubble, using a powerful new telescope, showed that the universe was far bigger than had been previously thought. Moreover, he noticed a previously unobserved phenomenon. When light reaches our eyes from a moving source, it creates a change in frequency. This may be expressed in terms of the colours of the spectrum. When a source is travelling towards us, its light is perceived to shift towards the high frequency (violet) end of the spectrum. When it moves away, we perceive a shift towards the low frequence (red) end of the spectrum. This theory, first worked out by the Austrian Christian Doppler, and called the "Doppler effect" after him, had major implications for astronomy. The stars appear to observers as a pattern of lights against a dark background. Noticing that most of the stars showed a shift towards the red end of the spectrum, Hubble's observations gave rise to the idea that the galaxies were moving away from us at a speed proportionate to the distance of the galaxy. This became known as Hubble's Law, although Hubble himself did not think that the universe was expanding.

Hubble observed that there was a correlation between the redshift and distance, as measured by the apparent brightness of the galaxies. It appeared that the most distant galaxies then observable were moving away at 25,000 miles per second. With the advent of the new 200-inch telescope in the 1960s, even more distant objects were detected, moving away at 150,000 miles per second. Upon these observations, the hypothesis of the "expanding universe" was built. In addition, the "field equations" of Einstein's general theory of relativity could be interpreted in such a way as to make them conform to this idea. By extension, it was argued that, if the universe was expanded, it must have been smaller in the past than now. The consequence of this was the hypothesis that the universe must have begun as a single dense core of matter. This was not originally Hubble's idea. It had already been advanced in 1922 by the Russian mathematician, Alexander Friedmann. Then in 1927, Georges-Henri Lemaître first put forward his idea of the "cosmic egg". From the standpoint of dialectical materialism, the idea of an eternally unchanging, closed universe, in a state of permanent equilibrium, is clearly incorrect. Therefore, the abandonment of this standpoint was undoubtedly a step forward.

The theories of Friedmann were given an important boost by the observations of Hubble and Wirtz. These appeared to indicate that the universe, or at least the part of it we can observe, was expanding. This was seized upon by Lemaître, a Belgian priest, who attempted to prove that, if the universe was finite in space, it must also be finite in time—it must have had *a beginning*. The usefulness of such a theory to the Catholic Church is beyond all doubt. It leaves the door wide open to the idea of a Creator, who, after being ignominiously expelled from the universe by science, now prepares his triumphal comeback as the Cosmic Ju-ju Man. "I felt at the time," said Hannes Alfvén years later, "that the motivation for his theory was Lemaître's need to reconcile his physics with the Church's doctrine of creation *ex nihilo*." [54] Lemaître was later rewarded by being made director of the Pontifical Academy of Science.

How the theory evolved

It is not actually correct to refer to "the big bang theory". In fact, there have been at least five different theories, each of which has run into trouble. The first, as we have seen, was put forward in 1927 by Lemaître. This was soon refuted on a number of different grounds—incorrect conclusions drawn from general relativity and thermo-dynamics, a false theory of cosmic rays and stellar evolution, etc. After the Second World War, the discredited theory was revived by George Gamow and others in a new form. A number of calculations were advanced by Gamow and others, (incidentally, not without a certain amount of scientific "creative accountancy") to explain the different phenomena which would flow from the big bang—density of matter, temperature, radiation levels, and so on. George Gamow's brilliant style of writing ensured that the big bang captured the popular imagination. Once again, the theory ran up against serious problems.

A whole number of discrepancies were found which invalidated, not only Gamow's model, but the "oscillating universe" model subsequently worked out by Robert Dicke and others, in an attempt to get round the problem of what happened before the big bang, by making the universe oscillate in a never-ending cycle. But Gamow had made one important prediction—that such an immense explosion would leave behind evidence in the form of "background radiation", a kind of echo of the big bang in space. This was used to revive the theory some years later.

From the beginning there was opposition to the idea. In 1948, Austrian astronomers Thomas Gold and Hermann Bondi advanced the "steady state" as an alternative, later popularised by Fred Hoyle. While accepting the expanding uni-verse, it attempted to explain it by the "continuous creation of matter from nothing". This was alleged to be happening all the time, but at a rate too slow to be detected by present-day technology. This means that the universe remains essentially the same for all time, hence the "steady state" theory. Thus matters went from bad to worse. From the "cosmic egg" to matter created out of nothing! The two rival the-ories slugged it out for over a decade.

The very fact that so many serious scientists were prepared to accept Hoyle's fantastic notion that matter was being created out of nothing is itself absolutely astonishing. In the event, this theory was shown to be false. The steady state theory assumed the universe to be homogeneous in time and space. If the universe were in

(54) Quoted by Lerner, op. cit., p. 214.

a "steady state" for all time, the density of a radio-emitting object ought to be constant, since the further we look out into space, the further back in time we see. However, observations showed that this was not the case; the further they looked out into space, the greater the intensity of the radio waves. This proved conclusively that the universe was in a constant state of change and evolution. It had not always been the same. The steady state theory was wrong.

In 1964, the steady state theory received the *coup de grace* with the discovery by two young astronomers in the USA, Arnas Penzias and Robert Wilson, of background radiation in space. This was immediately taken to be the "after-echo" of the big bang, predicted by Gamow. Even so, there were inconsistencies. The temperature of the radiation was found to be only 3.5°K, not the 20°K predicted by Gamow, or the 30°K predicted by his successor, Philip J.E. Peebles. This result is even worse than it looks. Since the amount of energy in a field is proportional to the 4th power of its temperature, the energy of the observed radiation was actually several thousand times less than that predicted.

American astrophysicist Robert Dicke and his Canadian counterpart Peebles took over the theory where Gamow had left off. Dicke realised that there was a handy way of getting round the sticky question of what happened before the big bang, if only they could get back to Einstein's idea of a closed universe. It could then be argued that the universe would expand for a time, then collapse to a single point (a "singularity"), or something near it, and then bounce back into expansion, in a kind of everlasting cosmic ping-pong game. The trouble was that Gamow had calculated the energy and density of the universe at levels just short of what would be needed to close the universe. The density was about two atoms per cubic meter of space; and the energy density, expressed as the predicted temperature of the background radiation, supposed to represent the remnants of the big bang, 20°K, i.e., 20 degrees above absolute zero. In fact, Gamow had fixed these figures in order to prove that the big bang produced heavy elements, something nobody now accepted. So Dicke unceremoniously ditched them, and selected new and equally arbitrary figures, which would fit in with *his* theory of a closed universe.

Dicke and Peebles predicted that the universe would be filled with radiation, mainly radio waves, with a temperature of 30°K. Later, Dicke claimed his group had predicted a temperature of 10°K, although this figure does not appear anywhere in his published notes, and is anyway a 100 times more than the observed result. This showed that the universe was more diffuse than Gamow had thought, with less gravity, which aggravated the basic problem of where all the energy for the big bang came from. As Eric Lerner points out:

"Far from confirming the Peebles-Dicke model, the Penzias-Wilson discovery clearly ruled out the closed oscillating model." [55] Thus arose a third version of the

(55) Lerner, op. cit., p. 152.

big bang—which became known as the standard model—an open universe in a permanent state of expansion.

Fred Hoyle did some detailed calculations, and announced that a big bang would produce only light elements—helium, deuterium and lithium (the latter two are actually quite rare). He calculated that if the density of the universe were about one atom per eight cubic metres, the amounts of these three light elements would be quite close to those actually observed. In this way, a new version of the theory was put forward which was nothing like the older theories. This no longer mentioned the cosmic rays of Lemaître, or the heavy elements of Gamow. Instead, the evidence put forward was the microwave background and three light elements. Yet none of this constitutes conclusive proof for the big bang. A major problem was the extreme smoothness of the background microwave radiation. The so-called irregularities in the background are so small that these fluctuations would not have had time to grow into galaxies—not unless there was a lot more matter (and therefore a lot more gravity) around than appears to be the case.

There were other problems, too. How does it come about that bits of matter flying in opposite directions all managed to reach the same temperature, and all at the same time (the "horizon" problem)? The partisans of the theory present the alleged origins of the universe as a model of mathematical perfection, all perfectly regular, a regular "Eden of symmetry whose characteristics conform to pure reason," as Lerner puts it. But the present universe is anything but perfectly symmetrical. It is irregular, contradictory, "lumpy". Not at all the stuff that well-mannered equations are made of down at Cambridge! One of the problems is why did the big bang not produce a smooth universe? Why did not the original simple material and energy just spread out evenly in space as an immense haze of dust and gas? Why is the present universe so "lumpy"? Where did all these galaxies and stars come from? So how did we get from A to B? How did the pure symmetry of the early universe give rise to the present irregular one we see before our eyes?

The 'inflation' theory

To get round this and other problems, Alan Guth, the American physicist, advanced his theory of the "inflationary universe". (It may be no coincidence that this idea was put forward in the 1970s, when the capitalist world was going through an inflationary crisis!) According to this theory, the temperature dropped so rapidly that there was no time for the different fields to separate out or for different particles to form. The differentiation took place only later, when the universe was much larger. This, then, is the most recent version of the big bang. It asserts that, at the time of the big bang, the universe experienced an exponential expansion, in which it doubled in size every 10^{-35} seconds (hence "inflation"). Whereas the earlier versions of the "standard model" envisaged the whole of the universe squashed to the size of a grapefruit, Guth went one better. He calculated that the universe did not begin as a grapefruit, but instead, it would be a billion times smaller than the nucleus of a hydrogen atom. Then it would expand at an incredible speed—many times the speed of light, which is 186,000 miles per second—until it reached a size 10^{90} times its initial volume, that is, 1 with 90 zeros after it!

Let us examine the implications of this theory. Like all the other big bang theories, it sets out from the hypothesis that all the matter in the universe was concentrated in a single spot. The fundamental mistake here is to imagine that the universe is equal to the observable universe, and that it is possible to reconstruct the entire history of the universe, as a linear process, without taking into account all the different phases, transitions, and different states through which matter passes.

Dialectical materialism conceives of the universe as infinite, but not static or in a permanent state of "equilibrium", as both Einstein and Newton did. Matter and energy cannot be created or destroyed, but are in a continual process of movement and change, which involves periodic explosions, expansion and contraction, attraction and repulsion, life and death. There is nothing intrinsically improbable about the idea of one, or many, great explosions. The problem here is a different one—a mystical interpretation of certain observed phenomena, such as the Hubble red shift, and an attempt to smuggle the religious idea of the creation of the universe into science by the back door.

To begin with, it is unthinkable that all the matter in the universe should be concentrated in a single point "of infinite density". Let us be clear what this means. Firstly, it is impossible to place an infinite amount of matter and energy in a finite space. Just to pose the question is sufficient to answer it. "Ah! say the big bangers, but the universe is not infinite, but finite, according to Einstein's general theory of relativity." In his book, Eric Lerner points out that an infinite number of different universes are allowed by Einstein's equations. Friedmann and Lemaître showed that many equations led to universal expansion. But by no means all of them imply a state of "singularity". Yet this is the one variant that is dogmatically advanced by Guth and co.

Even if we accept that the universe is finite, the notion of "singularity" leads us to conclusions of a clearly fantastic character. If we take the tiny corner of the universe which we are able to see as being the whole universe—an arbitrary assumption with no logical or scientific basis whatsoever—then we are talking about more than 100 billion galaxies, each containing about 100 billion main sequence stars (like our own sun). According to Guth, all this matter was concentrated in a space smaller than a single proton. When it had existed for a millionth of a trillionth of a trillionth, of a trillionth of a second with a temperature of trillions of trillions of trillions of degrees, there was only one field and only one kind of particle interaction. As the universe expanded and the temperature fell, the different fields are supposed to have "condensed" out of the original state of simplicity.

The question arises where all the energy came from to propel such an unprecedented expansion. In order to solve this riddle, Guth resorted to a hypothetical omnipresent force field (a "Higgs field"), the existence of which is predicted by some theoretical physicists, but for which there is not a shred of empirical evidence. "In Guth's theory," comments Eric Lerner, "the Higgs field which exists in a vacuum generates all the needed energy from nothing—*ex nihilo*. The universe, as he puts it, is one big 'free lunch', courtesy of the Higgs field." [56]

Dark matter?

Every time the big bang hypothesis runs into trouble, instead of abandoning it, its supporters just move the goal posts, introducing new and ever more arbitrary assumptions in order to shore it up. For example, the theory requires a certain amount of matter in the universe. If the universe was created 15 billion years ago, as the model predicts, there has simply not been enough time for the matter we observe to have congealed into galaxies like the Milky Way, without the help of invisible "dark matter". According to the big bang cosmologists, in order for galaxies to have been formed from the big bang, there must have been sufficient matter in the universe to bring about an eventual halt to its expansion through the law of gravitation. This would mean a density of approximately ten atoms per cubic metre of space. In reality, the amount of matter present in the observable universe is about one atom per ten cubic metres—a hundred times less than the amount predicted by the theory.

The cosmologists decided to represent the density of the universe as a ratio of the density needed to bring the expansion to a halt. They call this ratio omega. Thus, if omega equals 1, it would just be sufficient to halt the expansion. Unfortunately, the actual ratio was observed to be around .01 or .02. Approximately 99 per cent of the required matter had somehow "gone missing". How to solve the conundrum? Very simply. Since the theory demanded that the matter be there, they arbitrarily fixed the value of omega at close to 1, and then began a frantic search for the missing matter! The first problem facing the big bang was the origin of the galaxies. How did the extremely smooth background radiation produce such a "lumpy" irregular universe? The so-called ripples (anisotropies) in the radiation were supposed to have been a reflection of the formation of the clumps of matter around which the early galaxies coalesced. But the irregularities observed were too small to have been responsible for the formation of galaxies, unless there was a lot more matter, and therefore gravity, present than seems to be the case. To be exact, there needed to be 99 per cent more matter, which just wasn't there.

This is where the notion of "cold dark matter" comes in. It is important to realise that no one has ever seen this stuff. Its existence was put forward in the early 1980s,

(56) Lerner, op. cit., p. 158.

in order to fill up an embarrassing hole in the theory. Since only 1 or 2 per cent of the universe can actually be seen, the remaining 99 per cent or so was alleged to consist of invisible matter, which is dark and cold, emitting no radiation at all. Such strange particles, after a decade of searching for them, remain unobserved. But they nevertheless occupy a central place in the theory, simply because it demands that they should exist.

Fortunately, it is possible to work out quite accurately the amount of matter in the observable universe. As we have already pointed out, it is about one atom for every ten cubic metres of space, a mere one per cent of what is required by the big bang theory. But, as the journalists like to say, don't let the facts spoil a good story! If there is not enough matter in the universe to square with the theory, then there must be an awful lot of matter there which we can't see. As Brent Tully put it, "It's disturbing to see that there is a new theory every time there's a new observation."

At this stage, the defenders of the big bang decided to call on the aid of the Seventh Cavalry, in the person of particle physicists. The mission they were called upon to carry out puts all the exploits of John Wayne completely in the shade. The most he ever had to do was to find some unfortunate women and children carried off by the Indians. But when the cosmologists called in their colleagues who were busy investigating the mysteries of "inner space", their request was a trifle more ambitious. They wanted them to find the 99 per cent or so of the universe which had inconsiderately "gone missing". Unless they could find this missing matter, their equations would just not add up, and the standard theory of the origin of the universe would be in trouble!

In his book, *The Big Bang Never Happened,* Eric Lerner details a whole series of observations, the results of which have been published in scientific journals, which completely refute the idea of dark matter. Yet, in the teeth of all the evidence, the advocates of the big bang continue to behave like the learned professor who refused to look through the telescope to test the correctness of Galileo's theories. Dark matter must exist—because our theory demands it!

"The test of scientific theory," writes Lerner, "is the correspondence of predictions and observation, and the big bang has flunked. It predicts that there should be no objects in the universe older than twenty billion years and larger than 150 million light-years across. There are. It predicts that the universe, on such a large scale, should be smooth and homogeneous. The universe isn't. The theory predicts that, to produce the galaxies we see around us from the tiny fluctuations evident in the microwave background, there must be a hundred times as much dark matter as visible matter. There's no evidence that there's *any* dark matter at all. And if there is no dark matter, the theory predicts, no galaxies will form. Yet there they are, scattered across the sky. We live in one." [57]

(57) Lerner, op. cit., pp. 39-40.

Alan Guth succeeded in removing some of the objections to the big bang, but only by advancing the most fantastic and arbitrary version of the theory yet seen. It did not say what the "dark matter" was, but merely provided the cosmologists with a theoretical justification for it. The real significance was that it established the link between cosmology and particle physics that has lasted ever since. The problem is that the general tendency of theoretical physics, as in cosmology, has been to resort increasingly to a priori mathematical assumptions to justify their theories, making very few predictions that can be tested in practice. The resulting theories have an ever more arbitrary and fantastic character, and frequently seem to have more in common with science fiction than anything else.

In point of fact, the particle physicists who rushed to the aid of cosmology had plenty of problems of their own. Alan Guth and others were trying to discover a Grand Universal Theory (GUT), which would unify the three basic forces that operate on the small scale in nature—electromagnetism, the weak force (which causes radioactive decay), and the strong force (which holds the nucleus together, and is responsible for the release of nuclear energy). They hoped to repeat the success of Maxwell, a hundred years earlier, who had proved that electricity and magnetism were one and the same force. The particle physicists were only too willing to enter an alliance with the cosmologists, in the hope of finding the answer in the heavens for the difficulties they had found themselves in. In reality, their whole approach was similar. With scarcely any reference to observation, they based themselves on a series of mathematical models, and completely arbitrary assumptions, which were often little more than mere speculation. Theories have emerged thick and fast, each more incredible than the last. "Inflation" theory is mixed up with all this.

The neutrino to the rescue!

The determination with which the supporters of the big bang cling to their positions frequently leads them to perform the most amusing somersaults. Having searched in vain for the 99 per cent of missing "cold dark matter", they failed to find anything like the quantities required by the theory, to prevent the universe from expanding forever. On 18th December 1993, *The New Scientist* published an article entitled *Universe Will Expand Forever.* Here it was admitted that "a group of galaxies in the constellation of Cepheus contains far less invisible matter than had been thought a few months ago," and that the claims made earlier by American astronomers was "based on faulty analysis". A lot of scientific reputations are at stake, not to mention hundreds of millions of dollars in research grants. Could this fact have some connection with the fanaticism with which the big bang is defended? As usual, they saw what they wanted to see. The facts had to conform to the theory!

The evident failure to find the "cold dark matter", the existence of which is essential to the survival of the theory, was causing unease in the more thinking sections of the scientific community. An editorial of *The New Scientist*, published on the 4th June 1994 with the suggestive title *A Folly of Our Time?* compared the idea of dark matter with the discredited Victorian concept of the "ether", an invisible medium, by which light waves were believed to travel through space:

"It was invisible, ubiquitous, and, in the late 19th century, every physicist believed in it. It was, of course, the aether, the medium in which they thought light propagated, and it turned out to be a phantom. Light does not need a medium in which to propagate, unlike sound.

"Now, at the close of the 20th century, physicists find themselves in a curiously similar situation to their Victorian counterparts. Once again they are putting their faith in something which is invisible and ubiquitous. This time it is dark matter."

At this point, one would expect a serious scientist to begin to ask himself whether there was not something basically wrong with his theory. The same editorial adds:

"In cosmology, free parameters seem to be proliferating like wildfire. If the observations do not fit the theory, cosmologists seem happy to simply add new variables. By continually patching up the theory, we may be missing out on some Big Idea." Indeed. But, don't let the "facts" get in the way. Like a conjurer pulling a rabbit out of a hat, they suddenly discovered—*the neutrino!*

The neutrino, which is a subatomic particle, is described by Hoffmann as "fluctuating uncertainly between existence and non-existence." That is to say, in the language of dialectics, "it is and is not". How can such a phenomenon be reconciled with the law of identity, which categorically asserts that a thing either is or is not? Faced with such dilemmas, which reappear at every step in the world of subatomic particles described by quantum mechanics, there is frequently a tendency to resort to formulations such as the idea that the neutrino is a particle with neither mass nor charge. The initial opinion, still held by many scientists, was that the neutrino had no mass, and since electric charge cannot exist without mass, the inescapable conclusion was that the neutrino had neither.

Neutrinos are extremely small particles, and therefore difficult to detect. The existence of the neutrino was first postulated to explain a discrepancy in the amount of energy present in particles emitted from the nucleus. A certain amount of energy appeared to be lost, which could not be accounted for. Since the law of the conservation of energy states that energy can neither be created nor destroyed, this phenomenon required another explanation. Although it seems that the idealist physicist Niels Bohr was quite prepared to throw the law of conservation of energy overboard in 1930, this proved to be slightly premature! The discrepancy was explained by the discovery of a previously unknown particle—the neutrino.

Neutrinos formed in the sun's core at a temperature of 15 million degrees centigrade moving at the speed of light reach the sun's surface in three seconds. Floods of them stream through the universe, passing through solid matter, apparently without interacting on it. Neutrinos are so small that they pass straight through the earth.

So tiny are these elusive particles that their interaction with other forms of matter is minimal. They can pass through the earth, and even through solid lead, leaving no trace. Indeed, trillions of neutrinos are passing through your body even as you read these lines. But the likelihood that one could be trapped there is negligible, so you needn't worry. It has been estimated that a neutrino can pass through solid lead with a thickness of 100 light-years, with only a 50 per cent chance of being absorbed. That is why it remained undetected for so long. Indeed, it is difficult to imagine how a particle, which is so small that it was thought to have neither mass nor charge, and can pass through 100 light-years of lead, could ever be detected. But detected it was.

It seems that some neutrinos can be stopped by the equivalent of one tenth of an inch of lead. In 1956, using an ingenious experiment, American scientists succeeded in trapping an anti-neutrino. Then in 1968, they discovered neutrinos from the sun, although only one-third of the amount predicted by the current theories. Undoubtedly the neutrino possessed properties that could not immediately be detected. Given its extreme smallness, that was not surprising. But the idea of a form of matter that lacked the most basic properties of matter was clearly a contradiction in terms. In the event, the problem appears to have been resolved from two completely different sources. First, one of the discoverers of the neutrino, Nobel Prize winning physicist Frederick Reines, announced in 1980 that he had discovered the existence of *neutrino oscillation* in an experiment. This would indicate that the neutrino does have mass, but Reines' results were not seen as conclusive.

However, Soviet physicists, involved in an entirely separate experiment, showed that electron-neutrinos have a mass, which could be as much as 40 electron volts. Since this is only 1/13,000th of the mass of an electron, which in turn is only 1/2,000th of a proton, it is hardly surprising that the neutrino was for so long believed to have no mass.

Up till recently, the general view of the scientific establishment was that the neutrino had no mass and no charge. Now, all of a sudden, they have changed their mind and declared that the neutrino does indeed have mass—and, perhaps, quite a lot of it. This is the most astonishing conversion since Saint Paul fell off his horse on the road to Damascus! Indeed, such indecent haste must raise serious doubts about the motivation behind this miraculous conversion. Can it be that they were so desperate at their signal failure to deliver the goods with "cold dark matter" that they finally decided to do an about-turn on the neutrino? One can just imagine what Sherlock Holmes would have said to Doctor Watson!

Despite the enormous advances in the field of particle research, the present situation is confused. Hundreds of new particles have been discovered, but as yet there is no satisfactory general theory capable of introducing some order, as Mendeleyev did in the field of chemistry. At present, there is an attempt to unify the fundamental forces of nature by grouping them under four headings: gravity, electromagnetism, and the "weak" and "strong" nuclear forces, each of which functions at a different level.

Gravitation works on the cosmological scale, holding the stars, planets and galaxies together. Electromagnetism binds atoms into molecules, transports photons from the sun and stars, and fires the synapses of the brain. The strong force binds together protons and neutrons inside the nuclei of atoms. The weak force is expressed in the transmutation of unstable atoms during radioactive decay. Both the latter forces only operate at very short range. However, there is no reason to suppose that this arrangement represents the last word on the subject, in some respects it is an arbitrary notion.

There are big differences between these forces. Gravitation affects all forms of matter and energy, whereas the strong force only affects one class of particles. Yet gravitation is one hundred million trillion trillion trillion times weaker than the strong nuclear force. More importantly, it is not evident why there should be no opposite force to gravity, whereas electromagnetism is manifested both as positive and negative electrical charge. This problem, the solution of which was attempted by Einstein, remains to be solved, and has a vital bearing on the entire discussion about the nature of the universe. Each force is accounted for by a different set of equations, involving some twenty different parameters. These give results, but nobody knows why.

The so-called Grand Unified Theories ("GUTs") put forward the idea that matter itself might only be a passing phase in the evolution of the universe. However, the prediction made by the GUTs that protons decay has not been borne out, thus invalidating at least the simplest version of the GUTs. In an attempt to make sense of their own discoveries, some physicists have got entangled in ever more weird and wonderful theories, like the so-called supersymmetry theories ("SUSYs") which purport that the universe was originally built on more than four dimensions. According to this notion, the universe could have started with, for example, ten dimensions, but unfortunately all but four of them collapsed during the big bang, and are now too small to be noticed.

Apparently, these objects are the subatomic particles themselves, which are alleged to be quanta of matter and energy that condensed out of pure space. Thus they stagger from one metaphysical speculation to the next in a vain attempt to explain the fundamental phenomena of the universe. Supersymmetry postulates the universe as beginning in a state of absolute perfection. In the words of Stephen Hawking, "the early universe was simpler, and it was a lot more appealing, *because* it was a lot simpler." Some scientists even try to justify this kind of mystical speculation on aesthetic grounds. Absolute symmetry is alleged to be beautiful. Thus we find ourselves back in the rarefied atmosphere of Plato's idealism.

In reality, nature is not characterised by absolute symmetry, but is full of contradictions, irregularities, cataclysms, and sudden breaks of continuity. Life itself is a proof of this assertion. In any living system, absolute equilibrium signifies death. The contradiction that we observe here is as old as the history of human thought. It is the contradiction between the "perfect" abstractions of thought and the necessary irregularities and "imperfections" which characterise the real material world. The whole problem stems from the fact that the abstract formulae of mathematics, which may or may not be beautiful, most certainly do not adequately represent the real world of nature. To suppose such a thing is a methodological error of the first magnitude, and necessarily leads us to draw wrong conclusions.

Constant headaches, or Hubble trouble

At present there is a fierce dispute among the supporters of the big bang concerning the supposed age of the universe. In fact, the entire "standard model" is in crisis. We are treated to the spectacle of respectable people of science attacking each other in public with the most ungentlemanly language. And all over something called the Hubble Constant. This is the formula that measures the speed at which things are moving in the universe. This is of great importance for those who wish to discover the age and size of the universe. The trouble is that nobody knows what it is!

Edwin Hubble asserted that the speed with which the galaxies are moving apart was proportional to their distance from us—the further away, the faster they are moving. This expressed in Hubble's Law: v(elocity) = H x d(istance). In this equation, the H is known as Hubble's Constant. In order to measure this, we need to know two things: the speed and distance away of a particular galaxy. The speed can be calculated by the red shift. But the distance between galaxies cannot be measured with a slide-rule. In fact, no reliable instruments exist for measuring such immense distances. And here lies the rub! The experts cannot agree on the real value of the Hubble Constant, as was comically revealed in a Channel 4 TV programme:

"Michael Pierce says that, *without doubt*, the Hubble Constant is 85, Gustaf Tamman asserts 50, George Jacoby 80, Brian Schmidt 70, Michael Rowan Robinson 50, and John Tonry 80. The difference between 50 and 80 may not sound like much," says the accompanying Channel Four booklet, "but it is crucial to the age of the Universe. *If the Hubble is high, astronomers could be in the process of disproving their most important theory.*"

The importance of this is that the higher the "Hubble", the faster things are moving, and the sooner in the past was the moment when the big bang was supposed to have occurred. In recent years, new techniques of measuring the distance of galaxies have been applied, which have led astronomers to revise earlier estimates drastically. This has provoked consternation in the scientific community, since the estimates for the Hubble Constant have been getting higher all the time. The latest estimate puts the age of the universe at just 8 billion years. This would mean that there are stars that are older than the universe itself! This is a glaring contradiction—not a dialectical one, but simply nonsense.

"Well," comments Carlos Frank, quoted in the same booklet, "if it turns out that the ages of the stars are greater than the expansion time of the universe, as inferred by the measurement of the Hubble Constant and the measurement of the density of the universe, then there is a genuine crisis. You only have one option: you have to drop the basic assumptions upon which the model of the Universe is based. *In this case, you have to drop some, perhaps all, of the basic assumptions on which the big bang theory is based."* [58]

There is virtually no empirical evidence to bear out the big bang theory. Most of the work done to support it is of a purely theoretical character, leaning heavily on abstruse and esoteric mathematical formulae. The numerous contradictions between the preconceived "big bang" schema and the observable evidence have been covered up by constantly moving the goal posts in order to preserve at all costs a theory upon which so many academic reputations have been built.

According to this theory, there can be nothing in the universe older than 15 billion years. But there is evidence that contradicts this proposition. In 1986, Brent Tully of Hawaii University discovered huge agglomerations of galaxies ("superclusters") about a billion light years long, three hundred million light years wide and one hundred million light-years thick. In order for such vast objects to form, it would have taken between eighty and a hundred billion years, that is to say four or five times longer than what would be allowed by the "big bangers". Since then there have been other results that tend to confirm these observations.

The New Scientist (5th February, 1994) carried a report of the discovery of a cluster of galaxies by Charles Steidel of the Massachusetts Institute of Technology and Donald Hamilton of the California Institute of Technology in Pasadena with big implications for the big bang theory:

"The discovery of such a cluster spells trouble for theories of cold dark matter, which assume that a large fraction of the mass of the universe is in cold, dark objects such as planets or black holes. The theories predict that material in the early universe clumped together from the 'bottom up', so that galaxies formed first, then only later clumped to form clusters."

As usual, the initial reaction of astronomers is to resort to "move the goal posts", adjusting the theory to get round awkward facts. Mauro Giavalisco of the Baltimore Space Telescope Science Institute "believes it might just be possible to explain the birth of the first galaxy cluster at a red shift of 3.4 by fine-tuning the cold dark matter theory. But he adds a warning. 'If you found ten clusters at red shift 3.5, it would kill cold dark matter theories'."

We may take for granted that not just ten but a far larger number of these vast clusters exist and will be discovered. And these, in turn, will only represent a minute proportion of all the matter that stretches far beyond the limits of the observable universe and reaches out to infinity. All attempts to place a limit on the material uni-

---

(58) *The Rubber Universe*, pp. 11 and 14, our emphasis (Channel 4 publication, 1995).

verse are doomed to fail. Matter is boundless, both at the subatomic level, and with regard to time and space.

Big crunch and superbrain

> "Dies irae, dies illa
> Solvet saeclum in favilla."
> (Thomas of Celano, *Dies Irae*)

> ("That day, the day of wrath,
> will turn the universe to ashes."
> —Mediaeval Church chant for the dead.)

In the same way they cannot agree on the origin of the universe, so they also disagree on how it is all supposed to end up—except that they all agree that it will end badly! According to one school of thought, the expanding universe will eventually be brought to a halt by the force of gravity, whereupon the whole thing will collapse in on itself, leading to a "big crunch", where we will all end up just where we started, back inside the cosmic egg. Not so! exclaims another school of big bangers. Gravity is not strong enough to do this. The universe will simply keep on expanding indefinitely, getting thinner and thinner, like "Augustus who would not have any soup", until eventually it fades away into the black night of nothingness.

Decades ago, Ted Grant, using the method of dialectical materialism, showed the unsoundness both of the big bang theory of the origin of the universe and the alternative steady state theory put forward by Fred Hoyle and Herman Bondi. Subsequently, the steady state theory, which was based on the continuous creation of matter (from nothing), was shown to be false. The big bang theory therefore "won" by default, and is still defended by the majority of the scientific establishment. From the standpoint of dialectical materialism, it is arrant nonsense to talk about the "beginning of time", or the "creation of matter". Time, space, and motion are the mode of existence of matter, which can neither be created nor destroyed. The universe has existed for all time, as constantly changing, moving, evolving matter and (which is the same thing) energy. All attempts to find a "beginning" or an "end" to the material universe will inevitably fail. But how is one to explain this strange regression to a mediaeval view of the fate of the universe?

While it is pointless to look for a direct causal link between the processes at work in society, politics and the economy, and the development of science (the relationship is neither automatic nor direct, but far more subtle), it is hard to resist the conclusion that the pessimistic outlook of some scientists in relation to the future of the universe is not accidental, but somehow related to a general feeling that society has reached an impasse. The end of the world is nigh. This is not a new phenomenon. The same doom-laden outlook was present in the period of decline of the Roman Empire and at the close of the Middle Ages. In each case, the idea that the world was coming to an end reflected the fact that a particular system of society had become exhausted and was on the point of extinction. What was imminent was not the end of the world, but the collapse of slavery and feudalism.

Just take the following quote from *The First Three Minutes* by Nobel Prize winner Steven Weinberg:

"It is almost irresistible for humans to believe that we have some special relation to the universe, that human life is not just a more or less farcical outcome of a chain of accidents reaching back to the first three minutes, but that we were somehow built in from the beginning. As I write this I happen to be in an aeroplane at 30,000 feet, flying over Wyoming en route home from San Francisco to Boston. Below, the earth looks very soft and comfortable—fluffy clouds here and there, snow turning pink as the sunsets, roads stretching straight across the country from one town to another. It is very hard to realise that this all is just a tiny part of an overwhelmingly hostile universe. It is even harder to realise that this present universe has evolved from an unspeakably unfamiliar early condition, and faces a future extinction of endless cold or intolerable heat. The more the universe seems comprehensible, the more it also seems pointless." [59]

We have already seen how the big bang theory opens the door to religion and all kinds of mystical ideas. To blur the distinction between science and mysticism is to put back the clock 400 years. It is a reflection of the current irrational mood of society. And it invariably leads to conclusions of a thoroughly reactionary nature. Let us take just one apparently remote and obscure question: "Do protons decay?" As we have said, this is one of the predictions of one of the branches of modern particle physics known as the GUTs. All kinds of sophisticated experiments were conducted to test this. All ended in complete failure. Yet they persist in putting forward the same idea.

Here is a typical example of the type of literature issued by the advocates of the big crunch theory:

"In the final moments, gravity becomes the all-dominant force, mercilessly crushing matter and space. The curvature of space-time increases ever faster. Larger and larger regions of space are compressed into smaller and smaller volumes. According to conventional theory, the implosion becomes infinitely powerful, crushing all matter out of existence and obliterating every physical thing, including space and time themselves, at a space-time singularity.

"This is the end.

"The 'big crunch', as far as we understand it, is not just the end of matter. It is the end of *everything*. Because time itself ceases at the big crunch, it is meaningless

(59) Quoted in Lerner, op. cit., pp. 164-5.

to ask what happens next, just as it is meaningless to ask what happened before the big bang. There is no 'next' for anything at all to happen—no time even for inactivity or space for emptiness. A universe that came from nothing in the big bang will disappear into nothing at the big crunch, its glorious few zillion years of existence not even a memory."

The question that follows is a classic of unconscious humour: "Should we be depressed by such a prospect?" Paul Davies asks, presumably expecting a serious answer! He then proceeds to cheer us up by speculating on various means whereby humankind might escape destruction. Inevitably, we immediately find ourselves in a kind of never-never land half way between religion and science fiction.

"One might wonder whether a superbeing inhabiting the collapsing universe in its final moments could have an infinite number of distinct thoughts and experiences in the finite time available." So, before the final three minutes are up, humanity casts off its crude material body, and becomes pure spirit, able to survive the ending of everything by transforming itself into a superbrain.

"Any superbrain would need to be quick-witted and switch communications from one direction to another as the oscillations brought more rapid collapse in one direction and then another. If the being can keep pace, the oscillations could themselves provide the necessary energy to drive the thought processes. Furthermore, in simple mathematical models there appears to be an infinite number of oscillations in the finite duration terminating in the big crunch. This provides for an infinite amount of information processing, hence, by hypothesis, an infinite subjective time for the superbeing. Thus the mental world may never end, even though the physical world comes to an abrupt cessation at the big crunch." [60]

One really needs a superbrain to make head or tail of this! It would be nice to think that the author is joking. Unfortunately, we have read too many passages of this kind recently to be sure of this. If the Big Crunch signifies "the end of everything", where does this leave our friend the superbrain? To begin with, only an incorrigible idealist could conceive of a brain without a body. Of course, we are here in the presence, not of any old brain, but a superbrain. But even so, we assume that the presence of a spinal cord and a central nervous system would be of some use to it; that such a nervous system ought in all fairness, to posses a body; and that a body (even a superbody) generally requires some kind of sustenance, specially since the brain is known to be somewhat greedy, and absorbs a very high percentage of the total calories consumed even by a mere mortal. A superbrain would logically possess a superappetite! Sadly, since the big crunch is the end of everything, our unfortunate superbrain will evidently be placed in a rather strict diet for the rest of eternity. We can only hope that, being quick-witted, it will have had time to snatch a quick meal before its three minutes was up. With this edifying thought, we take our leave of the superbrain, and return to reality.

(60) P. Davies, op. cit., pp. 123, 124-5 and 126.

Is it not astonishing that, after two thousand years of the greatest advances of human culture and science, we find ourselves back in the world of the *Book of Revelations*? Engels warned more than a hundred years ago that, by turning their backs on philosophy, scientists would inevitably end up in the "spirit world". Unfortunately, his prediction has proven to be all too accurate.

A 'plasma universe'?

The standard model of the universe has led us into a scientific, philosophical, and moral dead-end. The theory itself is full of holes. Yet it still remains on its feet, though badly shaken, mainly for the lack of an alternative. Nevertheless, something is stirring in the world of science. New ideas are beginning to take shape, which not only reject the big bang, but which set out from the idea of an infinite, constantly changing universe. It is far too early to say which of these theories will be vindicated. One interesting hypothesis, that of the "plasma universe", has been put forward by the Swedish Nobel Prize winning physicist Hannes Alfvén. While we cannot deal with the theory in detail, we feel we should at least mention some of Alfvén's ideas.

Alfvén passed from the investigation of plasma in the laboratory to a study of how the universe evolves. Plasma consists of hot, electrically conducting gases. It is now known that 99 per cent of the matter in the universe is plasma. Whereas in normal gases, electrons are bound to an atom and cannot move easily, in a plasma, the electrons are stripped off by intense heat, allowing them to move freely. Plasma cosmologists envisage a universe "crisscrossed by vast electrical currents and powerful magnetic fields, ordered by the cosmic counterpoint of electromagnetism and gravity." [61] In the 1970s, the *Pioneer* and *Voyager* spacecrafts detected the presence of electrical currents and magnetic fields filled with plasma filaments around Jupiter, Saturn and Uranus.

Scientists like Hannes Alfvén, Anthony Peratt and others, have elaborated a model of the universe which is dynamic, not static, but which does not require a beginning in time. The phenomenon of the Hubble expansion needs an explanation. But the big bang is not necessarily it. A big bang will certainly produce an expansion, but an expansion does not require a big bang. As Alfvén puts it: "This is like saying that because all dogs are animals, all animals are dogs." The problem is not the idea of an explosion, which at some point gave rise to an expansion of part of the universe. There is nothing intrinsically improbable in this. The problem is the idea that all the matter in the universe was concentrated at a single point, and that the universe and time itself was born in a single instant called the big bang.

The alternative model suggested by Hannes Alfvén and fellow Swedish physicist Oskar Klein accepts that there could have been an explosion, caused by the combination of large amounts of matter and antimatter in one small corner of the visible universe, which generated huge quantities of energetic electrons and

(61) Lerner, op. cit., p. 14

positrons. Trapped in magnetic fields, these particles drove the plasma apart for hundreds of millions of years. "The explosion of this epoch, some ten or twenty billion years ago, sent the plasma from which the galaxies then condensed flying outward—in the Hubble expansion. But this was in no way a big bang that created matter, space, and time. It was just a big bang, an explosion in one part of the universe. Alfvén is the first to admit that this explanation is not the only possible one. 'The significant point,' he stresses, 'is that there are alternatives to the big bang'."

At a time when almost all other scientists believed that space was an empty vacuum, Alfvén showed that this was not the case. Alfvén pointed out that the entire universe is pervaded by plasma currents and magnetic fields. Alfvén did pioneering work in the field of sunspots and magnetic fields. Later, Alfvén proved that when a current flows through a plasma in the laboratory, it assumes the form of a filament in order to move along magnetic field lines. Starting out from this observation, he then concluded that the same phenomenon takes place in plasma in space. It is a general property of plasma throughout the universe. Thus, we have immense electrical currents flowing along naturally formed plasma filaments, which crisscross the cosmos.

"By forming the filamentary structures observed on the smallest and largest scales, matter and energy can be compressed in space. But it is clear that energy can be compressed in *time* as well—the universe is filled with sudden, explosive releases of energy. One example that Alfvén was familiar with is the solar flare, the sudden release of energy on the sun's surface, which generates the streams of particles that produce magnetic storms on earth. His 'generator' models of cosmic phenomena showed how energy could be produced gradually, as in a well-behaved power station, but not explosively, as in the flares. Understanding the explosive release of energy was the key to the dynamics of the cosmos."

Alfvén had proved the correctness of the Kant-Laplace Nebular Hypothesis. Now, if the stars and planets can be formed by the action of huge filamentary currents, there is no reason why whole solar systems cannot be formed in the same way:

"Again, the process is identical, but this time immensely larger: filaments sweeping through a protogalactic nebula pinch plasma into the building materials of the sun and other stars. Once the material is initially pinched, gravitation will draw some of it together, especially slower-moving dust and ice particles, which will then create a seed for the growth of a central body. Moreover, the filament's vortex motion will provide angular momentum to each of the smaller agglomerations within it, generating a new, smaller set of currents carrying filaments and a new cycle of compression that forms a solar system. (In 1989, this hypothesis now widely accepted, was definitively confirmed when scientists observed that the rotation axes of all the stars in a given cloud are aligned with the cloud's magnetic field—clearly, a magnetic-field-controlled stellar formation.)"

Alfvén's theories were, of course, rejected by the cosmologists, since they challenged not only the standard model, but even called into question the existence of black holes, which were then all the rage. He had already correctly explained the cosmic rays, not as the remnants of the big bang, but as the products of electromagnetic acceleration.

"Thus, in Alfvén and Klein's scenario, only a small part of the universe—that which we see—will have first collapsed and then exploded. Instead of coming from a singular point, the explosion comes from a vast region hundreds of millions of light-years across and takes hundreds of millions of years to develop—no 'origin of the universe' is required." [62]

Whether this particular theory is shown to be correct only time will tell. The important thing, as Alfvén himself points out, is that other alternative hypotheses to the big bang are possible. Whatever happens, we are sure that the model of the universe which is finally corroborated by science will have nothing in common with a closed universe with a big bang at one end and a big crunch at the other. The discovery of the telescope in 1609 was a decisive turning point in the history of astronomy. Since then, the horizon of the universe has been pushed further and further back. Today powerful radio telescopes probe deep into space. All the time new objects are being discovered, bigger and further away, with absolutely no end in sight. Yet man's obsession with the finite creates the persistent urge to place a "final limit" on everything. We see this same phenomenon repeated time and again in the history of astronomy.

It is ironic that, at a time when technology enables us to penetrate further than ever into the vastness of the universe, we witness a psychological regression to the mediaeval world of a finite universe, beginning with Creation and ending in the total annihilation of space, time and matter. An impassable line is drawn at this point, beyond which the human mind is not meant to enquire, since "we cannot know" what is there. It is the 20th century equivalent of the old maps, which showed the edge of the world, marked with the stern warning, "Here be Monsters".

Einstein and the big bang

In recent decades the prejudice has become deeply rooted that "pure" science, especially theoretical physics is the product of abstract thought and mathematical deduction alone. As Eric Lerner points out, Einstein was partly responsible for this tendency. Unlike earlier theories, such as Maxwell's laws of electromagnetism, or Newton's laws of gravity, which were firmly based on experiment, and soon confirmed by hundreds of thousands of independent observations, Einstein's theories were initially confirmed on the basis of only two—the deflection of starlight by the sun's gravitational field and a slight deviation in the orbit of Mercury.

(62) Lerner, op. cit., pp. 52, 196, 209 and 217-8.

The fact that relativity theory was subsequently shown to be correct has led others, possibly not quite up to Einstein's level of genius, to assume that this is the way to proceed. Why bother with time-consuming experiments and tedious observations? Indeed, why depend upon the evidence of the senses at all, when we can get straight to the truth through the method of pure deduction?

We see a steadily increasing tendency towards a purely abstract theoretical approach to cosmology, based almost exclusively on mathematical calculations and relativity theory. "The annual number of cosmology papers published skyrocketed from sixty in 1965 to over five hundred in 1980, yet this growth was almost solely in *purely* theoretical work: by 1980 roughly 95 per cent of these papers were devoted to various mathematical models, such as the 'Bianchi type XI universe'. By the mid-seventies, cosmologists' confidence was such that they felt able to describe in intimate detail events of the first one-hundredth second of time, several billion years ago. Theory increasingly took on the characteristic of myth—absolute, exact knowledge about events in the distant past but an increasingly hazy understanding of how they led to the cosmos we now see, and an increasing rejection of observation."

The Achilles' heel of Einstein's static, closed universe is that it would inevitably collapse in on itself because of the force of gravity. In order to get round this problem, he advanced the hypothesis of the "cosmological constant", a repulsive force that would counteract that of gravity, thus preventing the universe from collapse. For a time the idea of a static universe, held forever in a state of equilibrium by the twin forces of gravity and the "cosmological constant" received support—at least from the very small number of scientists who claimed to understand the extremely abstract and complicated theories of Einstein.

In 1970, in an article in *Science*, Gerard de Vaucouleur showed that, as objects in the universe get larger, so their density gets less. An object ten times bigger, for example, will be 100 times less dense. This has serious implications for the attempts to establish the average density of the universe, which is necessary to obtain in order to establish whether there is enough gravity to halt the Hubble Expansion. If the average density drops with increases in size, it will be impossible to define the average density for the universe as a whole. If De Vaucouleur is right, the density of the observed universe will be far less than had been thought, and the value of omega could be as little as .0002. In a universe with so little matter, the effects of gravity will be so weak that the difference between general relativity and Newtonian gravity will be insignificant and, therefore, "for all practical purposes, general relativity, the foundation of conventional cosmology, can be *ignored!*" Lerner continues: "De Vaucouleur's discovery shows that nowhere in the universe—except perhaps near a few ultradense neutron stars—is general relativity more than a subtle correction." [63]

The difficulties involved in grasping what Einstein "really meant" are proverbial. When some journalist asked the English scientist Eddington, whose work gave

(63) Lerner, op. cit., pp. 153-4, 221 and 222.

the first direct confirmation of Einstein's general theory of relativity, if it was true that there were only three people in the world who understood relativity, the latter replied, "Oh, really? And who is the third?" However, the Russian mathematician Alexander Friedmann in the early 1920s showed that Einstein's model of the universe was only one of an infinite number of possible cosmologies, some expanding, some contracting, depending on the value of the cosmological constant, and the "initial conditions" of the universe. This was a purely mathematical result, derived from Einstein's equations. The real significance of Friedmann's work was that it called into question the idea of a closed static universe, and showed that other models were possible.

Neutron stars

Contrary to the idea of Antiquity that the stars were eternal and changeless, modern astronomy has shown that stars and other heavenly bodies have a history, a birth and life and a death—gigantic, rarefied and red in youth; blue, hot and radiant in middle life; shrunken, dense and red once more in old age. An immense amount of information has been accumulated from astronomical observations involving powerful telescopes. At Harvard alone, a quarter of a million stars had already been arranged in forty classes before the Second World War through the work of Annie J. Cannon. Now a great deal more is known as a result of radio telescopes and space exploration.

The British astronomer Fred Hoyle has made a detailed investigation of the life and death of stars. The stars are fuelled by the fusion of hydrogen into helium at the core. A star in its early stages changes little in size or temperature. This is the present position of our own sun. Sooner or later, however, the hydrogen that is being consumed at the hot centre is turned into helium. This accumulates at the core until, when it reaches a certain size, quantity changes into quality. A dramatic change occurs, causing a sudden variation in size and temperature. The star expands enormously, while its surface loses heat. It becomes a red giant.

According to this theory, the helium core contracts, raising the temperature to the point where the helium nuclei can fuse to form carbon, releasing new energy. As it heats, it contracts still further. At this stage, the life of the star draws rapidly to a close, for the energy produced by helium fusion is far less than that produced by hydrogen fusion. At a given point, the energy required to keep the star's expansion against the pull of its own gravitational field begins to fail. The star contracts rapidly, collapsing in on itself to become a *white dwarf*, surrounded by a halo of gas, the remnant of the outer layers blown out by the heat of contraction. These are the basis of planetary nebulae. Stars may remain in this state for a long time, slowly cooling, until they no longer possess enough heat to glow. They then end up as *black dwarves*.

However, such processes seem relatively sedate in comparison to the scenario mapped out by Hoyle for bigger stars. When a large star reaches a late stage of development, in which its internal temperature reaches 3-4 billion degrees, iron begins to form at the core. At a certain stage, the temperature reaches such a point that the iron atoms are driven apart to form helium. At this point, the star collapses in on itself in about one second. Such a terrific collapse causes a violent explosion, which blasts all the outer material away from the star's centre. This is what is known as a *supernova*, like the one that astonished Chinese astronomers in the 11th century.

The question arises of what happens if a large star continues to collapse inwards under the pressure of its own gravity. Unimaginable gravitational forces would squeeze the electrons into the space already occupied by protons. According to a law of quantum mechanics known as the Pauli exclusion principle, no two electrons can occupy the same energy state in an atom. It is this principle acting on the neutrons that prevents further collapse. At this stage the star is now mainly composed of neutrons, hence its name. Such a star has a tiny radius, maybe only 10 km, or about 1/700th of the radius of a white dwarf, and with a density of more than a 100 million times that of the latter, which was already extremely high. A single matchbox full of such material would weigh as much as an asteroid a mile in diameter.

With such staggering concentrations of mass, the gravitational pull of a neutron star would absorb everything in the surrounding space. The existence of such neutron stars was theoretically predicted in 1932 by the Soviet physicist and Nobel Prize winner Lev D. Landau, and later studied in detail by J.R. Oppenheimer and others. For some time it was doubted whether such stars could exist. However, in 1967 the discovery of pulsars inside the remnants of supernova such as the Crab Nebula gave rise to the theory that pulsars are really neutron stars. There is nothing in all this that is inconsistent with the principles of materialism.

Pulsars are pulsating stars which gave out rapid bursts of energy at regular intervals. It is estimated that there may be 100,000 pulsars in our galaxy alone, of which hundreds have already been located. The source of these powerful radio waves was thought to be a neutron star. According to the theory, it would have to have an immensely strong magnetic field. In the grip of the neutron star's gravitational field, electrons could only emerge at the magnetic poles, losing energy in the form of radio waves in the process. The short bursts of radio waves could be explained by fact that the neutron star must be rotating. In 1969, it was noted that a light of a dim star in the Crab Nebula was flashing intermittently in line with the microwave pulses. This was the first sighting of a neutron star. Then, in 1982, a fast pulsar was discovered, with pulsations 20 times faster than those of the Crab Nebula—642 times a second.

In the 1960s, new objects were discovered by radio telescopes, the quasars. By the end of the decade, 150 were discovered—some of them estimated to be nine billion light years away, assuming the red-shift to be correct. To appear at all at such a vast distance must mean that these objects are 30 to 100 times more luminous than a normal galaxy. Yet they appeared to be small. This poses difficulties, which led some astronomers to refuse to accept that they could be so far away.

The discovery of quasars gave an unexpected boost to the big bang theory. The existence of collapsed stars with a tremendously strong gravitational field posed problems that could not be resolved by direct observation. This fact opened the door to a flood of speculations, involving the most peculiar interpretations of Einstein's general theory of relativity. As Eric Lerner points out:

"The glamour of the mysterious quasars quickly attracted young researchers to the arcane calculations of general relativity and thus to cosmological problems, especially those of a mathematical nature. After 1964 the number of papers published in cosmology leapt upward, but the growth was almost wholly in purely theoretical pieces—mathematical examinations of some problem in general relativity, which made no effort to compare results with observations. Already, in 1964, perhaps four out of five cosmology papers were theoretical, where only a third had been so a decade earlier." [64]

It is necessary to distinguish clearly between black holes, the existence of which has been derived from a particular interpretation of the general theory of relativity, and neutron stars, which have actually been observed. The idea of black holes has captured the imagination of millions through the writings of authors like Stephen Hawking. Roger Penrose, in an essay based on a BBC Radio lecture delivered in 1973, describes the theory of black holes as follows:

"What is a black hole? For astronomical purposes it behaves as a small, highly condensed dark 'body'. But it is not really a material body in the ordinary sense. It possesses no ponderable surface. A black hole is a region of empty space (albeit a strangely distorted one), which acts as a centre of gravitational attraction. At *one* time a material body *was* there. But the body collapsed inwards under its own gravitational pull. The more the body concentrated itself towards the centre the stronger became its gravitational field and the less was the body able to stop itself from yet further collapse. At a certain stage a point of no return was reached, and the body passed within its 'absolute event horizon'.

"I shall say more of this later, but for our present purposes, it is the absolute event horizon which acts as the boundary surface of the black hole. This surface is not material. It is merely a demarcation line drawn in space separating an interior from an exterior region. The interior region—into which the body has fallen—is defined by the fact that no matter, light, or signal of any kind can escape from it, while the exterior region is where it is still possible for signals or material particles to escape to the outside world. The matter which collapsed to form the black hole has fallen deep inside to attain incredible densities, apparently even to be crushed

(64) Lerner, op. cit., p. 149.

out of existence by reaching what is known as a 'space-time singularity'—a place where physical laws, as presently understood, must cease to apply." [65]

Stephen Hawking

In 1970, Stephen Hawking put forward the idea that the energy content of a black hole might occasionally produce a pair of subatomic particles, one of which might escape. This implies that a black hole can evaporate, although this would take an unimaginably long period of time. In the end, according to this view, it would explode, producing a large amount of gamma rays. Hawking's theories have attracted a lot of attention. His well-written best seller *A Brief History of Time, From the Big Bang to Black Holes*, was perhaps the book that more than any other drew the attention of the new theories of cosmology to the public's attention. The author's lucid style made complicated ideas seem both simple and attractive. It makes for good reading, but so do many works of science fiction. Regrettably, it appears to have become fashionable for the authors of popular works about cosmology to sound as mystical as possible, and to put forward the most outlandish theories, based on the maximum amount of speculation and the minimum amount of facts. Mathematical models have displaced observation almost entirely. The central philosophy of this school of thought is summed up in Stephen Hawking's aphorism "one cannot really argue with a mathematical theorem."

Hawking claims that he and Roger Penrose proved (mathematically) that the general theory of relativity "implied that the universe must have a beginning and, possibly, an end." The basis of all this is that the general theory of relativity is taken as absolutely true. Yet, paradoxically, at the point of the big bang general relativity suddenly becomes irrelevant. It ceases to apply, just as all the laws of physics cease to apply, so that *nothing whatsoever can be said about it*. Nothing, that is, except metaphysical speculation of the worst sort. But we will return to this later.

According to this theory, time and space did not exist before the big bang, when all the matter in the universe was alleged to have been concentrated at a single infinitesimally small point, known to mathematicians as a singularity. Hawking himself points out the dimensions involved in this remarkable cosmological transaction:

"We now know that our galaxy is only one of some hundred thousand million that can be seen using modern telescopes, each galaxy itself containing some hundred thousand million stars...We live in a galaxy that is about one hundred thousand light-years across and is slowly rotating; the stars in its spiral arms orbit around its centre about once every several hundred million years. Our sun is just an ordinary, average-sized, yellow star, near the inner edge of one of the spiral arms. We have certainly come a long way since Aristotle and Ptolemy, when we thought that the earth was the centre of the universe!" [66]

(65) T. Ferris, op. cit., p. 204.
(66) S.W. Hawking, *A Brief History of Time, From the Big Bang to Black Holes*, p. 34.

In point of fact, the very large quantities of matter mentioned here give no real idea of the amount of matter in the universe. New galaxies and super-clusters are being discovered all the time, and there is no end to this process. We may have come a long way since Aristotle in some respects. But in others, it seems that we are far, far behind him. Aristotle would never have made the mistake of talking about a time before time existed, or claiming that the entire universe was, in effect, *created from nothing*. In order to find ideas like these one would have to go back several thousand years to the world of the Judaic-Babylonian creation myth.

Whenever someone attempts to protest against these proceedings, he is instantly ushered into the presence of the great Albert Einstein, as a naughty schoolboy is dragged to the headmaster's study, and given a stern lecture on the need to show greater respect to general relativity, informed that one cannot argue with mathematical theorems, and sent home duly chastened. The main difference is that most headmasters are alive, and Einstein is dead, and therefore unable to comment on this particular interpretation of his theories. In fact, one would look in vain in all the writings of Einstein for any reference to the big bang, black holes and the like. Einstein himself, although he initially tended towards philosophical idealism, was implacably opposed to mysticism in science. He spent the last decades of his life fighting against the subjective idealist views of Heisenberg and Bohr, and, in fact, moved close to a materialist position. He would certainly have been horrified that mystical conclusions should be drawn from his theories. The following is a good example:

"All of the Friedmann solutions have the feature that at some time in the past (between ten and twenty thousand million years ago) the distance between neighbouring galaxies must have been zero. At that time, which we call the big bang, the density of the universe and the curvature of space-time would have been infinite. Because mathematics cannot really handle infinite numbers, this means that the general theory of relativity (on which Friedmann's solutions are based) predicts that there is a point in the universe where the theory itself breaks down. Such a point is an example of what mathematicians call a singularity. In fact, all our theories of science are formulated on the assumption that space-time is smooth and nearly flat, so they break down at the big bang singularity, where the curvature of space-time is infinite. This means that even if there were events before the big bang, one could not use them to determine what would happen afterward, because predictability would break down at the big bang. Correspondingly, if, as is the case, we know only what has happened since the big bang, we could not determine what happened beforehand. As far as we are concerned, events before the big bang can have no consequences, so they should therefore cut them out of the model and say that time had a beginning at the big bang."

Passages such as this forcefully remind one of the intellectual gymnastics of the Medieval Schoolmen, arguing about the number of angels who could dance on the end of a pin. This is not meant as an insult. If the validity of an argument is determined by its *internal consistency*, then the arguments of the Schoolmen were as valid as this. They were not fools, but highly skilled logicians and mathematicians, who erected theoretical constructs as elaborate and perfect in their way as medieval cathedrals. All that was necessary was to accept their premises, and everything fell into place. The problem is whether the original premise is valid or not. This is a general problem with all mathematics, and its central weakness. And this entire theory leans very heavily on mathematics.

"At the time which we call the big bang..." But if there was *no time*, how can we refer to it as "a time" at all? Time is said to have *begun* at that point. So what was there before time? A time when there was no time! The self-contradictory nature of this idea is glaringly obvious. Time and space are the mode of existence of matter. If there was neither time, nor space, nor matter, what was there? Energy? But energy, as Einstein explains, is just another manifestation of matter. A force field? But a force field is also energy, so the difficulty remains. The only way that time can be got rid of is if before the big bang there was—*nothing*.

The problem is: how is it possible to get from nothing to something? If one is religiously minded, there is no problem; God created the universe from nothing. This is the doctrine of the Catholic Church, of Creation *ex nihilo*. Hawking is uncomfortably aware of this fact, as he says in the very next line:

"Many people do not like the idea that time has a beginning, probably because it smacks of divine intervention. (The Catholic Church, on the other hand, seized on the big bang model and in 1951 officially pronounced it to be in accordance with the Bible.)"

Hawking himself does not want to accept this conclusion. But it is unavoidable. The whole mess arises out of a philosophically incorrect concept of time. Einstein was partly responsible for this, since he appeared to introduce a subjective element by confusing the measurement of time with time itself. Here again the reaction against the old mechanical physics of Newton has been carried to an extreme. The question is not whether time is "relative" or "absolute". The central issue to be addressed is whether time is *objective* or *subjective*; whether time is the mode of existence of matter or an entirely subjective concept existing in the mind and determined by the observer. Hawking clearly adopts a subjective view of time, when he writes:

"Newton's laws of motion put an end to the idea of absolute position in space. The theory of relativity gets rid of absolute time. Consider a pair of twins. Suppose that one twin goes to live on the top of a mountain while the other stays at sea level. The first twin would age faster than the second. Thus, if they met again, one would be older than the other. In this case, the difference in ages would be very small, but it would be much larger if one of the twins went for a long trip in a spaceship at nearly the speed of light. When he returned he would be much younger than the one who stayed on Earth. This is known as the twins paradox, but it is a paradox only if one has the idea of absolute time at the back of one's mind. In the theory of relativity there is no unique absolute measure of time that depends on where he is and how he is moving." [67]

That there is a subjective element in the measurement of time is not in dispute. We measure time according to a definite frame of reference, which can, and does, vary from one place to another. The time in London is different from the time in Sydney or New York. But this does not mean that time is purely subjective. The objective processes in the universe take place whether we are able to measure them or not. Time, space, and motion are objective to matter, and have no beginning and no end.

Here it is interesting to note what Engels had to say on the subject:

"Let us continue. So time had a beginning. What was there before this beginning? The universe, which was then in a self-identical, unchanging state. And as no changes succeed one another in this state, the more specialised idea of time transforms itself into the more general idea of *being*. In the first place, we are not in the least concerned here with what concepts change in Herr Dühring's head. The subject at issue is not the *concept of time*, but *real* time, which Herr Dühring will by no means rid himself of so cheaply. In the second place, however much the concept of time may be converted into the more general idea of being, this takes us not one step further. For the basic forms of all being are space and time, and being out of time is just as gross an absurdity as being out of space.

"The Hegelian 'timelessly past being' and the neo-Schellingian 'unpreconceivable being' are rational ideas compared with this being out of time. For this reason Herr Dühring sets to work very cautiously; actually it is of course time, but of such a kind as cannot really be called time; time does not in itself consist of real parts, and is only divided up arbitrarily by our understanding—only an actual filling of time with differentiable facts is susceptible of being counted—what the accumulation of empty duration means is quite unimaginable. What this accumulation is supposed to mean is immaterial here; the question is whether the world, in the state assumed here, has duration, passes through a duration in time. We have long known that we can get nothing by measuring such a duration without content, just as we can get nothing by measuring without aim or purpose in empty space; and Hegel calls this infinity *bad* precisely because of the tedium of this procedure." [68]

Do singularities exist?

A black hole and a singularity are not the same thing. There is nothing in principle that excludes the possible existence of stellar black holes, in the sense of a massive collapsed star where the force of gravity is so immense that not even light can escape from its surface. Even the idea is not new. It was predicted in the 18th cen-

(67) Hawking, op. cit., pp. 46-7 and 33.
(68) Engels, *Anti-Dühring*, pp. 64-5.

tury by John Mitchell who pointed out that a sufficiently massive star would trap light. He came to this conclusion on the basis of Newton's classical theory of gravitation. General relativity did not enter into it.

However, the theory advanced by Hawking and Penrose goes far beyond the observed facts, and, as we have seen, draws conclusions that lend themselves to all kinds of mysticism, even if this was not their intention. Eric Lerner considers the case for supermassive black holes at the centre of galaxies to be weak. Together with Anthony Peratt, he has shown how all the features associated with these supermassive black holes, quasars, etc., can be better explained by electromagnetic phenomena. However, he believes the evidence is considerably stronger for the existence of stellar sized black holes since this rests on detecting very intense X-ray sources which are too big to be neutron stars. But even here the observations are far from proving the case.

The abstractions of mathematics are useful tools for understanding the universe, on one condition: that we do not lose sight of the fact that even the best mathematical model is only a rough approximation of reality. The problems start when people begin confusing the model with the thing itself. Hawking himself unwittingly reveals the weakness of this method in the passage already quoted. He *assumes* that the density of the universe at the point of the big bang was infinite, without giving any reasons for this, and then adds, in a most peculiar line of argument, that "because mathematics cannot really handle infinite numbers" the theory of relativity breaks down at this point. To this, it is necessary to add, "and all the known laws of physics", since it is not only general relativity which breaks down with the big bang, but all of science. It is not just that we do not know what occurred before this. It is that we *cannot* know.

This is a return to Kant's theory of the unknowable Thing-in-Itself. In the past, it was the role of religion and certain idealist philosophers, like Hume and Kant, to place a limit upon human understanding. Science was permitted to go so far, and no further. At the point where human intelligence was not allowed to proceed, mysticism, religion and irrationality commenced. Yet the whole history of science is the story of how one barrier after another was removed. What was supposed to be unknowable for one generation became an open book for the next. The whole of science is based on the notion that the universe can be known. Now, for the first time, scientists are placing limits on knowledge, an extraordinary state of affairs and a sad comment on the present situation in theoretical physics and cosmology.

Consider the implications of the above passage: a) since the laws of science, including general relativity (which is supposed to provide the basis for the whole theory) break down at the big bang, it is impossible to know what, if anything, occurred before it, b) even if there were events before the big bang, they have no relevance to what happened afterwards, c) we cannot know anything about it, and so, d) we should simply "cut it out of the model and say that time began at the big bang."

The self-assurance with which these assertions are put forward is truly breath-taking. We are asked to accept an absolute limit on our ability to understand the most fundamental problems in cosmology, in effect, to ask no questions (because all questions about the time before there was time are meaningless) and that we should just accept without more ado that time began with the big bang. In this way, Stephen Hawking simply assumes what has to be proved. In the same way, the theologians assert that God created the universe, and when asked who created God, merely answer that such questions are beyond the minds of mortals. On one thing we can agree, however; the whole thing does indeed "smack of divine intervention". More than that, it necessarily implies it.

In his polemic against Dühring, Engels points out that it is impossible that motion should arise out of immobility, that *something* should arise out of *nothing*: "Without an act of Creation we can never get from nothing to something, even if the something were as small as a mathematical differential." [69] Hawking's principal defence seems to be that the alternative theory to the big bang, put forward by Fred Hoyle, Thomas Gold and Hermann Bondi—the so-called Steady State theory—was shown to be false. From the standpoint of dialectical materialism, there was never anything to choose between these two theories. One was as bad as the other. Indeed the Steady State theory, which suggested that matter was being continuously creat-ed in space out of nothing, was, if possible, even more mystical than its rival. The very fact that such an idea could be taken seriously by scientists is itself a damning comment on the philosophical confusion that has bedevilled science for so long.

The ancients already understood that "out of nothing comes nothing". This fact is expressed in one of the most fundamental laws of physics, the law of the conser-vation of energy. Hoyle's claim that only a very small amount was involved makes no difference. It is a bit like the naïve young lady who, in order to placate her irate father who found out she was going to have a baby, assured him that it was "only a little one". Not even the tiniest particle of matter (or energy, which is the same) can ever be created or destroyed, and therefore the Steady State theory was doomed from the outset.

Penrose's theory of a "singularity" was originally nothing to do with the origin of the universe. It merely predicted that a star collapsing under its own gravity would be trapped in a region whose surface eventually shrinks to zero size. In 1970, however, he and Hawking produced a joint paper in which they claimed to prove that the big bang itself was such a "singularity", provided only that "general relativ-ity is correct and the universe contains as much matter as we observe."

"There was a lot of opposition to our work, partly from the Russians because of their Marxist belief in scientific determinism, and partly from people who felt that the whole idea of singularities was repugnant and spoiled the beauty of Einstein's

(69) Engels, *Anti-Dühring*, p. 68.

theory. However, one cannot really argue with a mathematical theorem. So in the end our work became generally accepted and nowadays nearly everyone assumes that the universe started with a big bang singularity."

General relativity has proved a very powerful tool, but every theory has its limits, and one has the impression that it is being pushed to the limit here. How long it will be before it is replaced by a broader and more comprehensive set of ideas it is impossible to say, but it is clear that this particular application of it has led to a blind alley. As far as the amount of matter in the universe is concerned, the total amount will never be known, because it has no limit. Typically, they are so wrapped up in mathematical equations, that they forget reality. In practice, the equations have replaced reality.

Having succeeded in convincing a lot of people, on the basis that "one cannot really argue with a mathematical theorem," Hawking then proceeded to have second thoughts: "It is perhaps ironic," he says, "that, having changed my mind, I am now trying to convince other physicists that there was in fact no singularity at the beginning of the universe—as we shall see later, it can disappear once quantum effects are taken into account." The arbitrary nature of the whole method is shown in Hawking's extraordinary change of mind. He now says there is no singularity in the big bang. Why? What has changed? There is no more actual evidence than before. These twists and turns all take place in the world of mathematical abstractions.

Hawking's theory of black holes represents an extension of the idea of singularity to particular parts of the universe. It is full of the most contradictory and mystical elements. Take the following passage, which describes the extraordinary scenario of an astronaut falling into a black hole:

"The work that Roger Penrose and I did between 1965 and 1970 showed that, according to general relativity, there must be a singularity of infinite density and space-time curvature within a black hole. This is rather like the big bang at the beginning of time, only it would be an end of time for the collapsing body and the astronaut. At this singularity the laws of science and our ability to predict the future would break down. However, any observer who remained outside the black hole would not be affected by this failure of predictability, because neither light nor any other signal could reach him from the singularity. This remarkable fact led Roger Penrose to propose the cosmic censorship hypothesis, which might be paraphrased as 'God abhors a naked singularity'. In other words, the singularities produced by gravitational collapse occur only in places, like black holes, where they are decently hidden from outside view by an event horizon. Strictly, this is what is known as the weak cosmic censorship hypothesis: it protects observers who remain outside the black hole from the consequences of the breakdown of predictability that occurs at the singularity, but it does nothing at all for the poor unfortunate astronaut who falls into the hole." [70]

(70) Hawking, op. cit., pp. 50 and 88-9.

What sense can one make of this? Not content with the beginning (and end) of time for the universe as a whole, Penrose and Hawking now discover numerous parts of the universe where time has already ended! It has now been demonstrated that black holes exist (probably the remnants of massive collapsed stars), and contain tremendous concentrations of matter and gravity. But it seems extremely doubtful that this gravitational collapse could ever reach the point of a singularity, much less remain in this state forever. Long before this point was reached, such a tremendous concentration of matter and energy would result in a massive explosion.

The entire universe is proof that the process of change is never-ending, at all levels. Vast tracts of the universe may be expanding, while others are contracting. Long periods of apparent equilibrium are disrupted by violent explosions, like supernovas, which in turn provide the raw material for the formation of new galaxies, which goes on all the time. There is no disappearance or creation of matter, but only its continuous, restless change from one state to another. There can therefore be no question of the "end of time" inside a black hole, or anywhere else.

An empty abstraction

The whole mystical notion derives from the subjectivist interpretation of time, which makes it dependent on ("relative to") an observer. But time is an objective phenomenon, which is independent of any observer. The need to introduce the unfortunate astronaut into the picture does not arise from any scientific necessity, but is the product of a definite philosophical point of view, smuggled in under the banner of "relativity theory". You see, for time to be "real", it needs an *observer*, who can then interpret it from his or her point of view. Presumably, if there is no observer, there is no time! In a most peculiar piece of reasoning, this observer is protected against the malign influence of the black hole, by an arbitrary hypothesis, a "weak cosmic censorship", whatever that might mean. Inside the hole, however, there is no time at all. So outside, time exists, but a little distance away, time does not exit. At the boundary between the two states, we have the mysterious *event horizon*, the nature of which is shrouded in obscurity.

At least, it would appear that we must abandon all hope of ever understanding what goes on beyond the event horizon, since, to quote Hawking, it is "decently hidden from outside view." Here we have the 20th century equivalent of the Kantian Thing-in-Itself. And, like the Thing-in-Itself, it turns out to be not so difficult to understand after all. What we have here is a mystical idealist view of time and space, fed into a mathematical model, and mistaken for something real.

Time and space are the most fundamental properties of matter. More correctly, they are the mode of existence of matter. Kant already pointed out that, if we leave aside all the physical properties of matter, we are left with time and space. But this is, in fact, an empty abstraction. Time and space can no more exist separately from the physical properties of matter than one can consume "fruit" in general, as opposed to apples and oranges, or make love to Womankind. The accusation has been levelled against Marx without the slightest justification that he conceived of History as taking place without the conscious participation of men and women, as a result of Economic Forces, or some nonsense of the sort. In fact, Marx states quite clearly that History can do nothing, and that men and women make their own history, although they do not do so entirely according to their own "free will".

Hawking, Penrose and many others are guilty precisely of the mistake that was falsely attributed to Marx. Instead of the empty abstraction History, which is, in effect, personified, and endowed with a life and a will of its own, we have the equally empty abstraction Time, envisaged as an independent entity which is born and dies, and generally gets up to all kinds of tricks, along with its friend, Space, which arises and collapses and bends, a bit like a cosmic drunkard, and ends up swallowing hapless astronauts in black holes.

Now this kind of thing is fine in science fiction, but is not very useful as a means of understanding the universe. Clearly, there are immense practical difficulties in obtaining precise information about, say, neutron stars. In a sense, in relation to the universe, we find ourselves in a position roughly analogous to early humans in relation to natural phenomena. Lacking adequate information, we seek a rational explanation of difficult and obscure things. We are thrown back on our own resources— the mind and the imagination. Things seem mysterious when they are not understood. In order to understand, it is necessary to make hypotheses. Some of these will be found to be wrong. That in itself presents no problem. The whole history of science is full of examples where the pursuit of an incorrect hypothesis led to important discoveries.

However, we have a duty to attempt to ensure that hypotheses have a reasonably rational character. Here the study of philosophy becomes indispensable. Do we really have to go back to primitive myths and religion in order to make sense of the universe? Do we need to revive the discredited notions of idealism, which, in fact, are closely related to the former? Is it really necessary to re-invent the wheel? "One cannot argue with a mathematical theorem." Maybe not. But it is certainly possible to argue with false philosophical premises, and an idealist interpretation of time, which leads us to conclusions like the following:

"There are some solutions of the equations of general relativity in which it is possible for our astronaut to see a naked singularity: he may be able to avoid hitting the singularity and instead fall through a 'wormhole' and come out in another region of the universe. This would offer great possibilities for travel in space and time, but unfortunately it seems that these solutions may all be highly unstable; the least disturbance, such as the presence of an astronaut, may change them so that the astronaut could not see the singularity until he hit it and his time came to an end. In other words, the singularity would always lie in his future and never in his past. The strong version of the cosmic censorship hypothesis states that in a realistic solution, the singularities would always lie either entirely in the future (like the singularities of gravitational collapse) or entirely in the past (like the big bang). It is greatly to be hoped that some version of the censorship hypothesis holds because close to naked singularities it may be possible to travel into the past. While this would be fine for writers of science fiction, it would mean that no one's life would ever be safe: someone might go into the past and kill your father or mother before you were conceived!" [71]

"Time-travel" belongs to the pages of science fiction, where it can be a source of harmless amusement. But we are convinced that nobody ought to be afraid that their existence may be put at risk by some inconsiderate time-traveller doing away with their granny. Frankly, one only has to pose the question to realise that it is a patent absurdity. Time moves in only one direction, from past to future, and cannot be reversed. Whatever our friend the astronaut might find at the bottom of a black hole, he will not find that time has been reversed, or "stands still" (except in the sense that, since he would instantly be torn to pieces by the force of gravity, time would cease *for him*, along with a lot of other things).

We have already commented on the tendency to confuse science with science fiction. It is also noticeable that much of science fiction itself is permeated with a semi-religious, mystical and idealist spirit. Long ago, Engels pointed out that scientists who despised philosophy frequently fall victim to all kinds of mysticism. He wrote an article on the subject entitled *Natural Science and the Spirit World*, from which the following extract is taken:

"This school prevails in England. Its father, the much lauded Francis Bacon, already advanced the demand that his new empirical, inductive method should be pursued to attain, above all, by its means: longer life, rejuvenation—to a certain extent, alteration of stature and features, transformation of one body into another, the production of new species, power over the air and the production of storms. He complains that such investigations have been abandoned, and in his natural history he gives definite recipes for making gold and performing various miracles. Similarly Isaac Newton in his old age greatly busied himself with expounding the Revelation of St. John. So it is not to be wondered at if in recent years English empiricism in the person of some of its representatives—and not the worst of them—should seem to have fallen a hopeless victim to the spirit-rapping and spirit-seeing imported from America." [72]

There is no doubt that Stephen Hawking and Roger Penrose are brilliant scientists and mathematicians. The problem is that, if you begin with a wrong premise, you will inevitably draw the wrong conclusions. Hawking clearly feels uncomfortable with the idea that religious conclusions can be drawn from his theories. He mentions that in 1981 he attended a conference on cosmology in the Vatican, organised by the Jesuits, and comments:

(71) Hawking, op. cit., p. 89.
(72) Engels, *The Dialectics of Nature*, pp. 68-9.

"The Catholic Church had made a bad mistake with Galileo when it tried to lay down the law on a question of science, declaring that the sun went round the earth. Now, centuries later, it had decided to invite a number of experts to advise it on cosmology. At the end of the conference the participants were granted an audience with the Pope. He told us that it was all right to study the evolution of the universe after the big bang, but we should not inquire into the big bang itself because that was the moment of Creation and therefore the work of God. I was glad then that he did not know the subject of the talk I had just given at the conference—the possibility that space-time was finite but had no boundary, which means that it had no beginning, no moment of Creation. I had no desire to share the fate of Galileo, with whom I feel a strong sense of identity, partly because of the coincidence of having been born exactly 300 years after his death!" [73]

Clearly, Hawking wishes to draw a line between himself and the Creationists. But the attempt is not very successful. How can the universe be finite, and yet have no boundaries? In mathematics, it is possible to have an infinite series of numbers which starts with one. But in practice, the idea of infinity cannot begin with one, or any other number. Infinity is not a mathematical concept. It cannot be counted. This one-sided "infinity" is what Hegel calls *bad infinity*. Engels deals with this question in his polemic with Dühring:

"But what of the contradiction of 'the counted infinite numerical series'? We shall be in a position to examine it more closely a soon as Herr Dühring has performed the clever trick of *counting it* for us. When he has completed the task of counting from $-\infty$ (minus infinity) to 0, let him come again. It is certainly obvious that, wherever he begins to count, he will leave behind him an infinite series and, with it, the task which he has to fulfil. Just let him invert his own infinite series $1+2+3+4\ldots$ and try to count from the infinite end back to 1; it would obviously only be attempted by a man who has not the faintest understanding of what the problem is. Still more. When Herr Dühring asserts that the infinite series of lapsed time has been counted, he is thereby asserting that time has a beginning; for otherwise he would have been unable to start 'counting' at all. Once again, therefore, he smuggles into the argument, as a premise, what he has to prove. The idea of an infinite series which has been counted, in other words, the world-encompassing Dühringian Law of Determinate Number, is therefore a *contradiction in adjecto*, contains within itself a contradiction, and indeed an *absurd* contradiction.

"It is clear that an infinity which has an end but no beginning is neither more nor less infinite than one with a beginning but no end. The slightest dialectical insight should have told Herr Dühring that beginning and end necessarily belong together, like the North Pole and the South Pole, and that if the end is left out, the beginning just becomes the end—the *one* end which the series has; and vice versa. The whole deception would be impossible but for the mathematical usage of working with infinite series. Because in mathematics it is necessary to start from determinate, finite terms in order to reach the indeterminate, the infinite, all mathematical series, positive or negative, must start with 1, or they cannot be used for calculation. But the logical need of the mathematician is far from being a compulsory law for the real world." [74]

Stephen Hawking carried this relativistic speculation to an extreme with his work on black holes, which leads us right into the realms of science fiction. In an attempt to get round the awkward question of what happened before the big bang, the idea was advanced of "baby universes", coming into existence all the time, and connected by so-called wormholes. As Lerner ironically comments: "It is a vision that seems to beg for some form of cosmic birth control." [75] It really is astounding that sober scientists could take such grotesque ideas for good coin.

The idea of a "finite universe with no boundaries" is yet another mathematical abstraction, which does not correspond to the reality of an eternal and infinite, constantly changing universe. Once we adopt this standpoint, there is no need for mystical speculations about "wormholes", singularities, superstrings, and all the rest of it. An infinite universe does not require us to look for a beginning or an end, only to trace the endless process of movement, change and development. This dialectical conception leaves no room for Heaven or Hell, God or the Devil, Creation or the Last Judgement. The same cannot be said for Hawking who, quite predictably, ends up attempting to "know the mind of God".

The reactionaries rub their hands at this spectacle, and use the prevailing current of obscurantism in science for their own ends. William Rees-Mogg, big business consultant, and James D. Davidson write:

"We think it is extremely likely that the religious movement we see at work in many societies across the globe will be strengthened if we go through a very difficult economic period. Religion will be strengthened because the current thrust of science no longer undermines the religious perception of reality. Indeed, for the first time in centuries, it actually buttresses it." [76]

Thoughts in a vacuum

> "Why, sometimes, I've believed as many as six
> impossible things before breakfast." (Lewis Carroll)
> "With men this is impossible;
> but with God all things are possible." (Matthew, 19:26)
> "Nothing can be created out of nothing." (Lucretius)

(74) Engels, *Anti-Dühring*, pp. 62-3.
(75) Lerner, op. cit., p. 161.
(76) W. Rees-Mogg and J. Davidson, *The Great Reckoning: How the World Will Change in the Depression of the 1990s*, p. 447.

Just before finishing writing this book, we came across the latest contribution to cosmology of the big bang, which appeared in *The New Scientist* on the 25th of February 1995. In an article by Robert Matthews entitled *Nothing like a Vacuum*, we read the following:

"It is all around you, yet you cannot feel it. It is the source of everything, yet is nothing."

What is this amazing thing? A *vacuum*. What is a vacuum? The Latin word *vacuus*, from which it comes, means quite simply *empty*. The dictionary defines it as "space empty, or devoid of all matter or content; any space unoccupied or unfilled; a void, blank." This was the case up till now. But not any longer. The humble vacuum, in Mr. Matthews' words, has become "one of the hottest topics in contemporary physics."

"It is proving to be a wonderland of magical effects: force fields that emerge from nowhere, particles popping in and out of existence and energetic jitterings with no apparent power source."

Thanks to Heisenberg and Einstein (poor Einstein!), we have the "astonishing realisation that all around us 'virtual' subatomic particles are perpetually popping up out of nothing, and then disappearing again within about 10^{-23} seconds. 'Empty space' is thus not really empty at all, but a seething sea of activity that pervades the entire Universe." This is true and false. It is true that the whole universe is pervaded by matter and energy, and that "empty space" is not really empty, but full of particles, radiation and force-fields. It is true that particles are constantly changing, and that some have a life so fleeting that they are called "virtual" particles. There is absolutely nothing "astonishing" about these ideas, which were known decades ago. But it is entirely untrue that they pop "out of *nothing*". We have already dealt with this misconception above, and it is not necessary to repeat what was said.

Like an old record with a repeating groove, those who wish to introduce idealism into physics constantly harp on the idea that you can get something from nothing. This idea contradicts all the known laws of physics, including quantum physics. Yet we find here the incredible notion that energy can be obtained literally from nothing! This is like the attempts to discover *perpetual motion*, which were rightly ridiculed in the past.

Modern physics begins with the rejection of the old idea of the *ether*, an invisible universal medium, through which light waves were thought to travel. Einstein's theory of special relativity proved that light could travel through a vacuum, and did not require any special medium. Incredibly, after citing Einstein as an authority (as obligatory nowadays as crossing yourself before leaving church, and about as meaningful) Mr. Matthews proceeds to smuggle the ether back into physics:

"This does not mean that a universal fluid cannot exist, but it does mean that such a fluid must conform to the dictates of special relativity. The vacuum is not forced to be mere quantum fluctuations around an average state of true nothingness. It can be a permanent, non-zero source of energy in the Universe."

Now what precisely is one supposed to make of this? So far we have been told about "astonishing" new developments in physics, "wonderlands" of particles and have been assured that vacuums possess enough energy to solve all our needs. But the actual information provided by the article does not seem to say anything new. It is very long on assertions, but very short on facts. Perhaps it was the author's intention to make up for this by obscurity of expression. What is meant by a "*permanent non-zero source of energy*" is anyone's guess. And what is an "*average state of true nothingness*"? If what is meant is a true vacuum, then it would have been preferable to use two clear words instead of four unclear ones. This kind of deliberate obscurity is generally used to cover up muddled thinking, especially in this area. Why not speak plainly? Unless, of course, what is involved is a "true nothingness"—of content.

The whole thrust of the article is to show that a vacuum derives unlimited quantities of energy from nowhere. The only "proof" for this is a couple of references to the special and general theories of relativity, which are regularly used as a peg upon which to hang any arbitrary hypothesis. "Special relativity demands that the vacuum's properties must appear the same for all observers, whatever their speed. For this to be true it turns out that the pressure of the vacuum 'sea' must exactly cancel out its energy density. It is a condition that sounds harmless enough, but it has some astounding consequences. It means, for example, that a given region of vacuum energy retains the same energy density, no matter how much the region expands. This is odd, to say the least. Compare it with the behaviour of an ordinary gas, whose energy density decreases as its volume increases. It is as if the vacuum can draw on a constant reservoir of energy."

In the first place, we note that what was only a hypothetical "universal fluid" a couple of sentences ago has now become transformed into an *actual* vacuum "sea", though where all the "water" came from, nobody is quite sure. This is odd to say the least. But leave it there. Let us, like the author, assume what was to be proved, and accept the existence of this vast ocean of nothingness. It turns out that this "nothing" is now not only *something*, but a very substantial "something". As if by magic, it is filled with energy from a "constant reservoir". This is the cosmological equivalent of the *cornucopia*, the "horn of plenty" of Greek and Irish mythology, a mysterious drinking horn or cauldron that, however much one drank from it, was never empty. This was a gift from the gods. Now Mr. Matthews wishes to present us with something that makes this look like child's play.

If energy enters a vacuum, it must come from somewhere outside the vacuum. This is plain enough, since a vacuum cannot exist in isolation from matter and energy. The idea of empty space without matter is as nonsensical as the idea of matter without space. There is no such thing as a perfect vacuum on earth. The nearest thing to a perfect vacuum is space. But in point of fact, space is not empty, either. Decades ago, Hannes Alfvén pointed out that space was alive with networks of electrical currents and magnetic fields filled with plasma filaments. This is not the results of speculation or appeals to relativity theory, but is borne out by observation, including those of the *Voyager* and *Pioneer* spacecrafts that detected these currents and filaments around Jupiter, Saturn and Uranus.

So there is, indeed, plenty of energy in space. But not the kind of energy Mr. Matthews is talking about. Not a bit of it. Having established his "vacuum sea" he means to get his energy *directly from the vacuum*. No matter required! This is much better than the conjurer who pulls a rabbit out of a hat. After all, we all know the rabbit actually comes from somewhere. This energy comes from nowhere at all. It comes from a vacuum, by courtesy of the general theory of relativity: "One of the key features of Einstein's general relativity theory is that mass is not the only source of gravitation. In particular, pressure, both positive and negative can also give rise to gravitational effects."

By this point, the reader is thoroughly mystified. Now, however, all becomes clear (almost). "This feature of the vacuum," we are now told, "lies at the heart of perhaps the most important new concept in cosmology of the past decade: cosmic inflation. Developed principally by Alan Guth at MIT and Andrei Linde, now at Stanford, the idea of cosmic inflation arises from the assumption that the very early Universe was packed with unstable vacuum energy whose 'antigravitational' effect expanded the Universe by a factor of perhaps 10^{50} in just 10^{-32} seconds. The vacuum energy died away, leaving random fluctuations whose energy turned into heat. Because energy and matter are interchangeable, the result was the matter creation we now call the big bang."

So that's it! The whole arbitrary construction is meant to back up the inflationary theory of the big bang. As always, they move the goalposts continually, in order to prop up their hypothesis at all costs. It is like the supporters of the old Aristotle-Ptolemaic theory of the crystal spheres, which they continually revised, making it ever more complicated, in order to fit the facts. As we have seen, the theory has been having a bad time lately, what with the missing "cold dark matter" and the unholy mess about the Hubble constant. Badly in need of a little support, its supporters have obviously looked round for some explanation to one of the central problems of the theory—where did all the energy come from to cause the inflationary big bang. "The biggest free lunch of all time," Alan Guth called it. Now they want to pass the bill to somebody, or something, and come up with—a vacuum. We doubt whether this particular bill will ever be paid. And, in the real world, people who don't pay their bills are usually unceremoniously shown the door, even if they offer to produce the general theory of relativity in lieu of cash.

"From nothing, through nothing, to nothing," said Hegel. That is a fitting epitaph for the theory of inflation. There is actually only one way of getting something from nothing—by an act of Creation. And that is only possible through the intervention of a Creator. Try as they will, the supporters of the big bang will find that their footsteps will always lead them in this direction. Some will go quite happily, others protesting that they are not religious "in the conventional sense". But the movement back to mysticism is the inevitable consequence of this modern creation myth. Fortunately, an increasing number of people are becoming dissatisfied with this state of affairs. Sooner or later, a breakthrough will occur at the level of observation that will enable a new theory to emerge, allowing the big bang to be laid decently to rest. The sooner the better.

The origins of the solar system

Space is not really empty. A perfect vacuum does not exist in nature. Space is filled by a thin gas—"interstellar gas" first detected in 1904 by Hartmann. The concentrations of gas and dust become much greater and denser in the neighbourhood of galaxies, which are surrounded by "fog", mostly composed of atoms of hydrogen, ionised by radiation from the stars. Even this matter is not inert and lifeless, but is broken up into electrically-charged subatomic particles, subject to all kinds of movement, processes and change. These atoms occasionally collide and can change their energy state. Though an individual atom might only collide once every 11 million years, given the vast numbers involved, it is enough to give rise to a continuous and detectable emission, the "song of hydrogen", first detected in 1951.

Almost all of this is hydrogen, but there is also deuterium, a more complex form of hydrogen, oxygen and helium. It might seem impossible that combination should occur, given the extremely sparse distribution of these elements in space. But occur it does, and to a remarkable degree of complexity. The water molecule (H_2O), was found in space, as was that of ammonia (NH_3), followed by formaldehyde (H_2CO), and even more complex molecules, giving rise to a new science—astrochemistry. Finally, it has been proved that the basic molecules of life itself—*amino acids*—exist in space.

Kant (in 1755) and Laplace (in 1796) first advanced the nebular hypothesis of the formation of the solar system. According to this, the sun and planets were formed out of the condensation of an immense cloud of matter. This seemed to fit the facts, and, by the time Engels wrote *The Dialectics of Nature*, it was generally accepted. In 1900, however, Thomas C. Chamberlain and Forest Ray Moulton put forward an alternative theory—the planetesimal hypothesis. This was further developed by British scientists Sir James Hopwood Jeans and Sir Harold Jeffreys, who advanced the tidal hypothesis in 1918. This involved the idea that the solar system originated as a result of a collision of two stars. The problem with this theory is that, if it were true, planetary systems would be extremely rare phenomena. The vast distances separating stars mean that such collisions are 10,000 times less common than supernovae—themselves far from common occurrences. Once again, we see that, by attempting to solve a problem by resorting to an accidental external source like a stray star, we create more problems than we solve.

Eventually, the theory that was supposed to have displaced the Kant-Laplace model was shown to be mathematically unsound. Other attempts, like the "three-star collision" (Littleton) and Hoyle's supernova theory, were also ruled out in 1939, when it was proved that the material drawn from the sun in such a way would be too hot to condense into planets. It would merely expand into a thin gas. Thus, the catastrophe-planetesimal theory was overthrown. The nebular hypothesis has been reinstated, but on a higher level than before. It is not merely a repetition of the ideas of Kant and Laplace. For instance, it is now understood that the clouds of dust and gas envisaged in the model would have to be much bigger than they thought. On such huge scales, the cloud would experience *turbulence*, creating vast eddies, which would then condense into separate systems. This perfectly dialectical model was developed in 1944 by the German astronomer Carl F. von Weizsäcker, and perfected by the Swedish astrophysicist, Hannes Alfvén.

Weizsäcker calculated that there would be sufficient matter in the largest eddies to create galaxies in the process of a turbulent contraction, giving rise to sub-eddies. Each of these could produce solar systems and planets. Hannes Alfvén made a special study of the magnetic field of the sun. In the early stages, the sun was spinning at a great speed, but was eventually slowed down by its magnetic field. This passed on angular momentum to the planets. The new version of the Kant-Laplace theory, as developed by Alfvén and Weizsäcker, is now generally accepted as the most likely version of the origins of the solar system.

The birth and death of stars constitute a further example of the dialectical workings of nature. Before it runs out of nuclear fuel, the star experiences a prolonged period of peaceful evolution lasting millions of years. But on reaching the critical point, it experiences a violent end, collapsing under its own weight in less than a second. In the process, it gives off a colossal amount of energy in the form of light, emitting more in a few months than the sun emits in a billion years. Yet this light represents only a small fraction of the total energy of a supernova. The kinetic energy of the explosion is ten times greater. Perhaps ten times more than the latter is carried away in the form of neutrinos, emitted in a split-second flash. Most of the star's mass is scattered into space. Such a supernova explosion in the vicinity of the Milky Way hurled forth its mass, reduced to nuclear ashes, containing a large variety of elements. The earth and all that is in it, ourselves included, is entirely composed of this recycled stardust, the iron in our blood being a typical sample of recycled cosmic debris.

These cosmic revolutions, like the earthly variety, are rare events. In our own galaxy, only three supernovas have been recorded over the past 1000 years. The brightest of these, noted by Chinese observers in 1054, produced the Crab Nebula. Moreover, the classification of stars has led to the conclusion that there is no new kind of matter in the universe. The same matter exists everywhere. The main features of the spectra of all stars can be accounted for in terms of substances that exist on earth. The development of infrared astronomy provided the means of exploring the interior of dark interstellar clouds, which are probably where most new stars are formed. Radio astronomy has begun to reveal the composition of these clouds—mainly hydrogen and dust, but with an admixture of some surprisingly complex molecules, many of them organic.

And so the birth of our solar system some 4.6 billion years ago developed out of a cloud of shattered debris of a now extinct star. The present sun coalesced at the centre of the revolving flat cloud, whereas the planets developed at different points encircling the sun. It is believed that the outer planets—Jupiter, Saturn, Uranus and Pluto—are a sample of the original cloud: hydrogen, helium, methane, ammonia and water. The smaller inner planets—Mercury, Venus, Earth and Mars—are richer in heavier elements and poorer in gases like helium and neon, which were able to escape their weaker gravities.

Aristotle thought that everything on earth was perishable, but that the heavens themselves were changeless and immortal. Now we know differently. As we gaze with wonder at the immensity of the night sky, we know that every one of these heavenly bodies that light up the darkness will one day be extinguished. Not only mortal men and women, but the stars themselves that bear the names of Gods experience the agony and the ecstasy of change, birth and death. And, in some strange way, this knowledge brings us closer to the great universe of nature, from which we came and to which we must one day return. Our sun has at present enough hydrogen to last for billions of years in its present state. Eventually, however, it will increase its temperature to the point where life on earth will become impossible. All individual beings must perish, but the wonderful diversity of the material universe in all its myriad manifestations is eternal and indestructible. Life arises, passes away, and arises again and again. Thus it has been. Thus it will ever be.

Part three:
Life, mind and matter

10. The dialectics of geology

There is an English saying, "as solid as the ground under our feet." This comforting idea, however, is very far from the truth. The earth beneath our feet is not as solid as it seems. The rocks, the mountain ranges, the continents themselves, are in a continuous state of movement and change, the exact nature of which has only begun to be understood in the latter half of this century. Geology is the science that deals with the observation and explanation of all the phenomena that take place on and within the planet. Unlike other natural sciences such as physics and chemistry, geology bases itself, not on experiments, but on observation. As a result its development was heavily influenced by the way in which these observations were interpreted. These, in turn, were conditioned by the philosophical and religious trends of the day. This fact explains the tardy development of geology in relation to other earth sciences. Not until 1830 did Charles Lyell (1797-1895), one of the fathers of modern geology, show that the earth is far older than the book of *Genesis* says. Later measurements based on radioactive decay confirmed this, establishing that the earth and the moon are approximately 4.6 billion years old.

From the earliest period, men and women were aware of phenomena like earthquakes and volcanic eruptions that revealed the tremendous forces lying pent up beneath the earth's surface. But until the present century such phenomena were attributed to the intervention of the gods. Poseidon-Neptune was the "earth-shaker", while Vulcan-Hephistes, the lame blacksmith of the gods, lived in the bowels of the earth, and caused volcanoes to erupt with his hammer-blows. The early geologists of the 18th and 19th centuries were aristocrats and clergymen, who believed, with Bishop Ussher, that the world had been created by God on 23rd October 4004 B.C. In order to explain the irregularities of the earth's surface, such as canyons and high mountains, they developed a theory—catastrophism—which tried to make the observed facts fit in with the Biblical stories of cataclysms, like the Flood. Each catastrophe wiped out whole species, thus conveniently explaining the existence of the fossils which they found buried deep inside the rocks in coal mines.

It is no coincidence that the catastrophe theory of geology gained most ground in France, where the Great Revolution of 1789-94 had a decisive influence on the psychology of all classes, the echoes of which reverberated down the generations. For those inclined to forget, the revolutions of 1830, 1848, and 1870 provided a vivid reminder of Marx's penetrating observation that France was a country where the class struggle is always fought to the finish. For Georges Cuvier, the celebrated French naturalist and geologist of the 19th century, the earth's development is marked by "a succession of brief periods of intense change and that each period marks a turning point in history. In between, there are long uneventful periods of stability. Like the French Revolution, after upheaval, everything is different. Likewise, geographical time is subdivided into distinct chapters, each with its own basic theme." [1]

If France is the classical country of revolution and counter-revolution, England is the classical home of reformist gradualism. The English bourgeois revolution was, like the French, quite a bloody affair, in which a king lost his head, along with a lot of other people. The "respectable classes" in England have been trying hard to live this down ever since. They far prefer to dwell on the comically misnamed "Glorious Revolution" of 1688, an inglorious coup d'état in which a Dutch adventurer acted as the middleman in an unprincipled carve-up of power between the money-grubbing nouveaux riches of the City and the aristocrats. This has provided the theoretical basis for the Anglo-Saxon tradition of gradualism and "compromises".

Aversion to revolutionary change in any shape or form is translated into an obsessive concern to eliminate all traces of sudden leaps in nature and society. Lyell put forward a diametrically opposite view to catastrophism. According to him, the boundary line between different geological layers represented not catastrophes but simply recorded the shifting pattern of transitions between two neighbouring sedentary environments. There was no need to look for global patterns. Geological periods were merely a convenient method of classification, rather like the divisions of English history according to reigning monarchs.

Engels paid tribute to Lyell's contribution to the science of geology:

"Lyell first brought sense into geology by substituting for the sudden revolutions due to the moods of the Creator the gradual effects of a slow transformation of the earth." However, he also recognises his deficiencies: "The defect of Lyell's view— at least in its first form—lay in conceiving the forces at work on the earth as constant, both in quality and quantity. The cooling of the earth does not exist for him; the earth does not develop in a definite direction but merely changes in an inconsequent fortuitous manner." [2]

"These views," writes Peter Westbroek, "represent the dominant philosophies of the nature of geological history—on the one hand catastrophism, the notion of sta-

(1) P. Westbroek, *Life as a Geological Force*, p. 71.
(2) Engels, *The Dialectics of Nature*, p. 39, note.

bility interrupted by brief periods of rapid change, and on the other, gradualism, the idea of continuous fluctuation. In Coquand's time, catastrophism was generally accepted in France, but sympathy for this philosophy would soon fade, for purely practical reasons. Geological theory had to be built from scratch. The founders of geology were forced to apply the principle of the present as the key to the past as rigorously as possible. Catastrophism was of little use precisely because it claimed that the geological conditions were fundamentally different from those in the subsequent periods of stability. With the far more advanced geological theory now at our disposal, we can adopt a more flexible attitude. Interestingly, catastrophism is regaining momentum." [3]

The argument between gradualism and catastrophism is really an artificial one. Hegel already dealt with this by inventing the *nodal line of measurement*, in which the slow accumulation of quantitative changes gives rise to periodic qualitative leaps. Gradualism is interrupted, until a new equilibrium is restored, but at a higher level than before. The process of geological change corresponds exactly to Hegel's model, and this has now been conclusively proved.

Wegener's theory

At the beginning of the 20th century, Alfred Wegener, a German scientist, was struck by the similarity of the coastlines of eastern South America and the West Coast of Africa. In 1915, he published his theory of the transposition of continents, which was based on the assumption that, sometime in the past, all the continents had been part of a single great landmass (*Pangaea*), which later broke up into separate landmasses which drifted apart, eventually forming the present continents. Wegener's theory inevitably failed to give a scientific explanation of the mechanism behind continental drift. Nevertheless, it constituted a veritable revolution in geology. Yet it was indignantly rejected by the conservative geological community. The geologist Chester Longwell even went so far as to say that the fact that the continents fitted together so well was "a trick of the devil" to deceive us. For the next 60 years, the development of geology was hampered by the dominant theory of "isostacy", a steady state theory that only accepted vertical movements of the continents. Even on the basis of this false hypothesis major steps forward were made, preparing the ground for the negation of the theory that increasingly entered into conflict with the observed results.

As so often happens in the history of science, technological advance linked to the requirements of production, provided the necessary stimulus for the development of ideas. The search for oil by big companies like Exxon led to major innovations for the investigation of the geology of the seabed, and the development of powerful new methods of seismic profiling, deep-sea drilling and improved meth-

(3) P. Westbroek, op. cit., pp. 71-2.

ods for dating fossils. In the mid-1960s, Peter Vail, a scientist in Exxon's main Houston laboratory, began to study the irregularities in the linear patterns on the ocean floor. Vail was sympathetic to the old French view of interrupted evolution, and believed that these breaks in the process represented major geological turning points. His observations revealed patterns of sedimentary change that seemed to be the same all over the world. This was powerful evidence in favour of a dialectical interpretation of the geological process.

Vail's hypothesis was greeted with scepticism by colleagues. Jan van Hinte, another of Exxon's scientists, recalled: "We palaeontologists didn't believe a word he was saying. We were all brought up in the Anglo-Saxon tradition of gradual change, and this smelled of catastrophism." However, Jan van Hinte's own observations of the fossil and seismic record in the Mediterranean, revealed exactly the same as Vail's, and the ages of the rock corresponded to Vail's predictions. The picture that now emerges is clearly dialectical:

"It is a common feature in nature: the drop that makes the bucket overflow. A system that is internally stabilised is gradually undermined by some external influence until it collapses. A small impetus then leads to dramatic change, and an entirely new situation is created. When the sea level is rising, the sediments build up gradually on the continental shelf. When the sea goes down, the sequence becomes destabilised. It hangs on for some time, and then—Wham! Part of it slides into the deep sea. Eventually, sea levels begin to rise and bit by bit, the sediment builds up." [4]

Quantity changed into quality when in the late 1960s, as a result of deep-sea drilling on the ocean floor, it was discovered that the seabed of the Atlantic Ocean was moving apart. The "Mid-Ocean Ridge" (that is, an under-sea mountain chain located in the Atlantic) indicated that the American continent is moving away from the Euro-Asian landmass. This was the starting-point for the development of a new theory, that of *plate tectonics*, which has revolutionised the science of geology.

Here we have a further example of the dialectical law of the negation of the negation, as applied to the history of science. Wegener's original theory of continental drift is negated by the steady state theory of isostacy. This in turn is negated by plate tectonics, which marks a return to the older theory but on a qualitatively higher level. Wegener's theory was a brilliant and basically correct hypothesis, but he was unable to explain the exact mechanism whereby continental drift occurs. Now, on the basis of all the discoveries and scientific achievements of the past half-century, we not only know that continental drift is a fact, but we can explain exactly how it takes place. The new theory is on a far higher level than its predecessor, with a deeper understanding of the complex mechanisms through which the planet evolves.

This represents the equivalent in geology of the Darwinian revolution in biology. Evolution applies not only to animate but also to inanimate matter. Indeed, the

(4) P. Westbroek, op. cit., p. 84.

two interpenetrate and condition each other. Complex natural processes intercon-nect. Organic matter—life—arises inevitably from inorganic matter at a certain point. But the existence of organic matter in turn exercises a profound effect upon the physical environment. For example, the existence of plants producing oxygen had a decisive effect on the atmosphere and therefore on climatological conditions. The development of the planet and of life on earth provide a wealth of examples of the dialectics of nature, development through contradictions and leaps, long periods of slow "molecular" change alternate with catastrophic developments, from the col-lision of continents to the sudden extinction of whole species. Moreover, closer examination reveals that the sudden, apparently inexplicable leaps and catastrophes normally have their roots in the earlier periods of slow, gradual change.

What are plate tectonics?

The earth's molten surface eventually cooled down sufficiently to form a crust, under which gas and molten rock were trapped. The surface of the planet was con-tinually broken up by exploding volcanoes, spewing out lava pools. Gradually a thicker crust was formed, entirely made up of volcanic rock. At that time, the first small continents were formed out of the sea of molten rock (magma), and the ocean-ic crust began to form. Gases and steam from volcanic eruptions began to thin out the atmosphere, causing violent electrical storms. Owing to the higher thermal regime, this was a period of tremendous catastrophes, explosions, with the continen-tal crust forming then being blown apart, then forming again, partial melting, crys-tal formation and collisions, on a far vaster scale than anything seen since. The first micro-continents moved far faster and collided more frequently than today. There was a rapid process of generation and recycling of the continental crust. The forma-tion of the continental crust was the most fundamental event in the history of the planet. Unlike the seabed, the continental crust is not destroyed by subduction into the mantle, but increases its total volume in the course of time. The creation of the continents was thus an irreversible event.

The earth is made up of a number of layers of material. The main layers are the core (divided into the inner and outer core), the thick mantle, and the thin crust on the surface. Each layer has its own chemical composition and physical properties. As the molten earth cooled some four billion years ago, the heavier materials sank to the earth's centre, while the lighter elements stayed nearer the surface. The earth's inner core is a solid mass, compressed by colossal pressures. The crust forms a thin layer around the semi-liquid mantle, like the skin around an apple. From the cool thin crust, down 50 kilometres, the temperature is about 800°C. Deeper still, at around 2,000 km, the temperature rises to well over 2,200°C. At this depth the rocks behave more like liquids.

This crust supports the oceans and landmasses, as well as all forms of life. About seven-tenths of the crust is covered by water, which is a fundamental feature of the planet. The surface crust is very uneven, containing huge mountain ranges on its landmass, and under water ranges in the deep oceans. An example of one is the Mid-Atlantic Ridge, which forms the boundary between four of the earth's plates. The crust is made up of ten major plates that fit together like a jigsaw puzzle. However, along the edges of these plates "faults" are situated, where volcanic activity and earthquakes are concentrated. The continents are fixed into these plates and move as the plates themselves move.

At the border of these plates underwater volcanoes spew out molten rock from the bowels of the earth, creating new ocean floor. The seabed spreads away from the ridge like a conveyer belt, carrying with it huge rafts of continental crust. Volcanoes are the source of the transformation of enormous energy from the earth into heat. There are an estimated 430 active volcanoes at present. Paradoxically, volcanic explosions release energies that cause the rocks at the crust to melt. The earth's crust (lithosphere) is being continually changed and renewed. New lithosphere is constantly being created by the intrusion and extrusion of magma at the mid-ocean ridges through the partial melting of the mantle (asthenosphere). This creation of new crust at these faults pushes the old floor apart and with it the continental plates. This new lithosphere spreads away from the mid-ocean ridges as more material is added, and eventually, the very expansion of the ocean floor leads elsewhere to it submerging into the earth's interior.

This process explains the movement of continents. The constant subterranean turmoil in turn creates colossal heat, which builds up and produces new volcanic activity. These areas are marked by island arcs and mountain ranges and by volcanoes, earthquakes and deep ocean trenches. This keeps the balance between new and old, in a dialectical unity of opposites. As the plates themselves collide, they produce earthquakes.

This continuous activity under the earth's surface governs many phenomena affecting the development of the planet. The landmass, oceans and atmosphere are not only affected by the sun's rays, but also by gravity and the magnetic field surrounding the earth. "Continual change," says Engels, "i.e., abolition of abstract identity with itself, is also found in so-called inorganic things. Geology is its history. On the surface, mechanical changes (denudation, frost), chemical changes (weathering), and, internally, mechanical changes (pressure), heat (volcanic), chemical (water, acids, binding substances), in great upheaval, earthquakes, etc." Again, "Every body is continually exposed to mechanical, physical and chemical influences, which are always changing it and modifying its identity." [5]

Under the Atlantic Ocean there is an undersea volcanic mountain chain where new magma is constantly being created. As a result, the oceanic crust is being enlarged, and is pushing apart the continents of South America and Africa, and also

---

(5) Engels, *Dialectics of Nature*, 1946 edition, p. 163 and p. 162.

North America and Europe. However, if some areas are getting bigger, others must also be consumed. As the American continent is being pushed by colossal forces against the Pacific Ocean crust, the ocean plate is being forced to dip under America, where it dissolves, moves in currents, and eventually emerges—after millions of years—in another mid-ocean ridge.

These are not smooth, linear processes, but take place through contradictions and leaps of truly cataclysmic dimensions. There are times when the forces beneath the earth's outer crust meet with such resistance that they are forced to turn back upon themselves, and find some new direction. Thus, for a very long period, an ocean like the Pacific can be enlarged. However, when the balance of forces changes, the whole process goes into reverse. A vast ocean can be squeezed between two continents, and eventually disappear, forced between and under the continents. Such processes have occurred many times in the history of the planet over 4,600 million years. Two hundred million years ago, there was an ocean—Iethys—between Euro-Asia and Africa. Today the only remnant of that ocean is part of the Mediterranean Sea. The rest of that great ocean has been consumed and has vanished beneath the Carpathian Mountains and the Himalayas, destroyed by the collision of India and Arabia with Asia.

On the other hand, when a mid-ocean ridge is closed (that is, consumed under a continent) then new lithosphere will appear in another place. As a rule, the lithosphere breaks through at the weakest point. Unimaginable forces accumulate over millions of years, until eventually quantitative change produces a cataclysm. The outer shell is shattered, and the new lithosphere breaks through, opening up the way for the birth of new oceans. In the present day, we can see signs of this process in the volcanic valley of Afar in East Africa, where the continent is breaking up and a new ocean will be created in the next fifty million years. In effect, the Red Sea represents the very early stages in the development of an ocean separating South Arabia from Africa.

The understanding that the earth is not a static but dynamic entity gave a powerful impulse to geology, placing it on a really scientific basis. The great success of the plate tectonics theory is that it dialectically combines all the natural phenomena, overturning the conservative conceptions of the scientific orthodoxy based upon formal logic. Its basic idea is that everything upon earth is in constant movement, and that this takes place through explosive contradictions. Oceans and continents, mountains and basins, rivers, lakes and coastlines are in a process of constant change, in which periods of "calm" and "stability" are violently interrupted by revolutions on a continental scale. Atmosphere, climatic conditions, magnetism, even the location of magnetic poles of the planet are likewise in a permanent state of flux. The development of each individual process is influenced and determined, to one extent or another, by the interconnection with all the other processes. It is impossible to study one geological process in isolation from the rest. All of them combine to create a unique sum total of phenomena which is our world. Modern geologists are compelled to think in a dialectical way although they have never read a single line of Marx and Engels, just because their subject matter can be adequately interpreted in no other way.

Earthquakes and the genesis of mountains

As a young man, Charles Darwin found the fossil of a marine animal far inland. If it were true that marine animals had once lived in this place, then the existing theories of the earth's history were wrong. Darwin showed his find excitedly to an eminent geologist, who replied: "Oh, let's hope it's not true." The geologist preferred to believe that someone had dropped the fossil there, after a trip to the seaside! From the standpoint of common sense, it appears incredible that continents should move. Our eyes tell us that this is not so. The average velocity for that kind of movement is around 1-2 centimetres a year. Therefore, for normal purposes it may be discounted. However, over a much longer period of millions of years, these slight changes produce the most dramatic changes imaginable.

On the top of the Himalayas (almost 9,000 metres above sea level) there are rocks which contain fossils from marine organisms. This means that these rocks, which originated at the bottom of a prehistoric sea, the Iethys Ocean, were thrust upwards over a period of 200 million years to create the highest mountains in the world. Even this process was not a uniform one, but involved contradictions, with tremendous upheavals, advances and retreats, through thousands of earthquakes, massive destruction, breaks in continuity, deformations and folds. It is evident that the movement of the plates is caused by gigantic forces inside the earth. The entire make-up of the planet, its appearance and identity is determined by this. Humanity has direct experience of only a tiny fraction of these forces through earthquakes and volcanic eruptions. One of the basic features of the earth's surface is the mountain ranges. How do these develop?

Take a bunch of paper sheets and press it against a wall. The sheets will fold and deform under the pressure and they will "move" upwards, creating a curved feature. Now imagine the same process when an ocean is being pressurised between two continents. The ocean is being forced under one of the continents, but the rocks at that point will be deformed and fold, creating a mountain. After the total disappearance of the ocean, the two continents will collide, and the crust at that point will be thickened vertically as the continental masses are compressed. The resistance to subduction causes large nappe folds and thrust faults, and this uplift gives rise to a mountain chain. The collision between the Euro-Asian and the African plates (or parts of Africa) created a long mountain chain, starting from the Pyrenees in the West, passing through the Alps (collision of Italy and Europe), the Balkans, Hellenic, Tauridic, Caucasus (collision of South Arabia and Asia) and finally the Himalayas (collision of India–which was originally an island–and Asia). In the same manner, the Andes and Rocky mountains in America are located over the zone where the Pacific Ocean plate is dipping under the American continent.

It is not surprising that these zones are also characterised by intense seismic activity. The world's seismically active zones are exactly the borders between the different tectonic plates. In particular, zones where mountains are being created signify areas where colossal forces have been accumulated over a long time. When continents collide, we see the accumulation of forces acting on different rocks, at different locations and in different ways. Those rocks, which are composed of the hardest material, resist deformation. But, at a critical point, quantity is transformed into quality, and even the hardest rocks are broken or plastically deformed. This qualitative leap is expressed in earthquakes, which despite the spectacular appearance actually represent only a tiny movement of the earth's crust. The formation of a mountain chain requires thousands of earthquakes, leading to extensive folding, deformation and the movement upwards of rock.

Here we have the dialectical process of evolution through leaps and contradictions. The rocks, which are being compressed, present an initial barrier, offering resistance to the pressure of subterranean forces. However, when they are broken, they turn into their exact opposite, becoming channels for the release of these forces. The forces that operate under the surface are responsible for creating mountain chains and ocean trenches. But on the surface there are other forces operating in the opposite direction.

Mountains do not continuously rise higher and higher, because they are subject to opposing forces. On the surface we have weathering, erosion and transportation of matter from the mountains and the continents back to the oceans. Solid rocks are worn away by the action of strong winds, intense rain, snow and ice, which weaken and fracture the outer shell of the rocks. After a period, there is a further qualitative leap. The rocks gradually lose their consistency, small grains begin to separate from them. The effect of wind and water, especially rivers, transport millions of grains from higher levels to basins, lakes, but mainly oceans, where these rock-particles are gathered together again at the bottom of the sea. There they are buried again, as more and more material is accumulating above them and a new operation appears, the opposite one—rocks are being consolidated again. As a result, new rocks are created, which will follow the movement of the ocean bed until they are once again buried under a continent, where they will melt, possibly emerging once again at the top of a new mountain somewhere in the earth's surface.

Subterranean processes

The fact that the material under the solid surface is liquid is shown by the lava flows from volcanoes. Rocks are buried very deep in the earth's crust under big mountains and in subduction zones. Under such conditions they suffer a number of changes. As they sink deeper into the crust, the earth's internal activity leads to a rise in temperature. At the same time, the weight of the overlying rocks and mountains leads to a further tremendous increase in pressure. Matter is organised in specific combinations of elements which in the solid state form crystals called minerals. Different minerals come together to form rocks. Every rock has a combination of minerals, and every mineral has a unique combination of elements in a specific crystal form. The changes in temperature and pressure cause changes in the chemistry of most minerals through the substitution of one element for another. While some minerals, within certain limits, remain stable, at a critical point, matter is reorganised in different crystal forms. This causes a qualitative change in the minerals, which react, producing a new combination reflecting the new conditions. This is a qualitative leap, like the change of water to ice at 0°C. The result is that the entire rock is transformed into a new rock. Thus, under the pressure of environmental conditions, we have a sudden leap, involving a metamorphosis not only of minerals but of the rocks themselves. There is no one single mineral form that remains stable under all natural conditions.

In zones which experience the subduction of an ocean under a continent, rocks can be buried very deep in the crust. Under such extreme conditions, the rocks themselves begin to melt. However, this process does not happen all at once. We have the phenomenon of partial melting, because different minerals melt at different points. The melting material has a tendency to move upwards, since it is less dense than the surrounding rocks. But this movement is not without problems, owing to the resistance of the overlying rocks. The molten rock, or magma, will slowly move upwards until, faced with a solid barrier, it is temporarily forced to halt. In addition, the outer area of the magma will start to cool and consolidate into a solid layer that will act as an additional barrier in the path of the magma. But eventually, the elemental force of pressure from below gradually increases to a point where the barriers are broken, and the magma finally breaks through to the surface in a violent explosion, realising colossal pent-up forces.

It is therefore evident that these processes do not take place in an accidental way, as it may appear to the unfortunate victims of an earthquake, but correspond to fundamental laws, which we are now only beginning to understand. They take place in specific zones, located at the borders of the plates, especially in mid-ocean ridges and behind subduction zones. This is exactly the reason why there are active volcanoes in Southern Europe (Santorini in Greece, Etna in Italy), in Japan, where there are subduction zones (which led to the Kobe earthquake), in mid-Atlantic and the Pacific Ocean (volcanic islands and submerged volcanoes in mid-ocean ridges) and in East Africa (Kilimanjaro) where there is a continental drift and the creation of a new ocean.

It is well known to miners that the temperature of the earth's crust increases the further down you go. The main source of this immense heat, which is responsible for all the processes that take place in the bowels of the earth, is heat energy released by the decay of radioactive elements. Elements contain isotopes (atoms of the same element, but with different mass), some of which are radioactive—that is to say, they are unstable and break down with time—producing more heat and more stable isotopes. This continuous process of reaction is proceeding very slowly, because these isotopes have been decaying since the origin of the earth, when they must have been more abundant. Thus, heat production and heat flow must have been higher than at present, maybe two or three times more during the Archaean period than now.

The Archaean-Proterozoic boundary is likewise of major significance, representing a qualitative leap. Not only do we have the emergence of the first life-forms, but also another crucial change in the land mass—from many small continental plates in the Archaean, with its numerous plate collisions, to the formation of larger, thicker and more stable plates during the Proterozoic. These large continental masses were the result of the aggregation of many small proto-continental plates. This was the period of major mountain building, of which two major episodes can be distinguished—1.8 billion and one billion years ago. The remnant of the last event of this titanic process, in which the rocks were repeatedly metamorphosed, deformed and re-shaped, can be seen today in South Canada and North East Norway.

The gradualist theory of uniformitarianism, originally advanced by Hutton in 1778, has no application whatsoever to the early history of the earth. All the available evidence suggests that modern-style plate tectonics began in the early Proterozoic, whilst some earlier variant of the plate tectonic process seems most likely to have been in operation in Archaean times. More than 80 per cent of the present continental crust was created before the end of the Proterozoic period. Plate tectonics is the determining factor in all these processes. Mountain building, earthquakes, volcanoes and metamorphosis are all interconnecting processes, one depends on the other, each determines, influences, causes or is caused by the other, and all of them, taken together, constitute the evolution of the earth.

11. How life arose

Oparin and Engels

"What we do not know today we shall know tomorrow." This simple statement underlies the conclusion of a scientific paper on the *Origin of Life* written by the Russian biologist Aleksandr Ivanovich Oparin in 1924. It was the first time that a modern appreciation of the subject had been undertaken, and opened up a new chapter in the understanding of life. It was no accident that as a materialist and dialectician, Oparin approached this subject from an original perspective. This was a bold beginning, at the very dawn of biochemistry and molecular biology, and was backed up independently by the contribution of British biologist John B.S. Haldane—again a materialist—in 1929. This work produced the Oparin-Haldane hypothesis, on which the subsequent understanding of the origin of life is based. "In it," writes Asimov, "the problems of life's origin for the first time was dealt with in detail from a completely materialistic point of view. Since the Soviet Union is not inhibited by the religious scruples to which the Western nations feel bound, this, perhaps, is not surprising." [6]

Oparin always acknowledged his debt to Engels, and made no secret of his philosophical position:

"This problem [of life's origins] has however always been the focus of a bitter conflict of ideas between two irreconcilable schools of philosophy—the conflict between idealism and materialism," writes Oparin.

"A completely different prospect opens out before us if we try to approach a solution of the problem dialectically rather than metaphysically, on the basis of a study of the successive changes in matter which preceded the appearance of life and led to its emergence. Matter never remains at rest, it is constantly moving and developing and in this development it changes over from one form of motion to another

---

(6) Asimov, op. cit., p. 592.

and yet another, each more complicated and harmonious than the last. Life thus appears as a particular very complicated form of the motion of matter, arising as a new property at a definite stage in the general development of matter.

"As early as the end of the last century Frederick Engels indicated that a study of the history of the development of matter is by far the most hopeful line of approach to a solution of the problem of the origin of life. These ideas of Engels were not, however, reflected to a sufficient extent in the scientific thought of his time."

Engels was essentially correct when he described life as the mode of motion of proteins. However, today we can add that life is the function of the mutual reactions of nucleic acids and of proteins. As Oparin explained: "F. Engels, in common with biologists of his time, often used the terms 'protoplasm' and 'albuminous bodies'. The 'proteins' of Engels must therefore not be identified with the chemically distinct substances which we have now gradually succeeded in isolating from living things, nor with purified protein preparations composed of mixtures of pure proteins. Nevertheless Engels was considerably in advance of the ideas of his time when, in speaking of proteins, he specially stressed the chemical aspects of the matter and emphasised the significance of proteins in metabolism, that form of the motion of matter which is characteristic of life."

"It is only now that we have begun to be able to appreciate the value of the remarkable scientific perspicacity of Engels. The advances in protein chemistry now going on enabled us to characterise proteins as individual chemical compounds, as polymers of amino acids having extremely specific structures." [7] J.D. Bernal offers an alternative to Engels's definition of life as "a partial, continuous, progressive, multiform and conditionally interactive, self-realisation of the potentialities of atomic electron states." [8]

Although the Oparin-Haldane hypothesis laid the basis for a study of life origins, as a branch of science it is more correct to ascribe it to the revolution in biology in the mid-20th century. Theories concerning the origin of life are largely speculative. There are no traces in the fossil record. We are dealing here with the simplest and most basic life-forms imaginable, transitional forms which were quite unlike the idea of living things we have today, but which nevertheless represented the decisive leap from inorganic to organic matter. Perhaps, as Bernal comments, it is more correct to say the origin not of life, but the origin of the processes of life.

Engels explains that the Darwinian revolution "reduced the gulf between inorganic and organic nature to a minimum but removed one of the most essential difficulties that had previously stood in the way of the theory of descent of organisms. The new conception of nature was complete in its main features; all rigidity was dissolved, all fixity dissipated, all particularity that had been regarded as eternal

(7) A.I. Oparin, *The Origin of Life on Earth*, pp. xii and 230-1.
(8) J.D. Bernal, *The Origin of Life*, p. xv.

became transient, the whole of nature shown as moving in eternal flux and cyclical course." [9] The scientific discoveries since this was written have served to strengthen this revolutionary doctrine.

Oparin drew the conclusion that the original atmosphere of the earth was radically different from that of today. He suggested that instead of oxygen, the character of the atmosphere was reducing rather than oxidising. Oparin proposed that the organic chemicals on which life depends formed spontaneously in such an atmosphere under the influence of ultraviolet radiation from the sun. Similar conclusions were arrived at independently by J.B.S. Haldane:

"The Sun was perhaps slightly brighter than now and as there was no oxygen in the atmosphere the chemically active ultraviolet rays from the Sun were not, as they now are, mainly stopped by ozone (a modified form of oxygen) in the upper atmosphere, and oxygen itself lower down. They penetrated to the surface of the land and sea, or at least to the clouds. Now, when ultraviolet acts on a mixture of water, carbon dioxide, and ammonia, a vast variety of organic substances are made, including sugars and apparently some of the materials from which proteins are built up." [10]

In a more generalised form Engels pointed in the right direction fifty years previously: "If, finally, the temperature becomes so far equalised that over a considerable portion of the surface at least it does not exceed the limits within which protein is capable of life, then, if other chemical conditions are favourable, living protoplasm is formed." He continued, "Thousands of years may have passed before the conditions arose in which the next advance could take place and this formless protein produce the first cell by formation of nucleus and cell membrane. But this first cell also provided the foundation for the morphological development of the whole organic world; the first to develop, as it is permissible to assume from the whole analogy of the palaeontological record, were innumerable species of non-cellular and cellular protista..." [11] Although this process took place over a far longer timespan, this is a generally correct prognosis.

Just as Engels' ideas were ignored at the time by the scientific community, so were those of Oparin and Haldane. Only recently are these theories getting the recognition they deserve. Richard Dickerson writes:

"Haldane's ideas appeared in *The Rationalist Annual* in 1929, but they elicited almost no reaction. Five years earlier Oparin had published a small monograph proposing rather similar ideas about the origin of life, to equally little effect. Orthodox biochemists were too convinced that Louis Pasteur had disproved spontaneous generation once and for all to consider the origin of life a legitimate scientific question. They failed to appreciate that Haldane and Oparin were proposing something very special: not that life evolves from non-living matter today (the classical theory of

(9) Engels, *Dialectics of Nature*, p. 13.
(10) J.B.S. Haldane, *The Rationalist Annual*, 1929.
(11) Engels, *The Dialectics of Nature*, p. 16.

spontaneous generation, which was untenable after Pasteur) but rather that life once evolved from non-living matter under the conditions prevailing on the primitive earth and in the absence of competition from other living organisms." [12]

How did life arise?

There is no subject of such tremendous import for us as the question of how living, feeling, thinking creatures arose out of inorganic matter. This riddle has occupied the human mind from the earliest times, and has been answered in various ways. We can broadly identify three trends:

1st theory – God created all life, including humans.

2nd theory – life arose from inorganic matter, by spontaneous generation, as maggots from decaying flesh, or beetles from a dunghill (Aristotle).

3rd theory – life came from outer space in a meteorite, which fell on the earth, and then developed.

This transformation from inorganic to organic is a comparatively recent view. In contrast, the theory of spontaneous generation—that life originated from nothing—has a long history. From ancient Egypt, China, India and Babylon came the belief in spontaneous generation. It is contained in the writing of the ancient Greeks. "Here maggots arise from dung and rotting meat, here lice form themselves from human sweat, here fireflies are born from the sparks of a funeral pyre, and finally, frogs and mice originate from dew and damp earth...For them spontaneous generation was simply an obvious, empirically established fact the theoretical basis of which was of secondary importance," states Oparin. [13] Much of this was bound up with religious legends and myths. By contrast, the approach of the early Greek philosophers was materialist in character.

It was the idealist view of Plato (expressed also by Aristotle), which invested spontaneous generation with a supernatural quality and later formed the basis of mediaeval scientific culture and dominated people's minds for centuries. Matter does not contain life but is infused with it. Through Greek and Roman philosophical schools, it was borrowed and elaborated by the early Christian church to develop their mystical conception of the origin of life. St. Augustine saw in spontaneous generation a manifestation of divine will—the animation of inert matter by the "life-creating spirit." As Lenin points out, the scholastics and clerics seized upon that which was dead in Aristotle and not upon that which was alive. It was later developed by Thomas Aquinas in according with the teachings of the Catholic Church. A similar standpoint is held by the Eastern churches. The Bishop of Rostov, Dimitrii, in 1708 explained that Noah did not take in his ark those animals capable of spontaneous generation: "These all perished in the Flood and after the Flood they arose

(12) Scientific American, 239 [1978].
(13) A.I. Oparin, op. cit., p. 2.

anew from such beginnings." This was the dominant belief in Western society up until the mid-19th century.

The great Thomas Henry Huxley in his Edinburgh lecture in 1868 first clearly explained that life had one common physical basis: protoplasm. He stressed it was functionally, formally and substantially the same over the whole range of living things. In function, all organisms reveal movement, growth, metabolism and reproduction. In their form they are composed of nucleated cells; and in substance, they are all made up of proteins, a chemical compound of carbon, hydrogen, oxygen and nitrogen. This graphically reveals the underlying unity of life.

The French scientist Louis Pasteur, the father of microbiology, in a series of experiments finally discredited the theory of spontaneous generation. "Life could only come from life," said Pasteur. The discoveries of Pasteur dealt a crushing blow to the orthodox conception of spontaneous generation. The further triumph of Darwin's theory of evolution forced the vitalists (the idea of the "life force") to look at the origin of life in a new way. From now on their defence of idealism came in the argument of the impossibility of understanding this phenomenon on the basis of materialism.

As early as 1907, in a book called *Worlds in the Making*, the Swedish chemist Svente Arrhenius put forward the theory of panspermia, which concluded that if life could not occur spontaneously on the earth, then it must have been introduced from other planets. He described spores travelling through space to "seed" life in other planets. Any life spores entering our atmosphere, as with meteorites, would burn up. To counter these criticisms, Arrhenius argued that life was therefore eternal, and had no origin. But the evidence contradicted his theory. It was shown that the existence of ultraviolet rays in space would quickly destroy any bacterial spores. For example, microorganisms selected for their toughness, were put on the space capsule *Gemini 9* in 1966, and exposed to radiation from space. They lasted six hours. More recently, Fred Hoyle thought that life had been brought to earth in the tails of comets. This idea has been revamped by Francis Crick and Leslie Orgel who suggested that earth might have been deliberately seeded by intelligent life from outer space! But such theories really solve nothing. Even if we accept that life came to earth from another planet, that still does not answer the question of how life arises, but merely puts it back another stage—to the hypothetical planet of origin.

It is not necessary to travel to outer space for a rational explanation of the origins of life. The origins of life can be found in the processes at work in nature on our own planet over three and a half billion years ago, under very special conditions. This process can no longer be repeated, because any such organisms would be at the mercy of existing life forms which would make short work of them. It could only arise on a planet where no life existed, and also when there was little oxygen, since oxygen would combine with the chemicals needed to form life and break them down. The earth's atmosphere at that time was mainly made up of methane, ammonia and water vapour. Experiments in laboratories have shown that a mixture of water, ammonia, methane and hydrogen, subject to ultraviolet radiation produced two simple amino acids, and traces of more complicated ones. In the late 1960s, complex molecules were found to be present in gas clouds in space. It is therefore possible that, even at a very early stage in the earth's formation, the elements for the emergence of life, or near-life, were already present in the form of amino acids. More recent experiments have proven beyond all doubt that the proteins and nucleic acids, which are the basis of all life, could have emerged from the normal chemical and physical changes taking place in the primordial "soup".

According to Bernal, the unity of life is part of the history of life and, consequently, is involved in its origin. All biological phenomena are born, develop and die in accordance with physical laws. Biochemistry has demonstrated that all life on earth was the same at a chemical level. Despite the enormous variation between species, the basic mechanism of enzymes, coenzymes, and nucleic acids appear everywhere. At the same time, it forms a set of identical particles that hold themselves together by the principles of self-assembly in the most elaborate structures.

The revolutionary birth of life

It is now becoming clear that the earth in its early stages did not function in the same manner as today. Atmospheric composition, climate, and life itself, developed through a process of convulsive changes, involving sudden leaps, and all kinds of transformations, including retrogressions. Far from being a straight line, the evolution of the earth and of life itself is full of contradictions. The first period of the earth's history, known as *Archaean*, lasted until 1.8 billion years ago. In the beginning, the atmosphere consisted mainly of carbon dioxide, ammonia, water and nitrogen, but there was no free oxygen. Before this point, the earth was lifeless. So how did life arise?

As we have seen, up to the beginning of the 20th century, geologists believed that the earth had a very limited history. Only gradually did it become clear that the planet had a far older history, and moreover, one that was characterised by constant and sometimes cataclysmic change. We see a similar phenomenon in relation to the supposed age of the solar system, which turns out to be considerably older than what was previously believed. Suffice to say that the advances of technology after the Second World War, especially the discovery of nuclear clocks, provided the basis for far more accurate measurements, which gave rise to a giant leap forward in our understanding of the evolution of our planet.

Today we can say that the earth became a solid planet more than 4.5 billion years ago. For everyday thinking, this seems an unimaginably long time. Yet, when dealing with geological time, we enter an entirely different order of magnitudes. Geologists are accustomed to dealing with millions and billions of years, as we think of hours, days and weeks. It became necessary to create a different time-scale, capable of embracing such periods of time. This closes the "early" stages of the earth's history, and yet this convulsive period accounts for no less than 88 per cent of the total history of the planet. Compared to this, the entire history of the human race so far is no more than a fleeting moment. Unfortunately, the paucity of evidence from this period prevents us from obtaining a more detailed picture of the processes.

To understand the origin of life, it is necessary to know the composition of the earth's early environment and atmosphere. Given the likely scenario that the planet was formed from a dust cloud, its composition would have been largely hydrogen and helium. Today the earth contains large amounts of heavier elements, like oxygen and iron. In fact, it contains roughly 80 per cent of nitrogen and roughly 20 per cent of oxygen. The reason for this is that the lighter hydrogen and helium escaped from the earth's atmosphere as the gravitational pull was insufficient to hold them. The larger planets with greater gravitation, like Jupiter and Saturn, have retained their dense atmosphere of hydrogen and helium. By contrast, our much smaller moon, with its low gravity, has lost all its atmosphere.

The volcanic gases that formed the primitive atmosphere must have contained water, along with methane and ammonia. We presume these were released from the interior of the earth. This served to saturate the atmosphere and produce rain. With the cooling of the earth's surface, lakes and seas began to form. It is believed that these seas constituted a prebiotic (pre-life) "soup", where the chemical elements present, under the impact of ultraviolet light from the sun, synthesised to produce complex nitrogenous organic compounds, such as amino acids. This effect of ultraviolet was made possible by the absence of ozone in the atmosphere. This constitutes the basis of the Oparin-Haldane hypothesis.

All life is organised into cells, except for viruses. Even the simplest cell is an extremely complex phenomenon. The standard theory is that the heat from the earth itself would have been sufficient for complex compounds to form out of simple ones. The early life forms were able to store energy derived from the ultraviolet radiation from the sun. However, changes in the composition of the atmosphere cut off the supply of ultraviolet rays. Certain aggregates, which had developed the substance known as chlorophyll, were able to make use of the visible light that penetrated the ozone layer that filtered out the ultraviolet. These primitive algae consumed carbon dioxide and emitted oxygen, leading to the creation of the present atmosphere.

Throughout the whole course of geological time, we can observe the dialectical interdependence of atmospheric and biospheric activity. On the one hand, most of the free oxygen in the atmosphere resulted from biological activity (through the process of photosynthesis in plants). On the other hand, changes in the composition of the atmosphere, in particular the increase in the amounts of molecular oxygen present, triggered off major biological innovations, which enabled new forms of life to emerge and diversify.

How did the first living cell arise out of the primordial soup of amino acids and other simple molecules some four billion years ago? The standard theory, as expressed in 1953 by the Nobel Prize winning chemist Harold Urey and his student Stanley Miller, was that life arose spontaneously in an early atmosphere of methane, ammonia, and other chemicals, activated by lightning. Further chemical reactions would permit the simple compounds of life to develop into increasingly complex molecules, eventually producing the DNA double helix, or the single stranded RNA, both of which possess the power of reproduction.

The odds against this occurring by accident are truly staggering, as the Creationists love to point out. If the origin of life were a truly random event, then the Creationists would have a powerful case. It would really be a miracle! The basic structures of life and genetic activity in general depend upon incredibly complex and sophisticated molecules—DNA and RNA. In order to make a single protein molecule it would be necessary to combine several hundred amino acid building blocks in a precise order. This is a formidable task, even in a laboratory with the latest equipment. The odds against such a thing occurring by accident in some warm little pool would be astronomical.

This question has recently been approached from the point of view of complexity, an offshoot of chaos theory. Stuart Kauffman, in his work on genetics and complexity, raised the possibility that a kind of life arose as a result of the spontaneous emergence of order out of molecular chaos, through the natural workings of the laws of physics and chemistry. If the primordial soup was sufficiently rich in amino acids, it would not be necessary to wait for random reactions. A coherent, self-reinforcing web of reactions could be formed out of the compounds in the soup.

By means of catalysts different molecules could interact and fuse with each other to form what Kauffman calls an "autocatalytic set". In this way, order emerging from molecular chaos would manifest itself as a system that grows. This is not yet life as we know it today. It would have no DNA, no genetic code, and no cell membrane. Yet it would exhibit certain lifelike properties. For instance it could grow. It would possess a kind of metabolism—absorbing in a steady supply of "food" molecules in the form of amino acids and other simple compounds, adding them to itself. It would even have a primitive kind of reproduction, extending itself to spread over a wider area. This idea, which represents a qualitative leap or "phase transition" in the language of complexity, would mean that life had not arisen as a random event, but as a result of the inherent tendency of nature towards organisation.

The first animal organisms were cells able to absorb the energy built up by the plant cells. The changed atmosphere, the disappearance of ultraviolet radiation, and the presence of already existing life-forms rules out the creation of new life at the present time, unless it is achieved by artificial means under laboratory conditions. In the absence of any rivals or predators in the oceans, the earliest compounds would have spread rapidly. At a certain stage, there would be the qualitative leap with the formation of a nucleic acid molecule capable of reproducing itself: a living organism. In this way, organic matter arises out of inorganic matter. Life itself is the product of inorganic matter organised in a certain way. Gradually, over a long period of million of years, mutation would begin to appear, eventually giving rise to new forms of life.

Thus we can arrive at a minimum age for life on earth. One of the main obstacles to the evolution of life as we know it was the absence of an ozone screen in the upper atmosphere in Archaean times. This allowed the penetration of the surface layers of the oceans by universal radiation, including ultraviolet rays, which inactivate the life-inducing DNA molecule. The first primitive living organisms—*the prokaryotic cells*—were single-celled, but lacked a nucleus and were incapable of cell division. However, they were relatively resistant to the ultraviolet radiation, or even, according to one theory, dependent upon it. These organisms were the predominant form of life on earth for a period of some 2.4 billion years.

The prokaryotic unicellular creatures reproduced asexually through budding and fission. Generally, asexual reproduction creates identical copies unless a mutation develops, which is very infrequent. That explains the slowness of evolutionary change at this time. However, the emergence of the nucleated cell (eukaryotes) gave rise to the possibility of greater complexity. It seems likely that the evolution of the eukaryotes arose from a colony of prokaryotes. For instance, some modern prokaryotes can invade and live as components within eukaryotic cells. Some organelles (organs) of eukaryotes have their own DNA, which must be a remnant of their formally independent existence. Life itself has certain principal features, including metabolism (the total of the chemical changes that go on in the organism) and reproduction. If we accept the continuity of nature, the simplest organisms that exist today must have evolved from simpler and simpler processes. Moreover, the material bases of life are the commonest of all the elements of the Universe: hydrogen, carbon, oxygen and nitrogen.

Once life has appeared, it itself constitutes a barrier which prevents the re-emergence of life in the future. Molecular oxygen, a by-product of life, arises from the process of photosynthesis (where light is transformed into energy). "The life that we have on Earth today is, in fact, divided into two great categories long recognised by mankind—the oxygen breathing animals and the photosynthetic or light-growing plants", states Bernal. "Animals can live in the dark, but they need air to breathe, either free air or oxygen dissolved in water. Plants do not need oxygen—in fact they produce it in the sunlight—but they cannot live and grow for long in the dark. Which, therefore, came first? Or did some other form of life precede them? This alternative now seems almost certain. Detailed studies of the life histories, the internal cellular anatomy and the metabolism both of plants and animals show them to be divergently specialised dependants of some zoo-phyte. These must have been like some of the bacteria of today that can at the same time carry on the functions of animals and plants, and act both as oxidising and as photosynthetic agents." [14]

Early life forms

It is a striking fact that the chromosomes of all living organisms, from bacteria to humans, are similar in composition. All genes are made of the same kind of chemical substances—nucleoproteins. This is also true of viruses, the simplest known living things that stand on the threshold of organic and non-living matter. The chemical composition of the nucleoproteins permits a molecular entity to reproduce itself, the basic characteristic of life, both in genes and viruses.

Engels points out that the evolution of life cannot be understood without all kinds of transitional forms:

"Hard and fast lines are incompatible with the theory of evolution. Even the border-line between vertebrates and invertebrates is now no longer rigid, just as little is that between fishes and amphibians, while that between birds and reptiles dwindles more and more every day. Between *Compsognathus* and *Archaeopteryx* only a few intermediate links are wanting, and birds' beaks with teeth crop up in both hemispheres. 'Either...or' becomes more and more inadequate. Among lower animals the concept of the individual cannot be established at all sharply. Not only as to whether a particular animal is an individual or a colony, but also where in development *one* individual ceases and the other begins.

"For a stage in the outlook on nature where all differences become merged in intermediate steps, and all opposites pass into one another through intermediate links, the old metaphysical method of thought no longer suffices. Dialectics, which likewise knows no hard and fast lines, no unconditional, universally valid 'either...or' which bridges the fixed metaphysical differences, and besides 'either...or' recognises also in the right place 'both this—and that' and reconciles the opposites, is the sole method of thought appropriate in the highest degree to this stage. Of course, for everyday use, for the small change of science, the metaphysical categories retain their validity." [15]

The boundary-lines between living and non-living matter, between plants and animals, reptiles and mammals, are not so clearly drawn as one might suppose. Viruses, for example, form a class which cannot be said to be life as we generally understand it, and yet they clearly possess some of the attributes of life. As Ralph Buchsbaum states:

---

(14) J.D. Bernal, op. cit., p. 26.
(15) Engels, *Dialectics of Nature*, p. 282.

"The viruses are among the largest proteins known, and several different ones have already been prepared in pure crystalline form. Even after repeated crystallisations, a treatment no obviously living substance has ever been able to survive, viruses resume their activities and multiply when returned to favourable conditions. While no one has yet succeeded in growing them in the absence of living matter, it is clear that viruses help to bridge the gap that was formerly thought to exist between nonliving and living things. No longer can it be said that there is some sharp and mysterious distinction between the nonliving and the living, but rather there seems to be a gradual transition in complexity.

"If we imagine that the earliest self-propagating substances were something like viruses, it is not difficult to suppose that an aggregation of virus-like proteins could lead to the development of larger bacteria-like organisms, independent, creating their own food from simple substances, and using energy from the sun.

"Such a level of organisation may be compared to present-day forms like the *independent bacteria*, some of which conduct photosynthesis without chlorophyll, using, instead, various green or purple pigments. Others utilise the energy derived from the oxidation of simple slats of nitrogen, sulphur, or iron. These, for instance, can oxidise ammonia to nitrates, or hydrogen sulphide to sulphates, with the release of energy which is utilised in forming carbohydrates." [16]

The relatively brief interval between the formation of the planet and the cooling of its surface crust, meant that the emergence of life occurred in an amazingly short space of time. Stephen J. Gould explains: "life, for all its intricacy, probably arose rapidly about as soon as it could." [17] The microfossils of 3.5 billion years are, as expected, prokaryotic cells—that is without a nucleus (methanogens, bacteria, and blue-green algae). They are regarded as the simplest forms of life on earth, although even by this time there was diversity. Which means that between 3.5 and 3.8 billion years our common ancestor emerged, together with other forms that became extinct.

There was little, if any molecular oxygen atmosphere at this time. The organisms that existed at the time did not require oxygen—in fact it would have killed them. They grew by oxidising hydrogen and reducing carbon dioxide to methane. It has been suggested that these organisms must have been similar to eocyte cells that inhabit the very hot environment of volcanic vents. They obtain their energy not from oxygen but through converting sulphur to hydrogen sulphide.

"One can visualise," writes Richard Dickerson, "that before living cells evolved the primitive ocean was teeming with droplets possessing special chemistries that survived for a long time and then disappeared again." He continues:

"Those droplets that by sheer chance contained catalysts able to induce 'useful' polymerisations would survive longer than others; the probability of survival would be directly linked to the complexity and effectiveness of their 'metabolism'. Over

(16) R. Buchsbaum, *Animals Without Backbones*, Vol. 1, p. 12.
(17) S.J. Gould, *The Panda's Thumb*, p. 181.

the aeons there would be a strong chemical selection for the types of droplets that contained within themselves the ability to take molecules and energy from their surroundings and incorporate them into substances that would promote the survival not only of the parent droplets but also of the daughter droplets into which the parents were dispersed when they became too big. This is not life, but it is getting close to it." [18]

Given the lack of fossil evidence, it is necessary to examine the organisation of modern cells in order to cast light on their origins. For the simplest life forms to reproduce, a genetic apparatus containing nucleic acids must be present. If cells are the basic unit of life, we can be almost certain that the original organisms contained nucleic acids or closely related polymers. Bacteria, for example, are composed of a single cell and are likely to be the prototype of all living cells.

The bacterium *Escherichia coli* (E. coli) is so small that a million million of its cells could be enclosed into a volume of one cubic centimetre. It contains a cell wall, a membrane, which keeps essential molecules enclosed; it also selects and draws in useful molecules from outside the cell. It maintains the balance between the cell and its environment. The main metabolism of the cell takes place in the membrane, where hundreds of chemical reactions take place that use the nutrients in the environment for growth and development. The bacterium, E. coli, reproduces every twenty minutes. This unique transformation within the cell is made possible by a group of molecules called enzymes. These are catalysts which speed up the chemical reactions without being altered in the process. They work repeatedly, continuously transforming nutrients into products.

Reproduction is an essential element of life. When cell division occurs, a set of identical daughter cells is created. The mechanism for duplication, for making new protein molecules with exactly the same sequence as the parent cell, is encoded in the nucleic acids. They are unique in that they alone, with the assistance of certain enzymes, are able to reproduce themselves directly. The DNA (deoxyribonucleic acid) carries all the information needed to direct the synthesis of new proteins. However, the DNA cannot do this directly, but acts as a "master copy" from which messenger RNA (ribonucleic acid) copies are made that carry the information of the sequence to the synthesising system. This is known as the genetic code. Nucleic acids cannot replicate without enzymes, and enzymes cannot be made without nucleic acid. They must have developed in parallel. It is likely that in the original "soup" of elements there existed RNA molecules that were also enzymes, which developed on the basis of natural selection. Such RNA enzymes came together to form a helix, and become the basis for self-replicating RNA. The genetic replication is, however, not without occasional errors. In the bacterium E. coli the error rate is one in every 10 million base copies. In the course of millions of generations such

(18) Scientific American, 239, [1978].

errors—mutations—may have little effect, but alternatively, they may lead to profound changes in the organism, and on the basis of natural selection, lead to the formation of new species.

The next stage in organic evolution was the development of other polymers—combination of molecules—grouped together into whole families. A structure was needed to enclose the molecules: a semipermeable *cell membrane*. Cell membranes are complex structures, barely poised between a solid and liquid state. Small changes in the composition of the membrane can produce a qualitative change, as Chris Langton explains: "Twitch it ever so slightly, change the cholesterol composition a bit, change the fatty acid composition just a bit, let a single protein molecule bind with a receptor on the membrane, and you can produce big changes, biologically useful changes." [19]

Photosynthesis and sexual reproduction

As can be seen from what has already happened, the evolution of the cell is a relatively advanced stage of organic evolution. As the abundant components of the biotic soup became exhausted, it became necessary to evolve water-soluble organic materials from the atmosphere. From fermentation, the simpler but less efficient form of metabolism, photosynthesis was the next step. The special chlorophyll molecule had evolved. This allowed living organisms to capture solar energy for the synthesis of organic molecules. The first photosynthesizers removed themselves from the competition for dwindling natural energy-rich molecules and set themselves up as primary producers. Once the photosynthetic process was achieved, the future of life was assured. As soon as it emerges and produces enough oxygen, respiration becomes possible. In accordance with the laws of natural selection, once photosynthesis started it made its mark on all subsequent living things, and was undoubtedly so successful that it wiped out earlier forms of life.

This development represents a qualitative leap. The subsequent evolution to more complex forms is a drawn out process eventually leading to a new branch of life, the nucleated cell. At the top of the eukaryotic tree, several branches appear simultaneously, such as plants, animals and fungi. According to the American molecular biologist Mitchell Sogin the amount of oxygen affected the pace of evolution. The chemical composition of ancient rocks suggests that atmospheric oxygen increased in relatively distinct steps separated by long periods of stability. Some biologists believe that the explosion of life could have been triggered by oxygen reaching a certain level.

The nucleated cell—the *eukaryotes*—completely adapted to oxygen and showed little variation. The emergence of this revolutionary new life form allowed the existence of advanced sexual reproduction, which in turn, accelerated the pace of evo-

(19) Quoted in R. Lewin, *Complexity, Life at the Edge of Chaos*, p. 51.

lution. Whereas the prokaryotes consisted of only two groups of organisms, the bacteria and the blue-green algae (the latter produced oxygen through photosynthesis), the eukaryotes consist of all green plants, all animals and fungi. Sexual reproduction represents another qualitative leap forward. This requires the genetic material to be packaged inside the nucleus. Sexual reproduction allows the mixing of genes between two cells, the chances of variation being far greater. In reproduction, the chromosomes of the eukaryotic cells fuse to produce new cells. Natural selection serves to preserve favourable genetic variants in the gene pool.

One of the key aspects of life is reproduction. All animal and plant cells have the same basic internal structures. Reproduction and the passing on of parental characteristics (heredity) take place through the union of sex cells, the egg and sperm. The genetic material DNA through which the characteristics of life forms are transmitted from one generation to the next is contained in the nucleus of all cells. The cell structure, which is made up of cytoplasm, also contains a number of miniature organs called organelles. The internal structure of the organelles is identical to different types of bacteria, which seems to indicate that the composition of the animal and plant cell is the result of these once independent organs, with their own DNA, combining to form a co-operative whole. In the 1970s microtubules were discovered. These are protein rods, which fill every cell in the body like an internal scaffolding. This internal "skeleton" gives shape to the cell and appears to play a role in the circulation of protein and plasma products. The advent of the eukaryotic or nucleated cell constituted a biological revolution some 1,500 million years ago.

From asexual budding and fission emerged sexual reproduction. Such an advance served to mix up the hereditary material of two individuals, so that the offspring would differ from the parents. This provided the variation on which natural selection could work. In every animal and plant cell the DNA is arranged in pairs of chromosomes in the nucleus. These chromosomes carry the genes that determine individual characteristics. The new offspring, while combining the characteristics of its parents, is nevertheless different from them. It appears that the origin of sexual reproduction is connected with primitive organisms ingesting one another. The genetic material of two individuals was fused producing an organism with two sets of chromosomes. The larger organism then split into two parts with the correct amount of chromosomes. Single and paired chromosomes existed, but through time the paired condition became the normal mode of existence of plants and animals. This laid the basis for the evolution of multicellular organisms.

By about 700-680 million years ago, the first *metazoa* appeared. These were complex multicellular organisms that require oxygen for their growth. During that period the oxygen content of the atmosphere increased constantly, reaching its present level only 140 million years ago. The processes at work in evolution have a markedly dialectical character in which long periods of gradual quantitative change are interrupted by sudden explosions. Such a period occurred about 570 million years ago.

The Cambrian Explosion

It requires an effort of the imagination to recall just how recent a phenomenon complex forms of life on earth are. Picture a world in which the earth consisted of barren windswept rocks, in which the most complex forms of life were mats of algae and pond scum. This was the situation for the great majority of the earth's history. For thousands of millions of years the development of life was virtually static. Then suddenly, this stagnant world suddenly erupted in one of the most dramatic explosions in the history of life. The fossil record now reveals an extraordinary proliferation of different forms of life. The emergence of animals with shells and skeletons preserves this progress in tablets of stone. The explosion of new forms of life in the oceans was paralleled by the mass extinction of the older stromatolites, which had been the dominant life form in the Proterozoic period. The appearance of a vast multitude of many-celled creatures transformed the face of the earth for all time.

"Perhaps the most remarkable (and also the most perplexing) thing about the fossil record is its beginning," Frank H.T. Rhodes writes. "Fossils first appear in appreciable numbers in rocks of the Lower Cambrian age, deposited about 600 million years ago. Rocks of older (Pre-Cambrian) age are almost completely unfossiliferous, although a few traces of ancient organisms have been recorded from them. The difference between the two groups of rocks is every bit as great as this suggests: a palaeontologist may search promising-looking Pre-Cambrian strata for a lifetime and find nothing (and many have done just this); but once he rises up into the Cambrian, in come the fossils—a great variety of forms, well-preserved, worldwide in extent, and relatively common. This is the first feature of the oldest common fossils, and it comes as a shock to the evolutionist. For instead of appearing gradually, with demonstrably orderly development and sequence—they come in with what amounts to a geological bang." [20]

In spite of his genius, Darwin was unable to come to terms with the Cambrian explosion. Clinging to his gradualist conception of evolution, he assumed that this sudden leap was only apparent, and due to the incompleteness of the fossil record. In recent years, new and startling discoveries in palaeontology have led to a major revision in the interpretation of evolution. The old idea of evolution as an uninterrupted process of gradual change has been challenged in particular by Stephen Jay Gould, whose investigations into the fossil record of the Burgess Shale (an important fossil location in British Columbia) have transformed palaeontology.

Life developed, not in a straight line of uninterrupted evolutionary progress, but through a process aptly described by Stephen Jay Gould as punctuated equilibria in which long periods of apparent stability are interrupted by periods of sudden and cataclysmic change characterised by mass extinctions of species. For 500 million years the borderlines of geological periods are marked by such sudden upheavals in

---

(20) F.H.T. Rhodes, *The Evolution of Life*, pp. 77-8.

which the disappearance of some species clears the way for the proliferation of others. This is the biological equivalent of the geological processes of mountain formation and continental drift. It has nothing in common with the vulgar caricature of evolution understood as a simple process of gradual change and adaptation.

According to the classical theory of Darwin the emergence of the first complex multicellular forms of life must have been preceded by a long period of slow progressive change, which culminated in the "Cambrian explosion" 500 million years ago. However, the most recent discoveries show that this is not the case. The investigations of Gould and others show that for two-thirds of the history of life on earth—nearly 2.5 billion years—life remained confined to the lowest recorded level of complexity, prokaryotic cells, and nothing else.

"Another 700 million years of the larger and much more intricate eukaryotic cells, but no aggregation to multicellular animal life. Then, in the 100-million year wink of a geological eye, three outstandingly different faunas—from Ediacara to Tommotian, to Burgess. Since then, more than 500 million years of wonderful stories, triumphs, and tragedies, but not a single new phylum, or basic anatomical design, added to the Burgess complement."

In other words, the emergence of complex multicellular organisms, the basis of all life as we know it today, did not arise out of a slow, gradual "evolutionary" accumulation of adaptive changes, but in a sudden, qualitative leap. This was a veritable biological revolution, in which, "in a geological moment near the beginning of the Cambrian, nearly all modern phyla made their first appearance, along with an even greater array, of anatomical experiments that did not survive very long thereafter." During the Cambrian period, nine phyla (the basic unit of differentiation within the animal kingdom) of marine invertebrates appeared for the first time, including protozoa, coelenterata (jellyfish, sea-anemones), sponges, molluscs and trilobites. It took about 120 million years for the complete range of invertebrate phyla to evolve. On the other hand, we had the rapid demise of the stromatolites, which had been the dominant life form for two billion years.

"Modern multicellular animals make their first uncontested appearance in the fossil record some 570 million years ago—and with a bang, not a protracted crescendo. This 'Cambrian explosion' marks the advent (at least into direct evidence) of virtually all major groups of modern animals—and all within the minuscule span, geologically speaking, of a few million years." [21]

For S.J. Gould, "We find no story of stately progress, but a world punctuated with periods of mass extinction and rapid origination among long stretches of relative tranquillity." [22] And again: "The history of life is not a continuum of development, but a record punctuated by brief, sometimes geologically instantaneous, episodes of mass extinction and subsequent diversification. The geological time

(21) S.J. Gould, *Wonderful Life*, pp. 60, 64 and 23-4.
(22) S.J. Gould, *Ever Since Darwin*, p. 14.

scale maps this history, for fossils provide our chief criterion in fixing the temporal order of rocks. The divisions of the time scale are set at these major punctuations because extinctions and rapid diversifications leave such clear signatures in the fossil record." [23]

Plants and animals

During the Cambrian and Ordovician period—570-440 million years ago—there was an impressive rise of graptolites and trilobites, and a major growth of diversity in marine species all over the world, including the emergence of the first fish. This was the result of the extensive spreading of the sea floor, especially of the Iapetus Ocean. During the Silurian period (440-400 million years ago) the melting of the ice-sheets caused an important rise in the sea level. The shallow seas that covered much of Asia, Europe and North America were not a serious barrier to the migration of species and not accidentally this was the period when marine transgression reached its maximum extent.

By this time there was a somewhat odd distribution of the continents. The southern continents were loosely clustered together to form a proto-Gondwanaland (Africa, South America, Antarctica, Australia, India), but North America, Europe, and Asia were separate. There was a small proto-Atlantic Ocean (*Iapetus*) between Europe and North America, and the South Pole lay somewhere in North-West Africa. Subsequently, the continents drifted together to form one, single super-continent—*Pangaea*. This process began 380 million years ago, when the Iapetus Ocean disappeared, giving rise to the creation of the Caledonian-Appalachian mountain belt. This event resulted in the collision of the Baltic with Canada, uniting Europe with North America. By that time, continuing convergence caused the northwest corner of Gondwanaland to impinge on North America, creating a semi-continuous landmass, in which all continents were united.

Such a massive increase in land area in turn produced a revolutionary leap in the evolution of life itself. For the first time, a form of life attempted to move from the sea to the land, at its coastal margins. The first amphibians and land plants appeared. This was the starting-point for an explosive growth of animal and plant life. That period was marked by the elimination of the shallow seas environment, and, as a consequence, the mass extinction or sharp decline of many marine species. Evidently, the changing environment forced some species to move from the coastal areas to the land, or die. Some were successful, others not. The great majority of marine organisms adapted to life in the shelves and the reefs of the shallow seas became extinct. Amphibians eventually gave rise to reptiles. The first land plants underwent an explosive growth, creating huge forests with trees reaching heights of 30 metres. Many of the coal deposits now being exploited have their origin in this

(23) S.J. Gould, *Wonderful Life*, p. 54.

remote period, the products of the accumulated debris of millions of years, rotting on the floor of prehistoric forests.

Formal logic approaches the natural world with an ultimatum—either...or. A thing is either living or dead; an organism is either a plant or an animal, and so on. In reality, things are not so simple. In *Anti-Dühring*, Engels writes: "For everyday purposes we know and can definitely say, e.g., whether an animal is alive or not. But, upon closer inquiry, we find that this is sometimes a very complex question, as the jurists very well know. They have cudgelled their brains in vain to discover a rational limit beyond which the killing of the child in its mother's womb is murder. It is just as impossible to determine the moment of death, for physiology proves that death is not a sudden instantaneous phenomenon, but a very protracted process." [24]

We have already pointed out the difficulty in classifying very primitive organisms, such as viruses, which stand on the borderline between organic and inorganic matter. The same difficulty arises in distinguishing between plants and animals. Plants fall into three major divisions. The first (*Thallophyta*) includes the most primitive forms, either single-celled organisms, or loosely organised groups of cells. Are these plants or animals? It may be argued that they are plants because they contain chlorophyll. They "live" like plants.

Rhodes has this to say on the subject:

"But this simple answer does not solve our problem of recognising a plant—if anything, it makes it more confusing, for instead of providing a convenient clear-cut dividing line between plants and animals it points us to the hazy overlapping zone between the two kingdoms. And just as the viruses carried us back to the threshold of life, so these lowly thallophytes carry us to the ill-defined threshold that separates the plant world from the animal.

"Now many of the protozoans are, as we have seen, clearly animals—they move, grow, assimilate food, and excrete waste products very much as 'undoubted' animals do. But there are some tantalising exceptions. Let us look for a moment at the tiny unicellular organism *Euglena*, a common inhabitant of ponds and ditches. It has a more or less oval body which is moved through the water by movements of the flagellum; the creature can also crawl and perform worm-like movement: in other words it is capable of typically 'animal' movement—but it contains chlorophyll and obtains nutrition by photosynthesis!

"*Euglena* is really a living contradiction to most of our ideas about the differences between animals and plants, and the contradiction arises, not because we can't decide which of the two it is, but because it appears to be both. Other forms which are very closely related lack chlorophyll and behave as any other animal, using the long thread-like lash to swim, taking in and digesting food, and so on. The implication of this is clear. 'Plants' and 'animals' are abstract categories of our own mak-

(24) Engels, *Anti-Dühring*, pp. 26-7.

ing—conceived and formulated purely as a matter of convenience. Because of this, it by no means follows that all organisms must fit into one group or the other. Perhaps *Euglena* is a living remnant of the ancient and primitive group of minute aquatic organisms which were the ancestors of both animals and plants. But can we not resolve the conflict by considering chlorophyll as distinctive? Can we suppose that 'if chlorophyll—then a plant' will give us a sage rule? Unfortunately this too will not do, for some of these thallophytes (the fungi) which in other respects are very plant-like, do not possess chlorophyll. In fact, these fungi represent a problem family—for in various members within it, almost all the 'typical' plant characters (need for sunlight, absence of movement, and so on) break down. And yet, on balance, its members seem to be plants." [25]

The diversity of multicellular life represents a further qualitative leap in the evolution of life. The change from soft-bodied organism to ones with mineralised hard parts, as recorded in the Burgess Shale, represents the development of higher organisms. Certain substances like salt and calcium soak into the cell structure and tissues of sea creatures, which need to secrete them. Within the cell, the organelles which deals with metabolism or energy, mitochondria, absorb calcium and phosphate and ejects it as calcium phosphate. This mineral can be deposited within cells or can be used to build an internal or external skeleton.

The development of a skeleton usually takes place through the seeding of mineral crystals onto fibrous protein, called collagen. Collagen, which makes up around a third of all protein of vertebrates, can only be formed in the presence of free oxygen. The first move towards vertebrates seems to be the *Pikaia* of the Burgess Shale, a fish-like animal. The sea squirts also appear to be an evolutionary link between those animals that were fixed to the sea floor and obtained their food from filtered nutrients, and free-swimming fish. These fishes (*ostracoderms*) were covered with shell-like scales, with no teeth or jaws. This revolutionary leap in the Silurian period produced the first vertebrates.

It was in this period (410 million years ago) that the jaws evolved from the front gill, which allowed the hunting of other animals instead of sucking nutrition from the sea floor. "The first fishes did not have jaws," says Gould. "How could such an intricate device, consisting of several interlocking bones, ever evolve from scratch? 'From scratch' turns out to be a red herring. The bones were present in ancestors, but they were doing something else—they were supporting a gill arch located just behind the mouth. They were well designed for their respiratory role; they had been selected for this alone and 'knew' nothing of any future function. In hindsight, the bones were admirably preadapted to become jaws. The intricate device was already assembled, but it was being used for breathing, not eating." This was clearly a case, in Marxist terms, of elements of the new within the old. The first jawed fish, the

(25) F.H.T. Rhodes, op. cit., pp. 138-9.

acanthodians, or spiny sharks, gave rise to many kinds of bony fish. From these fishes evolved the first land vertebrates, the amphibians.

Gould continues: "Similarly, how could a fish's fin ever become a terrestrial limb? Most fishes build their fins from slender parallel rays that could not support an animal's weight on land. But one peculiar group of freshwater bottom-dwelling fishes—our ancestors—evolved a fin with a strong central axis and only a few radiating projections. It was admirably preadapted to become a terrestrial leg, but it had evolved purely for its own purposes in water—presumably for scuttling along the bottom by sharp rotation of the central axis against the substrate.

"In short, the principle of preadaption simply asserts that a structure can change its function radically without altering its form as much. We can bridge the limbo of intermediate stages by arguing for a retention of old functions while new ones are developing." [26]

The *Eusthenopteron* had muscular fins, and lungs as well as gills. During dry periods, these fishes ventured from the pools to breathe air through their lungs. Many of the Carboniferous amphibians spent much of their time on land, but returned to water to lay their eggs. From there, the evolutionary leap was in the direction of reptiles, which spent all their time on land and laid fewer eggs enclosed in a calcium carbonate shell. Commenting on these leaps in evolution, Engels writes: "From the moment we accept the theory of evolution all our concepts of organic life correspond only approximately to reality. Otherwise there would be no change. On the day when concepts and reality completely coincide in the organic world development comes to an end. The concept fish includes life in water and breathing through gills: how are you going to get from fish to amphibian without breaking through this concept? And it has been broken through, for we know a whole series of fish which have developed their air bladders further, into lungs, and can breathe air. How, without bringing one or both concepts into conflict with reality, are you going to get from egg-laying reptile to the mammal, which gives birth to living young? And in reality we have in the monotremata a whole sub-class of egg laying mammals—in 1843 I saw the eggs of the duck-bill in Manchester and with arrogant narrow-mindedness mocked at such stupidity—as if a mammal could lay eggs—and now it has been proved!" [27]

Mass extinctions

The Palaeozoic-Mesozoic boundary (250 million years ago) represents the greatest period of extinction in the entire fossil record. Marine invertebrates were especially affected. Whole groups became extinct, including the trilobites that had dominated the oceans for millions of years. Plant life was not seriously affected but 75 per cent of amphibians and over 80 per cent of reptile families disappeared. At present,

(26) S.J. Gould, *Ever Since Darwin*, pp. 107-8.
(27) MESC, *Engels to Schmidt, 12 March 1895*.

it is estimated that four or five families disappear every million years. But at the end of the Palaeozoic, we had the disappearance of 75-90 per cent of all species. By such catastrophic events did the evolution of the species unfold. Yet this process of mass extinctions did not represent a step back in the evolution of life. On the contrary, precisely this period prepared a mighty step forward in the development of life on earth. The gaps left in the environment by the disappearance of some species gave an opportunity to others to rise, flourish and dominate the earth.

The factors that influence the distribution, diversity and extinctions of life forms are endlessly varied. Furthermore, they are dialectically interrelated. Continental drift itself causes changes of latitude, and therefore climatological conditions. Variations in climate will create environments that are more or less favourable for different organisms. Tolerance to temperature fluctuations and climatic conditions are key factors in this process, giving rise to diversification. We see that diversity usually increases as we get closer to the equator.

The break-up of continents, their separation and collisions, all these factors change the conditions under which the species develop, cutting off one group from another. Physical isolation produces new adaptive variations, reflecting changes in the environment. Continental fragmentation thus tends to increase the diversity of life forms. Kangaroos survived only because Australia was isolated from the other continents very early, before the explosive rise of the mammals that caused the disappearance of large marsupials in all the other continents. Similarly, the destruction of oceans produces mass extinctions of marine species, yet at the same time creates the conditions for the development of new land plants and animals, as was the case at the inception of the Pangaean land mass. Death and birth are thus inseparably linked in the chain of evolutionary development, where the mass extinction of one species is the prior condition for the emergence and development of new ones, better equipped to cope with changed conditions.

The evolution of the species cannot be regarded as an isolated self-contained fact, but must be seen as the result of a constant and complex interaction of different elements—not only the infinitely large numbers of genetic mutations within living organisms, but also the continual changes in the environment: fluctuations in sea-level, water salinity, the circulation of oceanic currents, the supply of nutrients to the oceans, and, possibly, even factors like the reversal of the earth's magnetic field, or the impact of large meteorites on the earth's surface. The dialectical interplay of these diverse tendencies is what conditions the process of natural selection, which has produced forms of life far richer, more varied and more wonderful than the most fantastic inventions of poetry.

The epoch of the dinosaurs—the Mesozoic (850-65 million year ago)
The continental mass, Pangaea, created through the collision of the continents in the Palaeozoic era, remained intact for about 100 million years. This gave rise to a new

set of tectonic, climatic and biological conditions. Then in the Mesozoic era the process turned into its opposite. The super-continent began to break up. Vast glaciers covered the southern parts of Africa-America-Australia and Antarctica. During the Triassic (250-205 million years ago) dinosaurs evolved on the land and pleisiosaurus and ichthyosaurus in the sea, while the winged reptile pterosaurus later took to the air. Mammals evolved from the thraspid reptiles, but they developed very slowly. The explosive growth of the dinosaurs which dominated other vertebrate terrestrial life-forms did not permit a major development of mammals. They remained small both in size and numbers for millions of years, eclipsed by the shadow of their giant contemporaries, searching for food at night.

The Jurassic (205-145 million years ago) saw a major climatic change marked by the retreat of the glaciers, leading to a rise in global temperature towards the end of the period. The level of the seas rose by at least 270 meters during the Mesozoic, reaching almost double the present average level.

It takes a long time to fragment a supercontinent. The break-up of Pangaea began at the beginning of the Jurassic (180 million years ago) and the last continent was not separated until the early Cenozoic (40 million years ago). The first separation was on an east-west axis, where the creation of the Tethys Ocean split Pangaea into Laurasia in the North and Gondwanaland in the South. In turn, Gondwanaland split into three parts in the east—India, Australia and Antarctica. During the late Mesozoic a North-South split appeared, creating the Atlantic Ocean which separated North America from Laurasia and South America from Africa. India moved to the north and collided with Asia, while Africa also moved to the north and partly collided with Europe after the destruction of the Tethys Ocean. Of this mighty ocean, only a tiny part remained as the Mediterranean Sea. In the Pacific, Atlantic and Indian Oceans, periods of rapid expansion of the sea floor assisted the movement of the continental fragments.

Throughout the Mesozoic, dinosaurs were the dominant group of vertebrates. Despite the separation of the continents, they were firmly established all over the world. But at the end of this period—65 million years ago—there was a new period of mass extinctions, in which the dinosaurs vanished from the face of the earth. Most of the terrestrial, marine and flying reptiles (dinosaurs, ichthyosaurs and pterosaurs) were wiped out. Of the reptiles, only the crocodiles, snakes, turtles and lizards survived. This spectacular elimination of species was not confined to the dinosaurs, however. In fact, about one-third of all living species became extinct, including the ammonites, bellemnites, some plants, bryozoa, bivalve molluscs, echinoids and others.

The remarkable success of the dinosaurs was a result of their perfect adaptation to the existing conditions. The total population was at least as big as that of mammals today. At present, everywhere in the world, there is a mammal, big or small, occupying every available ecological space. We can be sure that 70 million years ago, those spaces were occupied by an immense variety of dinosaurs. Contrary to the common impression of the dinosaurs as huge, lumbering creatures, they existed in all sizes. Most were relatively small, many walked upright on their hind legs, and could run very fast. Many scientists now believe that at least some of the dinosaurs lived in groups, looked after their young, and possibly even hunted in packs. The Mesozoic-Cenozoic boundary (65 million years ago) represents yet another revolutionary turning point in the evolution of life. A period of mass extinction prepared the way for a huge evolutionary leap forward, opening the way for the rise of the mammals. But before we deal with this process, it is worthwhile considering the question of why the dinosaurs disappeared.

Why did the dinosaurs disappear?

This question has been hotly debated in recent years, and, despite very confident claims, particularly on behalf of the meteorite-catastrophe theory, is still not decisively resolved. There are in fact many theories which have attempted to explain a phenomenon which, both because of its spectacular appearance and because of its implications for the emergence of our own species, has captured the popular imagination in a unique way. Nevertheless, it is necessary to remind ourselves that this was not a unique event in the chain of evolution. It was not the only mass extinction, or the biggest, or necessarily the one with the most far-reaching evolutionary consequences.

The theory which currently enjoys most support and which certainly has been given the most sensational publicity is based on the assertion that the impact of a huge meteorite falling somewhere on the earth's surface caused an effect rather similar to the "nuclear winter" which would follow a major nuclear war. If the impact were sufficiently large, it would throw great quantities of dust and debris into the atmosphere. The dense clouds thus formed would prevent the sun's rays from reaching the earth's surface, resulting in a prolonged period of darkness and falling temperatures.

There is empirical evidence to suggest that some kind of explosion took place, which may have been caused by a meteorite. The theory has gained ground in recent years with the discovery of a thin layer of clay amongst fossil remains, which would be consistent with the effect of dust produced by such a large impact. The idea has, for example, seemingly been accepted by Stephen J. Gould. Nevertheless, there are questions that have still to be answered. First of all, the dinosaurs did not disappear overnight, or even in a few years. In fact, the extinction occurred over several million years—a very short time in geological terms, but sufficiently long to cast some doubt on the idea of a meteoric catastrophe.

While the meteorite hypothesis cannot be ruled out, it has one major disadvantage. As we have pointed out, there have been many mass extinctions along the evolutionary road. How is this to be explained? Do we really have to resort to an external phenomenon such as a sudden meteor impact to do so? Or does the rise and fall of species have something to do with tendencies that are inherent within the process of evolution itself? Even at the present time, we can observe the phenomenon of the rise and fall of animal populations. Only recently have we come close to understanding the laws that govern this complex process. By looking for explanations that lie outside the given phenomenon, we run the risk of abandoning the search for a real understanding. Moreover, a solution that seems attractive because it removes all difficulties at a stroke can create even greater difficulties than the ones it was alleged to have solved.

Several other suggestions have been put forward. The period under consideration was characterised by widespread volcanic activity. This, and not a meteorite impact, could well have caused a change in the climate that the dinosaurs were unable to cope with. It has also been suggested that the disappearance of the dinosaurs was connected with competition from the mammals. There is a parallel here with the disappearance of most of the original marsupial population of South America under pressure from the mammals from the North. Indeed, it is possible that the extinction of these creatures was the result of a combination of these circumstances—volcanic activity, destruction of the existing environment, excessive specialisation, and competition for reduced food resources by a species better equipped to cope with the changed conditions. It is unlikely that this particular controversy will be resolved in the near future. What is not in dispute is that, at the end of the Mesozoic some fundamental change ended the domination of the dinosaurs. The main thing is that *it is not necessary* to introduce external factors to explain this phenomenon:

"'You don't have to look for sunspots, climatic upheavals or any other weird explanation to account for the disappearance of the dinosaurs,' said Lovejoy. 'They did fine as long as they had the world to themselves, as long as there was no better reproductive strategy around. They lasted more than a hundred million years; humans should as well. But once a breakthrough adaption was made, once dinosaurs were confronted by animals that could reproduce successfully three or four times as fast as they could, they were through'." [28]

The *cosmic terrorist*—or how not to make a hypothesis

The problem becomes clear the moment we pose the question in the following way: very well, let's accept that the extinction of the dinosaurs was caused by an *accident* in the form of a sudden meteorite impact. How do we explain all the other mass extinctions? Were they all caused by meteorites? The question is not as pointless as it might seem. Attempts have indeed been made to show that all the large-scale extinctions were the result of periodic storms of meteorites from the asteroid belt.

(28) Quoted in D.C. Johanson and M.A. Edey, *Lucy, The Beginning of Humankind*, p. 327.

This is the substance of the so-called Nemesis theory put forward by Richard Muller of the University of California.

Certain palaeontologists (David Raup and Jack Sepkoski) have claimed that mass extinctions occur at regular intervals of approximately 26 million years. However, others basing themselves on the same evidence have found no such regularity in this phenomenon. There is a similar disagreement among geologists, some of whom claim to see evidence of regular periodicity in the occurrence of big craters, while others disagree. In short, there is no conclusive evidence either for the idea of regular intervals between mass exterminations or of regular bombardment of the earth by comets or meteorites.

Such a field lends itself easily to the most arbitrary and senseless speculations. Moreover, it is precisely such sensational "theories" which tend to get most publicity, irrespective of their scientific merit. The "Nemesis" theory is a case in point. If we accept, as Muller does, that mass exterminations occur regularly every 26 million years, and if we further accept, as he does, that mass extinctions are caused by meteorite storms, then it must follow that the earth must have been visited by meteorites every 26 million years, as regular as the clock.

The difficulty in such a notion is quite clear—even to Muller, who writes:

"I found it incredible that an asteroid would hit precisely every 26 million years. In the vastness of space, even the Earth is a very small target. An asteroid passing close to the sun has only slightly better than one chance in a billion of hitting our planet. The impacts that do occur should be randomly spaced, not evenly strung out in time. What could make them hit on a regular schedule? Perhaps some cosmic terrorist was taking aim with an asteroid gun. Ludicrous results require ludicrous theories."

And Muller went on to make up precisely such a ludicrous theory, in order to justify the preconceived idea that *all* mass extinctions were indeed caused by meteorite impacts, and that these happen regularly every 26 million years. He describes a heated argument with Luis Alvarez, the originator of the original theory that the dinosaurs were wiped out by an asteroid crashing into the earth, who was sceptical about Muller's ideas. The following extract from this dialogue gives us an interesting insight into the methodology whereby certain hypotheses are born:

"'Suppose someday we found a way to make an asteroid hit the Earth every 26 million years. Then wouldn't you have to admit that you were wrong, and that all the data should have been used?'

"'What is your model?' he demanded. I thought he was evading my question.

"'It doesn't matter! It's the possibility of such a model that makes your logic wrong, not the existence of any particular model'.

"There was a slight quiver in Alvarez's voice. He, too, seemed to be getting angry. 'Look, Rich,' he retorted, 'I've been in the data-analysis business a long time, and most people consider me quite an expert. You just can't take a no-think approach and ignore something you know'.

"He was claiming authority! Scientists aren't allowed to do that. Hold your temper, Rich, I said to myself. Don't show him you're getting annoyed.

"'The burden of proof is on you,' I continued, in an artificially calm voice. 'I don't have to come up with a model. Unless you can demonstrate that no such models are possible, your logic is wrong'.

"'How could asteroids hit the Earth periodically? What is your model?' he demanded again. My frustration brought me close to the breaking point. Why couldn't Alvarez understand what I was saying? He was my scientific hero. How could *he* be so stupid?

"Damn it! I thought. If I have to, I'll win this argument on *his* terms. I'll invent a model. Now my adrenaline was flowing. After another moment's thought, I said: 'Suppose there is a companion star that orbits the sun. Every 26 million years it comes close to the Earth and does something, I'm not sure what, but it makes asteroids hit the Earth. Maybe it brings the asteroids with it'."

The completely arbitrary nature of the method used to arrive at a hypothesis without the slightest basis in fact is glaringly obvious. With such an approach, we really leave the realm of science and enter that of science fiction, where, in the words of the old song, "anything goes". In fact, Muller himself is honest enough to confess that "I hadn't meant my model to be taken that seriously, although I had felt that my point would be made if the model could withstand assault for at least a few minutes." [29] But we live in an age of credulity. The "Nemesis" theory, which is quite clearly not a scientific model, but an arbitrary guess, is now being taken with the utmost seriousness by many astronomers who are sweeping the skies, busily searching for clues of the existence of this invisible "death-star", this cosmic terrorist who, having made short work of the dinosaurs, will one day return to the scene of the crime, and finish us all off!

The problem here is one of method. When Napoleon asked Laplace where God fitted into his mechanical scheme of the universe, he gave the famous reply: "Sire, je n'ai pas besoin de cette hypothèse." ("Sire, I have no need for that hypothesis"). Dialectical materialism sets out to discover the inherent laws of motion of nature. Whereas accident plays a role in all natural processes, and it cannot, in principle be excluded that, for example, the extinction of the dinosaurs was caused by a stray asteroid, it is completely misleading and counterproductive to seek the causes of mass exterminations in general in external phenomena, wholly unrelated to the processes under consideration. The laws which govern the evolution of the species must be sought for and found in the process of evolution itself, which includes both long periods of slow change, but also other periods where change is enormously accelerated, giving rise both to mass exterminations of some species and the emergence and strengthening of new ones.

(29) Quoted in T. Ferris, op. cit., pp. 262-3, 265 and 266.

It is the lack of ability to grasp the process as a whole, to understand its contradictory, complex, non-linear character—that is to say, the lack of a dialectical approach—which leads to these arbitrary attempts to solve problems by recourse to extraneous factors, like a *deus ex machina*, the proverbial rabbit pulled out of a conjurer's hat. Along this road lies only the deadest of dead-ends. Moreover, the extraordinary propensity for the acceptance of the wildest scenarios—almost all involving the idea of some impending cosmic catastrophe, signifying, at the very least, the end of the world—is something which tells us a lot about the general psychological make-up of society in the last decade of the 20th century.

12. The revolutionary birth of humankind

The era known as the Cenozoic begins with the mass extinctions 65 million years ago and has continued right up to the present. During this era, the continents continued to drift, separate and collide. This created new environmental conditions. In the first 20 million years, temperatures continued to rise, and a tropical zone appeared, in which conditions in Britain, for example, resembled those of a Malaysian jungle. The most important development in evolution in this era was the extraordinarily rapid rise of the mammals, which took over the environments vacated by the reptiles. By 40 million years ago, primates, elephants, pigs, rodents, horses, sea cows, porpoises, whales and bats, as well as most orders of modern birds and many families of plants, had all appeared.

The rise of the mammals might be seen as a kind of triumphal procession, in which evolution progresses ever upwards, in an unbroken line, culminating finally in the birth of humankind, the crowning glory of creation. But this was far from the case. Evolution was never a straight line, as we have seen. Periods of intense growth were, in this period also, followed by dramatic reversals, death and extinction. The two main periods of extinction are linked with sharp environmental changes. By 40-30 million years ago, we observe the beginnings of a cooling process. Temperature fell continuously for the next 25 million years, only stabilising at its present level five million years ago. That period witnessed the first recent period of extinctions affecting mammals.

The primates, the ancestors of apes and of humans, were spread all over the world. The period of extinction of the dinosaurs had an effect on many of these families. The new environmental conditions led to the development of a new species—the proto-apes, better adapted to the changed conditions. It is worth mentioning that the new conditions mainly influenced Africa and Euro-Asia, and not America. By this time, Antarctica reached the South Pole and began to be covered in ice. For the next 10-20 million years, there was a further period of explosive growth of mammals—the biggest ever—in which many species of apes appeared. However, the basic design of the apes remained unchanged throughout this period, until a new sharp climatic shift brought about a transformation. There are considerable disagreements among palaeontologists on the question of when and how the hominids separated from the apes. There are indications from bones that as far back as 14 million years ago there was already a species that resembled modern apes. Scientists believe that these bones belong to a species which lived both in Africa and Euro-Asia from 14-7 million years ago. It appears to have been a very successful species, and represents the common ancestor of humans, apes and gorillas. Then, 10-7 million years ago, there was a new and dramatic environmental change.

Glaciers already covered Antarctica. Now the ice-sheet spread, not only in the South, but in the North, where it covered Alaska, North America, and North Europe. Since more and more water was trapped in the ice, the sea level began to decline. It has been estimated that the fall in sea levels was more than 150 metres at that time. As a result, new landmasses appeared, joining the continents; land bridges were formed connecting Europe and Africa, Asia and America, Britain and Europe, thus making possible further migrations of species. The Mediterranean Sea completely evaporated. The climate around the equator became very dry, causing extensive desertisation, together with a massive decline of jungles and forests, and the emergence of vast expanses of savannahs and open land. By this time, Asia was separated from Africa by deserts, thus cutting off the African apes from their Asian cousins. Inevitably, this was another period of extinction and death. But it was equally a period of the birth of new species. At a certain point, possibly seven million years ago, the development of mammals resulted in the emergence of the first hominids (human-like primates).

It is now generally accepted that humankind originated in Africa. By 5.3 million years ago, the Mediterranean assumed its present form, and a new species of ape developed in Africa, which, in the course of a million years, developed in three different directions, giving rise eventually to apes, hominids and gorillas. The separation of these three branches occurred about 4-5 million years ago as a result of environmental pressure in Eastern Africa. The spread of the glaciers to South Africa resulted in a dramatic change in Eastern Africa—severe depletion of forests, because of reduced rainfall and a generally drier climate. This was probably the driving-force which led to the separation of the three species of proto-apes. Hitherto, they had lived in trees. Now they had three options:

1) Part of them remained in the forests. These must have been the most skilful, strongest and most successful in extracting food from limited sources. However, the decline of the forest habitat must have severely depleted their numbers. The remnant of this branch is represented by the modern gorillas.

2) Another group, forced to move to the margins of the forests, with fewer trees and less food resources, eventually were forced to increase their food-gathering

range by moving on the ground, while remaining near the trees for protection. This group is represented by the modern chimpanzees.

3) A third group, probably made up of the weaker and less skilful section of the species, were compelled by intense competition for scarce food resources to move out of the forest altogether. They were thus forced not only to move on the ground, but to cover long distances in order to find the food necessary for their survival. They were compelled to develop an entirely new way of living, radically different to that of other primates.

Environmental pressures in Asia caused by climatic changes also drove some groups of monkeys to the fringes of the forests. These developed into the modern baboons, which move on the ground in search of food, but return to the trees for protection. Primates exhibit a variety of modes of locomotion. The tarsier leaps and clings; the gibbon swings from limb to limb; the orangutan is "four-handed"; the gorilla is a knuckle walker; the monkey is a true quadruped; only hominids have ventured to become completely bipedal.

"Other specialisations have gone with handedness. If one is going to jump and snatch, one had better be able to judge distances accurately. If not, one will come up empty-handed at best; at worst, one will miss the branch entirely and fall. The way to precise distance judgment is via binocular vision: focusing two eyes on an object to provide depth perception. That requires that the eyes be set in the front of the skull and facing forward, not on the sides of the head, as a squirrel's eyes are. Primate ancestors developed such vision. Their skulls become rounded to accommodate the new position of the eyes, and with that change in shape came an enlargement of the skull capacity and the opportunity to have a larger brain. At the same time, the jaw became smaller. With hands, an animal does not have to do all its foraging and hunting with its teeth. It can afford a shorter jaw and fewer teeth. Modern apes and monkeys—and humans—have sixteen teeth in each jaw. Their ancestors had as many as twenty two." [30]

The pioneering American psychologist Jerome Bruner, in his writings on the mental development of children, has stressed that skilled behaviour has much in common with language production on the one hand and problem-solving on the other. The simplest skills almost all involve the use of the hand or hands and the visual guidance. On the development of the human hand, Bruner writes the following:

"The hands of man are a slow-growing system, and it is many years before humans can exhibit the kind of manual intelligence that has distinguished our species from others—the using and making of tools. Indeed, historically, the hands were regarded even by students of primate evolution as of no particular interest.

(30) D.C. Johanson and M.A. Edey, op. cit., p. 320.

Wood Jones would have us to believe that there was little morphological difference between the monkey hand and that of man, but that the difference was in the function to which they were put by the central nervous system. Yet, as Clark and Napier have pointed out, it is the evolutionary direction of morphological change in the hand, from tree shrews through New World monkeys through Old World monkeys to man, that should reveal how the function of the hand has changed and, with it, the nature of the implementation of human intelligence.

"That change has been steadily in the direction of a very special form of despecialisation. The hand is free from its locomotor function, from its brachiating function, and from such specialised requirements as were answered by claws and by exotic forms of finger pads. Becoming more despecialised in function means becoming more varied in the functions that can be fulfilled. Without losing its capacity for phalangeal divergence needed for weight-wearing, convergence for cupping food, prehensility for holding and climbing, or opposability—all part of an early primate heritage—the hand in the later primate evolution achieves several new functional capacities while undergoing appropriate morphological change as well. A combined capacity for power and precision grip is added.

"The flexibility of the palm and thumb increases through changes in the hamate and trapezium bones in their articulation. The thumb lengthens and its resting angle to the hand increases. The terminal phalanges broaden and strengthen, particularly the thumb. Napier may exaggerate when he says, 'The present evidence suggests that the stone implements of early man were as good (or as bad) as the hand that made them.' For surely, initially stupid hands become clever when employed in a clever programme devised by the culture." [31]

The first hominid fossils were found in East Africa, and belong to the species known as *Australopithecus afarensis*, which lived around 3.9-3.0 million years ago. These ape-like creatures were able to walk upright, possessed hands with thumbs fully opposed to the fingers, and therefore capable of manipulating tools. Their cranial capacity was larger than other apes (450 ccs.). As yet, no tools have been found in connection with these early hominids, but are clearly in evidence when we come to the first clearly identifiable human species, the aptly-named *Homo habilis* ("handyman"), which walked upright, had a height of 1.20 metres and had a brain capacity of 800 cubic centimetres.

At what point does the real separation of humans from hominid apes take place? Palaeontologists have argued for a long time over this question. The answer was given by Engels in his masterly essay *The Part Played by Labour in the Transition of Ape to Man*. But it was already anticipated by Marx and Engels much earlier in their pioneering work, *The German Ideology*, written in 1845:

---

(31) J.S. Bruner, *Beyond the information Given*, pp. 246-7.

"Men can be distinguished from animals by consciousness, by religion or any-thing else you like. They themselves begin to distinguish themselves from animals as soon as they begin to *produce* their means of subsistence, a step which is conditioned by their physical organisation. By producing their means of subsistence men are indirectly producing their material life." [32]

Role of toolmaking

In an extremely superficial attempt to discredit the materialist view of the origin of the human species, it is often stated that humans are not the only animals to "use tools". This argument is completely hollow. While many animals (not only monkeys and chimpanzees, but even some birds and insects) may be said to use "tools" for certain activities, these are limited to whatever natural materials they find to hand—sticks, stones etc. Moreover, such use either consists of accidental activity, as when a monkey throws a stick to dislodge fruit from a tree, or limited actions, which may be highly complex but are entirely the result of genetic conditioning and instinct. The actions are always the same. There is no question of intelligent planning, fore-sight or creativity, except to a very limited degree in the higher species of mammals, but the most advanced of the apes have nothing resembling the productive activity of even the most primitive hominids.

The essential point is not that humans "use tools". It is the fact that humans are the only animals that make tools, and not as an isolated or accidental activity, but as the essential condition for their existence upon which everything else depends. Thus, although from a genetic point of view humans and chimpanzees are almost identical, and the behaviour of these animals in some respects appears remarkably "human", the most intelligent chimpanzee is quite incapable of making even the most rudimentary stone tools produced by *Homo erectus*, a creature standing on the evolutionary threshold of humanity.

In his most recent book, *The Origin of Humankind*, Richard Leakey, makes this point:

"Chimpanzees are adept tool users, and use sticks to harvest termites, leaves as sponges, and stones to crack nuts. But—so far, at any rate—no chimpanzee in the wild has ever been seen to manufacture a stone tool. Humans began producing sharp edged tools 2.5 million years ago by hitting two stones together, thus beginning a trail of technological activity that highlights human prehistory." [33]

Compare these lines to what Engels wrote in 1876:

"Many monkeys use their hands to build nests for themselves in the trees or even, like the Chimpanzee, to construct roofs between the branches for protection against the weather. With their hands they seize hold of clubs to defend themselves against enemies, or bombard the latter with fruits and stones. In captivity, they carry

(32) MECW, Vol. 5, p. 31.
(33) Richard Leakey, *The Origin of Humankind*, p. 36.

out with their hands a number of simple operations copied from human beings. But it is just here that one sees how great is the gulf between the undeveloped hand of even the most anthropoid of apes and the human hand that has been highly perfected by the labour of hundreds of thousands of years. The number and general arrangement of the bones and muscles are the same in both; but the hand of the lowest savage can perform hundreds of operations that no monkey's hand can imitate. No simian hand has ever fashioned even the crudest stone knife." [34]

Nicholas Toth has spent many years attempting to reconstruct the methods by which early humans produced tools, and has come to the conclusion that even the most basic processes of flaking stone requires not only considerable care and manual dexterity, but also a degree of foresight and planning.

"To work efficiently, the stone knapper has to choose a rock of the correct shape, bearing the correct angle at which to strike; and the striking motion itself requires great practice in order to deliver the appropriate amount of force in the right place. 'It seems clear that early tool-making proto-humans had a good intuitive sense of the fundamentals of working stone, ' Toth wrote in a paper in 1985. 'There's no question that the earliest toolmakers possessed a mental capacity beyond that of apes,' he recently told me. 'Toolmaking requires a coordination of significant motor and cognitive skills'." [35]

There is a close correlation between the hand, the brain, and all the other organs of the body. The part of the brain connected with the hands is vastly greater than that which is connected with any other part of the body. Darwin already grasped the fact that the development of certain parts of the organism is linked with the development of other parts which apparently have no relation to them. He called this phenomenon the law of the correlation of growth. The development of manual dexterity through labour provided the stimulus for a rapid development of the brain.

The development of humankind was not an accident, but the result of necessity. The upright stance of early hominids was necessary to allow them to move freely on the savannah in search of food. The head had to be positioned at the top of the body in order to detect the presence of predators, as we see in some other savannah-dwelling animals, such as the meerkat. Limited food sources created the necessity to gather and transport, which was the driving force for the development of the hand.

Apes were not built to walk on two legs and do so rather clumsily. The anatomy of even the earliest hominids reveals a bone structure clearly adapted to upright walking. The upright posture has severe disadvantages in many respects. It is impossible to run as fast on two legs as on four. In many ways, bipedalism is an unnatural posture, which explains the prevalence of back pains that have plagued the human animal from the cave to the present. The great advantage of bipedalism is that it freed the hands for labour. This was humanity's great leap forward. Labour

(34) Engels, *The Dialectics of Nature*, pp. 229-30.
(35) R. Leakey, op. cit., p. 38.

is, together with nature, the source of all wealth. But, as Engels points out, it is infinitely more than this:

"It is the primary basic condition for all human existence, and this to such an extent that, in a sense, we have to say: labour created man himself."

The development of the hand through labour is closely connected to the development of the body as a whole.

"Thus the hand is not only the organ of labour, it is also the product of labour. Only by labour, by adaptation to ever new operations, by inheritance of the thus acquired special development of muscles, ligaments, and, over longer periods of time, bone as well, and by the ever-renewed employment of these inherited improvements in new, more and more complicated operations, has the human hand attained the high degree of perfection that has enabled it to conjure into being the pictures of Raphael, the statues of Thorwaldsen, the music of Paganini.

"But the hand did not exist by itself. It was only one member of an entire, highly complex organism. And what benefited the hand, benefited also the whole body it served." [36]

The same thing applies to language. Even though apes are capable of producing a range of sounds and gestures that may be seen as a kind of embryonic "language", all attempts to teach them to talk have ended in failure. Language, as Engels explains, is a product of collective production, and can only arise in a species the life-activity of which depends exclusively on co-operation in order to produce tools, a complex process which must be consciously learnt and passed on from one generation to the next. On this, Noam Chomsky remarks:

"Anyone concerned with the study of human nature and human capacities must somehow come to grips with the fact that all normal humans acquire language, whereas acquisition of even its barest rudiments is quite beyond the capacities of an otherwise intelligent ape."

In recent times, it has become customary to try to show that language is not peculiar to humans. While there is no doubt that systems of communication exist among animals, it is entirely incorrect to describe this as language. Human speech arises from human society and human co-operative productive activity, and is qualitatively different to any other system of communication in the animal world, even the most complex.

"Human language appears to be a unique phenomenon, without significant analogue in the animal world. If this is so, it is quite senseless to raise the problem of explaining the evolution of human language from more primitive systems of communication that appear at lower levels of intellectual capacity."

And again: "As far as we know, possession of human language is associated with a specific type of mental organisation, not simply a higher degree of intelli-

(36) Engels, *The Dialectics of Nature*, pp. 228 and 230-1.

gence. There seems to be no substance to the view that human language is simply a more complex instance of something to be found elsewhere in the animal world. This poses a problem for the biologist, since, if true, it is an example of true 'emergence'—the appearance of a qualitative different phenomenon at a specific stage of complexity of organisation" [37]

The rapid expanse in brain size brought additional problems, especially in relation to childbirth. Whereas a newborn ape has a brain size of 200 cubic centimetres—about half that of an adult—that of a human baby (385 cubic centimetres) is only about a quarter of the size of the adult human brain (about 1350 cubic centimetres). The form of the human pelvis, adapted to walking in an upright position limits the size of the pelvic opening. Thus, all human babies are born "prematurely", as a result of the large brain and the restrictions imposed by the biological engineering of bipedalism.

The complete helplessness of the newborn human baby is evident in comparison with any other species of higher mammals. It has been suggested by Barry Bogin, a biologist at the University of Michigan, that the slow rate of bodily growth in human infants, as compared to apes, is connected with the long time needed to absorb the complex rules and techniques of human society. Even the difference in body size between children and adults helps to establish a teacher-pupil relationship, where the young learn from the old, whereas among the apes rapid growth soon leads to physical rivalry. When the long process of learning is complete, the body catches up with a sudden leap in growth during adolescence.

"Humans become human through intense learning not just of survival skills but of customs and social mores, kinship and social laws—that is, culture. The social milieu in which helpless infants are cared for and older children are educated is much more characteristic of humans than it is of apes." [38]

Social organisation

Life on the open savannah with a multitude of predators was a dangerous affair. Humans are not strong animals, and the early hominids were much smaller than modern humans. They possessed neither strong claws nor powerful teeth, nor could they outrun lions and other four-footed predators. The only way to survive was by developing a highly organised and co-operative community for the collective exploitation of scarce food resources. But the decisive step was without doubt the manufacture of artefacts, beginning with the stone scrapers, used for a variety of purposes. Despite their deceptively simple appearance, these were already highly sophisticated and versatile tools, the production of which implies a significant degree of organisation, planning, and at least the elements of a division of labour. Here we have the real beginnings of human society. In the words of Engels:

(37) N. Chomsky, *Language and Mind*, pp. 66-7 and 70.
(38) R. Leakey, op. cit., p. 45.

"As already said, our simian ancestors were gregarious; it is obviously impossible to seek the derivation of man, the most social of all animals, from non-gregarious immediate ancestors. The mastery over nature, which begins with the development of the hand, with labour, widened man's horizon at every new advance. He was continually discovering new, hitherto unknown, properties of natural objects. On the other hand, the development of labour necessarily helped to bring the members of society closer together by multiplying cases of mutual support, joint activity, and by making clear the advantage of this joint activity to each individual. In short, men in the making arrived at the point where they had something to say to one another. The need led to the creation of its organ; by modulation the undeveloped larynx of the ape was slowly but surely transformed for ever more developed modulation, and the organs of the mouth gradually learned to pronounce one articulate letter after another." [39]

The production of tools, the beginnings of a division of labour, originally between men and women, the development of language, and a society based on co-operation—these were the elements which marked the real emergence of humankind. This was not a slow, gradual process, but represents yet another revolutionary leap, one of the most decisive turning points in evolution. In the words of the palaeontologist Lewis Binford, "Our species had arrived—not as a result of gradual, progressive processes but explosively in a relatively short period of time." [40]

The relation between labour and all the other factors was explained by Engels:

"First labour, after it, and then with it, articulate speech—these were the two most essential stimuli under the influence of which the brain of the ape gradually changed into that of man, which for all its similarity to the former is far larger and more perfect. Hand in hand with the development of the brain went the development of its most immediate instruments—the sense organs. Just as the gradual development of speech is necessarily accompanied by a corresponding refinement of the organ of hearing, so the development of the brain as a whole is accompanied by a refinement of all the senses. The eagle sees much farther than man, but the human eye sees considerably more in things than does the eye of the eagle. The dog has a far keener sense of smell than man, but it does not distinguish a hundredth part of the odours that for man are definite features of different things. And the sense of touch, which the ape hardly possesses in its crudest initial form, has been developed only side by side with the development of the human hand itself, through the medium of labour."

The earliest hominids had a predominantly vegetarian diet, although the use of even the most primitive tools like digging sticks gave them access to supplies of food not available to other apes. This diet was supplemented by small quantities of meat, obtained mainly by scavenging. The real breakthrough came when the pro-

(39) Engels, *The Dialectics of Nature*, pp. 231-2.
(40) Quoted in Leakey, op. cit., p. 67.

duction of tools and weapons permitted humans to pass over to hunting as the primary source of food. The consumption of meat undoubtedly led to a rapid further increase in brain size:

"A meat diet," writes Engels, "contains in an almost ready state the most essential substances required by the organism for its metabolism. It shortened the time required, not only for digestion, but also for the other vegetative bodily processes corresponding to those of plant life, and thus gained further time, material, and desire for the active manifestation of animal life in the proper sense of the term. And the further that man in the making became removed from the plant kingdom, the higher he rose also above animals. Just as becoming accustomed to a plant diet side by side with meat converted wild cats and dogs into the servants of man, so also adaptation to a flesh diet, side by side with a vegetable diet, considerably contributed to giving bodily strength and independence to man in the making. The most essential effect, however, of a flesh diet was on the brain, which now received a far richer flow of the materials necessary for its nourishment and development, and which therefore could become more rapidly and perfectly developed from generation to generation." [41]

Exactly the same point is made by Richard Leakey, who relates it to a fundamental change in social organisation. In most other primates, there is fierce competition between males to mate with the females. This is reflected in the very considerable differences in body size between, say, male and female savannah baboons. Such a difference can be seen in the earliest hominids, such as *Australopithecus afarensis.* This suggests a social structure closer to the apes than to humans. In other words, physical adaptations such as bipedalism, vital as it undoubtedly was as a precondition for human evolution, does not yet entitle us, contrary to what Richard Leakey suggests, to characterise these early hominids as humans.

Among savannah baboons, the males (who are twice the size of the females) leave the troop as soon as they reach maturity, and join another troop, where they immediately enter into competition with the established males for access to the females. Thus, in Darwinian terms, these males have no (genetic) reason for co-operating with each other. Among chimpanzees, on the other hand, for reasons not yet understood, the males remain in the group where they were born, and the females migrate. The male chimpanzees, being genetically related, have a Darwinian reason to co-operate, which they do, both to defend the group against outsiders, and even occasionally combining to hunt a monkey to supplement their diet. The difference in body size between male and female chimpanzees is only 15-20 per cent, reflecting the predominantly co-operative nature of this society.

Whereas the difference in size between male and female members of the *Australopithecus afarensis* group was so great that they were at first thought to be

(41) Engels, *The Dialectics of Nature*, pp. 233-4 and 237.

fossils from two entirely different species, the situation is radically different when we come to the earliest members of the human species, where males were no more than 20 per cent larger than females, as with chimpanzees, our closest genetic relatives. On this, Leakey remarks:

"As the Cambridge anthropologists Robert Foley and Phyllis Lee have argued, this change in body-size differential at the time of the origin of the genus *Homo* surely represents a change in social organisation, too. Very probably, early *Homo* males remained with their natal groups with their brothers and half brothers, while the females transferred to other groups. Relatedness, as I've indicated, enhances co-operation among the males.

"We can't be certain what prompted this shift in social organisation: enhanced co-operation among males must have been strongly beneficial for some reason. Some anthropologists have argued that defence against neighbouring troops of *Homo* became extremely important. Just as likely, and perhaps more so, is a change centred on economic needs. Several lines of evidence point to a shift in diet for *Homo*—one in which meat became an important energy and protein source. The change in tooth structure in early *Homo* indicates meat eating, as does the elaboration of a stone-tool technology. Moreover, the increase in brain size that is part of the *Homo* package may even have *demanded* that the species supplement its diet with a rich energy source." [42]

It is well known that the brain is a metabolically expensive organ, which in modern humans absorbs 20 per cent of energy consumed, despite only amounting two per cent of total body weight. The Australian anthropologist Robert Martin has explained that the increase in brain size in early *Homo* could only have occurred on the basis of an enhanced energy supply, which could only come from meat, with its concentration of calories, proteins and fat. Originally, this would have come from scavenging, and some hunting activity (which, as we know, occurs even among chimpanzees). But later there is little doubt that hunting played an increasing role in providing a more varied and nutritional diet, with far-reaching evolutionary consequences.

Hypotheses on human development

In recent years, there has been a fierce controversy about the role of hunting in early human society. There has been a tendency to play down the role of hunting, insisting more on the role of food gathering and scavenging. While this question is still not decisively resolved, it is difficult not to share Leakey's view that the argument against the hunter-gatherer model of early human society has gone too far. It is also interesting to note the way in which these controversies tend to reflect certain prej-

(42) R. Leakey, op. cit., p. 54.

udices or social pressures and fads that have nothing whatsoever to do with the issues at stake.

In the early years of the 20th century, the idealist standpoint predominated. Mankind became human thanks to the brain, with its higher thoughts, which propelled all development. Later, the view of "Man the Toolmaker" re-emerged, although in a rather idealised version, in which tools, but not weapons, were said to be the motor-force of evolution. The terrible events of the Second World War then produced a reaction against this, in the form of the theory of "Man the Killer Ape," put forward "possibly because it seemed to explain (or even excuse) the horrible events of the war," as Leakey shrewdly remarks

In the 1960s, there was a great interest in the !Kung San—the incorrectly named "Bushmen" of the Kalahari desert, a group of people living in apparent harmony with their natural environment, and exploiting it in complex ways. This fitted in well with the growing interest in environmental issues in Western society. In 1966, however, the idea of "Man the Hunter" re-emerged strongly at a major anthropological conference in Chicago. This, however, fell foul of the supporters of "Women's Liberation", in the 1970s. Since hunting is usually seen as a male activity, it was assumed—quite unjustifiably—that to accept it would be somehow to downgrade the role of women in early society. The powerful feminist lobby put forward the hypothesis of "Woman the Gatherer", in which it was argued that the gathering of food, mainly plants, which could be shared, was the basis on which a complex human society evolved.

The central role of women in early society is undeniable, and was clearly explained by Engels in his classic work *The Origins of the Family, Private Property and State*. However, it is a serious error to read into the record of the past conceptions—or, still worse, prejudices—derived from present-day society. The cause of the emancipation of women will not be advanced a single step by attempting to make the reality of history fit into a pattern which appeals to certain current fashions but is devoid of any real content. We do not make the future of humanity any more hopeful by painting the past in rosier colours. Nor will we encourage people to become vegetarians by denying the fundamental role played by meat eating, hunting, yes, and even cannibalism, in developing the human brain.

"With all respect to the vegetarians, it has to be recognised that man did not come into existence without a flesh diet, and if the latter, among all peoples known to us, has led to cannibalism at some time or another (the forefathers of the Berliners, the Weletabians or Wilzians, used to eat their parents as late as the tenth century), that is of no consequence to us today." [43]

Similarly, a division of labour must have existed between men and women in the earliest human societies. The mistake, however, is to confuse the division of labour

---

(43) Engels, *The Dialectics of Nature*, p. 237.

in early society, where neither private property nor the family as we know it today existed, with inequality and the oppression of women in modern class society. In the majority of existing hunter-gatherer societies known to anthropologists, the elements of a division of labour exists, in which the men hunt and the women gather plants for food.

"The camp is a place of intense social interaction, and a place where food is shared"; comments Leakey, "when meat is available, this sharing often involves elaborate ritual, which is governed by strict social rules."

There is good reason to suppose that a similar situation existed in early human society. Instead of the caricature of Social Darwinism, which attempts to extrapolate the laws of the capitalist jungle to cover the whole of human history and prehistory, all the available evidence indicates that the entire basis of early human society was co-operation, collective activity, and sharing. Glynn Isaac of Harvard University made a significant advance in anthropological thinking in a major article published in *Scientific American* in 1978. Isaac's food sharing hypothesis emphasises the social impact of collective food gathering and sharing. In a 1982 speech on the centenary of Darwin's death, he said: "The adoption of food-sharing would have favoured the development of language, social reciprocity and the intellect." In his latest book, *The Making of Mankind*, Richard Leakey wrote that "the food-sharing hypothesis is a strong candidate for explaining what set early humans on the road to modern man."

The last two million years have been characterised by a unique climate cycle. Long periods of intense cooling and glacier advances have been interrupted by short periods of rising temperatures and glacial retreat. Ice ages have an average duration of 100,000 years, whereas the interglacial periods last for approximately 10,000. Under these extreme conditions, mammals were compelled to develop more advanced forms or to disappear. Out of a total of 119 mammalian species living in Europe and Asia two million years ago, only nine still survive. The big majority of the rest either developed as more advanced species, or disappeared. Once again, birth and death are inseparably linked in the contradictory, bitter-sweet, dialectical process of evolution.

The last ice age gave way to a new inter-glacial period, which has lasted until the present, but will eventually come to an end. *Homo erectus* gave way to a more advanced hominid—*Homo sapiens*—about 500,000 years ago. The human race (*Homo sapiens sapiens*) represents one evolutionary line from *Homo sapiens*, branching off about 100,000 years ago. The other line—*Homo sapiens neanderthalensis*—either disappeared or was absorbed around 40,000 years ago. Thus, the human race developed during a period characterised by intense cooling. These conditions represented a severe struggle for survival. However, there were other periods in which conditions improved, stimulating massive growth and waves of human migration. The age of humankind begins to dawn.

Engels and human origins

How do the ideas of Engels, *The Part Played by Labour in the Transition of Ape to Man*, stand in the light of the most recent theories of evolution?

One of the foremost modern palaeontologists is Stephen J. Gould. In his book *Ever Since Darwin*, he gives the following appraisal of Engels' essay:

"Indeed, the nineteenth century produced a brilliant exposé from a source that will no doubt surprise most readers—Fredrick Engels. (A bit of reflection should diminish surprise. Engels had a keen interest in the natural sciences and sought to base his general philosophy of dialectical materialism upon a 'positive' foundation. He did not live to complete his 'dialectics of nature', but he included long commentaries on science in such treatises as the *Anti-Dühring*.) In 1876, Engels wrote an essay entitled, *The Part Played by Labour in the Transition from Ape to Man*. It was published posthumously in 1896 and, unfortunately, had no visible impact upon Western science.

"Engels considers three essential features of human evolution: speech, a large brain, and upright posture. He argues that the first step must have been a descent from the trees with subsequent evolution to upright posture by our ground-dwelling ancestors. 'These apes when moving on level ground began to drop the habit of using their hands and to adopt a more and more erect gait. This was the decisive step in the transition from ape to man.' Upright posture freed the hand for using tools (labour, in Engels's terminology); increased intelligence and speech came later." [44]

Despite everything, idealist theories of human evolution still conduct a stubborn rearguard action against materialism, as we see from the following extract from a book published as recently as 1995:

"The force that is likely to have driven our evolution [is]…the process of cultural evolution. As our cultures evolved in complexity, so did our brains, which then drove our bodies towards greater responsiveness and our cultures towards still greater complexity in a feedback loop. Big and clever brains led to more complex cultures and bodies suited to take advantage of them, which in turn led to yet bigger and cleverer brains." [45]

Idealists have repeatedly attempted to assert that man is distinguished from the "lower" animals by his superior intelligence. Evidently, early man, for some unexplained reason, first "became intelligent", then began to speak, use tools, paint pictures and so on. If this were true, one would expect it to be reflected in a significant increase in brain size very early on. However, the fossil record proves that this is not the case.

In the course of the last three decades, there have been a series of tremendous advances in the science of palaeontology, new and exciting fossil discoveries and a new way of interpreting them. According to one recent theory, the first bipedal apes

(44) S. J. Gould, *Ever Since Darwin*, pp. 210-1.
(45) Christopher Wills, *The Runaway Brain, The Evolution of Human Uniqueness*, p. xxii.

evolved as far back as seven million years ago. Subsequently, in a process known to biologists as "adaptive radiation", there was a proliferation of bipedal species (that is, species which walked on two legs), with the evolution of many different species of bipedal apes, each adapted to different environmental conditions. About 2-3 million years ago, one of these species developed a significantly larger brain— *Homo erectus*. These were the first hominids to use fire; to use hunting as a significant source of food; to run in the same way as modern humans and to make tools according to a definite preconceived mental plan. Thus, the increase in brain size coincides with the first appearance of tool-making activity, approximately 2.5 million years ago. Thus, for 5 million years, there was no significant expansion of brain size, and then a sudden leap, which is clearly identified with the production of tools.

Molecular biology indicates that the earliest hominid species appeared about five million years ago, in the form of a bipedal ape with long arms and curved fingers. The proto-human *Australopithecus* had a small brain—only 400 cubic centimetres. The qualitative leap took place with *Homo habilis*, who had a brain size of more than 600 cubic centimetres—i.e., an astonishing increase of 50 per cent. The next big advance was with *Homo erectus*, with a brain size of between 850 and 1100 cubic centimetres.

Not until the emergence of *Homo sapiens sapiens* about 100,000 years ago does the size of the brain reach modern levels—1350 ccs. Thus, the earliest hominids did not posses large brains. *Human evolution was not powered by the brain. On the contrary, the enlarged brain was the product of human evolution, especially the making of tools.* The qualitative leap in brain size takes place with *Homo habilis* ("handyman") and is clearly identified with the production of stone tools. In fact a new qualitative leap takes place in the transition from *Homo erectus* to *Homo sapiens*. "The human mind appeared on Earth with astonishing suddenness," writes John McCrone. "Just 70,000 years—the merest eye-blink of geological time—covers our ancestors' transition from smart ape to self-conscious *Homo sapiens*.

"On the far side of the evolutionary divide stands *Homo erectus*, a clever beast with a brain almost as big as a modern human's, a simple tool culture and a mastery of fire—yet mentally still somehow lacking. On our own side stands *Homo sapiens* with the rituals and symbolic art—the cave paintings, beads and bracelets, decorative lamps and burial graves—that mark the arrival of a self-aware mind. *Something sudden and dramatic must have happened,* and it is this event that could be the starting point for human consciousness." [46]

Can apes make tools?

It has recently become fashionable to blur the difference between humans and the rest of the animal kingdom to the point where it virtually disappears. In a way, this is preferable to the kind of idealist nonsense of the past. Humans are animals, and

(46) New Scientist, 29th January 1994, p. 28.

share a number of characteristics with other animals, especially our nearest relatives, the apes. The genetic difference between humans and chimpanzees is only about two per cent. Yet here too, quantity becomes quality. *This two per cent represents a qualitative leap, which has decisively separated humankind from all other species.*

The discovery of the rare species of bonobo chimpanzees, which are even closer to humans than other chimpanzees, has aroused a lot of interest. In their book *Kanzi, The Ape at the Brink of the Human Mind,* Sue Savage-Rumbaugh and Roger Lewin have given a detailed account of their investigations into the mental capacities of a captive bonobo, Kanzi. There is no doubt that the level of intelligence displayed by Kanzi is significantly higher than that so far seen in non-humans, and in some respects resembles that of a human child. Above all, it shows the existence of the potential for, say, tool making. This is a powerful argument in favour of the theory of evolution.

Nevertheless, the significant thing about the experiments that attempt to get the bonobo to make a stone tool is that they were unsuccessful. In the wild, chimpanzees use "tools" such as "fishing sticks" to get termites out of their nest, and even use stones as "anvils" to crack nuts. These operations show a high level of intelligence, and undoubtedly prove that humankind's nearest relations possess some of the mental prerequisites needed for more advanced activities. But as Hegel once remarked, when we want to see an oak tree, we are not satisfied if we are shown an acorn instead. The *potential* for making tools is not the same as actually making them, any more than the mere possibility of winning £10 million on the lottery is the same thing as actually winning. Moreover, this potential, on closer examination turns out to be extremely relative.

Modern chimpanzees occasionally hunt small monkeys. But they do not use weapons or tools for this; *they use their teeth.* Early humans were able to butcher large carcasses, for which they needed sharp stone tools. No doubt, the earliest hominids used only ready-made implements like sticks for digging up roots. This is just the kind of thing we see with modern chimpanzees. If humans had stuck to a mainly vegetarian diet, there would have been no need to make stone tools. But the ability to make stone tools gave them access to a whole new supply of food. This remains true even if we accept that early humans were not hunters but mainly scavengers. They would still need stone tools to cut through the tough hides of large animals.

The proto-humans of the Oldowan culture in East Africa already possessed quite advanced techniques for making stone tools by the process known as flaking. They selected the right sort of stones, and rejected others; they used the correct angle for striking and so on. All this shows a high level of sophistication and skill, which is absent from the "work" of Kanzi, despite the active intervention of humans aimed at encouraging the bonobo to produce a tool. After repeated efforts, the experimenters were forced to admit that:

"So far Kanzi has exhibited a relatively low degree of technological finesse in each of [the four criteria] compared to that seen in the Early Stone Age record."

And they conclude:

"There is, therefore, a clear difference in the stone-knapping skills of Kanzi and the Oldowan tool-makers, which seems to imply that these early humans had indeed ceased to be apes." [47]

Among other differences separating even the most primitive hominids from the highest of the apes are important changes in body structure related to the upright stance. The structure of the bonobo's arms and wrists, for instance, is different from that of humans. The long, curled fingers and short thumb prevent it from gripping a stone effectively enough to strike a powerful glancing blow. This fact has already been pointed out by others:

The chimpanzee's hand has a fairly well developed opposable thumb, "but it is stubby and meets the forefinger along its side, not at its tip. In the hominid hand, the thumb is much larger and is twisted so that it faces the forefinger. This is a logical concomitant to bipedalism and produces a great increase in dexterity. All hominids seem to have had this kind of hand—even afarensis, the oldest one now known. Its hand is scarcely distinguishable from a modern man's." [48]

Despite all the efforts to blur the dividing lines, the difference between even the most advanced apes and the most primitive hominids has been established beyond doubt. Ironically, these experiments, intended to disprove the idea of humans as tool-making animals, *proved exactly the opposite.*

Humans and language

In the same way that attempts have been made to show that tool making is not a fundamental feature of humanity, so some have tried to show the same thing in relation to language. The part of the brain known as Broca's area is associated with language, and was thought to be unique to humans. It is now known that this area also exists in other animals. This fact has been used to dispute the idea that the acquisition of language is unique to humans. But this argument seems extremely feeble. The fact remains that no species other than humans depend upon language for their existence as a species. Language is essential to the social mode of production, which is the basis of human society.

In order to prove that other animals can communicate to some extent, it is not necessary to study the behaviour of bonobos. Many of the lower species have quite sophisticated systems of communication—not just mammals, but also birds and insects. Ants and bees are social animals and have highly developed forms of communication. These, however, cannot be taken as implying intelligent thought, or thought at all. They are inborn and instinctive. They also are quite limited in scope.

(47) S. Savage-Rumbaugh and R. Lewin, *Kanzi, The Ape at the Brink of the Human Mind*, p. 218.
(48) D.C. Johanson and M.A. Edey, *Lucy, The Begginnings of Humankind*, p. 325.

The same actions are repeated endlessly and mechanically and are no less effective for that. But few would regard this as *language* as we understand it.

A parrot can be taught to repeat whole sentences. Does this mean it can talk? It is fairly clear that, while it can imitate sounds quite well, it has no understanding of what the sounds actually mean. But the conveyance of meaning is the essence of intelligible language. Things are different with the higher mammals. Engels, who was a keen hunter, was not sure to what extent dogs and horses did not partially understand human speech and feel frustrated at not being able to talk. Certainly, the level of understanding shown by the bonobo Kanzi in captivity is quite remarkable. In spite of all this, there are specific reasons why no animal other than humans has a language. Humans alone possess a vocal tract that permits the production of consonants. No other animal can pronounce consonants. Some can make clicking and hissing sounds. In fact, consonants can only be pronounced together with vowels, or they would be reduced to clicks and hisses. The ability to pronounce consonants is a product of walking on two feet, as the study on Kanzi shows:

"Man alone has a vocal tract that permits the production of consonants sounds. These differences between our vocal tract and that of apes, while relatively minor, are significant and may be linked to the refinement of bipedal posture and the associated need to carry the head in a balanced, erect position over the centre of the spine. A head with a large heavy jaw would cause its bearer to walk with a forward list and would inhibit rapid running. To achieve balanced upright posture, it was essential that the jaw structure recede and thus that the sloped vocal tract characteristic of apes become bent at a right angle. Along with the reduction of the jaw and the flattening of the face, the tongue, instead of residing entirely in the mouth, was lowered partially down into the throat to form the back of the oropharynx. The mobility of the tongue permits modulation of the oropharyngeal cavity in a manner that is not possible in the ape, whose tongue resides entirely in the mouth. Similarly, the sharp bend in the supralaryngeal airway means that the distance between the soft palate and the back of the throat is very small. By raising the soft palate, we can block off the nasal passage-ways, permitting us to form the turbulence necessary to create consonants."

Without consonants, we cannot easily distinguish between one word and another. We would just have howls and screeches. These can convey a certain amount of information, but it is necessarily limited:

"Speech is infinitely varied and currently only the human ear can readily find the meaningful units in these infinitely varied patterns. The consonants permit us to accomplish this feat." Human infants are able to categorise consonants in a way similar to adults from a very early age, as anyone who has listened to "baby talk" will know. It consists precisely of constantly repeated experiments with combinations of consonants and vowels— "ba-ba, pa-pa, ta-ta, ma-ma", and so on. Even at this early stage, the human infant is performing a task which no other animal is capable of.

Should we then conclude that the only reason that other animals lack speech is physiological? That would be a serious mistake. The shape of the vocal tract, and the physical ability to combine vowels and consonants are the physical preconditions for human speech, but no more than that. Only the development of the hand, inseparably connected with labour and the need to develop a highly co-operative society, made possible the enlarged brain and language. It seems that the area of the brain related to the use of tools and language have a common origin in the early development of the nervous system of a child, and only become separated from the age of two, when Broca's area establishes differentiated circuits with the anterior prefrontal cortex. This, in itself, is striking proof of the close link between tool making and language. Language and manipulative skills developed together, and this evolution is reproduced in the development of human infants today.

Even the earliest hominids of the Oldowan culture had manipulative skills far in advance of the apes. They were not just "upright chimpanzees". The manufacture of even the simplest stone tool is far more complex than it seems. It requires planning and foresight. *Homo habilis* had to plan ahead. He had to know that at some time in the future he would need a tool, even though, he had no such need in the moment when he discovered the appropriate material. The careful selection of the right kind of stone, and the rejection of others; the searching out of the right angle to strike a blow; this showed a level of thinking ability qualitatively different to that of apes. It seems unlikely that at least the rudiments of language were not present at this stage. But there is further evidence which points in this direction. Humans are unusual in that 90 per cent are right-handed. Such a preference for one hand is not found in other primates. Individual apes may be right-handed or left-handed, but the population as a whole will break down into two equal halves. The phenomenon of handedness is closely connected with manipulative skills and language:

"Handedness is associated with localisation of function to the opposite brain hemisphere. The location of manipulative skills in the left hemispheres of (most) right-handers is accompanied by the location there of language skills, too. The right hemisphere has become specialised for spatial skills."

This phenomenon is absent in *Australopithecus*, but has been found in the earliest known skulls of *Homo habilis*, the first toolmaker. It is highly unlikely that this is a coincidence. By the time we reach *Homo erectus*, the evidence becomes overwhelming:

"These three lines of anatomical evidence—of the brain, the vocal apparatus, and the capacity for tool-use—provide the principal support for the notion of long, gradual changes on the road to language. Along with these changes in the brain and the vocal apparatus, there occurred concomitant gradual changes in the hand, changes that made it an increasingly suitable instrument for tool construction and use." [49]

(49) S. Savage-Rumbaugh and R. Lewin, op. cit., pp. 226-7, 228 and 237-8.

The emergence of humankind represents a qualitative leap in evolution. Here, for the first time, matter becomes aware of itself. In place of unconscious evolution, we have the commencement of history. In the words of Frederick Engels:

"With man we enter *history*. Animals also have a history, that of their descent and gradual evolution to their present position. This history, however, is made for them, and in so far as they themselves take part in it, this occurs without their knowledge and desire. On the other hand, the more that human beings become removed from animals in the narrower sense of the word, the more they make their history themselves, consciously, the less becomes the influence of unforeseen effects and uncontrolled forces on this history, and the more accurately does the historical result correspond to the aim laid down in advance.

"If, however, we apply this measure to human history, to that of even the most developed peoples of the present day, we find that there still exists here a colossal disproportion between the proposed aims and the results arrived at, that unforeseen effects predominate, and that the uncontrolled forces are far more powerful than those set into motion according to plan. And this cannot be otherwise as long as the most essential historical activity of men, the one which has raised them from the animal to the human state and which forms the material foundation of all their other activities, namely the production of their requirements of life, i.e., in our day social production, is above all subject to the interplay of unintended effects from uncontrolled forces and achieves its desired end only by way of exception, but much more frequently the exact opposite...

"Only conscious organisation of social production, in which production and distribution are carried on in a planned way, can lift mankind above the rest of the animal world as regard the social aspect, in the same way that production in general has done this for mankind in the specifically biological aspect. Historical evolution makes such an organisation daily more indispensable, but also with every day more possible. From it will date a new epoch of history, in which mankind itself, and with mankind all branches of its activity, and particularly natural science, will experience an advance that will put everything preceding it in the deepest shade." [50]

(50) Engels, *Dialectics of Nature*, pp. 48-9.

13. The genesis of mind

The brain puzzle

"Organic nature grew out of dead nature; living nature produced a form capable of thought. First, we had matter, incapable of thought; out of which developed thinking matter, man. If this is the case—and we know it is, from natural science—it is plain that matter is the mother of mind; mind is not the mother of matter. Children are never older than their parents. 'Mind' comes later, and we must therefore consider it the offspring, and not the parent ... matter existed before the appearance of a thinking human; the earth existed long before the appearance of any kind of 'mind' on its surface. In other words, matter exists objectively, independently of 'mind'. But the psychic phenomena, the so-called 'mind', never and nowhere exists without matter, were never independent of matter. Thought does not exist without a brain; desires are impossible unless there is a desiring organism... In other words: psychic phenomena, the phenomena of consciousness, are simply a property of matter organised in a certain manner, a 'function' of such matter." (Nikolai Bukharin)

"The interpretation of brain mechanisms represents one of the last remaining biological mysteries, the last refuge of shadowy mysticism and dubious religious philosophy." (Steven Rose)

For centuries, as we have seen, the central issue of philosophy was the question of the relation between thought and being. Now at last the great strides forward made by science are beginning to shed light on the real nature of the mind and how it works. These advances provide striking confirmation of the materialist outlook. This is particularly the case in relation to the controversies over the brain and neurobiology. The last hiding place of idealism is under attack, which does not prevent the idealists from staging a stubborn rearguard action, as the following quotation shows:

"When it became impossible to investigate *this non-material element of creation* many dismissed it. They came to think that only matter was real. And so our deepest thoughts were reduced to nothing but the products of brain cells working according to the laws of chemistry...We may study the electrical brain responses that accompany thought, but we cannot reduce Plato to nerve pulses, or Aristotle to alpha-waves...Descriptions of physical movements will never reveal their meaning. Biology can only examine the interlocking world of neurons and synapses." [51]

What we call "mind" is just the mode of existence of the brain. This is an immensely complicated phenomenon, the product of many millions of years of evolution. The difficulty in analysing the complex processes that occur within the brain and nervous system, and the equally complex interrelations between mental processes and the environment, has meant that a proper understanding of the nature of thought has been delayed for centuries. This has enabled idealists and theologians to speculate on the allegedly mystical nature of the "soul", conceived as a non-material substance which deigned to take up temporary residence in the body. The advances of modern neurobiology mean that the idealists are finally being driven from their ultimate refuge. As we begin to unlock the secrets of the brain and nervous system, it becomes progressively easier to explain the mind, without recourse to supernatural agents, *as the sum total of brain activity*.

In the words of neurobiologist Steven Rose, mind and consciousness are "the inevitable consequence of the evolution of particular brain structures which developed in a series of evolutionary changes in the pathway of humanity's emergence...consciousness is a consequence of the evolution of a particular level of complexity and degree of interaction among the nerve cells (neurons) of the cerebral cortex, while the form it takes is profoundly modified for each individual brain by its development in relationship with the environment." [52]

The mind—a machine?

The conceptions of the human brain have changed considerably over the past 300 years, since the birth of modern science and the emergence of capitalist society. The way in which the brain has been perceived has historically been coloured by the existing religious and philosophical prejudices. For the Church, the mind was "God's house". The mechanistic materialism of the 18th century regarded it as a clockwork machine. More recently, it has been described as an improbable sum of probabilistic events. In mediaeval times, when the Catholic ideology dominated everything, the soul was said to permeate all portions of the body; brain, body, mind or matter were indistinguishable. With the appearance of Copernicus, Galileo and

(51) Blackmore and Page, *Evolution: the Great Debate*, pp. 185-6, our emphasis.
(52) Steven Rose, *The Conscious Brain*, p. 31.

finally Newton and Descartes, with its views of mechanical materialism, there was a shift in this viewpoint.

For Descartes the world was machine-like, and living organisms merely particular types of clockwork or hydraulic machines. It is this Cartesian machine image which has come to dominate science and to act as the fundamental metaphor legitimating a particular world view, which takes the machine as a model for the living organism and not the reverse. Bodies are indissoluble wholes that lose their essential characteristics when they are taken to pieces. Machines, on the contrary, can be dismantled to be understood and then put back together. Each part serves a separate and analysable function, and the whole operates in a regular manner that can be described by the operation of its separate parts impinging on each other.

At each stage, the image of the brain has faithfully reflected the limitations of the science of the period. The mechanistic world-outlook of the 18th century reflected the fact that the most advanced science of the day was mechanics. Had the great Newton not explained the entire universe in terms of the laws of mechanics? Why then should the human body and mind work in any other way? Descartes accepted this point of view when he described the human body as a kind of automaton. But since Descartes was a devout Catholic, he could not bring himself to accept that the immortal soul could be part of this machine. It had to be something entirely separate, situated in a special area of the brain, the so-called pineal gland. From this obscure corner of the brain, the Spirit took up temporary residence in the body, and gave life to the machine.

"So developed the inevitable but fatal disjunction of Western scientific thought," says Steven Rose, "the dogma known in Descartes' case and that of his successors as 'dualism'; a dogma which, as we shall see, is the inevitable consequences of any sort of reductionist materialism which does not in the end wish to accept that humans are 'nothing but' the motion of their molecules. Dualism was a solution to the paradox of mechanism which would enable religion and reductionist science to stave off for another two centuries their inevitable major contest for ideological supremacy. It was a solution which was compatible with the capitalist order of the day because in weekday affairs it enabled humans to be treated as mere physical mechanisms, objectified and capable of exploitation without contradiction, while on Sundays ideological control could be reinforced by the assertion of the immortality and free will of an unconstrained incorporeal spirit unaffected by the traumas of the workday world to which its body has been subjected." [53]

In the 18th and 19th centuries, the conception of the mind being the "ghost in the machine" changed. With the advent of electricity, the brain and nervous system were perceived as an electrical maze. At the turn of the century, the telephone exchange analogy emerges, where the brain processes messages from different

(53) S. Rose, *Molecules and Minds*, p. 23.

organs. With the era of mass production came the model of business organisation, as typified in this quote from a child's encyclopaedia:
"Imagine your brain as the executive branch of big business. It is divided, as you see here, into many departments. Seated at the big desk in the headquarters office is the General Manager—your conscious self—with telephone lines running to all departments. Around you are your chief assistants—the Superintendents of Incoming Messages, such as Vision, Taste, Smell, Hearing, and Feeling (the last two hidden behind the central offices). Nearby also are the Superintendents of Outgoing Messages which control Speech and the movement of Arms, Legs, and all other parts of the body. Of course, only the most important messages ever reach your office. Routine tasks such as running the heart, lungs, and stomach, or supervising the minor details of muscular work are carried out by the Managers of Automatic Actions in the Medulla Oblongata and the Manager of Reflex Actions in the Cerebellum. All other departments form what the scientists call Cerebrum."

With the advent of the computer, which can carry out staggering calculations, the parallel with the brain became inevitable. The very way computers stored information was called *memory*. More and more powerful computers were built. How close could a computer get to the human brain? Eventually, science fiction brought us the *Terminator* films, where computers had surpassed human intelligence and fought to take over the world. Yet as Steven Rose in his latest book explains: "Brains do not work with *information* in the computer sense, but with *meaning*. And meaning is a historically and developmentally shaped process, expressed by individuals in interaction with their natural and social environment. Indeed, one of the problems of studying memory is precisely that it is a dialectical phenomenon. Because each time we remember, we in some senses do work on and transform our memories; they are not simply being called up from store and, once consulted, replaced unmodified. Our memories are recreated each time we remember." [54]

What is the brain?

The human brain is the highest point attained by evolution of matter. Physically it weighs about 1.5 kilograms, which is heavier than most human organs. Its surface is wrinkled like a walnut and has a colour and consistence resembling cold porridge. It is, however, extremely complex biologically. It contains a vast number of cells (neurons), possibly numbering 100 billion in total. But even this is dwarfed when we discover that each neuron is embedded in a mass of smaller cells called glia, which serves to support the neurons.

The brain is largely composed of the cerebrum, which is divided into two equal parts. The surface area is known as the cortex. The size of the cortex distinguishes humans from all other organisms. The cerebrum is split into regions or lobes, which

(54) S. Rose, *The Making of Memory*, p. 91.

correspond roughly to particular body functions and in processing sensory information. Behind the cerebrum lies the cerebellum, which supervises all the tiny muscular movements of the body. Below these parts is a thick stalk or brain stem, which is the continuation of the spinal cord. This carries the nerve fibres from the brain through the spinal cord and throughout the body's nervous system, bringing everything into communication with the brain.

The increased brain size, which decisively sets humans apart from other animals, is mainly accounted for by the enlargement of the thin outer layer of nerve cells known as the neocortex. However, this expansion did not take place uniformly. The frontal lobes, associated with planning and foresight, expanded much more than the rest. The same is true of the cerebellum, at the rear part of the skull, which is associated with the ability to acquire automatic skills, a host of everyday actions which we perform without thinking, such as riding a bike, changing gear while driving or doing up pyjama buttons.

The brain itself contains a circulatory system that brings nutrients to regions distant from a blood supply. It receives a large proportion of blood, which carries vital oxygen and glucose. Although the adult brain makes up only 2 per cent of body weight, its oxygen consumption is 20 per cent of the total—and as much as 50 per cent in an infant. Twenty per cent of the body's glucose consumption occurs in the brain. Fully one fifth of the blood pumped by the heart passes through the brain. The nerves transmit information electrically. The signal that passes down a nerve does so as a wave of electricity; a pulse which passes from the cell body to the end of the nerve fibre. So the language of the brain is composed of electrical impulses, not only the amount but the frequency. "The information upon which such predictions are based," writes Rose, "depends on the arrival of data at the body surface in terms of light and sound of varying wavelengths and intensities, fluctuations in temperature, pressure on particular points of the skin, concentration of certain chemical substances which are detected by nose or tongue. Within the body this data is transformed into a series of electrical signals passing along particular nerves to the central brain regions where the signals interact with one another producing certain types of response."

The neuron is composed of a whole number of properties (dendrites, cell body, axon, synapses), which carry out this relay of information (messages arrive at the synapses from the axon). In other words, the neuron is the unit of the brain system. Thousands of motor neurons are involved in any coordinated muscular action. More complex actions will involve millions—though even a million represents only about 0.01 per cent of the total available in the human cortex. But the brain cannot be understood as an assemblage of separate parts. While analysis of the detailed make up of the brain is vital, it can only go so far.

"There are many levels at which one can describe the behaviour of the brain," states Rose. "One can describe the quantum structure of atoms, or the molecular properties of the chemicals which compose it; the electron-micrographic appearance of the individual cells within it; the behaviour of its neurons as an interacting system; the evolutionary or developmental history of these neurons as a changing pattern in time; the behavioural response of the individual human whose brain is under discussion; the familial or social environment of that human, and so on." [55] In order to understand the brain, it is necessary to grasp the complex dialectical interrelations of all its parts. It is necessary to bring together a whole host of sciences: ethology, psychology, physiology, pharmacology, biochemistry, molecular biology, and even cybernetics and mathematics.

Evolution of the brain

In ancient mythology, the goddess Minerva sprang fully armed from the head of Jupiter. The brain was not so fortunate. Far from being created in a single instant, it evolved into its present complex system over a period of millions of years. It came into existence at quite a primitive level of evolution. Single celled organisms show certain behaviour patterns (e.g. movement towards light or nutrients). With the advent of multi-cellular life, a sharp division takes place between animal and plant life. While possessing internal signalling devices that enable plants to "communicate", plant evolution turned away from the evolution of nerves and brain. The movement in the animal kingdom required rapid communication between cells in different parts of the body.

The simplest organisms are self sufficient, possessing all their requirements within a single cell. Communication between one part of the cell and another is relatively simple. On the other hand, multi-cellular organisms are qualitatively different and permit the development of specialisation between cells. Certain cells can deal primarily with digestion, others providing a protective layer, and others circulation, etc. Chemical signalling (hormones) exists in the most primitive multicellular organisms. Even at such a primitive level specialised cells can be found. It is a step towards a nervous system. The more complex organisms, such as flatworms have developed a nervous system, where the neurons are clustered together into a *ganglion*. It has been established that the ganglion is the evolutionary link between nerves and the brain. These clumps of nerve cells occur in insects, crustaceans and molluscs.

The development of a head and the location of eye spots and mouth are an advantage in receiving information about the direction in which the animal is moving. In conformity with this development a group of ganglia are clustered in the head of a flatworm. It represents the evolution of the brain—despite its primitive form. The flatworm also exhibits learning—a key property of the developed brain. It represents a revolutionary leap forward in evolutionary terms.

(55) S. Rose, *The Conscious Brain*, p. 28.

American neuroscientists have found that the basic cellular mechanisms for the formation of memory in humans are also present in snails. Professor Eric Kandel of Columbia University studied the learning and memory of a marine snail called *Aplysia californica*, and found that it exhibited some basic features found in humans. The difference is that, while the human brain has some 100 billion nerve cells, *Aplysia* only has a few thousand, and they are large. The fact that we share these mechanisms with a marine snail is a sufficient answer to the stubborn attempts of idealists to present humankind as some kind of unique creation, separate and apart from other animals. For almost every function of the brain depends in some way upon memory. No divine intervention is required to explain this phenomenon. Natural processes tend to be very conservative. Having hit upon an adaptation which proves useful for performing certain functions, it is constantly replicated throughout evolution, enlarged and improved upon to the degree that this bestows an evolutionary advantage.

Evolution has introduced many innovations in the brains of animals, especially the higher primates and humans with their very large brains. Whereas *Aplysia* can "remember" something for several weeks, its memory only involves a level of mental activity known as *habit* in humans. Such a memory is involved in, say, remembering how to swim. Research into brain-damaged people suggests that the faculty of remembering facts and habit are stored separately in the brain. A person can lose his memory for facts, but still ride a bicycle. The memories that fill a human mind are, of course, infinitely more complex than the processes that go on in the nervous system of a snail.

The continued enlargement of the brain required a drastic change in animal evolution. The nervous system of arthropods or molluscs cannot develop further as a result of a fundamental design problem. The nerve cells are arranged in a ring around the gut, and if expanded would increasingly restrict the gut—a limit sharply revealed in the spider, where the gut is so narrowed by its nerve ring that it can only digest its food as a thin liquid. Insects cannot grow beyond a certain size because their structures would break under their own weight. The brain size has reached its physical limits. Giant insects in horror movies are confined to the realms of science fiction.

The further development of the brain requires the separation of the nerves from the gut. The emergence of vertebrate fish provides the model for the subsequent development of the spinal cord and brain. The skull cavity can house an enlarged brain and the nerves run from the brain through the backbone down the spinal cord. From the eye pits developed an image-forming eye, which could present optical patterns to the nervous system. The emergence of amphibians and reptiles on land saw the great development of the fore-brain region which takes place at the expense of the optic lobes.

Harry Jerison of the University of California developed the idea of the correlation of brain size to body size, and tracked its evolutionary development. He discovered reptiles were small-brained 300 million years ago and remain so today. His graph of reptilian brain size against body size produced a straight line, which includes the dinosaurs. However, the evolution of the early mammals some 200 million years ago marked a leap in relative brain size. These small nocturnal animals were four or five times brainier than the average reptile. This was largely due to the development of the cerebral cortex, which is unique to mammals. This remained the same relative size for some 100 million years. Then, some 65 million years ago, it developed rapidly. According to Roger Lewin, within 30 million years brain development "had increased four to fivefold, with the biggest increases coinciding with the evolution of ungulates (hoofed mammals), carnivores and primates." (*New Scientist*, 5th December, 1992.)

As monkeys, apes and humans evolved, brain size became much bigger. Taking body size into account, monkey's brains are two to three times the average for modern mammals, whereas the human brain is about six times the size. The development of the brain was not of a continuous gradual development but one of fits, starts, and leaps. "Though this broad-brush picture misses important details, the main message is clear enough", says Roger Lewin, "the brain's history involves long periods of constancy punctuated by bursts of change."

In under three million years—an evolutionary leap—the brain tripled in relative size, producing a cortex that accounts for 70-80 per cent of brain volume. The first bipedal hominid species evolved somewhere between 10 and seven million years ago. However, their brains were relative small, on a par with the ape. Then, about 2.6 million years ago, a rapid expansion took place with the emergence of *Homo*. "A leap in the evolution of the ancestors of modern humans took place," says geologist Mark Maslin of Kiel University. "What evidence there is," explains Lewin, "suggests that brain expansion began some 2.5 million years ago, a period coinciding with the first appearance of stone tools." With labour, as Engels explained, came the expansion of the brain and the development of speech. Primitive animal communication gave way to language—a qualitative advance. This must have also depended upon the development of vocal cords. The human brain is capable of making abstractions and generalisations beyond that of the chimpanzee, to which we are closely related.

With the increase in brain size came the increase in complexity and the reorganisation of neural circuitry. The main beneficiary is the front section of the cortex, the prefrontal zone, which is about six times the size of that in apes. Because of its size, this zone can project more fibres to the midbrain, displacing connections there from other brain regions. "This may be significant for the evolution of language", says Terrence Deacon of Harvard University, who notes that the prefrontal zone is home to certain human speech centres. For humans, this reality of consciousness is revealed in self-awareness and thought.

"With the emergence of consciousness," observes Steven Rose, "a qualitative evolutionary leap forward has occurred, making for the critical distinction between humans and other species, so that humans have become vastly more varied and subject to complex interactions than is possible in other organisms. The emergence of consciousness has qualitatively changed the mode of human existence; with it, a new order of complexity, a higher order of hierarchical organisation, becomes apparent. But because we have defined consciousness not as a static form but as a *process* involving interaction between individual and environment, we can see how, as human relationships have become transformed during the evolution of human society, so human consciousness too has been transformed. Our cranial capacity or cell number may not be so different from the early *Homo sapiens*, but our environments—our forms of society—are very different and hence so too is our consciousness—which also means that so too are our brain states." [56]

Importance of speech

The impact of speech—especially the development of "inner speech"—on our brain development is of decisive importance. It is not a new idea, but was known to the ancient Greeks and the philosophers of the 17th century, particularly Thomas Hobbes. In *The Descent of Man,* Charles Darwin explained: "A long and complex train of thought can no more be carried on without the aid of words, whether spoken or silent, than a long calculation without the use of figures of algebra." In the 1930s the Soviet psychologist Lev Vygotsky attempted to reestablish the whole of psychology on this basis.

Using examples of child behaviour, he explained why children spend a lot of time talking aloud to themselves. They are rehearsing the habits of planning that they would later internalise as inner speech. Vygotsky showed that this inner speech underpinned the human ability to recollect and recall memories. The human mind is dominated by an inner world of thoughts, stimulated by our sensations, which is capable of generalisation and perspective. Animals also have memories, but they seem to be locked into the present, reflecting the immediate environment. The development of human inner speech allows humans to recall and develop ideas. In other words, inner speech played a key role in the evolution of the human mind.

Although Vygotsky's early death cut short his work, his ideas have been taken up and expanded, with an important input from anthropology, sociology, linguistics and educational psychology. In the past, memory was examined as a unitary biological system, containing short and long-term memory. It could be examined neurophysiologically, biochemically and anatomically. But today a more dialectical approach, involving other sciences, is being pioneered.

"In this reductionist approach", argues Rose, "it follows that the proper task of the sciences of the organism is to collapse the individual's behaviour into particular

(56) S. Rose, *The Conscious Brain*, p. 179.

molecular configurations; while the study of populations of organisms comes down to the search for DNA strands which code for reciprocal or selfish altruism. Paradigm cases of this approach over the last decade have been the attempts to purify RNA, protein, or peptide molecules that are produced by learning and which 'code' for specific memories; or the molecular biologist's search for an organism with a 'simple' nervous system which can be mapped by serial electron microscope sections and in which the different wiring diagrams associated with different behavioural mutations can be identified."

Rose concludes that "the paradoxes that this type of reductionism gets itself into are probably more vicious than those of the systems modellers. They have been apparent, of course, since Descartes, whose reduction of the organism to an animal machine powered by hydraulics had to be reconciled, for the human, with a free-willed soul in the pineal gland. As then, so today, mechanistic reductionism forces itself into sheer idealism before it is through." [57]

In the brain's evolution few parts are totally discarded. As new structures develop, the old ones are reduced in importance and size. With the development of the brain comes the increased capacity to learn. The transformation from ape to man was originally assumed to have begun with brain development. The size of an ape's brain (by volume) ranges from 400 to 600 cubic centimetres; the human brain is 1,200 to 1,500 ccs. It was believed the "missing link" would be essentially ape-like, but with a larger brain. Again it was considered that an enlarged brain preceded upright posture.

This first brain theory was decisively challenged by Engels as an extension of the false idealist view of history. The erect posture in walking was the decisive step in the transition from ape to man. It was their bipedal nature that freed their hands, which lead later to the expansion of the brain. "First comes labour," says Engels, "after it and then side by side with it, articulate speech—these were the two most essential stimuli under the influence of which the brain of the ape gradually changed into that of man." [58] Subsequent discovery of fossilised remains confirmed Engels's view. "The confirmation was complete beyond all scientific doubt. The African creatures being unearthed had brains no larger than those of apes. They had walked and run like humans. The foot differed little from that of modern man, and the hand was halfway to human conformation." [59]

Despite the growing evidence supporting Engels' views on human origins, the conception of brain-first development is still alive and kicking today. In a recent book entitled *The Runaway Brain, The Evolution of Human Uniqueness*, the author, Christopher Wills states: "We know that at the same time as our ancestors' brains were growing larger, their posture was *becoming more upright*, fine motor skills were developing, and vocal signals were graduating into speech." [60]

(57) S. Rose, *Molecules and Mind*, pp. 96-7.
(58) Engels, *Dialectics of Nature*, p. 284.
(59) S.L. Washburn and R.L. Moore, *Ape into Man: A Study of Human Evolution*.
(60) C. Wills, op. cit., p. 8, our emphasis.

Man becomes increasingly conscious of his environment and himself. Unlike other animals, humans can generalise their experience. Whereas animals are dominated by their environment, humans change their environment to suit their needs. Science has confirmed Engels' statement that "Our consciousness and thinking, however suprasensuous they may seem, are the product of a material, bodily organ, the brain. Matter is not a product of mind, but mind itself is merely the highest product of matter. This is, of course, pure materialism." [61] As the brain develops, so does the capacity to learn and generalise. Important information is stored in the brain, probably in many different parts of the system. This information is not erased as the molecules in the brain are renewed. Within fourteen days, 90 per cent of the brain's proteins are broken down and renewed by identical molecules. Nor is there any reason to believe that the brain has stopped evolving. Its capacity remains infinite. The development of classless society will see a new leap forward in mankind's understanding. For instance, the advances of genetic engineering are only in their infancy. Science opens up enormous opportunities and challenges. The brain and human intelligence will evolve to meet these future challenges. But for every problem solved, many more questions will be raised, in a never-ending spiralling of development.

Language and thought of the child

There appears to be a certain analogy between the development of human thought in general and the development of the language and thought of the individual human being through childhood and adolescence to adulthood.

This point was made by Engels in *The Part Played by Labour in the Transition of Ape to Man:*

"For, just as the developmental history of the human embryo in the mother's womb is only an abbreviated repetition of the history, extending over millions of years, of the bodily evolution of our animal ancestors, beginning from the worm, so the mental development of the human child is only a still more abbreviated repetition of the intellectual development of these same ancestors, at least of the later ones." [62]

The study of the development from embryo to adult is called *ontogeny*, whereas the study of evolutionary relationships between species is called *phylogeny*. Both are strangely linked together, but not as a crude mirror image. For instance, during its development in the womb, the human embryo resembles a fish, an amphibian, a mammal, and appears to pass through phases which recall the stages of animal evolution. All humans are alike in many respects, particularly the substances and structures of the brain. Chemically, anatomically and physiologically there is amazingly little variation. At conception, the fertilised ovum develops into two hollow balls of

(61) MESW, Vol. 3, p. 348.
(62) Engels, *The Dialectics of Nature*, p. 241.

cells. The first recognised development takes place within eighteen days, as thickening where the balls touch become the *neural groove*. The forward part enlarges, later to develop into a brain. Other differentiation takes place which will become the eyes, nose and ears. The blood circulation and nervous systems are the first to function in embryo life, with the heartbeat commencing in the third week of conception.

The neural groove becomes a channel and then a tube. In time it will be transformed into the spinal cord. At the head end, swellings appear in the tube to form the forebrain, midbrain and hindbrain. Everything is set for the rapid development of the central nervous system. There is a qualitative leap in the rate of cell division approximating the final cellular structure. By the time the embryo is 13 mm long, the brain has developed into the five-vesicle brain. The stalks that form the optic nerves and eyes emerge. By the end of the third month, the cerebral cortex and cerebellum can be identified, as well as the thalamus and hypothalamus. With the fifth month the wrinkled cortex begins to take shape. All the essentials are developed by the ninth month, although further development will take place after birth. Even then, the weight of the brain is only about 350 grams, compared with 1,300 to 1,500 grams of an adult. It will be 50 per cent of its adult weight at six months, 60 per cent at a year, and 90 per cent at six years. By the age of ten, it would be 95 per cent of its adult weight. The rapid growth of the brain is reflected in the size of the head. The size of a baby's head is large for its body compared to an adult. The brain of a newborn baby is closer than any other organ to its adult state of development. At birth the brain is ten per cent of the entire body weight compared to only two per cent in the adult.

The physical structures of the brain (its biochemistry, cellular architecture and electrical circuitry) are modified by the effects of the brain's response to the environment. Ideas and memories are encoded in the brain in terms of complex changes in the neural system. Thus, all the processes of the brain interact, to give rise to the unique phenomenon of consciousness—matter aware of itself. For Canadian psychologist Donald Hebb, the key lies in the synaptic junctions between two nerve cells, which remains the basis of today's ideas. Particular sets of circuitry and firing patterns between the synapses may encode the memory, but it will not necessarily be localised to a single network of the brain. It can be encoded in both the hemispheres and many times over. The entire scope of the individual's environment, especially in the early years of development, continuously leaves unique impressions on the brain processes and behaviour. "A variety of the most subtle changes in environment, especially during childhood," says Rose, "can produce long-lasting changes in its chemistry and function."

Without this dialectical interaction between brain and environment, then the individual's development would simply be prescribed by the genetic code. The behaviour of individuals would be precoded and predictable from the beginning.

However, the environment plays a decisive role in development. A changed set of circumstances can bring about a remarkable change in the individual.

Eyes, hand and brain

The development of the language and thought of the child was first subjected to a rigorous analysis in the pioneering work of the Swiss epistemologist Jean Piaget. Some aspects of his theories have been questioned, especially the lack of flexibility with which he interpreted the way children move from one to another of his stages. Nevertheless, this was pioneering work, in a field that had been virtually ignored, and many of his theories retain considerable validity. Piaget was the first one to give an idea of the dialectical process of the development from birth, through childhood to adolescence, as Hegel was the first to provide a systematic exposition of dialectical thinking in general. The defects of both systems should not be allowed to obscure the positive content of their work. Although Piaget's stages are undoubtedly rather schematic, and his research methods open to question, they nevertheless retain value as a general over-view of early human development.

Piaget's theories were a reaction against the views of the behaviourists, whose leading representative, American psychologist Burrhus F. Skinner, was particularly influential in the 1960s in the USA. The behaviourist approach is completely mechanistic, based on a linear pattern of cumulative development. According to this, children learn most efficiently when they are subjected to a linear programme of material devised by expert teachers and curriculum planners. Skinner's educational theories fit in very well with the capitalist mentality. Children will only learn, according to this theory, if they are rewarded for doing so, just as a worker who gets extra pay for overtime.

The behaviourists adopted a typically mechanical position on the development of language. Noam Chomsky pointed out that Skinner adequately described how a baby learned the first few words (mainly nouns), but he did not however explain how these were put together. Language is not just a string of words. It is precisely the combination of the words in a certain dynamic relationship that makes language such a rich, effective, flexible and complex instrument. Here, most decidedly, the whole is greater than the sum of the parts. It is really an incredible feat for a child of two to learn the rules of grammar, as any adult who has tried to learn a foreign language will agree.

Compared to this crude and mechanistic dogma, Piaget's theories represented a great step forward. Piaget explained that learning comes naturally to children. It is the job of the teacher to bring out those tendencies which are already present in all children. Moreover, Piaget correctly pointed out that the process of learning is not a straight line, but is punctuated by qualitative breakthroughs. Although Piaget's original stages are open to question, there is no doubt that this dialectical approach, in general, was valid. What was valuable in Piaget's work was that the development of the child was presented as a contradictory process in which each stage was based on the previous one, both overcoming and preserving it. The genetically conditioned base provides the ready-made material, which from the first moment enters into a dialectical interaction with the environment. The newborn baby is not conscious, but driven by deep-rooted biological instincts that urgently demand satisfaction. These powerful animal instincts do not disappear, but remain as an unconscious substratum, underlying our activities.

To use the language of Hegel, what we have here is the transition from being-in-itself to being-for-itself—from potential to actual, from an isolated, helpless, unconscious being, a plaything of natural forces to a conscious human being. The movement towards self-consciousness, as Piaget correctly explained, is a struggle, which passes through different phases. The newborn baby does not clearly distinguish itself from its surroundings. Only slowly does it become aware of the distinction between the *self* and the external world. "The period from birth to the acquisition of language," writes Piaget, "is marked by an extraordinary mental development." Elsewhere, he describes the first 18 months of existence as "a Copernican revolution on a small scale." [63] The key to this process is the gradual dawning of the realisation of the relation between the subject (self) and the object (reality), which must be understood.

Vygotsky and Piaget

The earliest and best of the critics of Piaget was Vygotsky, the Soviet educationalist who, in the period 1924-34, worked out a consistent alternative to Piaget's ideas. Tragically, Vygotsky's ideas were only published in the Soviet Union after the death of Stalin, and became known in the West in the 1950s and 60s, when they exercised a powerful influence on many, like Jerome Bruner. At the present time, they are widely accepted by educationalists.

Vygotsky was in advance of his time in explaining the important role of gestures in the development of language. This has been revived more recently by psycholinguists unravelling the origins of language. Bruner and others have pointed to the enormous impact of gestures on the later development of language in a child. Whereas Piaget placed more emphasis on the biological aspect of the development of the child, Vygotsky concentrated more on culture, as have people like Bruner. An important part in culture is played by tools, whether they are the sticks and stones of early hominids, or pencils, rubbers and books of today's children.

Recent research has shown that babies are more capable at an earlier stage than Piaget thought. His ideas about very young babies seem to have been overtaken, but much of his research remains valid. Coming from a biological background, it was inevitable that he should place heavy stress on this aspect of the child's develop-

(63) Piaget, *The Mental Development of the Child*, p. 19.

ment. Vygotsky approached the question from a different point of view, but nevertheless, there are common points. For example, in his study of the early years of childhood, he deals with "nonlinguistic thought" such as Piaget outlined in his account of "sensorimotor activity", such as using a rake to reach another toy. Alongside this, we notice the incomprehensible sounds of the baby ("baby-talk"). When the two elements combine, there is an explosive development of language. For each new experience, the toddler wants to know the name. While Vygotsky took a different route, the trail was blazed by Piaget.

"The process of growing up is not a linear progression from incompetence to competence: to survive, a newborn baby must be competent at being a newborn baby, not at being a tiny version of the adult it will later become. Development is not just a quantitative process but one in which there are transformations in quality—between suckling and chewing solid food, for instance, or between sensorimotor and cognitive behaviour." [64]

Only gradually, over a long period and by a difficult process of adjustment and learning, does the child cease to be a bundle of blind sensations and appetites, a helpless object, and become a conscious, self-directing free agent. It is this painful struggle to pass from the unconscious to the conscious, from utter dependence on the environment to the domination of the environment, which provides the striking parallel between the development of the individual infant and that of the human species. Of course, it would be wrong to imply that the parallel is a precise one. Every analogy holds good only within definite limits. But it is hard to resist the conclusion that in at least some aspects such parallels do, in fact, exist. From lower to higher; from simple to complex; from unconscious to conscious—such features recur constantly in the evolution of life.

The animals depend more than humans upon the senses, and have better hearing, eyesight and sense of smell. It is noticeable that keenness of eyesight reaches a high point in late childhood, and thereafter diminishes. On the other hand, the higher intellectual functions continue to develop through life, and well into old age. To trace the path whereby humans pass from the unconscious to the level of real consciousness is one of the most fascinating and important tasks in science.

At birth, the baby knows only reflexes. But this does not at all signify passivity. From the very first moment of its existence, the baby's relation with its environment is *active* and *practical*. It does not think only with its head, but with its whole body. The development of the brain and consciousness is directly related to its practical activity. One of the first reflexes is sucking. Even here the process of learning from experience is present. Piaget points out that the baby suckles better after one or two weeks than at first. Later on comes a process of discrimination, where the child begins to recognise things. Later still, the child begins to draw its first generalisa-

(64) Steven Rose, Leon J. Kamin and Richard Lewontin, *Not In Our Genes*, p. 96.

tions, not only in thought but in action. It does not only suckle at the breast, but also sucks the air, and then his fingers. The Spanish have a saying: "I don't suck my thumb," meaning "I'm not stupid." As a matter of fact, the ability to introduce a thumb into the mouth is quite a difficult task for a baby, which usually appears at about two months, and marks a significant step forward, denoting a certain level of co-ordination of hand and brain.

Immediately after birth the child has difficulty in focusing its attention on particular objects. Gradually, it becomes able to concentrate on specific objects, and anticipates where they are so that it can move its head in order to see them. This development, analysed by Bruner, takes place during the first two or three months, and involves not only the purely visual field, but also activity—the orientation of the eyes, head, and body towards the object of attention. At the same time, the mouth becomes the link between vision and manual movement. Gradually, it begins a process of visually guided reaching-grasping-retrieving, which always concludes by bringing the hand to the mouth.

For the newborn child, the world is first and foremost something to be sucked. Later, it is something to be looked at and listened to, and, when a sufficient level of co-ordination permits it, something to be manipulated. This is not yet what we could call consciousness, but it is the starting-point of consciousness. A very lengthy process of development is needed for these simple elements to become integrated into *habits and organised perceptions*. Later on, we get systematic thumb-sucking, the turning of the head to the direction of a sound, following a moving object with the eyes (indicating a level of generalisation and anticipation). After five weeks or more, the baby smiles, and recognises some people rather than others, although this cannot be taken to mean that the baby possesses a notion of a person, or even an object. This is the stage of the most elementary sense perception.

In its relations to the objective world, the baby has two possibilities: either to incorporate things (and people) into its activities, and thus to *assimilate* the material world, or to readjust its subjective wishes and impulses to the external world, i.e., to *accommodate to reality*. From a very early age, the baby tries to "assimilate" the world to itself, by introducing it into its mouth. Later, it learns to adjust to external reality, gradually begins to distinguish and perceive different objects, and remembers them. It acquires, through experience, the ability to carry out a number of operations, like reaching and grasping. Logical intelligence arises first from concrete operations, from *practice*, and only much later as abstract deductions.

Piaget identified six clearly defined "stages" in the development of the child. The stage of reflexes or hereditary functions includes primary instinctive tendencies such as *nutrition*. The need to obtain food is a powerful inborn impulse, controlling the reflexes of the newborn child. This is a common feature which humans share with all animals. The newborn child, lacking the elements of higher thought, is nonetheless a natural materialist, who expresses his firm belief in the existence of the physical world in exactly the same way as all animals—by eating it. It takes a great deal of intellectual refinement before clever philosophers succeed in convincing people that we cannot really say whether the material world is out there or not. This supposedly complicated and profound philosophical question is in fact resolved by a baby in the only possible way—*through practice*.

From the age of two, the child enters a period of symbolic thought and *preconceptual representation*. The child begins to use picture images as symbols to replace the real things. Parallel to this is the development of language. The next stage is *conditional representation*, recognising other points of reference in the world, and simultaneously is developed coherent language. This is followed by *operational thinking* from seven to twelve years of age. The child begins to recognise relationships between objects and to deal with more abstract conceptions.

It is precisely practice, and the interaction of inborn, genetically conditioned tendencies, which provide the key to the mental development of the child. Piaget's second stage is that of primary motor habits, accompanied by the first "organised perceptions" and primary "differentiated feelings". The third stage is that of "sensorimotor intelligence" or practice (which is prior to speech). Then comes the phase of "intuitive intelligence" involving spontaneous relations between individuals, especially submission to adults; the phase of "concrete intellectual operations" which includes the development of *logic* and *moral and social feelings* (from 7 to 11 or 12 years); and finally, a phase of *abstract intellectual operations*—the formation of personality and emotional and intellectual integration in adult society (adolescence).

Human progress is closely linked to the development of thought in general, and science and technology in particular. The capacity for rational, abstract thought does not come easily. Even now, the minds of most people rebel against thought that leaves behind the familiar world of the concrete. This ability appears quite late in the mental development of the child. We see this in children's paintings, which depict *what the child actually sees*, not what they ought to see, according to the laws of perspective, and so on. Logic, ethics, morality, all appear late in the child's intellectual development. In the first period, every action, every movement, every thought, is the product of necessity. The notion of "free will" has nothing whatever to do with the mental activities of the child. Hunger and fatigue lead to desire for food or sleep, even in the youngest baby.

The possession of a capacity for abstract thought, even on the most primitive level, makes the subject master of the most distant events, both in space and time. This is as true for the child as it was for early humans. Our earliest ancestors did not clearly distinguish themselves from other animals or inanimate nature. Indeed, they had not fully emerged from the animal kingdom, and were very much at the mercy of the forces of nature. The elements of self-awareness seem to exist in chimpanzees, our nearest relatives, though not in monkeys. But only in humans does the potential for abstract thought reach its full expression. This is closely related to language, one of the fundamental distinguishing features of humankind.

The neocortex, which makes up 80 per cent of the volume of the human brain, is the part responsible for relations with groups, and is related to thinking in general. There is a close connection between social life, thought and language. The self-centred nature of the newborn baby gradually gives way to a realisation that there is an external world, people and society, with its own laws, demands and restrictions. Quite late on, between three and six months, according to Piaget, the phase of grasping begins, involving first pressure, then manipulation. This is a decisive step, leading to a multiplication of the baby's powers and the formation of new habits. After this, development becomes speeded up. The dialectical nature of the process is indicated by Piaget:

"The point of departure is always a reflex cycle, but a cycle the exercise of which, instead of repeating itself without more ado, incorporates new elements and constitutes with them still wider organised totalities, thanks to progressive differentiations." Thus the development of the child is not a straight line or a closed circle, but a spiral, where long periods of slow change are interrupted by sudden leaps forward, and each stage involves a qualitative advance.

Piaget's third stage is that of "practical intelligence" or the "sensorimotor stage as such". The exact nature and delineation of these "stages" is, of course, debatable, but the general thrust remains valid. Intelligence is closely related to the manipulation of objects. The development of the brain is directly linked to the hand. As Piaget says: "But it is a question of an exclusively practical intelligence, which is applied to the manipulation of objects, and which, in place of words and concepts, only makes use of perceptions and organised movements in *schemes of action*." [65] From this we see that the basis of all human knowledge is experience, activity and practice. The hands, in particular, play a decisive role.

The emergence of language

Before speech develops as such, the baby makes use of all kinds of signs, eye contact, cries and other body language, to exteriorise its wants. In the same way, it is clear that before the earliest hominids could speak, they must have used other means to signal to one another. The rudiments of such communication exist in other animals, especially the higher primates, but only in humans does speech exist as such. The long struggle of the child to master speech, with its complex underlying patterns and logic, is synonymous with the acquisition of consciousness. A similar road must have been traversed by early humans.

The throat of the human infant, like that of apes and other mammals, is so constructed that the vocal passage is low down. In this way, it is capable of making the

---

(65) Piaget, op. cit., p. 22.

kind of cries that animals make, but not articulate speech. The advantage of this is that it can cry and eat at the same time, without choking. Later on, the vocal passage migrates upwards, reflecting a process that actually occurred during the course of evolution. It is unthinkable that human speech would have arisen all at once, without all kinds of transitional forms. This took place over millions of years, in which there were undoubtedly periods of rapid development, as we see in the development of the human infant.

Can thought exist without language? That depends on what is meant by "thought". The *elements* of thought exist in animals, especially the higher mammals, which also possess certain means of communication. Among the chimpanzees, the level of communication is quite sophisticated. But in none of these can we speak of either language or thought anything remotely on the human level. The higher develops from the lower, and could not exist without it. Human speech originates in the incoherent sounds of the baby, but it would be foolish to identify the two. In the same way, it is a mistake to try to show that language existed before the human race.

The same is true of thought. To use a stick to get hold of an object that is out of reach is an act of intelligence. But this appears quite late in the development of the child—about 18 months. This involves the use of a tool (a stick) in a coordinated move, in order to realise a preconceived aim. It is a deliberate, planned action. This kind of activity can be seen among apes, and even monkeys. The use of objects found ready to hand—sticks, stones, etc.—as adjuncts to food-gathering activities is well documented. At twelve months, the child has learnt to experiment by throwing an object in different directions to "see what happens".

This is a repeated purposeful activity, designed to get results. It implies an awareness of *cause and effect* (if I do this, then that will happen). None of this knowledge is innate. It is learned through experience. It takes the child 12-18 months to grasp the notion of cause and effect. A most powerful piece of knowledge! It must have taken early humans millions of years to learn the same lesson, which is the real basis of all rational thought and purposeful action. All the more absurd that, at a time when our knowledge of nature has reached such dazzling heights, certain scientists and philosophers should wish to drag thought back to what is really a primitive and childish state, by denying the existence of causality.

In the first two years of life, an intellectual revolution takes place, in which the notions of space, causality and time are formed, not, as Kant imagined, out of thin air, but as a direct result of practice and experience of the physical world. All human knowledge, all the categories of thought, including the most abstract ones, are derived from this. This materialist conception is clearly proven by the development of the child. Initially, the infant does not distinguish between reality and itself. But at a certain point, the realisation dawns that what it sees is something outside itself, something which will continue to exist even when it is no longer seen. This is the great breakthrough, the "Copernican revolution" of the intellect. Those philosophers who assert that the material world does not exist, or that this cannot be proven, are, in a literal sense of the word, expressing an *infantile* idea.

The baby who cries when its mother leaves the room shows that it understands that she has not disappeared just because she is no longer in its field of vision. It cries in the certainty that this action will bring about her return. Up to the first year, the child believes that what is out of sight has, in effect, ceased to exist. By the end of the second year, it already recognises cause and effect. Just as there is no Chinese Wall separating thought from action, so there is no absolute dividing line between the intellectual life of the child and its emotional development. Feelings and thoughts are, in fact, indivisible. They constitute the two complementary aspects of human behaviour. Everyone knows that no great enterprise is achieved without the element of the will. Emotions are a most powerful lever for human action and thought, and play a fundamental role in human development. But at every stage, the intellectual development of the child is inextricably bound up with activity. As intelligent behaviour emerges, emotional states of mind are associated with actions—cheerfulness or sadness are linked with the success or failure of intentional acts.

The emergence of language represents a profound modification in the behaviour and experience of the individual, both from an intellectual and emotional standpoint. It is a qualitative leap. The possession of language creates, to quote Piaget, "the ability to reconstruct his past actions in the form of narration and to anticipate his future actions through verbal representations." With language, past and future become real for us. We can rise above the restrictions of the present, plan, predict and intervene according to a conscious plan.

Language is a product of social life. Human social activity is unthinkable without language. It must have been present, in one form or another, in the earliest truly human societies, from the very earliest times. Thought itself is a kind of "internal language". With language comes the possibility of real human social intercourse, the creation of a culture and tradition which can be learned and passed on orally, and later on in writing, as opposed to mere imitation. It also makes possible genuine human relations, where feelings of antipathy, sympathy, love and respect can be expressed in a more coherent, developed way. In embryo, these elements are present from the first six months in the form of imitation. The first words are pronounced, usually isolated nouns. Then the child learns to put two words together. Nouns are gradually connected with verbs and adjectives. Finally, the mastering of grammar and syntax entails extremely complex patterns of logical thought. This is a tremendous qualitative leap for every individual as it was for the species.

Very young children can be said to have a "private" language, which is not language in the real sense, but only sounds which represent experiments and attempts to copy adult speech. Articulate speech grows out of these sounds, but the two must not be confused. Language, by it very nature, is not private, but social. It is inseparable from social life and collective activity, in the first place, co-operation in production, which lies at the basis of all social life from the earliest times. Language represents a colossal leap forward. Once the process started, it would have enormously speeded up the development of consciousness. This can be seen also in the development of the child.

Language represents the beginnings of the socialisation of human activity. Before this, early pre-humans must have communicated by other means: cries, body language and other gestures. Indeed, modern humans continue to do so, particularly in moments of great stress or emotion. But the limitations of this kind of "language" are self-evident. They are hopelessly inadequate to convey more than immediate situations. The level of complexity, abstract thought and planning needed for even the simplest human societies based on co-operative production cannot be expressed by such means. Only through language is it possible to escape from the immediate present, recall the past, and foresee the future. Only though language is it possible to establish a really human form of communication with others, to share one's "inner life" with them. Thus we talk of "dumb animals" as a distinction from humans, the only animals that possess speech.

Socialisation of thought

Through language, the child is initiated into the wealth of human culture. Whereas with other animals, the factor of genetic inheritance is predominant, in human society, the cultural factor is decisive. The human infant has to go through a very long period of "apprenticeship" in which it is completely subordinated to adults, particularly its parents, who, largely by means of language, initiate it into the mysteries of life, society and the world. The child finds itself confronted with a ready-made model to copy and imitate. Later this is expanded to include other adults and children, especially through play. This process of socialisation is not easy or automatic, but it is the basis of all intellectual and moral development. All parents have noticed with amusement how small children will withdraw into a world of their own, and quite happily conduct a "conversation" with themselves for long periods, while playing on their own. The development of the child is intimately linked to the process of breaking away from this primitive state of egocentricity, and relating to others and to external reality in general.

In Piaget's original scheme, the period from two to seven years marks the transition from the simply "practical" ("sensorimotor") phase of the intelligence, to thought as such. This process is characterised by all kinds of transitional forms between the two. It reveals itself in play, for example. From seven to twelve, games appear with rules, implying common objectives, as opposed to playing with dolls, say, which is highly individual. The logic of primary infancy can be described as *intuition*, which is still present in adults—what Hegel calls "immediate" thought. At a later stage, well known to parents, the child begins to ask *why*? This naïve curiosity is the beginning of rational thinking—the child is no longer willing just to take things as they are, but seeks a rational ground for them. It grasps the fact that all things have a cause, and tries to grasp what this is. It is not satisfied with the mere fact that "B" happens to occur *after* "A". It wishes to know why it has occurred. Here too the child of between three to seven years of age shows itself to be wiser than some modern philosophers.

Intuition, to which a certain aura of magic and poetry has been traditionally attached, is, in fact, the lowest form of thinking, characteristic of very small children and people on a low level of cultural development. It consists of the immediate impressions provided by the senses, which provoke us to react "spontaneously", that is, in an unthinking way, to a given circumstance. The rigours of logic and consistent thought do not enter into it. Such intuitions can sometimes be spectacularly successful. In such cases, the apparently spontaneous nature of the "flash of inspiration" provides the illusion of a mysterious insight coming "from within" and divinely inspired. In fact, intuition comes, not from the obscure depths of the soul, but from the *interiorisation of experience*, which is obtained, not in a scientific way, but in the form of images and the like.

A person with considerable experience of life can frequently arrive at an accurate assessment of a complicated situation on the basis of the scantiest information. Similarly, a hunter can display almost a "sixth sense" about the animals he is tracking. In the case of truly great minds, flashes of inspiration are considered to represent a quality of genius. In all these cases, what appears to be a spontaneous idea is, in fact, the distilled essence of years of experience and reflection. More often, however, mere intuition leads to a highly unsatisfactory, superficial and distorted form of knowledge. In the case of children, "intuition" marks the primitive, immature phase of thought, before they are able to reason, define and judge. It is so inadequate that it is generally regarded as comical by adults, who have long since left this phase behind. In all these cases, it goes without saying that there is nothing mystical involved.

In the first stages of life, the child does not distinguish between itself and its physical environment. Only gradually, as we have seen, does the child begin to distinguish between the subject ("I") and the object (the physical world). It begins to understand the real relationship between its environment and itself in practice, through manipulation of objects and other physical operations. The primitive unity is broken down, and a confusing multiplicity of sights, sounds and objects emerges. Only later does the child begin to grasp the connections between things. Experiments have shown that the child is consistently more advanced in deeds than in words.

There is no such thing as a "purely intellectual act". This is particularly clear in the case of small children. It is commonplace to counterpose the *heart* and the *head*. This, too, is a false opposition. The emotions play a part in the solution of intellectual problems. Scientists become excited over the solution of the most abstruse equations. Different schools of thought clash heatedly over problems of philosophy, art, and so on. On the other hand, there is no such thing as pure acts of affection. Love, for example, presupposes a high degree of understanding between two people. Both the intellect and the emotions play a role. The one presupposes the other, and they intervene and condition each other, to a greater or lesser degree.

As the degree of socialisation advances and develops, the child becomes more aware of the need for what Piaget calls "inter-personal sentiments"—the emotional relations between people. Here we see that the social bond itself involves contradictory elements of attraction and repulsion. The child learns this first in relation to its parents and family, and then forms close bonds with broader social groups. Feelings of sympathy and antipathy are developed, linked to the socialisation of actions, and the appearance of moral sentiments—good and bad, right and wrong, which mean much more than "I like" or "I dislike". They are not subjective but objective criteria derived from society.

These powerful bonds are an important part of the evolution of human society, which, from the outset was based on co-operative social production and mutual dependence. Without this, humanity would have never emerged from the animal world. Morality and tradition are learned through language, and passed on from generation to generation. Compared to this, the factor of biological inheritance appears quite secondary, although it remains the raw material from which humanity is constructed.

With the commencement of proper schooling, from about the age of seven, the child begins to develop a strong sense of socialisation and co-operation. This is shown in games with rules—even a game of marbles requires a knowledge and acceptance of quite complicated rules. Like the rules of ethics and the laws of society, they must be accepted by all, in order to be viable. A knowledge of rules and how they are to be applied goes together with a grasp of something as complicated as the grammatical and syntactical structure of language.

Piaget makes the important observation that "all human behaviour is at the same time social and individual." Here we have a most important example of the unity of opposites. It is entirely false to counterpose thought to being, or individual to society. They are inseparable. In the relationship between *subject* and *object*, between the individual and the environment (society) the mediating factor is *human practical activity* (labour). The communication of thought is language (exteriorised reflection). On the other hand, thought itself is interiorised social intercourse. At seven years of age, the child begins to understand logic, which consists precisely of a system of relations, permitting the coordination of points of view.

In a brilliant passage, Piaget compares this stage with the early stage of Greek philosophy, when the Ionian materialists parted company with mythology, in order to arrive at a rational understanding of the world:

"It is surprising to observe that, among the firsts (new forms of explanation of the uniters) to appear, there are some which present a notable similarity to that given by the Greeks precisely in the epoch of decline of mythological explanations, properly so-called."

Here we see, in a very striking way, how the forms of thought of each individual child in its early development, provides a rough parallel to the development of human thought in general. In the early stages, there are parallels with primitive *animism*, where the child thinks that the sun shines, because it was born. Later the child imagines that clouds come from smoke, or air; stones are made of earth, etc. This recalls the early attempts to explain the nature of matter in terms of water, air, and so on. The great significance of this is that it was a naïve attempt to explain the universe in materialist, scientific terms, rather than in terms of religion and magic. The child of seven begins to grasp the notion of time, space, speed, etc. However, this takes time. Contrary to Kant's theory that the notion of time and space are inborn, the child cannot grasp such abstract ideas until they are experimentally demonstrated. *Thus, idealism is shown to be false by a study of the processes of developing of human thought itself.*

14. Marxism and Darwinism

Darwin's gradualism

" It is sometimes said that the standpoint of dialectics is identical with that of evolution. There can be no doubt that these two methods have points of contact. Nevertheless, between them there is a profound and important difference which, it must be admitted, is far from favouring the teaching of evolution. Modern evolutionists introduce a considerable admixture of conservatism into their teaching. They want to prove that there are no leaps either in nature or in history. Dialectics, on the other hand, knows full well that in nature and also in human thought and history leaps are *inevitable*. But it does not overlook the undeniable fact that the same *uninterrupted process* is at work in all phases of change. It only endeavours to make clear to itself the series of conditions under which gradual change must necessarily lead to a leap." [66] (Plekhanov)

Darwin regarded the pace of evolution as a gradual process of orderly steps. It proceeded at a constant rate. He adhered to Linnaeus' motto: "Nature does not make leaps." This conception was reflected elsewhere in the scientific world, most notably with Darwin's disciple, Charles Lyell, the apostle of gradualism in the field of geology. Darwin was so committed to gradualism, that he built his whole theory on it. "The geological record is extremely imperfect," stated Darwin, "and this fact will to a large extent explain why we do not find interminable varieties, connecting together all the extinct and existing forms of life by the finest graduated steps. He who rejects these views on the nature of the geological record will rightly reject my whole theory." This Darwinism gradualism was rooted in the philosophical views of Victorian society. From this "evolution" all the leaps, abrupt changes and revolutionary transformations are eliminated. This anti-dialectical outlook has held sway

(66) G. Plekhanov, *Selected Philosophical Works*, Vol. 1, p. 480.

over the sciences to this present day. "A deeply rooted bias of Western thought predisposes us to look for continuity and gradual change," says Gould.

However, these views have given rise to a heated controversy. The present fossil record is full of gaps. It reveals long-term trends, but they are also very jerky. Darwin believed that these jerks were due to the gaps in the record. Once the missing pieces were discovered, it would reveal a gradual smooth evolution of the natural world. Or would it? Against the gradualist approach, palaeontologists Niles Eldredge and Stephen Jay Gould have put forward a theory of evolution called punctuated equilibria, suggesting that the fossil record is not as incomplete as had been thought. The gaps could reflect what really occurred. That evolution proceeds with leaps and jumps, punctuated with long periods of steady, gradual development.

"The history of life is not a continuum of development, but a record punctuated by brief, sometimes geologically instantaneous, episodes of mass extinction and subsequent diversification," says Gould. Rather than a gradual transition, "modern multicellular animals make their first uncontested appearance in the fossil record some 570 million years ago—and with a bang, not a protracted crescendo. This 'Cambrian explosion' marks the advent (at least into direct evidence) of virtually all major groups of modern animals—and all within the minuscule span, geologically speaking, of a few million years." [67]

Gould also points to the feature that the boundaries of geological time coincide with turning points in the evolution of life. This conception of evolution comes very close to the Marxist view. Evolution is not some smooth, gradual movement from lower to higher. Evolution takes place through accumulated changes which burst through in a qualitative change, through revolutions and transformations. Already at the end of the 19th century, the Marxist George Plekhanov polemicised against the gradual conception of evolution:

"German idealist philosophy," he noted, "decisively revolted against such a misshapen conception of evolution. Hegel bitingly ridiculed it, and demonstrated irrefutably that both in nature and in human society *leaps* constituted just as essential a stage of evolution as gradual quantitative changes. 'Changes in being,' he says, 'consists not only in the fact that one quantity passes into another quantity, but also that quality passes into quantity and vice versa. Each transition of the latter kind represents an *interruption in gradualness*, and gives the phenomenon a new aspect, qualitatively distinct from the previous one'." [68]

"Evolution" and "revolution" are two sides of the same process. In rejecting gradualism, Gould and Eldredge have sought an alternative explanation of evolution, and have been influenced by dialectical materialism. Gould's paper on "Punctuated Equilibria" draws parallels with the materialist conception of history. Natural selection theory is a good explanation of how species get better at doing

(67) S. J. Gould, *Wonderful Life*, pp. 54 and 24.
(68) G. Plekhanov, *The Development of the Monist View of History*, pp. 96-7.

what they do, but provides an unsatisfactory explanation for the formation of new species. The fossil record shows six major mass extinctions took place at the beginning and end of the Cambrian period (600 million and 500 million years ago respectively), and the ends of the Devonian (345 million years ago), the Permian (225 million), the Triassic (180 million) and the Cretaceous (63 million). A qualitatively new approach is needed to explain this phenomenon.

The evolution of a new species is marked by the evolution of a genetic make-up that allows members of the new species to breed with each other, but not with members of other species. New species arise from a branching off from ancestral stocks. That is, as Darwin explained, one species descended from another species. The tree of life shows that more than one species can be traced back to one ancestral stock. Humans and chimpanzees are different species, but had one common extinct ancestor. Change from one species into another takes place rapidly between two stable species. This transformation does not take place in one generation or two, but over possibly hundreds of thousands of years. As Gould comments: "This may seem like a long time in the framework of our lives, but it is a geological instant…If species arise in hundreds or thousands of years and then persist, largely unchanged, for several million, the period of their origin is a tiny fraction of one per cent of their total duration."

The key to this change lies in geographical separation, where a small population has become separated from the main population at its periphery. This form of speciation, called *allopatric*, allows a rapid evolution to take place. As soon as an ancestral species is separated, the inter-breeding stops. Any genetic changes build up separately. However, in the smaller population, genetic variations can spread very quickly in comparison to the ancestral group. This can be brought about by natural selection responding to changing climatic and geographical factors. As the two populations diverge, they eventually reach a point where two species are formed. Quantitative changes have given rise to a qualitative transformation. If they ever meet in the future, then so genetically divergent are they, that they are unable to breed successfully; either their offspring will be sickly or sterile. Eventually, similar species with the same way of life would tend to compete, leading eventually to the extinction of the least successful.

As Engels commented: "The organic process of development, both of the individual and of species, by differentiation, is the most striking test of rational dialectics." Again, "The further physiology develops, the more important for it becomes these incessant, infinitely small changes, and hence the more important for it also the consideration of differences *within* identity, and the old abstract standpoint of formal identity, that an organic being is to be treated as something simply identical with itself, as something constant, becomes out of date." Engels then concludes: "If *there* the individuals which become adapted survive and develop into a new species by continually increasing adaption, while the other more stable individuals die away and finally die out, and with them the imperfect intermediate stages, then this can and does proceed *without any Malthusianism,* and if the latter should occur at all it makes no change to the process, at most it can accelerate it." [69]

Gould correctly says that the theory of punctuated equilibria is not in contradiction to the main tenet of Darwinism, natural selection, but, on the contrary, enriches and strengthens Darwinism. Richard Dawkins in his book *The Blind Watchmaker* attempts to downgrade Gould and Eldredge's recognition of dialectical change in nature. He sees little difference between "real" Darwinian gradualism and "punctuated equilibria". He states: "The theory of punctuated equilibrium is a gradualist theory, albeit it emphasises long periods of stasis intervening between relatively short bursts of gradualistic evolution. Gould has misled himself by his own rhetorical emphasis…" Dawkins then concludes, "in reality, all are 'gradualists'."

Dawkins criticises the punctuationists for attacking and misrepresenting Darwin. He says we need to see Darwin's gradualism in its context—as an attack on creationism. "Punctuationists, then, are really just as gradualist as Darwin or any other Darwinian; they just insert long periods of stasis between spurts of gradual evolution." But this is not a secondary difference, it is the essence of the matter. To criticise the weakness of Darwinism is not to undermine its unique contribution, but to synthesise it with an understanding of real change. Only then can Darwin's historic contribution be fully rounded out as an explanation of natural evolution. As Gould correctly says, "The modern theory of evolution does not require gradual change. In fact, the operation of Darwinian processes should yield what we see in the fossil record. It is gradualism that we must reject, not Darwinism." [70]

No progress?

The fundamental thrust of Gould's argument is undoubtedly correct. What is more problematical is his idea that evolution does not travel an inherently progressive path:

"Increasing diversity and multiple transitions seem to reflect a determined and inexorable progression toward higher things," states Gould. "But the palaeontological record supports no such interpretation. There has been no steady progress in the higher development of organic design. For the first two thirds to five-sixths of life's history, monerans alone inhabited the earth, and we detect no steady progress from 'lower' to 'higher' prokaryotes. Likewise, there has been no addition of basic designs since the Cambrian explosion filled our biosphere (although we can argue for limited improvement *within* a few designs—vertebrates and vascular plants, for example)." [71]

---

(69) Engels, *Dialectics of Nature,* pp. 154, 162 and 235, 1946 edition.
(70) S.J. Gould, *The Panda's Thumb,* p. 151.
(71) S.J. Gould, *Ever Since Darwin,* p. 118.

Gould argues, particularly in his book *Wonderful Life*, that the number of animal phyla (basic body plans) was greater soon after the "Cambrian explosion" than today. He says diversity has not increased and there are no long-term trends in evolution, and the evolution of intelligent life is accidental.

Here it seems to us that Eric Lerner's criticisms of Gould are correct:

"Not only is there a huge difference between the contingencies that lead to the evolution of a particular species and a long-term trend in evolution, such as towards greater adaptability or intelligence, but Gould rests his case on facts that are an example of just such a trend!" says Lerner. "Over time, evolution has tended to concentrate more and more on specific modes of development. Nearly all chemical elements were in existence ten billion years ago or more. The types of compounds vital to life—DNA, RNA, proteins, and so on—were all present on earth some four billion years ago. The main kingdoms of life—animals, plants, fungi, and bacteria—have existed for two billion years; there have been no new ones in that time. As Gould shows, the main phyla have existed for six hundred million years, and the major orders (a lower grouping) for about four hundred million years.

"As evolution has sped up, it has become more and more specific, and the earth has been transformed by the social evolution of a single species, our own. This is exactly the sort of long-term trend that Gould, despite his great contribution to evolutionary theory, is ideologically determined to ignore. Yet it exists, as does the trend towards intelligence." [72]

The fact that evolution has resulted in greater complexity, from lower organisms to higher ones, leading to human beings with large brains capable of the most complex tasks, is proof of its progressive character. That does not mean that evolution takes place in a straight ascending line, as Gould correctly argues; there are breaks, retrogressions, and pauses within the general progress of evolution. Although natural selection takes place in response to environmental changes (even of a local character), it nevertheless has led to greater complexity of life forms. Certain species have adapted to their environment and have existed in that form for millions of years. Other species have become extinct having lost out in competition with other more advanced models. That is the evidence of the evolution of life over the past 3.5 billion years.

The reason for Gould's emphatic rejection of the notion of progress in evolution has more to do with social and political reasons than strictly scientific ones. He knows that the idea of evolutionary progress and "higher species" have been systematically misused in the past in order to justify racism and imperialism—the alleged superiority of the white man was supposed to give the nations of Europe the right to seize the land and wealth of the "lesser breeds without the law" in Africa and Asia. As late as the 1940s respectable men of science were still publishing "evo-

(72) E.J. Lerner, op. cit., p. 402.

lutionary trees" showing the white man on top, with the black and other "races" on separate and lower branches, a little higher than the gorillas and chimpanzees. When questioned about his rejection of the notion of progress in evolution as "noxious", Gould justified himself as follows:

"'Progress is not intrinsically and logically noxious,' he replied. 'It's noxious in the context of Western cultural traditions.' With roots going back to the seventeenth century, progress as a central social ethic reached its height in the nineteenth century, with the industrial revolution and Victorian expansionism, Steve explained. Fears of self-destruction in recent decades, either militarily inflicted or through pollution, have dulled the eternal optimism of the Victorian and Edwardian eras. Nevertheless, the assumed inexorable march of scientific discovery and economic growth continue to fuel the idea that progress is a good and natural part of history. 'Progress has been a prevailing doctrine in the interpretation of historical sequence,' Steve continued, 'and since evolution is the grandest history of all, the notion of progress immediately got transferred to it. You are aware of some of the consequences of that'." [73]

One can sympathise with Gould's reaction to such ignorant and reactionary rubbish. It is also true that terms like "progress" may not be ideal from a strictly scientific point of view when applied to evolution. There is always the risk that it could imply a *teleological* approach, that is, the conception of nature as operating according to a pre-established plan, worked out by a Creator. However, as usual, the reaction has swung too far the other way. If the word progress is inadequate, it could be substituted by, say, *complexity*. Can it be denied that there has been real development in living organisms since the first single-celled animals until now?

There is no need to return to the old one-sided view of Man, the culminating point of evolution, in order to accept that the past 3.5 billion years of evolution has not just meant change, but actual development, passing from simpler forms to more complex living systems. The fossil record bears witness to this. For example, the dramatic increase in average brain size with the evolution of mammals from reptiles, some 230 million years ago. Similarly, there was a qualitative leap in brain size with the emergence of humans, and this, in turn, did not take place as a smooth quantitative process, but as a series of leaps, with *Homo habilis, Homo erectus, Homo neanderthalis*, and finally *Homo sapiens*, representing decisive turning points.

There is no reason to suppose that evolution has reached its limit, or that human beings will experience no further development. The process of evolution will continue, although it will not necessarily take the same form as in the past. Profound changes in the social environment, including genetic engineering, can modify the process of natural selection, giving human beings for the first time the possibility of determining their own evolution, at least to some degree. This will open up an entirely new chapter in human development, especially in a society guided by the

(73) R. Lewin, op. cit., p. 140.

free and conscious decisions of men and women, and not the blind play of market forces and the animal struggle for survival.

Marxism and Darwinism

> "The kinds of values upheld in Marxist doctrine are almost diametric opposites from those which emerge from a scientific approach on our present terms." (Roger Sperry, winner of the 1981 Nobel Prize for Medicine.)

> "The church takes her stand against the inroads of chaos and the twentieth century gods of Progress and a materialistic world-view... *Genesis* then rings true as ever, whether one follows an evolutionary account of biological origins or not." (Blackmore and Page, *Evolution: The Great Debate*)

Using the method of dialectical materialism, Marx and Engels were able to discover the laws that govern history and the development of society in general. Unconsciously using a similar method, Charles Darwin was able to uncover the laws of evolution of plants and animals. "Darwin applied a consistent philosophy of materialism to his interpretation of nature," states palaeontologist Stephen Jay Gould. "Matter is the ground of all existence; mind, spirit, and God as well, are just words that express the wondrous results of neuronal complexity."

Charles Darwin's theory of evolution revolutionised our outlook on the natural world. Before him, the prevailing view amongst scientists was that species were immutable, having been created by God for specific functions in nature. Some accepted the idea of evolution, but in a mystical form, directed by vital forces which left room for the decisive intervention of the Supreme Being. Darwin represents a decisive break with this idealist outlook. For the first time, primarily though not exclusively through a process of natural selection, evolution provided an explanation of how species have changed over billions of years, from the simplest forms of unicellular organisms to the most complex forms of animal life, including ourselves. Darwin's revolutionary contribution was to discover the mechanism that brought about change, thereby putting evolution on a firm scientific basis.

There is a rough analogy here with the role played by Marx and Engels in the field of the social sciences. Long before them, others had recognised the existence of the class struggle. But not until Marx's analysis of the Labour Theory of Value and the development of historical materialism, was it possible to provide this phenomenon with a scientific explanation. Marx and Engels gave enthusiastic support to Darwin's theory, which provided confirmation for their ideas, as applied to nature. On 16th January 1861, Marx wrote to Lassalle: "Darwin's book is very important and serves me as a natural scientific basis for the class struggle in history. One has to put up with the crude English method of development, of course. Despite all deficiencies, not only is the death-blow dealt here for the first time to 'teleology' in the natural sciences but its rational meaning is empirically explained."

Darwin's *Origin of Species* appeared in 1859, the same year that Marx published his *Preface to the Critique of Political Economy*, which fully rounded out the materialist conception of history. Darwin had worked out the theory of natural selection more than twenty years earlier, but refrained from publication for fear of the reaction to his materialist views. Even then, he only referred to human origins with the phrase "light will be thrown on the origin of man and his history." Only when he could not hide them any longer was *The Descent of Man* published in 1871. Such were its disquieting ideas, Darwin was rebuked for publishing "at a moment when the sky of Paris was red with the incendiary flames of the Commune." He studiously avoided the question of religion, although he clearly had rejected Creationism. In 1880, he wrote: "It seems to me (rightly or wrongly) that direct arguments against Christianity and Theism hardly have any effect on the public; and that freedom of thought will best be promoted by that gradual enlightening of human understanding which follows the progress of science. I have therefore always avoided writing about religion and have confined myself to science."

Darwin's materialist conception of nature was a revolutionary break-through in providing a scientific conception of evolution. However, Marx was by no means uncritical of Darwin. In particular, he criticised his "crude English method" and showed how Darwin's deficiencies were based upon the influences of Adam Smith and Malthus. Lacking a definite philosophical standpoint, Darwin inevitably fell under the influence of the prevailing ideology of the times. The Victorian English middle-classes prided themselves on being practical men and women, with a gift for making money and "getting on in life". The "survival of the fittest", as a description of natural selection, was not originally used by Darwin, but by Herbert Spencer in 1864. Darwin was not concerned with progress in Spencer's sense—human progress based on the elimination of the "unfit"—and was unwise to adopt his phrase. Likewise, the phrase "struggle for existence" was used by Darwin as a metaphor, but it was distorted by conservatives, who used Darwin's theories for their own end. To Social Darwinists, the most popular catchwords of the Darwinian "survival of the fittest" and "struggle for existence", when applied to society suggested that nature would ensure the best competitors in a competitive situation would win, and that this process would lead to continuing improvement. It followed from this that all attempts to reform social processes were efforts to remedy the irremediable, and that, as they interfered with the wisdom of nature, they could lead only to degeneration. As the celebrated Ukranian geneticist Theodosius Dobzhansky put it:

"Since Nature is 'red in tooth and claw', it would be a big mistake to let our sentiments interfere with Nature's intentions by helping the poor, the weak, and the generally unfit to the point where they will be as comfortable as the rich, the strong, and the fit. In the long run, letting Nature reign will bring the greatest benefits. 'Pervading all Nature we may see at work a stern discipline which is a little cruel that it may be very kind,' wrote Herbert Spencer." [74]

Darwin and Malthus

> "Population, when unchecked, increases in a geometrical ratio. Subsistence only increases in an arithmetical ratio." (Thomas Robert Malthus, *The Principle of Population*.)

The *laissez faire* economics of Adam Smith may have given Darwin an insight into natural selection, but as Engels remarked: "Darwin did not know what a bitter satire he wrote on mankind, and especially on his countrymen, when he showed that free competition, the struggle for existence, which the economists celebrate as the highest historical achievement, is the normal state of the *Animal Kingdom*." [75] Darwin was inspired by Malthus's *Essay on Population* written in 1798. This theory purports to show that population grows geometrically and food supplies only arithmetically, unless checked by famine, war, disease, or restraint. It was shown to be false.

Unlike Spencer, Darwin understood "fitness" in relation only to a given environment, not to an absolute scale of perfection. In fact, neither of the two terms with which Darwin's name is chiefly associated, "evolution" and "survival of the fittest", occurs in early editions of *The Origin of the Species*, where his key ideas are expressed by the words "mutability" and "natural selection". On the 18th June 1862, Marx wrote to Engels: "Darwin, whom I have looked up again, amuses me when he says he is applying the 'Malthusian' theory *also* to plants and animals, as if with Mr. Malthus the whole point were not that he does *not* apply the theory to plants and animals but only to human beings—and with geometrical progression—as opposed to plants and animals." Engels also rejected Darwin's crude description or jargon, and says: "Darwin's mistake lies precisely in lumping together in 'natural selection' or the 'survival of the fittest', two absolutely separate things:

"1. Selection by the pressure of over-population, where perhaps the strongest survive in the first place, but where the weakest in many respects can also do so.

"2. Selection by greater capacity of adaption to altered circumstances, where the survivors are better suited to these *circumstances*, but where this adaption as a whole can mean regress just as well as progress (for adaption to parasitic life is always regress).

"The main thing: that each advance in organic evolution is at the same time a regression, fixing *one-sided* evolution and excluding evolution along many other directions. This, however, (is) *a basic law*." [76]

(74) T. Dobzhansky, *Mankind Evolving*, pp. 139-40.
(75) Engels, *Dialectics of Nature*, p. 19, 1946 edition.
(76) Engels, *Dialectics of Nature*, p. 236, 1946 edition.

Clearly, there exists a struggle for survival—though not in the Spencerian sense—in nature where scarcity exists, or danger to the members of a species through predators. "However great the blunder made by Darwin in accepting the Malthusian theory so naïvely and uncritically," says Engels, "nevertheless anyone can see at the first glance that no Malthusian spectacles are required to perceive the struggle for existence in nature—the contradiction between the countless host of germs which nature so lavishly produces and the small number of those which ever reach maturity, a contradiction which in fact for the most part finds its solution in a struggle for existence—often of extreme cruelty." [77]

Many species produce vast numbers of seeds or eggs to maximise their survival rate, particularly in the early years of life. On the other hand, the human species has survived in other ways, as its development is very slow, and where a great deal of energy and effort is invested in raising very few, late maturing offspring. Our advantage lies within our brain, and its capacity for learning and generalisation. Our population growth is not controlled by the death of large numbers of our offspring, and so cannot be compared *crudely* to other species.

History itself provides the final answer to Malthus. A.N. Whitehead has pointed out that from the tenth to the 20th century, a continually rising population in Europe was accompanied by generally rising living standards. This cannot be squared with the Malthusian theory, even if the question of "checks" is introduced, a means of "delaying the inevitable outcome". A thousand years should be sufficient to demonstrate the correctness or otherwise of any theory. "The plain truth," as Whitehead says, "is that during this period and over that area (i.e., Europe) the so-called checks were such that the Malthusian Law represented a possibility, *unrealised and of no importance*." [78]

Whitehead points out that the alleged "checks" were not even in proportion to the density of the population. For example, the plagues were mainly the result, not of population size, but of *bad sanitation*. Not birth control, but soap, water, and proper drains would have been the remedy. The Thirty Years War cut the population of Germany by half—quite a drastic "check" on population growth. The war had several causes, but excessive population has never been mentioned as one of them. Nor, to the best of our knowledge, has it played a noticeable role in any of the other wars in which European history is so rich. For example, the peasant uprisings at the end of the Middle Ages in France, Germany and England were not caused by excess population. As a matter of fact, they occurred precisely at a time when the population had been decimated by the Black Death. At the beginning of the 16th century, Flanders was thickly populated, yet enjoyed far higher living standards than Germany, where the grinding poverty of the peasants contributed to the Peasants' War.

(77) Engels, *Anti-Dühring*, p. 86.
(78) A.N. Whitehead, *Adventures of Ideas*, p. 77, our emphasis.

Malthus' theories are worthless from a scientific point of view but have consistently served as an excuse for the most inhuman application of so-called market policies. In the Irish potato famine of the 1840s, as a result of which the population of Ireland was reduced from over eight million to 4.5 million, the English landlords in Ireland continued to export wheat. Following sound free market principles, the "Liberal" government in London refused to introduce any measure which might interfere with free trade or prices, and cancelled the supply of cheap maize to the Irish, therefore condemning millions to death by starvation. The Malthusian principles of the English government were defended by Charles Grenville, secretary to the Privy Council thus:

"...The state of Ireland is to the last degree deplorable, and enough to induce despair: such general disorganisation and demoralisation, a people with rare exceptions besotted with obstinacy and indolence, reckless and savage—all from high to low intent on doing as little and getting as much as they can, unwilling to rouse and exert themselves, looking to this country for succour, and snarling at the succour which they get; the masses brutal, deceitful and idle, the whole state of things contradictory and paradoxical. While menaced with the continuance of famine next year, they will not cultivate the ground, and it lies unsown and untilled. There is no doubt that the people never were so well off on the whole as they have been this year of famine. Nobody will pay rent, and the savings banks are overflowing. With the money they get from our relief funds they buy arms instead of food, and then shoot the officers who are sent over to regulate the distribution of relief. While they crowd to the overseers with demands for employment, the landowners cannot produce hands, and sturdy beggars calling themselves destitute are apprehended with large sums in their pockets. 28th November, 1846."

The real state of affairs was described by Doctor Burritt, who was horrified to see men working on roads with their limbs swollen to almost twice their normal size. The body of a twelve-year-old boy was "swollen to nearly three times its usual size and had burst the ragged garment which covered him." Near a place called Skull, "we passed a crowd of 500 people, half naked and starving. They were waiting for soup to be distributed amongst them. They were pointed out to us, and as I stood looking with pity and wonder at so miserable a scene, my conductor, a gentleman residing at East Skull and a medical man, said to me: 'Not a single one of those you now see will be alive in three weeks: it is impossible.' ... The deaths here average 40 to 50 daily. Twenty bodies were fortunate in getting buried at all. The people build themselves up in their cabins, so that they may die together with their children and not be seen by passers-by." [79]

There was no more reason for these people to die of hunger than it is for millions to starve today, while farmers are paid not to grow food in the European Union and USA. They are not victims of the laws of nature, but of the laws of the market.

(79) P. Johnson, *Ireland, a Concise History*, pp. 102 and 103.

From the beginning, Marx and Engels denounced the false theories of Malthusianism. Answering the arguments of "Parson Malthus", in a letter to Lange dated 29th March 1865 Engels wrote: "The pressure of population is not upon the means of subsistence but upon the means of *employment*; mankind could multiply more rapidly than modern bourgeois society can demand. To us a further reason for declaring this bourgeois society a barrier to development which must fall."

The introduction of machinery, new scientific techniques and fertilisers means that world food production can easily keep abreast of population growth. The spectacular growth in the productivity of agriculture is taking place when the proportion of the population involved in it continues to fall. The extension of the agricultural efficiency already attained in the advanced countries to the entire farming world would yield a huge increase in production. Only a very small part of the vast biological productivity of the ocean is used at present. Hunger and starvation exist mainly due to the destruction of food surpluses to keep up the price of food and the need to maintain the profit levels of the agro-monopolies.

The widespread hunger in the so-called Third World is not the product of "natural selection", but very definitely a man-made problem. Not the "survival of the fittest", but greed for profits of a handful of big banks and monopolies is what condemns millions to a life of desperate poverty and actual starvation. Just to pay back the interest on their accumulated debts, the poorest countries are compelled to grow cash crops for export, including rice, cocoa and other food, which could be used to feed their own people. In 1989, Sudan was still exporting food, while its people starved to death. In Brazil, it is estimated that about 400,000 children die of hunger every year. Yet Brazil is one of the biggest exporters of food. The same discredited ideas continue to re-surface from time to time, as an attempt is made to blame the nightmare conditions of the Third World on the fact that there are "too many people" (meaning black, yellow and brown people). The fact that in the absence of pensions poor peasants need to have as many children as possible (especially sons) to keep them in old age is conveniently ignored. Poverty and ignorance causes the so-called population problem. As living standards and education increase, the growth in population tends to fall automatically. Meanwhile, the potential for increased food production is immense, and is being held down artificially in order to boost the profits of a few wealthy farmers in Europe, Japan and the USA. The scandal of mass starvation in the late 20th century is even more repugnant *because it is unnecessary*.

'Social Darwinism'

Although they greatly admired Darwin, Marx and Engels were by no means uncritical of his theories. Engels understood that Darwin's ideas would be later refined and developed—a fact confirmed by the development of genetics. He wrote to Lavrov in November 1875: "Of the Darwinian doctrine I accept the *theory of evolution*, but Darwin's method of proof (struggle for life, natural selection) I consider only a first, provisional, imperfect expression of a newly discovered fact." And again in his book *Anti-Dühring*: "The theory of evolution itself is however still in a very early stage, and it therefore cannot be doubted that further research will greatly modify our present conceptions, including strictly Darwinian ones, of the process of the evolution of species."

Engels sharply criticised Darwin's one-sidedness as well as the Social Darwinism that was to follow. "Hardly was Darwin recognised," states Engels, "before these same people saw everywhere nothing but *struggle*. Both views are justified within narrow limits, but both are equally one-sided and prejudiced...Hence, even in regard to nature, it is not permissible one-sidely to inscribe only 'struggle' on one's banners. But it is absolutely childish to desire to sum up the whole manifold wealth of historical evolution and complexity in the meagre and one-sided phrase 'struggle for life'. That says less than nothing." He then goes on to explain the roots of this error: "The whole Darwinian theory of the struggle for life is simply the transference from society to organic nature of Hobbes' theory of *Bellum Omnium Contra Omnes* (the war of each against all—ed.), and of the bourgeois economic theory of competition, as well as the Malthusian theory of population. When once this feat has been accomplished (the unconditional justification for which, especially as regards the Malthusian theory, is still very questionable), it is very easy to transfer these theories back again from natural history to the history of society, and altogether too naïve to maintain that thereby these assertions have been proved as eternal natural laws of society." [80]

The Social Darwinian's parallels with the animal world fitted in with the prevailing racist arguments that human character was based upon the measurement of men's skulls. For Daniel G. Brinton, American linguist and anthropologist, "the European or white race stands at the head of the list, the African or Negro at its foot" (1890). Cesare Lombroso, an Italian physician, in 1876, argued that born criminals were essentially apes, a throwback in evolution. It was part of the desire to explain human behaviour in terms of innate biology—a tendency that can still be observed today. The 'struggle for survival' was seen as innate in all animals including man, and served to justify war, conquest, profiteering, imperialism, racialism, as well as the class structure of capitalism. It is the forerunner of the cruder varieties of sociobiology and the theories of the *Naked Ape*. After all, was it not W.S. Gilbert whose satire proclaimed:

"Darwinian Man, though well-behaved,
At best is only a monkey shaved!"

Darwin stressed that "Natural Selection has been the most, but not the exclusive, means of modification." He explained that the adaptive changes in one part could

(80) Engels, *Anti-Dühring*, pp. 92 and 208-9.

lead to modifications of other features that have no bearing on survival. However, as opposed to the idealist conception of life, epitomised by the Creationists, the Darwinians scientifically explained how life evolved on the planet. It was a natural process which can be explained by the laws of biology, and the interaction of organisms with their environment. Independently of Darwin, another naturalist, Alfred Russel Wallace, had also constructed the theory of natural selection. This prompted Darwin to go into print after more than twenty years delay. However, an essential difference between Darwin and Wallace, was that Wallace believed all evolutionary change or modification to be determined solely by natural selection. But the rigid hyper-selectionist Wallace would end up rejecting natural selection when it concerned the brain and intellect, concluding that God had intervened to construct this unique creation!

Darwin explained that the evolution of life, with its rich and varied forms, was an inevitable consequence of the reproduction of life itself. Firstly, like breeds like, with minor variations. But secondly, all organisms tend to produce more offspring than survive and breed. Those offspring which have the greatest chance of survival are those more equipped to adapt to their surroundings, and, in turn, their offspring will tend to be more like them. The characteristics of these populations will, over time, increasingly adapt to their environment. In other words, the "fittest" survive and spread their favoured characteristics through populations. In nature, Darwinian evolution is a response to changing environments. Nature "selects" organisms with characteristics best able to adapt to its surroundings. "Evolution by natural selection," says Gould, "is no more than a tracking of these changing environments by differential preservation of organisms better designed to live in them." Thus, natural selection directs the course of evolutionary change. This discovery by Darwin was described by Leon Trotsky as "the highest triumph of the dialectic in the whole field of organic matter."

15. The selfish gene?

Genetics

It was not until the late 1930s that Darwin's mechanism for evolution—natural selection—obtained widespread acceptance. At this time, leading scientific figures like Ronald A. Fisher, J.B.S. Haldane, and Sewall Wright became the founding fathers of neo-Darwinism, which fused natural selection with Mendelian genetics. The theory of heredity was essential for the connection between the theory of evolution and cell theory. In the 19th century, biologists Schleiden, Schwann, and Virchow explained that cells were the basic unit of all living things. In 1944, Canadian Bacteriologist Oswald Avery identified DNA in the cell nucleus as the material forming the basis of heredity. The discovery by Francis Crick and James Watson of the double helix of DNA further clarified the pathway of evolution. Darwin's variations in offspring were due to changes in DNA, arising from random mutations and internal molecular rearrangements, on which natural selection would act.

Gregor Johann Mendel, an Austrian monk, and amateur botanist in the 1860s made a careful study of the inherited characteristics of plants, which discovered the phenomenon of genetic inheritance. Mendel, a shy and modest man, sent his findings to an eminent biologist, who, as one might have expected, dismissed the whole idea as nonsense. Deeply discouraged, Mendel hid his ideas from the world and returned to his plants. His revolutionary work was only rediscovered in 1900, when the science of genetics was really born. Improvements in microscopes made it possible to see inside the cell, leading to the discovering of genes and chromosomes.

Genetics allows us to understand the ever-continuing development of life. The evolution of life meant the appearance of a self-replicating molecule which could transmit the characteristics of the life-form to future generations. Such a mechanism is deoxyribonucleic acid (DNA). This self-reproducing DNA molecule is not concentrated in a particular part of the body, but is contained in every animal or plant cell. The highest evolved species, a product of over three billion years of evolution, is the human species. At adulthood, humans are made up of a trillion cells, but at conception there existed only a singled-celled embryo. How does this happen? The secret is in the DNA. Within this single cell was contained the DNA molecule that held the genetic code for the construction of a human being. The genetic information carried by the genes is stored in a chemically coded form. One gene is a section of DNA that has the information to make a particular type of protein.

The genes contained in every cell are that part of the organism that contains all the necessary information for creating animals and plants. Most genes carry information that direct cells to make proteins. Some genes tell the cells in an embryo where they are and whether they should grow into an arm or a leg. The sequences of bases stored in the genes determine what the living creature will be. The heredity information is stored in the nucleus of each cell in the form of chains of genes called chromosomes. Like a living textbook, two sets of chromosomes carry all the genes allotted to an individual, defining the nature of the structure of the proteins that do most of the work in the body.

Only in the 1950s was the chemical composition of genes identified as DNA. In 1953 Francis Crick and James Watson made a revolutionary breakthrough in genetics with their discovery of the famous double-helix model of the nucleic-acid molecule, for which they shared the Nobel Prize in 1962. This makes clear how chromosomes are duplicated in cell division. DNA is present in the simplest life-forms: a virus possesses a single DNA molecule. All life as we know it depends on DNA in the last analysis. The discovery and development of genetics further unlocked the secrets of evolution. The laws of evolution discovered by Darwin were enriched by the understanding of genetics, through the work of Fisher, Haldane and Wright, the founders of neo-Darwinism.

The gene is the unit of heredity. The entire collection of genes possessed by an organism is called the genome. At present scientists are engaged in a project to identify all the genes of the human genome, which number around 100,000*. The genes themselves in each generation of cells reproduce themselves; proteins in the shape of special enzymes play an important role in the process. Through this self-reproduction, genes are formed once again for each new cell. So the genes indirectly produce the proteins that construct and maintain all cells. From bacterial cells, plant cells and animal cells; cells specialised to form leaf and stem, muscle and bone, liver and kidney, and many more, including the brain. Each cell contains the same complement of genes as was present in the original cell. Each human cell probably contains the genetic information needed to make any type of human cell, and there-

---

* This was written before the results of the Human Genome Project were known. This has shown that the actual number of human genes is far less than what scientists supposed. See the comments in the preface to the second edition.

fore an entire human being, but in each cell only a selected portion of that information is used. It is analogous to a book of instructions, where only certain pages, and even only certain lines and words are selected to code the necessary proteins needed in the production of various cells.

The effect of sexual reproduction is to mix or shuffle the genes. The sex cells (egg or sperm) only contain 23 chromosomes each in humans, but when fused make up the normal 46 chromosomes. The new cell would, in the words of Dawkins, be "a mosaic of maternal genes and paternal genes." As the two sets of chromosomes merge, if two gene signals differ, then one characteristic will prevail over the other. The gene for brown eyes, for instance, is dominant to that for blue. They are what is termed as recessive and dominant genes. Sometimes a hybrid compromise is produced.

It is through reproduction that variation is achieved. From an evolutionary view this is vital. The asexual reproduction of primitive organisms makes identical copies of the parent cell, where mutation is very infrequent. On the other hand, sexual reproduction, with the new combination of genes from two sources, increases the possibilities of genetic variation and has the effect of accelerating the rate at which evolution can proceed. Each life form carries the DNA code of genetic information. The evidence of our common ancestry is the similarity of cell structure of all living things. The mechanism of inheritance is the same, where DNA determines that mice look like mice, humans look like humans, and bacteria look like bacteria. Some organisms, such as bacteria, possess only one main DNA molecule, whereas our own cells, and those of higher organisms, contain a number of separate bundles of DNA (chromosomes).

Genes and environment

Over the last 25 years, the twin ideologies of reductionism and biological determinism have been dominant in all branches of biology. The method of reductionism tries to explain the properties of complex wholes—proteins for example—in terms of the properties of the atoms and even the fundamental particles of which they are composed. The further down you went, the better (it was claimed) was the understanding. Further, they assert that the units that compose the whole exist before the whole, that a chain of causation runs from the parts to the whole, that the egg always comes before the chicken.

Biological determinism is very closely related to reductionism. It claims, for example, that the behaviour of human beings is determined by the genes possessed by individuals and leads to the conclusion that all human society is governed by the sum of the behaviour of all the individuals in that society. This genetic control is equivalent to the older ideas expressed by the term "human nature". Again scientists may argue that this is not what they mean, but the ideas of determinism and of genes as "fixed unalterable entities" abound in their statements and are taken up with glee by right wing politicians. For them, social inequalities are unfortunate, but they are innate and unalterable; they are therefore impossible to remedy by social means, as to do so would "go against nature". This idea has been expressed by Richard Dawkins in *The Selfish Gene*, which is used as a textbook in American universities.

The mechanism of evolution is conditioned by the dialectical interrelationship between genes and environment. Prior to Darwin, French naturalist Jean-Baptiste Lamarck put forward a different theory of evolution, which asserts that the individual adapts itself directly to its environment and passes on these modifications to its offspring. This mechanical interpretation has been completely discredited, although the idea that environment directly alters heredity resurfaced in Stalinist Russia in the guise of Lysenkoism. Human evolution has both a "nature" and a "history". The genetic raw material enters into a dynamic relationship with the social, economic and cultural environment. It is impossible to understand the process of evolution by taking either one of the two in isolation, as there is a constant interaction between the biological and "cultural" elements.

It has been conclusively proved that acquired traits (derived from the environment) are not biologically transmitted. Culture is passed on from one generation to another exclusively by teaching and example. That is one of the decisive features that set human society apart from the rest of the animal kingdom, although the *elements* of this can also be observed in the higher apes. It is impossible to deny the vital role of genes in human development, nor is this in the slightest degree in contradiction with materialism. Does it follow, then, that "it's all in the genes?" Let us quote the words of Dobzhansky:

"Most contemporary evolutionists are of the opinion that adaptation of a living species to its environment is the chief agency impelling and directing biological evolution."

And again: "Culture is, however, an instrument of adaptation which is vastly more efficient than the biological processes which led to its inception and advancement. It is more efficient among other things because it is more rapid—changed genes are transmitted only to the direct descendants of the individuals in whom they first appear; to replace the old genes, the carriers of the new ones must gradually outbreed and supplant the former. Changed culture may be transmitted to anybody regardless of biological parentage, or borrowed ready-made from other peoples."[81]

Biologists divide the organism into two parts, the genetic make-up, known as the genotype, and the apparent qualities, the phenotype. It is a common error to regard the relation between the two as a simple relation of cause and effect. The *genotype*, so the argument goes, comes before the *phenotype*, and is therefore the decisive element in the equation. We are born with a given set of genes, which cannot be altered, and this decides our fate, as surely as the position of the planets in astrology. This

(81) T. Dobzhansky, op. cit., p. 21.

kind of genetic mechanistic determinism is the mirror image of the quack theories of Trofim Denisovich Lysenko. It is Lamarckism turned inside out. In reality, the genotype, or genes found in the nucleus of every cell, is more or less fixed—give or take the occasional mutation. The phenotype, or the total morphological, physiological and behaviour properties of the individual, is not fixed. On the contrary, it changes constantly throughout the life of the organism by interaction between the genotype and the environment and between the phenotype and the environment. In other words, it is a product of dialectic inter-action of organism and environment. If Albert Einstein had been born in a New York slum, or a village in India, it does not take much intelligence to see that his genetic potential would have counted for very little.

The study of genetics provides the conclusive answer to idealism. No organism can exist without a genotype. And no genotype can exist outside a *spaciotemporal continuum*—an environment. The genes interact with the environment to give rise to the process of human development. As a matter of fact, if hereditary were perfect, there could be no evolution, since heredity is a conservative force. It is essentially a mechanism for self-copying. But there is a built-in contradiction in the genes, whereby occasionally an imperfect copy is produced—a mutation. There are an infinite number of such *accidents*, most of which are not only useless but positively harmful to the organism.

A single mutation cannot transform one species into another. The information contained in the gene does not remain there in splendid isolation. It enters into contact with the physical world, where it is tested, processed, articulated and modified. If a particular variant provides a better protein than another in a given environment, it will prosper, while the others are eliminated. At a certain point, small variations reach a qualitative stage, and a new species is formed. This is the meaning of natural selection. For some four billion years, the genes of every living thing—plants and animals, including humans—have been formed in this way. It is not a one-way process. The idea of the genetic determinists, that the genes are pre-eminent, has been described by Francis Crick, one of the discoverers of the DNA code, as the central dogma of molecular biology. It is no more valid than the dogma of the Immaculate Conception. In the dialectical relationship between the organism and the environment, information about the phenotype flows back into the genotype. The genes are "selected" by the environment, which determines which will survive, and which perish.

The role of the genetic code plays a vital role in establishing the "framework" of human beings, whereas the environment works to fill out and develop behaviour and personality. They are not isolated factors, but dialectically fuse together to produce the individual and his or her unique characteristics. No two persons are identical. However, although it is not possible to alter a person's hereditary make-up, it is entirely possible to alter the environment. The way to improve an individual's potential is to improve their environment. This idea has provoked a heated argument over many years: is it possible to over-ride or change genetic "deficiencies" through an improved environment? The leading early geneticist Francis Galton tried to demonstrate that genius was hereditary, and favoured a policy of selective breeding to maintain the intellectual stock. The idea that middle-class and upper class whites were genetically superior to other races and classes permeated Victorian society. It became the ideology of the eugenics movement which advocated forced sterilisation to prevent the biologically unfit from propagation. Unsound scientific data using IQ (intelligence quota) testing was used to support biological determinism and social inequalities based on race, sex or class that cannot be altered as they reflect innate inferior genes.

'Intelligence' and genes

The American sociobiologist Edward O. Wilson expresses the biological determinist view as follows:

"If the planned society—the creation of which is inevitable in the coming century—were to deliberately steer its members past those stresses and conflicts that once gave the destructive *phenotypes* (aggression and selfishness) their Darwinian edge, the other *phenotypes* (co-operation and altruism) might dwindle with them. In this, the *ultimate genetic sense*, social control would rob man of his humanity." [82]

In other words, by getting rid of the bad aspects of humanity, we may get rid of the good at the same time! Again, Wilson confuses genotype with phenotype by implying that the phenotype (not the genotype) is fixed and unchanging. It is not. Genotypes do not "code" for traits in the phenotype and there is no gene that is equivalent to altruism in the phenotype. Every living thing is the result of a continuous interaction between the genes, the environment, and the phenotype itself. However, we must also avoid falling into the other trap of believing the organism is putty in the "hands" of genes and the environment. It too is an active part of the process. All living things interact with their environment in a dialectical way.

"To suppose that a sex cell transports a particle called 'intelligence' which will make its possessor smart and wise no matter what happens to him is, indeed, ridiculous," affirms Dobzhansky. "But it is evident that the people we meet are not all alike in intelligence, abilities, and attitudes, and it is not unreasonable to suppose that these *differences* are caused partly by the natures of these people and partly by their environments."

Although this clearly demonstrates the materialist and dialectical character of life processes, genetics has given rise to heated controversy and opened the door to idealism and reactionary conceptions. A one-sided fashion of genetics inevitably

(82) E.O. Wilson, *Sociobiology—The New Synthesis*, p. 575.

ends up in error and confusion. Thus, certain geneticists have fallen into the trap of biological determinism or genetic determinism. This is also the case with sociobiologists like E.O. Wilson and Richard Dawkins. Commenting on this, Steven Rose asks:

"Does evolutionary theory imply that certain aspects of human—capitalism, nationalism, patriarchy, xenophobia, aggression and competition—are 'fixed' in our 'selfish genes'? Some biologists have claimed to answer this question in the affirmative, and political theorists of the right—from libertarian monetarists to neo-fascists have seized upon their pronouncements as providing 'scientific' justification for their political philosophies." The only conclusion from this is that capitalism and all its ills are "natural", being derived from biological facts. Theories of racial and sexual inequality have also sought to base themselves on certain interpretations of science.

Simplistic and crude metaphors of evolution, such as "survival of the fittest" and "the struggle for existence", made their way through Herbert Spencer into the vocabulary of social Darwinism. Within biology was found the very confirmation of capitalism, class inequalities and imperialism. It appears that the sociobiologists of the E.O. Wilson mould are following in their footsteps with their views of human nature and biological determinism. Marx and Engels explained that "man makes himself". Human nature, like consciousness, is a product of the prevailing social and economic conditions. That is why human nature has changed throughout history, following the development of society itself. For the sociobiologist, human characteristics appear biologically fixed through our genes, giving sustenance to the myth that "you can't change human nature".

In point of fact, so-called human nature has been transformed and re-transformed many times in the course of human history, as Dobzhansky points out:

"Darlington (1953) believes that 'individual adaptability is indeed one of the great illusions of common-sense observation. It is an illusion responsible for some of the chief errors of political and economic administration today. Individuals and populations cannot be shifted from one place or occupation to another after an appropriate period of training to fit the convenience of some master planner, any more than hill farmers can be turned into deep-sea fishermen or habitual criminals can be turned into good citizens.'

"Despite all the inadequacy and uncertainty of our knowledge of human genetics, there is plenty of evidence contrary to Darlington's view, and this evidence is conclusive.

"History abounds in proofs that individuals and populations can successfully be shifted from one place or occupation to another. Industrial revolutions in many countries throughout the world have amply shown this. The near ancestors of millions of industrial workers have been mostly 'timeless' peasants tilling the soil. The movement from the soil to industrial cities is even now under way, and on a grand scale, in some 'underdeveloped' countries." [83]

IQ testing

A term frequently misused by genetic determinists is heredity, especially in the field of IQ testing. The psychologists Hans Eysenck in Britain, Richard Herrnstein and Arthur Jensen in the US have promoted the idea that intelligence is largely inherited. They also maintain that the average IQ of blacks is genetically lower than that of whites, and of Irish in Ireland to English in England. Eysenck apparently believes that blacks and the Irish have been selectively bred for "low IQ" genes. In point of fact, IQ tests have been shown to be inherently flawed. There is no such thing as a unit of measurement for "intelligence", as there is for height or weight. The IQ is an imaginary concept based upon arbitrary assumptions.

The IQ test originated at the beginning of the century when Alfred Binet established a simple test to help identify children with learning difficulties. For Binet it was a means of identification of difficulties that could then be remedied through "mental orthopaedics". He certainly did not believe that this measure was of some "fixed" intelligence, and for those who contemplated such ideas Binet's rebuke was sharp: "We must protest and react against this brutal pessimism."

The basis of Binet's test was simple enough: older children should be able to carry out mental tasks that younger children could not. He thus assembled tests suitable for each age group; those considered brighter or less able were judged accordingly. Where children encountered difficulties, then remedial action should be undertaken. However, this system in the hands of others was used to draw different conclusions. With the death of Binet, the advocates of eugenics saw their opportunity to reinforce their determinist message. Intelligence was now considered innate and fixed through heredity and corresponded with social class and racial origin. As Lewis Terman introduced the Stanford-Binet tests into the US, he made it plain that low intelligence "is very common among Spanish-Indian and Mexican families of the South-West and also among negroes. Their dullness seems to be racial, or at least inherent in the family stocks from which they come...Children of this group should be segregated in special classes...They cannot master abstractions, but they can often be made efficient workers...There is no possibility at present of convincing society that they should not be allowed to reproduce, although from a eugenic point of view they constitute a grave problem because of their unusually prolific breeding."

This constituted the tone of the US educational establishment in regard to testing. A new twist was also introduced to extend its scientific scope: standards were set for adults, and the ratio between age and mental age—the "intelligence quotient", or IQ.

(83) T. Dobzhansky, op cit., p. 264.

In Britain, it was English psychologist Sir Cyril Lodowic Burt who translated and championed even more obsessively than his American counterparts Binet's tests. He claimed that men were more intelligent than women on the basis of alleged studies. The same gentleman alleged that he possessed the strongest scientific evidence that Christians were more intelligent than Jews, Englishmen than Irishmen, upper-class Englishmen than lower-class Englishmen, and so on. Not surprisingly, Burt himself just happened to be an upper class, Christian English male! By such means the oppressors justify oppression, the wealthy and powerful justify their privileges, on the grounds that their victims are "inferior". For some 65 years, until his death in 1971, Burt continued his work on eugenics and IQ testing, being duly knighted for his services to mankind. He helped to establish the notorious "eleven plus" education system, which segregated children between "secondary modern" and grammar schools. Burt explained: "Capacity must obviously limit content. It is impossible for a pint jug to hold more than a pint of milk; and it is equally impossible for a child's educational attainments to rise higher than his educable capacity permits."

So Binet's tests were twisted beyond recognition to reinforce the class character of society. There were those born to be hewers of coal and carriers of water, and those who would rule over society. The tests were not used to remedy, but to segregate. Whatever the modification of the IQ test, they all have the same roots: a preconceived "intelligence" that is the hallmark on which all are judged. However these tests are overwhelmingly influenced by culture and social stereotypes that determine the results. Again they are linked to school performance, and reflect those results. However, the idea that it is possible to identify or measure "intelligence" in this crude fashion is fundamentally false. After all, what is intelligence? How can it be quantified? It is not like weight or height. Intelligence is not fixed, as Burt claimed, but elastic. The potential of a human brain is limitless. To allow a human being to fulfil this potential is the task of society. Environmental facts can greatly restrict potential or enhance it. Bring up children in bad social conditions, and they will be disadvantaged in comparison with those brought up with all their needs provided. Social background is extremely important. If you change the environment, you change the child. Despite the claims of the biological determinists, intelligence is not fixed or genetically predetermined.

The obsession to statistically plot "intelligence" through the bell-shaped curve is an attempt to enforce social conformity. Those outside of the norm are said to be "abnormal" and in need of treatment. Alternately, it is genetic, and determines our class, race, and life. But in reality, whereas our genotype is fixed, our phenotype changes constantly. The loss of an arm or leg is irreversible but not heritable. Wilson's disease is heritable but with drugs not irreversible. "Nor, of course," says Rose, Kamin, and Lewontin, "does the phenotype develop linearly from the genotype from birth to adulthood. The 'intelligence' of an infant is not merely a certain small percentage of that of the adult it will become, as if the 'pint jug' were being steadily filled."

Burt's frantic attempts to shore up the genetic basis of IQ, led him systematically to falsify his records and data. His celebrated IQ study of separated identical twins resulted in his incredible assertion that there was no correlation between the environments of the separated pairs. For him, everything was determined by the twin's genes. He was the idol of the genetic determinists, and his work gave them the ammunition to further their cause. In 1978, D.D. Dorfman, an American psychologist, proved conclusively that this respectable scientist and English gentleman had simply invented his results. After his exposure as a fraud, his supporters were forced to change tack, simply berating Burt for his scientific carelessness! Burt's work was the IQ equivalent to the Piltdown Man. And yet at the time—despite fifteen years of glaring inconsistencies—his researches were hailed by the scientific establishment as proof of the inheritability of IQ. Despite Burt's demise, the establishment still clung to his reactionary philosophy as the cornerstone of their class outlook.

The more recent studies, involving separated identical twins in Britain, America and Denmark, do not in any meaningful way prove the inheritability of IQ. These studies have been convincingly answered by Steven Rose, Leon J. Kamin and Richard Lewontin. Their conclusion? "We do not know what the heritability of IQ really is. The data simply do not allow us to calculate a reasonable estimate of genetic variation for IQ in any population. For all we know, the heritability may be zero or 50 per cent. *In fact, despite the massive devotion of research effort to studying it, the question of heritability of IQ is irrelevant to the matters at issue.* The great importance attached by determinists to the demonstration of heritability is a consequence of their erroneous belief that heritability means unchangeability."

"Neither for IQ nor for any other trait can genes be said to determine the organism," they continue. "There is no one-to-one correspondence between the genes inherited from one's parent and one's height, weight, metabolic rate, sickness, health, or any other nontrivial organic characteristic...every organism is the unique product of the interaction between genes and environment at every stage of life." [84]

Eugenics

Eugenics was a word coined in 1883 by Francis Galton, who was a cousin of Darwin's. The desire to "improve" the human stock is frequently related to pseudo-scientific theories put forward by those who wish to demonstrate the "superiority" of a particular group—race, nation, social class, or sex, in terms of blood or "good breeding". Such reactionary nonsense is usually given a spurious "scientific" air to convey an impression of intellectual respectability to the most irrational and abhor-

---

(84) See S. Rose, L. Kamin and R. Lewontin, *Not in our Genes*, pp. 84, 86, 87, 96, 116 and 95.

rent prejudices. America, the "land of the free", saw the triumph of the eugenics movement in the enactment of laws for the compulsory sterilisation of the "biologically inferior". The state of Indiana passed the first sterilisation act in 1907. This practice could be carried out on those considered insane, imbecilic or moronic, as recommended by a board of experts. In the mid-1920s John Scopes taught evolution using a book entitled *A Civic Biology*, by George W. Hunter, which contained the infamous case of Jukes and Kallikaks.* Under the heading *Parasitism and Its Cost to Society—the Remedy*, it says:

"Hundreds of families such as those described above exist today, spreading disease, immorality and crime to all parts of this country. The cost to society of such families is very severe. Just as certain animals or plants become parasitic on other plants or animals, these families have become parasitic on society. They not only do harm to others by corrupting, stealing or spreading disease, but they are actually protected and cared for by the state out of public money. Largely for them the poorhouse and the asylum exist. They are true parasites.

"If such people were lower animals, we would probably kill them off to prevent them spreading. Humanity will not allow this, but we do have the remedy of separating the sexes in asylums or other places and in various ways preventing intermarriage and the possibilities of perpetrating such a low and degenerate race."

By the 1930s, over 30 states in America had passed sterilisation laws, expanding those eligible for treatment to alcoholics and drug addicts, and even blindness and deafness in others. The campaign reached its height in 1927, when the Supreme Court, by 8-1 votes, upheld the Virginia sterilisation law in *Buck v. Bell*. This case involved an eighteen year old white girl called Carrie Buck, who was involuntarily incarcerated in the State Colony for Epileptics and Feeble-Minded, and was the first person to be sterilised under the act. She was chosen, according to Harry Laughlin, the superintendent of the Eugenics Record Office (who wanted to eliminate "the most worthless one-tenth of our present population"), as she, her daughter and her mother were genetically mentally subnormal. This information was largely accrued from the Stanford-Binet test of IQ—which was later proved to be totally wrong. The judge in the case, O.W. Holmes, stated "Three generations of imbeciles are enough." Carrie's sister Doris was also covertly sterilised under the same law. Carrie's child, Vivian, died in 1932 of an illness. Her teachers described her as "very bright".

---

*The Jukes and the Kallikaks were names given to two imaginary families used as examples during the latter 19th century and early 20th century to argue that anti-social behaviour or low intelligence was genetically determined. This idea that traits considered socially inferior could be transmitted genetically was used to argue in favour of eugenics, or the pseudo-scientific breeding of human beings, the *Jukes Family* representing inherited criminal tendencies and the *Kallikak Family* inherited mental retardation.

By January 1935, around 20,000 forced sterilisations for eugenic purposes were carried out in the US. Laughlin wanted the net to include "homeless, tramps and paupers" and was taken up most fervently in Nazi Germany, where the *Erbgesundheitsrecht* led to the sterilisation of some 375,000, including 4,000 for blindness and deafness. In the USA, in the end, 30,000 were sterilised against their will. While classical eugenics has been discredited, new versions such as psychosurgery have emerged. This proclaims the idea that surgery on the brain can alleviate social problems, notably violence. Two American psychosurgeons, Vernon Mark and Frank Ervin, went so far as to argue that city riots in the US are caused by mental problems (*deranged amygdalas*) and may be cured by brain surgery on certain ghetto leaders. Research into this area of biology is being financed by the US law enforcement agencies.

Seeking suitable candidates for brain surgery, a revealing letter from 1971 between the Director of Corrections, Human Relations Agency, Sacramento, and the Director of Hospitals and Clinics, University of California Medical Center, shows the mentality of sections of the "scientific" community. The Director asks for suitable prison candidates "who have shown aggressive, destructive behaviour, possibly as a result of severe neurological disease," to conduct "surgical and diagnostic procedures…to locate centres in the brain which may have been previously damaged and which could serve as the focus for episodes of violent behaviour," for surgical removal.

The reply suggests a candidate who "was transferred…for increasing militancy, leadership ability and outspoken hatred for white society…he was identified as one of several leaders in the work strike of April 1971…Also evident at approximately the same time was an avalanche of revolutionary reading material." These crank ideologies are the theoretical backdrop of political reaction. In 1980, Dr. K. Ray Nelson, the then director of the Lynchburg Hospital where Carrie Buck was sterilised, discovered that over 4,000 operations had been carried out, the last as late as 1972. The IQ tests used in the Buck case have long been discredited. These reactionary ideas of forced sterilisation are not simply confined to the "dark ages" of the past, but are alive today, sustained on pseudo-scientific theories, particularly in America. Even now, there are sterilisation laws on the statute books of 22 US states.

Crime and genetics

Since the early 1970s the proportion of Americans in prison has more than tripled. In Britain those behind bars is at record levels. Prisons are so overcrowded that inmates are kept in police cells. "The UK in 1991 had a higher proportion of its population in jail than every Council of Europe nation apart from Hungary," comments the *Financial Times* (10th March 1994). Despite this violent crime remains high in both countries. This crisis has witnessed a flowering of reactionary ideas attempting to link criminal behaviour to biological factors. "For every 1 per cent that we reduce violence, we save the country $1.2 billion," says American psychologist Adrian Raine. As a result, the US National Institute of Health has increased its budget for violence-related research to $58 million. And in December 1994 the National Science Foundation began promoting proposals for a $12 million, five-year research consortium. "With the expected advances, we're going to be able to diagnose many people who are biologically brain-prone to violence," claims Stuart Yudofsky, chair of the psychiatry department at Baylor College of Medicine in the *Scientific American* of March 1995.

It has become fashionable in certain circles to attribute all kinds of things to genetic or biological disorders, rather than recognising that social problems arise from social conditions. The school of genetic determinism has drawn all types of reactionary conclusions, reducing all social problems to the level of genetics. Not long ago, research apparently revealed that many violent criminals had an extra Y chromosome, but more recent studies show the connection to be irrelevant. Now evidence of less activity in the frontal cortex of the brain of murderers is attracting attention as the link between biology and violence. There is a proposal for a Federal Violence Initiative to identify at least 100,000 inner-city children "whose alleged biochemical and genetic defects will make them prone to violence in later life."

The dangers of phoney research leading to genetic links to race and criminal or antisocial behaviour are ever present. False conclusions can be drawn from the statistic that in the US, where 12.4 per cent of the population are blacks, they account for 44.8 per cent of arrests for violent crime. In the same article in *Scientific American* we read: "There is reason to be concerned that ostensibly objective biological studies, blindly ignoring social and cultural differences, could misguidedly reinforce racial stereotypes." Due to this threat, boycotts have taken place over blood and urine samples being taken from racial minorities. So, according to Raine, "all the biological and genetic studies conducted to date have been done on whites."

Raine continues: "Imagine you are the father of an eight-year old boy. The ethical dilemma is this: I could say to you, 'Well, we have taken a wide variety of measurements, and we can predict with 80 per cent accuracy that your son is going to become seriously violent within 20 years. We can offer you a series of biological, social and cognitive intervention programmes that will greatly reduce the chance of his becoming a violent offender.' What do you do? Do you place your boy in those programmes and risk stigmatising him as a violent criminal even though there is a real possibility that he is innocent? Or do you say no to the treatment and run an 80 per cent chance that your child will grow up to (a) destroy his life, (b) destroy your life, (c) destroy the lives of his brothers and sisters and, most important, (d) destroy the lives of the innocent victims who suffer at his hands?"

Firstly, it is not possible to predict a child's future criminal behaviour at all—let alone with 80 per cent accuracy. And secondly, this puts the blame for crime on the individual. This reactionary argument fails to see crime, violence, and other social ills, as a product of the society we live under. It is a society based upon human exploitation and the maximisation of profit that results in mass unemployment, homelessness, poverty, and the denigration of life. These social conditions, in turn, produce crime, violence, and brutality. This is nothing to do with genes or biology, and everything to do with the barbarism of capitalist society.

The biological determinists are used to bolster up reactionary social ideas. It is not society that is to blame for crime, poverty, unemployment, etc., but the individual, through their genes or defective biology. The answer, therefore, is brain or genetic surgery. Others look for abnormal levels of testosterone, or slower heartbeats as the explanation of human violence. Some scientists have pointed to the low levels of serotonin, a chemical that in the body affects, amongst other things, the functioning of the brain. Thus, C.R. Jeffery wrote in the *Journal of Criminal Justice Education*: "By increasing the level of serotonin in the brain, we can reduce the level of violence." So serotonin boosters, like the antidepressant Prozac, are administered to patients to cure their aggression. The falsehood of this view is explained by the fact that this chemical can rise or drop in different parts of the brain at different times, with different effects. Environment can also affect levels. However, these "facts" are not allowed to get in the way, or prevent these people from making outrageous claims to bolster their reactionary views.

Jeffery advocates that "Science must tell us what individuals will or will not become criminals, what individuals will or will not become victims, and what law enforcement strategies will or will not work." Yudofsky reinforces Jeffery's enthusiasm with his assertion: "We are now on the verge of a revolution in genetic medicine. The future will be to understand the genetics of aggressive disorders and to identify those who have greater tendencies to become violent." He believes that hyperactive children should be tested, and, if necessary, given beta-blockers, anticonvulsants or lithium. Yudofsky says these drugs will be "cost effective" and a tremendous "opportunity for the pharmaceutical industry." It is not difficult to see on which side his bread is buttered.

"There are areas where we can begin to incorporate biological approaches," argues Diana Fishbein. "Delinquents need to be individually assessed." She goes on to advocate compulsory treatment for criminals, but if this is unsuccessful, "they should be held indefinitely." Masters believes that "we now know enough about the serotonergic system so that if we see a kid doing poorly in school, we ought to look at his serotonin levels."

Racism and genetics

The United States senate was told in 1899 that "God has not been preparing the English-speaking and Teutonic peoples for a thousand years for nothing but vain and idle self-admiration…He has made us adept in government that we may administer government among savages and senile people."

William Bradford Shockley, the co-inventor of the transistor, argued that, since blacks are genetically less intelligent than whites, they should not be given equal opportunities, a view also held by the well-known psychologist Hans J. Eysenck. Human nature is seen as the source and explanation of all social ills, having drawn certain distorted parallels with the lifestyles of other animals. The broader claims of sociobiology are that racism and nationalism are natural extensions of tribalism, which, in turn, is a product of "kin selection". "Nationalism and racism," states E.O. Wilson, "are culturally nurtured outgrowths of simple tribalism." This idea has even been suggested by Richard Dawkins: "Conceivably, racial prejudice could be interpreted as an irrational generalisation of a kin-selected tendency to identify with individuals physically resembling oneself and to be nasty to individuals different in appearance." [85]

According to the father of sociobiology, E.O. Wilson, "in hunter-gatherer societies, men hunt and women stay at home. This strong bias persists in most agricultural and industrial societies and *on that ground alone appears to have a genetic origin.*" He says that men are "naturally" polygamous, while women are "naturally" monogamous. The characteristic of sociobiology is the comparison of human social relations with the animal world, as justification for male dominance and class structure. "The genetic bias," says Wilson, "is intense enough to cause a substantial division of labour even in the most free and most egalitarian of future societies." This is the theme, based on the animal world, which zoologist Desmond Morris attempts to popularise.

The recent attempts to prove that intelligence is inherited has centred around IQ testing. *The Bell Curve* by Charles Murray regurgitates the old argument that genetics explains the gap between the average IQ of American whites and blacks. The fundamental arguments in this book have been repeatedly demolished. According to psychiatrist Peter Breggin, it is an attempt to "resurrect the King Kong image of Afro-Americans as violent and stupid." (*The Guardian*, 13th March 1995). But the most crushing evidence against the theories of genetic determinism come from a recent book entitled *The History and Geography of Human Genes* by population geneticists Luca Cavalli-Sforza, Paolo Menozzi and Alberto Piazza. The book is a remarkable synthesis of more than 50 years research in population genetics. It is the most authoritative account to date of how humans vary at the level of their chromosomes. The firm conclusion of the book is that, once the genes for surface traits such as colouration and stature are discounted, the human 'races' are remarkably alike under the skin. That variation between individuals is far greater than the variation among groups. According to the magazine *Time*, "In fact, the diversity among individuals is so enormous that the whole concept of race becomes meaningless at the genetic level. The authors say there is 'no scientific basis' for theories touting the genetic superiority of any one population over another." (16th January 1995.)

(85) R. Dawkins, *The Selfish Gene*, p. 108.

In reviewing the book, the *Time* article states: "Despite the difficulties, the scientists made some myth-shattering discoveries. One of them jumps right off the book's cover: a colour map of the world genetic variation has Africa on one end of the spectrum and Australia on the other. Because Australia's aborigines and sub-Saharan Africans share such superficial traits as skin colour and body shape, they were widely assumed to be closely related. But their genes tell a different story. Of all humans, Australians are most distant from the Africans and most closely resemble their neighbours, the Southeast Asians." The review concludes, "What the eye sees as racial differences—between Europeans and Africans, for example—are mainly adaptions to climate as humans moved from one continent to another." The book also confirms that the birthplace of humanity and so the starting point for the original human migrations was Africa, thereby demonstrating that the split from the African branch is the oldest on the human family tree.

The use of biological and genetic theories to justify reactionary policies is not a new phenomenon, although in the last decade or so it has been given a new lease of life by the general tendency of Western governments to go onto the offensive against the welfare state and all the other social conquests of the working class. The law of the market—that is *the law of the jungle*—is back in fashion. That includes, of course, the universities, where there are always enough people willing to swim with the prevailing current, which does their career prospects no harm whatsoever.

There are many honest academics who approach their subject in a dispassionate manner, but it would indeed be naïve to believe that the fact that a person has a string of letters after his or her name makes them immune from the pressures of the society in which they live, whether they are aware of it or not. In 1949, N. Pastore conducted a study into the opinions of twenty-four psychologists, biologists and sociologists concerning the so-called *nature-nurture* problem. Out of twelve "liberals or radicals", eleven said the environment was more important than heredity, and one the opposite. In the conservative camp, the result was exactly the opposite—eleven hereditarians and only one environmentalist! Dobzhansky found this result "disconcerting". For our part, we find it quite predictable.

Roger Scruton draws the social lessons: "Bioeconomics says that government programmes that force individuals to be less competitive and selfish than they are genetically programmed to be are preordained to fail." This fitted in perfectly with the reemergence of genetic determinism in America, and their proof that blacks were inferior to whites, and the working class was inferior to the middle and upper classes. The scientific backing for such fallacies is used to create an aura of so-called respectability and objectivity.

Richard Dawkins

Richard Dawkins, who came to fame with his controversially entitled book *The Selfish Gene*, has been at the centre of a heated polemic over genetics. Molecular biologists have identified the importance of DNA in replicating copies of DNA molecules. They possess coded instructions that produce the building blocks of life, amino acids. These make up proteins which shape cells and organs. Because of this, some molecular biologists and also sociobiologists have argued that all natural selection acts ultimately at the level of the DNA. This has led a number of scientists to have become so obsessed with the wondrous nature of the gene, that not a few are unable see the wood for the trees. Some have given the gene mystical qualities from which reactionary ideas are drawn. The idea that a person's physical, mental and moral characteristics are handed down unaltered and unalterable from genes is certainly not supported by the facts of genetic science. Yet it has cropped up again and again in literature and has had a serious effect on social policy throughout the 20th century.

The gene transmits its influence from parent to offspring. It can only be defined as a difference between a number of different genes (called *allelles*) influencing the same thing (e.g. blue/brown allelles for eye colour). The difference is identified by means of biochemical, physiological, structural or behavioural testing/observation (after other sources of variation, like environment, have been excluded).

Unfortunately, many scientists and others use misleading shorthand for the above definition. Particularly, that a gene that *contributes* to an individual animal behaving differently becomes the gene *for* its distinctive behaviour. Dawkins is not the only scientist that falls into this trap. In the 1970s many spoke of a gene *coding* for physical and behavioural characteristics. Also a gene must be compared with another for the same trait. It is not an entity that stands alone in its own right. As J.B.S. Haldane correctly pointed out, genetics is the science of *differences* not similarities. Quite simply, you and I can both be selfish—the differences between us cannot. You cannot apply personal characteristics to a comparison. In his book, *The Selfish Gene*, Dawkins jumps back and forth from one definition to the other, claiming that they are interchangeable—which they are not. The result has been to encourage biological determinism. A whole generation of American and other scientists are being brought up on this confusion.

The scientific research into genetics shows the possibilities for medicine, where gene disorders such as Huntington's chorea, Duchenne muscular dystrophy, and others have been identified. However, there are widespread assertions that in some way genes are responsible for all kinds of things, like homosexuality and criminality. This genetic determinism reduces all social problems to the level of genetics. In February 1995, a conference on *Genetics of Criminal and Anti-Social Behaviour* was held in London. Ten of the thirteen speakers were from the United States where a similar conference in 1992 with racist overtones was abandoned because of public pressure. While the chairperson, Sir Michael Rutter of the London Institute of Psychiatry stated "there can be no such thing as a gene for crime", other participants, like Dr. Gregory Carey of the Institute of Behavioural Genetics, University of Colorado, maintained that genetic factors as a whole were responsible for 40-50 per cent of criminal violence. Although he said it would be impractical to "treat" criminality through genetic engineering, others said there were good prospects for developing drugs to control excessive aggression, once the responsible genes had been found. He suggested, however, that *abortion should be considered when ante-natal testing indicates a child is likely to be born with genes predisposing it to aggression or antisocial behaviour.* His view was endorsed by Dr. David Goldman from the Laboratory of Neurogenetics at the US National Institute of Health in Maryland. "The families should be given the information and should be allowed to decide privately how to use it." (*The Independent*, 14th February 1995.)

According to Professor Hans Brunner of Nijmegen University Hospital in Holland, men in a family who inherited a particular genetic abnormality of the X chromosome that led to a deficiency in an enzyme concerned with messages in the brain have shown "impulsive aggression" including arson and attempted rape. Dr. David Goldman and Professor Matti Virkkunen of the University of Helsinki said they were discovering aggression-related genetic variations in the way people process brain chemicals. "Pharmaceutical companies are already interested in our findings," said Virkkunen. (*The Financial Times*, 14th February, 1995.)

Steven Rose described the conference as "troublesome, disturbing and unbalanced." The event was attacked in a letter by fifteen scientists. Dr. Zakari Erzinclioglu, director of the Centre for Forensic Science at Durham University, called it "very disturbing, simple minded and mischievous." Ashley Montague pointed out that "it is not 'criminal genes' that make criminals, but in most cases 'criminal social conditions'."

Richard Dawkins' *The Selfish Gene*, originally published in 1976, makes some startling assertions. "We are born selfish," says Dawkins. Although he says that "genes have no foresight" and "they do not plan ahead" Dawkins imbues genes with a consciousness and a "selfish" identity. They strive to replicate themselves, as if they are consciously planning how best this could be achieved:

"Certainly in principle, and also in fact, the gene reaches out through the individual body wall and manipulates objects in the world outside, some of them inanimate, some of them other living beings, some of them a long way away. With only a little imagination we can see the gene as sitting at the centre of a radiating web of extended phenotypic power. And an object in the world is the centre of a converging web of influences from many genes sitting in many organisms. The long reach of the gene knows no obvious boundaries." [86] Because for Dawkins individual organisms do not survive from one generation to another, while genes do, it follows that natural selection acts on what survives, namely, the genes. Therefore, all selection acts ultimately at the level of DNA. At the same time, each gene is in competi-

(86) R. Dawkins, *The Selfish Gene*, pp. 3 and 265-6.

tion with each other to reproduce themselves in the next generation. "What after all, is so special about genes? The answer is that they are replicators."

In this view, the replicator of life is the gene; thus the organism is simply the vehicle for the genes ("survival machines—robot vehicles blindly programmed to preserve the selfish molecules known as genes"…"they swarm in huge colonies, safe inside gigantic lumbering robots"). It is a recasting of Samuel Butler's famous aphorism that a hen is simply the egg's way of making another egg. An animal, for Dawkins, is only DNA's way of making more DNA. He imbues the genes with certain mystical qualities, which is essentially teleological.

"I suspect," says Dawkins in his defence, "that both Rose and Gould are determinists in that they believe in a physical, materialistic basis for all our actions. So am I…whatever view one takes on the question of determinism, the insertion of the word 'genetic' is not going to make any difference." He then adds, "if you are a full-blooded determinist you will believe that all your actions are determined by physical causes in the past…what difference can it possibly make whether some of those physical causes are *genetic*? Why are genetic determinists thought to be any more ineluctable, or blame-absolving, than 'environmental ones'?" [87]

Everything in nature has a cause and an effect, in which an effect in its turn becomes a cause. Dawkins mixes up determinism and fatalism: "An organism is a tool of DNA." Genetic determinism has a precise meaning, where genes are said to "determine" the exact nature of the phenotype. There is no doubt that genes have a powerful effect in the form of the organism, but its entity will be *decisively* influenced by the environment. For example, if two identical twins are placed into two totally different environments, two different characters will be produced. As Rose explains, "In reality, however, selection must act at a multitude of levels. Individual gene-sized lengths of DNA may or may not be selected in their own right, but that DNA is expressed against the background of the entire genotype; particular assemblies of genes or whole genotypes must therefore themselves represent another level of selection. Further, the genotype exists within a phenotype, and whether that phenotype survives or not depends on its interaction with others. Hence it will only be selected against the background of the population in which it is embedded." [88]

Dawkins was forced to backtrack to some extent, modifying his arguments in the later editions of *The Selfish Gene* (1989) and in *The Extended Phenotype: The Long Reach of the Gene* (1982). He says his flamboyant language left him open to mis-representation and misunderstanding: "It is all too easy to get carried away, and allow hypothetical genes cognitive wisdom and foresight in planning their 'strategy'." He nevertheless defends his fundamental argument and views life "in terms of genetic replicators preserving themselves by means of their extended phenotypes." And that "natural selection is differential survival of genes." Dawkins now says

(87) R. Dawkins, *The Extended Phenotype: The Long Reach of the Gene*, pp. 10-11.
(88) S. Rose, *Molecules and Minds*, pp. 64-5.

"genes may modify the effects of other genes, and may modify the effects of the environment. Environmental events, both internal and external, may modify the effects of genes, and may modify the effects of other environmental events." But this concession aside, Dawkins' main thesis remains.

For instance, he says: "Contraception is sometimes attacked as 'unnatural'. So it is, very unnatural. The trouble is, so is the welfare state. I think that most of us believe the welfare state is highly desirable. But you cannot have an unnatural welfare state, unless you also have unnatural birth control, otherwise the end result will be misery even greater than that which obtains in nature." He continues, "the welfare state is perhaps the greatest altruistic system the animal kingdom has ever known. But any altruistic system is inherently unstable, because it is open to abuse by selfish individuals, ready to exploit it. Individual humans who have more children than they are capable of rearing are probably too ignorant in most cases to be accused of conscious malevolent exploitation."

According to Dawkins child adoption is against the instincts and interests of our "selfish genes". "In most cases we should probably regard adoption, however touching it may seem, as a misfiring of an in-built rule," says Dawkins. "This is because the generous female is doing her own genes no good by caring for the orphan. She is wasting time and energy that she could be investing in the lives of her own kin, particularly future children of her own. It is presumably a mistake which happens too seldom for natural selection to have 'bothered' to change the rule by making the maternal instinct more selective."

He says that "if a female is presented with reliable evidence that a famine is expected, it is in her own selfish interests to reduce her own birth-rate." Dawkins also believes that natural selection would favour children who cheat, lie, deceive and exploit and that "when we look at wild populations we may expect to see cheating and selfishness within families. The phrase 'the child should cheat' means that genes which tend to make children cheat have an advantage in the gene pool." [89] He concludes that the organism is a tool of DNA, rather than the other way around.

These comments are interesting not so much for what they tell us about genes, but for what they reveal about the state of society in the last decade of the 20th century. In certain societies, powerful muscles or the ability to run fast can confer a genetic advantage. If a similar advantage is attributed to the propensity to lie, cheat and exploit, it must mean that such features are the qualities most necessary to succeed in modern society, and this is perfectly correct from the standpoint of the advocates of "market values". While it is extremely questionable that such qualities can, in fact, be passed on through the genetic mechanism, it is certainly the fact that they form the most essential features of the *egoism of the bourgeois*. The "war of each against all", as old Hobbes puts it, is the basic standpoint of capitalist society.

(89) R. Dawkins, *The Selfish Gene*, pp. 126, 109, 129 and 150.

Is it true that such a mentality is a genetically conditioned part of "human nature"? Let us remind ourselves that capitalism and its values has only existed at most for the last 200 years out of approximately 5,000 years of recorded history, and 100,000 years of human development. Human society, for the overwhelming majority of its existence, has been based on the principle of *co-operation*. Indeed, human beings could never have raised themselves above the level of animals without this. Far from being an essential component of the human psyche, competition is a recent phenomenon, a reflection of a society based on the production of commodities, which twists and perverts human nature into patterns of behaviour that would have been considered abhorrent and unnatural in the past.

It is too easy to blame some mysterious phenomenon such as "our genes" for the grasping self-centred morality of the market place. Moreover, this is not a question of zoology, but of social class. Individual capitalists compete against each other and do not hesitate to use any methods to ruin their rivals—lying, cheating, industrial espionage, insider dealing, predatory take-overs—these are considered to be normal commercial practice. From the standpoint of the working class, things are very different. It is not a question of individual morality, but precisely of social survival (the sociological equivalent of "the survival of the fittest"). The only power the working class possesses against the employers is the power of unity. That is precisely of *co-operation*.

Without organisation, beginning at the trade union level, the working class is only raw material for exploitation. The workers' need to combine in the defence of their interests is a lesson that has to be learned over and over again. Selfishness and "individualism" (in the bourgeois sense of the word) is quite self-defeating for the working class. Every strikebreaker is presented as a great defender of "individual freedom" by the millionaire press because it is in the interest of the employers to atomise the working class, to reduce it to its component parts, utterly at the mercy of Capital. Here too, the dialectical law holds good that the whole is greater that the sum of the parts. Consciously or not, those who present selfishness as an ideal, or at least as "human nature", have taken up a definite position in relation to the struggle between wage labour and Capital, and cannot complain if they are criticised for providing grist to the Thatcherite mill.

Dawkins sees evolution not as the outcome of a struggle of organisms, but as a struggle between genes seeking to copy themselves. The bodies they inhabit are secondary. He discards the Darwinian principle that individuals are the units of selection. This is a fundamentally false idea. Natural selection deals with organisms, with bodies. It favours some bodies because they are better suited to their environment. The gene is a piece of DNA enclosed within the cell nucleus, large numbers of which contribute to the development of most body parts. This in turn is affected by a whole series of environmental factors, internal and external. Selection does not work directly on parts. Natural selection works on bodies because they are in some way "fitter", i.e., stronger, fiercer, warmer, and so on. If there is a particular gene for strength or other such specific attributes, then Dawkins may be correct. But that is not the case. There is not one gene for one bit of anatomy. For instance, the instructions for the construction of the ear are contained in a host of separate genes, half of which have come from either parent.

As Stephen Jay Gould explained: "It [natural selection] accepts or rejects entire organisms because suites of parts, interacting in complex ways, confer advantages…Organisms are much more than amalgamations of genes. They have a history that matters; their parts interact in complex ways. Organisms are built by genes acting in concert, influenced by environments, translated into parts that selection sees and parts invisible to selection. Molecules that determine the properties of water are poor analogues for genes and bodies." [90]

This analysis is backed up by Steven Rose in his criticism of Dawkins which we have already quoted. Dawkins' method leads him into the swamp of idealism, when he attempts to argue that human culture can be reduced to units he calls *memes*, which, apparently, like genes, are self-replicating and compete for survival. This is clearly wrong. Human culture is passed down from generation to generation, not through *memes*, but through education in the broadest sense. It is not biologically inherited but has to be painstakingly relearned and developed by each new generation. Cultural diversity is bound up not with genes but social history. Dawkins' approach is essentially reductionist.

Societies are broken down to organisms, organisms to cells, cells to molecules, and molecules to atoms. For Dawkins, human nature and motivation are to be understood by analysing human DNA. The same is true of James Watson (the discoverer, with Francis Crick and Rosalind Franklin, of the double helix) who said: "What else is there but atoms?" They never allow the existence of either multiple levels of analysis or complex modes of determination. They ignore the essential relations between cells and the organism as a whole. This empirical method, which emerged with the scientific revolution at the birth of capitalism, was progressive in its day, but has now become a fetter on the advancement of science and the understanding of nature.

The future of genetics

"Until very recently, the only access to the genes which shape the natural world was through environmental change. Now those genes can be manipulated directly. That makes a change easy, immediate and comprehensible; the technology that enables direct genetic manipulation also opens genes' activity up to inspection. But at the same time it makes change arbitrary, because genes that no animal would spontaneously

(90) S.J. Gould, *The Panda's Thumb*, pp. 77-8.

evolve become possible. These new techniques give humanity unprece-dented powers to change the world—and to change itself." (*The Economist*, 25th February 1995.)

Over the past three decades, colossal advances have been made in the field of molecular genetics. In 1972, the first gene was isolated and reproduced ("cloned") in a laboratory. The consequences of this were so worrying, that scientists consid-ered a voluntary moratorium on the recombination of the cloned genes into the DNA of other organisms. But now the introduction of cloned genes into humans has become almost routine. By the first decade of the next century scientists will know the true names of all the proteins in the human body. Such knowledge has tremen-dous implications for the future—for good or ill.

Until this moment, the gene was shrouded in mystery, like Kant's Thing-in-Itself. The gene was the stern master of human destiny, implacable, unalterable, unfathomable. To talk about our genes was not only to talk about our inheritance. It was to talk about our fate. And fate is a court against which there is no appeal. Until this moment. But now, for the first time in the history of life on our planet, the pos-sibility exists of human beings controlling their own destiny, at the deepest levels. Contrary to the nonsense of the genetic reactionaries, it was never true that genes completely determined human evolution. Although they play a major role in human life, genes do not control it. At most, they establish certain parameters that limit or permit. But now the genotype itself, for the first time, is being brought under con-trol. This is a revolutionary development, pregnant with great consequences for the future of humanity.

The emergence of life out of inorganic matter was a giant evolutionary leap. After a whole series of transformations, the development of a thinking brain as the product of social life and collective labour was another giant step. Matter becomes conscious of itself. Now, for the first time in four billion years, human beings are in the process of mastering the secrets of their own evolution. Natural selection ceas-es to be a blind, mysterious force. The all-powerful genotype can be brought under the control of the phenotype. Humankind has the potential to determine its own des-tiny, and modify the harsh dictates of natural selection.

"Just as organisms are interpretations of genetic information within a specific environment," writes Oliver Morton, "so the use of this genetic knowledge will depend on the environments—economic and ethical, personal and political—in which that use is made. But those uses, good or ill, will surely be made. The genes that imperiously limited and permitted will be bent to human will; limits will become movable, permissions stretched. Genes have never been the complete mas-ters of human destiny, but nor have they been humanity's servants. Until now." (*The Economist*, 25th February 1995)

It is as futile to bemoan these discoveries as it was for desperate groups of work-ers to break machines in the early days of the Industrial Revolution. The discoveries of science and technology are a vital part of the development of society, allowing humankind to gain greater control over the constraints imposed by nature. Only in this way can humanity become truly free. The problem is not what the human mind discovers. The problem is how the discoveries are used. The advances of science open a new and breathtaking horizon of unlimited human development. But there is another, darker side to all this. The 20th century carries a terrible message of what horrors can come from capitalism in its epoch of historical decline. The techniques of genetic engineering in the hands of uncontrolled monopolies, interested only in making big profits, poses a ghastly threat.

The entire development of technology, which is constantly breaking down all barriers, and uniting the world in a way that has never been seen before, is an argument in favour of a world planned economy. Not the monstrous caricature of Stalinism, but a democratically run society, in which men and women would achieve conscious control over their lives and destinies. On the basis of a harmonious planned economy, pooling the resources of the entire planet, a vista of unlimited development opens up. On the one hand, we have the task of nurturing our own world, of making it fit for human beings, of repairing the ravages caused by the greed of irresponsible multinationals. On the other, we have before us the greatest challenges yet contemplated by our species—the exploration of space, linked to the question of the future survival of humankind. The science of genetic engineering, now in its infancy, may in the future be linked to the demands of long space voyages. At present, this is in the realm of speculation. Yet the history of the last hundred years has shown just how rapidly ideas that seemed to be fantastic have been overtaken by reality.

What we see at this moment in time is a colossal *potential*. In the context of a democratic, harmoniously planned economy, where men and women freely and consciously determine their destinies, the science of genetics will cease to be a block on human progress and will take its proper place in the study and transformation of life itself. This is not fantasy, but corresponds to actual possibilities. In the words of Oliver Morton:

"The possibilities of this biology are almost endless. The natural world, including the human body and mind, will become malleable. Implanted organs may refashion the brain, designer viruses rebuild old tissue. Human organs grown in animals for transplant are already being designed. New types of creature may appear; creatures to marvel at. If humanity can find no peer among the stars, it could create new intelligences on earth. The genetic difference between man and chimp is small; new sentient species are not inconceivable.

"All this will be made possible by genetics. But, at the same time, the pre-eminence of the gene will fade away. Genes have lost their privileged position as the carriers of information. Biological information will be stored in minds and computers as well as in genes, and the genes will become just one of the many means of manipulating the world, appropriate for some things and not for others, just like therapeutic proteins...

"What was once unique to genes is now in humanity's grip. That grip could soon have all the power that has at times been attributed to genes and more. The same intelligence will be able to shape the gene and the environment, which between them make all organisms what they are. The control of biological information on this scale—of the raw data and the way that it is processed—means the control of biology, of life itself." (*The Economist*, 25th February 1995.)

Part four:
Order out of chaos

16. Does mathematics reflect reality?

"The fact that our subjective thought and the objective world are subject to the same laws, and hence, too, that in the final analysis they cannot contradict each other in their results, but must coincide, governs absolutely our whole theoretical thought." (Engels)

The content of "pure" mathematics is ultimately derived from the material world. The idea that the truths of mathematics are a special kind of knowledge that is inborn or of divine inspiration does not bear serious examination. Mathematics deals with the quantitative relations of the real world. Its so-called axioms only appear to be self-evident to us because they are the product of a long period of observation and experience of reality. Unfortunately, this fact seems to be lost on many present-day theoretical mathematicians who delude themselves into thinking that their "pure" subject has nothing to do with the crude world of material things. This is a clear example of the negative consequences of carrying the division of labour to the extreme.

From Pythagoras onwards, the most extravagant claims have been made on behalf of mathematics, which has been portrayed as the queen of the sciences, the magic key opening all doors of the universe. Breaking free from all contact with the physical world, mathematics appeared to soar into the heavens, where it acquired a god-like existence, obeying no rule but its own. Thus, the great mathematician Henri Poincaré, in the early years of this century, could claim that the laws of science did not relate to the real world at all, but represented arbitrary conventions destined to promote a more convenient and "useful" description of the corresponding phenomena. Certain theoretical physicists now openly state that the validity of their mathematical models does not depend upon empirical verification, but on the aesthetic qualities of their equations.

The theories of mathematics have been, on the one side, the source of tremendous scientific advance, and, on the other, the origin of numerous errors and mis-

conceptions which have had, and are still having profoundly negative consequences. The central error is to attempt to reduce the complex, dynamic and contradictory workings of nature to static, orderly quantitative formulae. Nature is presented in a formalistic manner, as a single-dimensional point, which becomes a line,
which becomes a plane, a cube, a sphere, and so on. However, the idea that pure
mathematics is absolute thought, unsullied by contact with material things is far
from the truth. We use the decimal system, not because of logical deduction or "free
will", but because we have ten fingers. The word "digital" comes from the Latin
word for fingers. And to this day, a schoolboy will secretly count his material fingers beneath a material desk, before arriving at the answer to an abstract mathematical problem. In so doing, the child is unconsciously retracing the way in which
early humans learned to count.

The material origins of the abstractions of mathematics were no secret to
Aristotle: "The mathematician," he wrote, "investigates abstractions. He eliminates
all sensible qualities like weight, density, temperature, etc., leaving only the quantitative and continuous (in one, two or three dimensions) and its essential attributes."
Elsewhere he says: "Mathematical objects cannot exist *apart from* sensible (i.e.,
material) things." And "We have no experience of anything which consists of lines
or planes or points, as we should have if these things were material substances,
lines, etc., may be prior *in definition* to body, but they are not on that account prior
in substance." [1]

The development of mathematics is the result of very material human needs.
Early man at first had only ten number sounds, precisely because he counted, like a
small child, on his fingers. The exception were the Mayas of Central America who
had a numerical system based on twenty instead of ten, probably because they
counted their toes as well as their fingers. Living in a simple hunter-gatherer society, without money or private property, our ancestors had no need of large numbers.
To convey a number larger than ten, he merely combined some of the ten sounds
connected with his fingers. Thus, one more than ten is expressed by "one-ten",
(undecim, in Latin, or ein-lifon—"one over"—in early Teutonic, which becomes
"eleven" in modern English). All the other numbers are only combinations of the
original ten sounds, with the exception of five additions—hundred, thousand, million, billion and trillion.

The real origin of numbers was already understood by the great English materialist philosopher of the 17th century Thomas Hobbes: "And it seems, there was a
time when those names of number were not in use; and men were fayn to apply their
fingers of one or both hands, to those things they desired to keep account of; and
that thence it proceeded, that now our numeral words are but ten, in any Nation, and
in some but five, and then they begin again." [2]

(1) Aristotle, *Metaphysics*, pp. 120, 251 and 253.
(2) T. Hobbes, *Leviathan*, p. 14.

Alfred Hooper explains: "Just because primitive man invented the same number of number-sounds as he had fingers, our number-scale today is a *decimal* one, that is, a scale based on *ten*, and consisting of endless repetitions of the first ten basic number-sounds…Had men been given twelve fingers instead of ten, we should doubtless have a *duo-decimal* number-scale today, one based on twelve, consisting of endless repetitions of twelve basic number-sounds." [3] In fact, a duodecimal system has certain advantages in comparison to the decimal one. Whereas ten can only be exactly divided by two and five, twelve can be divided exactly by two, three, four and six.

The Roman numerals are pictorial representations of fingers. Probably the symbol for five represented the gap between thumb and fingers. The word "calculus" (from which we derive "calculate") means "pebble" in Latin, connected with the method of counting stone beads on an abacus. These and countless other examples serve to illustrate how mathematics did not arise from the free operation of the human mind, but is the product of a lengthy process of social evolution, trial and error, observation and experiment, which gradually becomes separated out as a body of knowledge of an apparently abstract character. Similarly, our present systems of weights and measures have been derived from material objects. The origin of the English unit of measurement, the foot, is self-evident, as is the Spanish word for an inch, "pulgada", which means a thumb. The origin of the most basic mathematical symbols + and – has nothing to do with mathematics. They were the signs used in the Middle Ages by the merchants to calculate excess or deficiency of quantities of goods in warehouses.

The need to build dwellings to protect themselves from the elements forced early humans to find the best and most practical way of cutting wood so that their ends fitted closely together. This meant the discovery of the right angle and the carpenters' square. The need to build a house on level ground led to the invention of the kind of levelling instrument depicted in Egyptian and Roman tombs, consisting of three pieces of wood joined together in an isosceles triangle, with a cord fastened at the apex. Such simple practical tools were used in the construction of the pyramids. The Egyptian priests accumulated a huge body of mathematical knowledge derived ultimately from such practical activity.

The very word "geometry" betrays its practical origins. It means simply "earth-measurement". The virtue of the Greeks was to give a finished theoretical expression to these discoveries. However, in presenting their theorems as the pure product of logical deduction, they were misleading themselves and future generations. Ultimately, mathematics derives from material reality, and, indeed, could have no application if this were not the case. Even the famous theorem of Pythagoras,

(3) A. Hooper, *Makers of Mathematics*, pp. 4-5.

known to every school pupil, that a square drawn on the longest side of a right triangle is equal to the sum of the squares drawn on the other two sides, had been already worked out in practice by the Egyptians.

Contradictions in mathematics

Engels, and before him Hegel, pointed to the numerous contradictions that abound in mathematics. This was always the case, despite the claims of perfection and almost papal infallibility made by mathematicians for their "sublime science". This fashion was started by the Pythagoreans, with their mystical conception of Number, and the harmony of the universe. Very soon, however, they found out that their harmonious and orderly mathematical universe was plagued with contradictions, the solution of which drove them to despair. For example, they found that it was impossible to express the length of the diagonal of a square in numbers.

The later Pythagoreans discovered that there were many numbers, like the square root of two, which could not be expressed in numbers. It is an "irrational number". But although the square root of two cannot be expressed as a fraction, it is useful to find the length of the side of a triangle. Present-day mathematics contains a veritable menagerie of such strange animals, still untamed, despite all efforts to domesticate them, but which, once accepted for what they are, render valuable services. Thus we have irrational numbers, imaginary numbers, transcendental numbers, transfinite numbers, all displaying strange and contradictory features, and all indispensable to the workings of modern science.

The mysterious π (Pi) was well known to the ancient Greeks, and generations of schoolchildren have learned to identify it as the ratio between the circumference and diameter of a circle. Yet, strangely, its exact value cannot be found. Archimedes calculated its approximate value by a method known as "exhaustion". It was between 3.14085 and 3.14286. But if we try to write down the exact value, we get a strange result: π = 3.14159265358979323846264338327950...and so on ad infinitum. Pi (π) which is now known as a transcendental number, is absolutely necessary to find the circumference of a circle, but cannot be expressed as the solution to an algebraic equation. Then we have the square root of minus one, which is not an arithmetical number at all. Mathematicians refer to it as an "imaginary number", since no real number, when multiplied by itself, can give the result of minus one, because two minuses give a plus. A most peculiar creature, this—but not a figment of the imagination, despite its name. In *Anti-Dühring*, Engels points out that:

"It is a contradiction that a negative magnitude should be the square of anything, for every negative magnitude multiplied by itself gives a positive square. The square root of minus one is therefore not only a contradiction, but even an absurd contradiction, a real absurdity. And yet $\sqrt{-1}$ is in many cases a necessary result of correct mathematical operations. Furthermore, where would mathematics—lower or higher—be, if it were prohibited from operating with $\sqrt{-1}$?" [4] Engels' remark is even more true today. This contradictory combination of plus and minus plays an absolutely crucial role in quantum mechanics, where it appears in a whole host of equations, which are fundamental to modern science.

That this mathematics involves startling contradictions is not open to doubt. Here is what Hoffman has to say about it:

"That such a formula should have any connection with that world of strict experiment which is the world of physics is in itself difficult to believe. That it was to be the deep foundation of the new physics, and that it should actually probe more profoundly than anything before towards the very core of science and metaphysics is as incredible as must once have seemed the doctrine that the earth is round." [5]

Nowadays, the use of the so-called imaginary numbers is taken for granted. The square root of minus one is used for a whole range of necessary operations, such as the construction of electrical circuits. Transfinite numbers, in turn, are needed to understand the nature of time and space. Modern science, and particularly quantum mechanics, could not manage without the use of mathematical concepts, which are frankly contradictory in character. Paul Dirac, one of the founders of quantum mechanics, discovered the "Q" numbers, which defy the laws of ordinary mathematics which state that a multiplied by b is the same thing as b multiplied by a.

Does the infinite exist?

The idea of the infinite seems difficult to grasp, because, at first sight, it is beyond all human experience. The human mind is accustomed to dealing with finite things, reflected in finite ideas. Everything has a beginning and an end. This is a familiar thought. But what is familiar is not necessarily true. The history of mathematical thought has some highly instructive lessons on this score. For a long time, mathematicians, at least in Europe, sought to banish the concept of infinity. Their reasons for so doing are obvious enough. Apart from the evident difficulty in conceptualising infinity, in purely mathematical terms it involves a contradiction. Mathematics deals with definite magnitudes. Infinity by its very nature cannot be counted or measured. This means that there is a real conflict between the two. For that reason, the great mathematicians of ancient Greece avoided infinity like the plague. Despite this, from the beginnings of philosophy, men speculated about infinity. Anaximander (610-547 B.C.) took it as the basis of his philosophy.

The paradoxes of Zeno (c. 450 B.C.) point to the difficulty inherent in the idea of infinitesimal quantity as a constituent of continuous magnitudes by attempting to prove that movement is an illusion. Zeno "disproved" motion in different ways. He argued that a body in motion, before reaching a given point, must first have travelled half the distance. But before this, it must have travelled half of that half, and

(4) Engels, *Anti-Dühring*, p. 154.
(5) B. Hoffman, *The Strange Story of the Quantum*, p. 95.

so on ad infinitum. Thus, when two bodies are moving in the same direction, and the one behind at a fixed distance from the one in front is moving faster, we assume that it will overtake the other. Not so, says Zeno. "The slower one can never be over-taken by the quicker." This is the famous paradox of Achilles the Swift. Imagine a race between Achilles and a tortoise. Suppose that Achilles can run ten times faster than the tortoise, which has 1000 metres start. By the time Achilles has covered 1000 metres, the tortoise will be 100 metres ahead; when Achilles has covered that 100 metres, the tortoise will be one metre ahead; when he covers that distance, the tortoise will be one tenth of a metre ahead, and so on to infinity.

Zeno's paradoxes do not prove that movement is an illusion, or that Achilles, in practice, will not overtake the tortoise, but they do reveal brilliantly the limitations of the kind of thinking now known as formal logic. The attempt to eliminate all con-tradiction from reality, as the Eleatics did, inevitably leads to this kind of insoluble paradox, or antinomy, as Kant later called it. In order to prove that a line could not consist of an infinite number of points, Zeno claimed that, if it were really so, then Achilles would never overtake the tortoise. There really is a logical problem here. As Alfred Hooper explains:

"This paradox still perplexes even those who know that it is possible to find the sum of an infinite series of numbers forming a geometrical progression whose com-mon ratio is less than 1, and whose terms consequently become smaller and small-er and thus 'converge' on some limiting value." [6]

In fact, Zeno had uncovered a contradiction in mathematical thought that would have to wait two thousand years for a solution. The contradiction relates to the use of the infinite. From Pythagoras right up to the discovery of the differential and inte-gral calculus in the 17th century, mathematicians went to great lengths to avoid the use of the concept of infinity. Only the great genius Archimedes approached the sub-ject, but still avoided it by using a roundabout method. The early atomists, starting with Leukippus, who may have been a pupil of Zeno, stated that the atoms "indivis-ible and infinite in number, move about ceaselessly in empty space, of infinite extent."

Modern physics accepts that the number of instants between two seconds is infi-nite, just as the number of instants in a span of time with neither beginning nor end. The universe itself consists of an infinite chain of cause and effect, ceaselessly changing, moving and developing. This has nothing in common with the crude and one-sided notion of infinity contained in the infinite series of numbers in simple arithmetic, in which "infinity" always "starts" with the number one! This is what Hegel called "Bad Infinity".

The greatest of Greek mathematicians, Archimedes (287-212 B.C.) made effec-tive use of indivisibles in geometry, but considered the idea of infinitely large and small as without logical foundation. Likewise, Aristotle argued that, since a body

(6) A. Hooper, *Makers of Mathematics*, p. 237.

must have form, it must be bounded, and therefore cannot be infinite. While accepting that there were two kinds of "potential" infinities—successive addition in arithmetic (infinitely large), and successive subdivision in geometry (infinitely small)—he nevertheless polemicised against geometers who held that a line segment is composed of infinitely many fixed infinitesimals, or indivisibles.

This denial of the infinite constituted a real barrier to the development of classical Greek mathematics. By contrast, the Indian mathematicians had no such scruples and made great advances, which, via the Arabs, later entered Europe. The attempt to banish contradiction from thought, in accordance with the rigid schemas of formal logic held back the development of mathematics. But the adventurous spirit of the Renaissance opened men's minds to new possibilities, which were, in truth, infinite. In his book *The New Science* (1638), Galileo pointed out that every integer (whole number) has only one perfect square, and every perfect square is the square of only one positive integer. Thus, in a sense, there are just as many perfect squares as there are positive integers. This immediately leads us into a logical contradiction. It contradicts the axiom that the whole is greater than any of its parts, inasmuch as not all the positive integers are perfect squares, and all the perfect squares form part of all the positive integers.

This is only one of the numerous paradoxes that have plagued mathematics ever since the Renaissance when men began to subject their thoughts and assumptions to a critical analysis. As a result of this, slowly, and in the teeth of stubborn resistance from conservative minds, one by one the supposedly unassailable axioms and "eternal truths" of mathematics have been overthrown. We arrive at the point where the entire edifice has been shown to be unsound and in need of a thoroughgoing reconstruction on more solid, yet more flexible foundations, which are already in the process of being laid, and which will inevitably have a dialectical character.

The calculus

Many of the so-called axioms of classical Greek mathematics were already undermined by the discovery of the differential and integral calculus, the greatest breakthrough in mathematics since the Middle Ages. It is an axiom of geometry that straight and curved are absolute opposites, and that the two are incommensurable, that is, the one cannot be expressed in terms of the other. Yet, in the last analysis, straight and curved in the differential calculus are regarded as equal. As Engels points out, the basis for this was laid a long time before it was elaborated by Leibniz and Newton: "The turning point in mathematics was Descartes' *variable magnitude*. With that came motion and hence *dialectics* in mathematics, and *at once, too, of necessity the differential and integral calculus*, which moreover immediately begins, and which on the whole was completed by Newton and Leibniz, not discovered by them." [7]

(7) Engels, *The Dialectics of Nature*, pp. 341-2.

The discovery of the calculus opened up a whole new horizon for mathematics and science in general. Once the old taboos and prohibitions were lifted, mathematicians were free to investigate entirely new areas. But they made use of infinitely large and small numbers uncritically, without considering their logical and conceptual implications. The use of infinitely small and great quantities was regarded as a kind of "useful fiction", which, for some incomprehensible reason, always gave the correct result. In the section on *Quantity* in the first volume of *Science of Logic*, Hegel points out that, while the introduction of the mathematical infinite opened up new horizons for mathematics, and led to important results, it remained unexplained, because it clashed with the existing traditions and methods:

"But in the method of the mathematical infinite mathematics finds a radical contradiction to that very method which is characteristic of itself, and on which it rests as a science. For the calculation of the infinite admits of, and demands, modes of procedure which mathematics, when it operates with finite magnitudes, must altogether reject, and at the same time it treats these infinite magnitudes as finite Quanta, seeking to apply to the former those same methods which are valid for the latter." [8]

The result was a long period of controversy concerning the validity of the calculus. Berkeley denounced it as in open contradiction to the laws of logic. Newton, who made use of the new method in his *Principia*, felt obliged to conceal the fact from the public, for fear of an adverse reaction. In the early 18th century, Bernard Fontenelle finally had the courage to state categorically that inasmuch as there are infinitely many natural numbers, an infinite number exists as truly as do finite numbers, and that the reciprocal of infinity is an infinitesimal. However, he was contradicted by Georges de Buffon, who rejected the infinity as an illusion. Even the great intellect of Jean le Rond d'Alembert was incapable of accepting this idea. In the article in his *Encyclopaedia* on the Differential, he denied the existence of infinity, except in the negative sense of a limit on finite quantities.

The concept of "limit" was in fact introduced in an attempt to get round the contradiction inherent in infinity. This was especially popular in the 19th century, when mathematicians were no longer prepared simply to accept the calculus unthinkingly, as the earlier generation had been content to do. The differential calculus postulated the existence of infinitesimally small magnitudes of varying orders—a first differential, a second differential, and so on to infinity. By introducing the concept of "limit" they at least created the appearance that an actual infinity was not involved. The intention was to make the idea of infinity seem subjective, to deny it objectivity. The variables were said to be *potentially* infinitely small, in that they become less than any given quantity, as *potentially* infinite, in that they become larger than any preassigned magnitude. In other words, "as big or small as you like!" This sleight of hand did not remove the difficulty, but only provided a fig leaf to cover up the logical contradictions involved in the calculus.

(8) Hegel, *Science of Logic*, Vol. 1, p. 257.

The great German mathematician Karl Frederick Gauss (1777-1855) was prepared to accept the mathematical infinite, but expressed horror at the idea of real
infinity. However, his contemporary Bernhard Bolanzo, setting out from Galileo's
paradox, began a serious study of the paradoxes implicit in the idea of a "completed infinite". This work was further developed by Richard Dedekind (1813-1914)
who characterised the infinite as something positive, and pointed out that, in fact,
the positive set of numbers can be regarded as negative (that is, as one that is not
infinite). Finally, Georg Cantor (1845-1918) went far beyond the definition of infinite sets and developed an entirely new arithmetic of "transfinite numbers".
Cantor's papers, beginning in 1870, are a review of the whole history of the infinite,
beginning with Democritus. Out of this, there developed a whole new branch of
mathematics, based on the theory of sets.

Cantor showed that the points in an area, however large, or in a volume or a continuum of still higher dimension, can be matched against the points on a line or a
segment, no matter how small it may be. Just as there can be no last finite number,
so there can be no last transfinite number. Thus, after Cantor, there can be no argument about the central place of the infinite in mathematics. Moreover, his work
revealed a series of paradoxes that have plagued modern mathematics, and have yet
to be resolved.

All modern scientific analysis relies on the concept of continuity, that is to say,
that between two points in space, there is an infinite number of other points, and
also that, between any two points in time there is an infinite number of other
moments. Without making these assumptions, modern mathematics simply could
not function. Yet such contradictory concepts would have been indignantly rejected, or at least regarded with suspicion, by earlier generations. Only the dialectical
genius of Hegel (a great mathematician incidentally) was capable of anticipating all
this in his analysis of finite and infinite, space, time and motion.

Yet despite all the evidence, many modern mathematicians persist in denying the
objectivity of infinity, while accepting its validity as a phenomenon of "pure" mathematics. Such a division makes no sense at all. For unless mathematics was able to
reflect the real, objective world, what use would it be? There is a certain tendency
in modern mathematics (and, by extension, incredibly, in theoretical physics) to
revert to idealism in its most mystical form, alleging that the validity of an equation
is purely a question of its aesthetic value, with no reference to the material world.

The very fact that mathematical operations can be applied to the real world and
get meaningful results indicates that there is an affinity between the two. Otherwise,
mathematics would have no practical application, which is clearly not the case. The
reason why infinity can be used, and must be used, in modern mathematics is
because it corresponds to the existence of infinity in nature itself, which has
imposed itself upon mathematics, like an uninvited guest, despite all the attempts to
bar the door against it.

The reason why it took so long for mathematics to accept infinity was explained very well by Engels:

"It is clear that an infinity which has an end but no beginning is neither more or less infinite than one with a beginning but no end. The slightest dialectical insight should have told Herr Dühring that beginning and end necessarily belong together, like the North Pole and the South Pole, and that if the end is left out, the beginning just becomes the end—the *one* end which the series has; and vice versa. The whole deception would be impossible but for the mathematical usage of working with infinite series. Because in mathematics it is necessary to start from determinate, finite terms in order to reach the indeterminate, the infinite, all mathematical series, positive and negative, must start with 1, or they cannot be used for calculation. But the logical need of the mathematician is far from being a compulsory law for the real world." [9]

Crisis of mathematics

From our school days we are taught to look upon mathematics, with its self-evident truths "axioms" and its rigorous logical deductions as the last word in scientific exactitude. In 1900, all this seemed certain, although in the International Congress of mathematicians held that year, German mathematician David Hilbert set forth a list of the 23 most significant unsolved mathematical problems. From that point things have got steadily more complicated, to the point where it is possible to talk of a real crisis in theoretical mathematics. In his widely read book, *Mathematics: The Loss of Certainty*, published in 1980, Morris Kline describes the situation thus:

"Creations of the early 19th century, strange geometries and strange algebras, forced mathematicians, reluctantly and grudgingly, to realise that mathematics proper and the mathematical laws of science were not truths. They found, for example, that several differing geometries fit spatial experience equally well. All could not be truths. Apparently mathematical design was not inherent in nature, or if it was, man's mathematics was not necessarily the account of that design. The key to reality had been lost. This realisation was the first of the calamities to befall mathematics.

"The creation of these new geometries and algebras caused mathematicians to experience a shock of another nature. The conviction that they were obtaining truths had entranced them so much that they had rushed impetuously to secure these seeming truths at the cost of sound reasoning. The realisation that mathematics was not a body of truths shook their confidence in what they had created, and they undertook to re-examine their creations. They were dismayed to find that the logic of mathematics was in sad shape."

(9) Engels, *Anti-Dühring*, p. 63.

At the beginning of the 20th century, they set about trying to solve the unsolved problems, remove the contradictions, and elaborate a new and foolproof system of mathematics. As Kline explains:

"By 1900 the mathematicians believed they had achieved their goal. Though they had to be content with mathematics as an approximate description of nature and many even abandoned the belief in the mathematical design of nature, they did gloat over their reconstruction of the logical structure of mathematics. But before they had finished toasting their presumed success, contradictions were discovered in the reconstructed mathematics. Commonly these contradictions were referred to as paradoxes, a euphemism that avoids facing the fact that contradictions vitiate the logic of mathematics.

"The resolution of the contradictions was undertaken almost immediately by the leading mathematicians and philosophers of the times. In effect four different approaches to mathematics were conceived, formulated, and advanced, each of which gathered many adherents. These foundational schools all attempted not only to resolve the known contradictions but to ensure that no new ones could ever arise, that is, to establish the consistency of mathematics. Other issues arose in the foundational efforts. The acceptability of some axioms and some principles of deductive logic also became bones of contention on which the several schools took differing positions."

The attempt to eliminate contradictions from mathematics only led to new and insoluble contradictions. The final blow was struck in 1930, when Kurt Gödel published his famous theorems, which provoked a crisis, even calling into question the fundamental methods of classical mathematics:

"As late as 1930 a mathematician might perhaps have been content with accepting one or another of the several foundations of mathematics and declared that his mathematical proofs were at least in accord with the tenets of that school. But disaster struck again in the form of a famous paper by Kurt Gödel in which he proved, among other significant and disturbing results, that the logical principles accepted by the several schools could not prove the consistency of mathematics. This, Gödel showed, cannot be done without involving logical principles so dubious as to question what is accomplished. Gödel's theorems produced a debacle. Subsequent developments brought further complications. For example, even the axiomatic-deductive method so highly regarded in the past as the approach to exact knowledge was seen to be flawed. The net effect of these newer developments was to add to the variety of possible approaches to mathematics and to divide mathematicians into an even greater number of differing factions." [10]

The impasse of mathematics has produced a number of different factions and schools, none of which accept the theories of the others. There are the Platonists

(10) Quoted in T. Ferris, op. cit., pp. 521-2 and 522-3.

(yes, that's right), who regard mathematics as an absolute truth ("God is a mathematician"). There are the Conceptualists, whose conception of mathematics is entirely different to that of the Platonists, but it is merely the difference between objective and subjective idealism. They see mathematics as a series of structures, patterns and symmetries which people have invented for their own purposes—in other words, mathematics has no objective basis, but is purely the product of the human mind! This theory is apparently popular in Britain.

Then we have the Formalist school, which was formed at the beginning of the 20th century, with the specific aim of eliminating contradictions from mathematics. David Hilbert, one of the founders of this school, saw mathematics as nothing more than the manipulation of symbols according to specific rules to produce a system of tautological statements, which have inner consistency, but otherwise no meaning whatsoever. Here mathematics is reduced to an intellectual game, like chess—again a completely subjective approach. The Intuitionist school is equally determined to separate mathematics from objective reality. A mathematical formula, according to these people, is not supposed to represent anything existing independently of the act of computation itself. This has been compared to the attempt of Bohr to use the discoveries of quantum mechanics to introduce new views of physical and mathematical quantities as divorced from objective reality.

All these schools have in common an entirely idealist approach to mathematics. The only difference is that the neo-Platonists are objective idealists, who think that mathematics originated in the mind of God, and the rest—intuitionists, formalists and conceptualists—believes that mathematics is a subjective creation of the human mind, devoid of any objective significance. This, then, is the sorry spectacle presented by the main schools of mathematics in the last decade of the 20th century. But it is not the end of the story.

Chaos and complexity

In recent years, the limitations of mathematical models to express the real workings of nature have been the subject of intense discussion. Differential equations, for example, represent reality as a continuum, in which changes in time and place occur smoothly and uninterruptedly. There is no room here for sudden breaks and qualitative changes. Yet these actually take place in nature. The discovery of the differential and integral calculus in the 18th century represented a great advance. But even the most advanced mathematical models are only a rough approximation to reality, valid only within certain limits. The recent debate on chaos and anti-chaos has centred on those areas involving breaks in continuity, sudden "chaotic" changes which cannot be adequately conveyed by classical mathematical formulae.

The difference between order and chaos has to do with linear and non-linear relationships. A linear relationship is one that is easy to describe mathematically: it can be expressed in one form or another as a straight line on a graph. The mathematics may be complex, but the answers can be calculated and can be predicted. A non-linear relationship, however, is one that cannot easily be resolved mathematically. There is no straight-line graph that will describe it. Non-linear relationships have been historically difficult or impossible to resolve and they have been often ignored as experimental error. Referring to the famous experiment with the pendulum, James Gleick writes that the regularity Galileo saw was only an approximation. The changing angle of the body's motion creates a slight non-linearity in the equations. At low amplitudes, the error is almost non-existent. But it is there. To get his neat results, Galileo also had to disregard non-linearities that he knew of: friction and air resistance.

Much of classic mechanics is built around linear relationships that are abstracted from real life as scientific laws. Because the real world is governed by non-linear relationships, these laws are often no more than approximations, which are constantly refined through the discovery of "new" laws. These laws are mathematical models, theoretical constructions whose only justification consists of the insight they give and their usefulness in controlling natural forces. In the last twenty years the revolution in computer technology has transformed the situation by making non-linear mathematics accessible. It is for this reason that it has been possible, in a number of quite separate faculties and research establishments, for mathematicians and other scientists to be able to do the sums for "chaotic" systems where they could not be done in the past.

James Gleick's book *Chaos, Making a New Science* describes how chaotic systems have been examined by different researchers using widely different mathematical models, and yet with all the studies pointing to the same conclusion: that there is "order" in what was previously thought of as pure "disorder". The story begins with studies of weather patterns, in a computer simulation, by an American meteorologist, Edward Lorenz. Using at first twelve and then later only three variables in non-linear relationships, Lorenz was able to produce in his computer a continuous series of conditions constantly changing, but literally never repeating the same conditions twice. Using relatively simple mathematical rules, he had created "chaos".

Beginning with whatever parameters Lorenz chose himself, his computer would mechanically repeat the same calculations over and over again, yet never get the same result. This "aperiodicity" (i.e., the absence of regular cycles) is characteristic of all chaotic systems. At the same time, Lorenz noticed that although his results were perpetually different, there was at least the suggestion of "patterns" that frequently cropped up: conditions that approximated to those previously observed, although they were never exactly the same. That corresponds, of course, to everyone's experience of the real, as opposed to computer-simulated weather: there are "patterns", but no two days or two weeks are ever the same.

Other scientists also discovered "patterns" in apparently chaotic systems, as widely different as in the study of galactic orbits and in mathematical modelling of electronic oscillators. In these and other cases, Gleick notes, there were "suggestions of structure amid seemingly random behaviour." It became increasingly obvious that chaotic systems were not necessarily unstable, or could endure for an indefinite period. The well known "red-spot" visible on the surface of the planet Jupiter is an example of a continuously chaotic system that is stable. Moreover, it has been simulated in computer studies and in laboratory models. Thus, "a complex system can give rise to turbulence and cohesion at the same time." Meanwhile, other scientists used different mathematical models to study apparently chaotic phenomena in biology. One in particular made a mathematical study of population changes under a variety of conditions. Standard variables familiar to biologists were used with some of the computed relationships being, as it would be in nature, non-linear. This non-linearity could correspond, for example, to a unique characteristic of the species that might define it as a propensity to propagate, its "survivability".

These results were expressed on a graph plotting the population size, on the vertical axis, against the value of non-linear components, on the horizontal. It was found that as the non-linearity became more important—by increasing that particular parameter—so the projected population went through a number of distinct phases. Below a certain crucial level, there would be no viable population and, whatever starting point, extinction would be the result. The line on the graph simply followed a horizontal path corresponding to zero population. The next phase was a steady state, represented graphically as a single line in a rising curve. This is equivalent to stable population, at a level that depended on the initial conditions. In the next phase there were two different but fixed populations, two steady states. This was shown as a branching on the graph, or a "bifurcation". It would be equivalent in real populations to a regular periodic oscillation, in a two-year cycle. As the degree of non-linearity increased again, there was a rapid increase in bifurcations, first to a condition which corresponded to four steady states (meaning a regular cycle of four years), and that very quickly afterwards it was 8, 16, 32, and so on.

Hence, within a short spread of values of the non-linear parameter, a situation had developed which, for all practical purposes, had no steady state or recognisable periodicity—the population had become "chaotic". It was also found that if the non-linearity was increased further throughout the "chaotic" phase, there would be periods when apparent steady states returned, based on a cycle of 3 or 7 years, but in each case giving way as non-linearity increased, to further bifurcation's representing 6, 12, and 24 year cycles in the first case, or 14, 28, and 56 year cycles in the second. Thus, with mathematical precision, it was possible to model a change from stability with either a single steady state or regular, periodic behaviour, to one that was, for all measurable purposes, random or aperiodic.

This may indicate a possible resolution to debates within the field of population science between those theorists who believe that unpredictable population variations are an aberration from a "steady state norm", and others who believe that steady state is the aberration from "chaotic norm". These different interpretations may arise because different researchers have effectively taken a single vertical "slice" of the rising graph, corresponding to only one particular value for non-linearity. Thus, one species could have a norm of a steady or a periodically oscillating population and another could exhibit chaotic variability. These developments in biology are another indication, as Gleick explains, that "chaos is stable; it is structured." Similar results began to be discovered in a wide variety of different phenomena. "Deterministic chaos was found in the records of New York measles epidemics and in 200 years of fluctuations of the Canadian lynx population, as recorded by the trappers of the Hudson's Bay Company." In all these cases of chaotic processes, there is exhibited the "period-doubling" that is characteristic of this particular mathematical model.

Mandelbrot's fractals

Another one of the pioneers of chaos theory, Benoit Mandelbrot, a mathematician at IBM, used yet another mathematical technique. In his capacity as a researcher for IBM, he looked for—and found—"patterns" in a wide variety of natural "random" processes. He found, for instance, that the background "noise" that is always present in telephone transmissions, follows a pattern that is completely unpredictable, or chaotic, but is nevertheless mathematically definable. Using a computer at IBM, Mandelbrot was able to produce chaotic systems graphically, yet only using the simplest mathematical rules. These pictures, known as "Mandelbrot sets", showed an infinite complexity, and when a computer drawing was "blown up" to show finer detail, the vast, seemingly limitless variety continued.

The Mandelbrot sets have been described as possibly the most complex mathematical object or model ever seen. Yet within its structure, there were still patterns. By repeatedly "magnifying" the scale and looking at finer and finer detail (something the computer could do indefinitely because the whole structure was based on a given set of mathematical rules) it could be seen that there were regular repetitions—similarities—at different scales. "The degree of irregularity" was the same at different scales. Mandelbrot used the expression "fractal" to describe the patterns evident within the irregularity. He was able to construct a variety of fractal shapes, by slightly altering the mathematical rules. Thus he was able to produce a computer simulation of a coastline which, at any scale (at any magnification) always exhibited the same degree of "irregularity" or "crinkliness".

Mandelbrot compared his computer-induced systems to examples of geometries that were also fractal shapes, repeating the same pattern over and over again on different scales. In the so-called Menger Sponge, for example, the surface area within it approaches infinity, while the actual volume of the solid approaches zero. Here, it is as if the degree of irregularity corresponds to the "efficiency" of the sponge in taking up space. That may not be as far fetched as it may sound because, as

Mandelbrot showed, there are many examples of fractal geometry in nature. The branching of the windpipe to make two bronchioles and their repeated branching right down to the level of the tiny air passages in the lungs follows a pattern that can be shown to be fractal. In the same way it can be shown that the branching of blood vessels is fractal. In other words, there is a "self-similarity", a repeating geometric pattern of branching, at whatever scale is examined.

The examples of fractal geometry in nature are almost limitless and in his book, *The Fractal Geometry of Nature*, Mandelbrot sought to demonstrate just that. It has been found that the spectrum of the timing of a normal heartbeat follows fractal laws, perhaps due to the fractal arrangement of nerve fibres in the heart muscle. The same is true of the rapid involuntary eye movements that are a feature of schizophrenia. Thus, fractal mathematics is now routinely used in a variety of scientific fields, including physiology and disciplines as widely separated as earthquake studies and metallurgy.

Yet another indications of the deterministic basis of chaos has been shown in studies of phase transitions and by the use of what mathematical modellers call "attractors". There are many examples of phase transitions. It can mean the change from the smooth "laminar" flow of a fluid to turbulent flow, the transition from solid to liquid or liquid to gas, or the change within a system from conductivity to "super-conductivity". These phase transitions may have crucial consequences in technological design and construction. An aircraft, for example would lose lift if the laminar airflow over the wing became turbulent; likewise, the pressure needed to pump water will depend on whether or not the flow in the pipe is turbulent.

The use of phase-scale diagrams and *attractors* represents yet another mathematical device that has found a wide variety of applications in apparently random systems. As in the case of other chaos studies, there has been the discovery of common patterns, in this case "strange attractors" in a variety of research programmes, including electric oscillators, fluid dynamics and even in the distribution of stars in globular clusters. All these various mathematical devices—period doubling; fractal geometry; strange attractors—were developed at different times by different researchers to examine chaotic dynamics. But all their results point in the same direction: that there is an underlying mathematical lawfulness in what was always considered to be random.

A mathematician, Mitchell Feigenbaum, pulling a number of threads together, has developed what he has called a "universal theory" of chaos. As Gleick says "he believed that his theory expressed a natural law about systems at the point of transition between order and turbulence...his universality was not just qualitative, it was quantitative...it extended not just to patterns but to precise numbers."

Marxists would recognise here the similarity with the dialectical law known as the law of transformation of quantity to quality. This idea describes the transition between one period of more or less gradual development, when change can be measured or "quantified", and the next when change has been so "revolutionary", there has been such a "leap", that the entire "quality" of the system has been altered. Gleick's use of the terms in a similar sense here is yet another indication of the way modern scientific theory is stumbling towards materialist dialectics.

The central point about the new science is that it deals with the world as it really is: as a constantly shifting dynamic system. Classical linear mathematics is like formal logic, which deals with fixed and unchanging categories. These are good enough as approximations, but do not reflect reality. Dialectics, however, is the logic of change, of processes and as such it represents an advance on formalism. In the same way, chaos mathematics is a step forward from the rather "unreal" science that ignored uncomfortable irregularities of life.

Quantity and quality

The idea of the transformation of quantity into quality is implicit in modern mathematics in the study of continuity and discontinuity. This was already present in the new branch of geometry, topology, invented in the early years of the 20th century by the great French mathematician, Jules Henri Poincaré (1854-1912). Topology is the mathematics of continuity. As Ian Stewart explains it: "Continuity is the study of smooth, gradual changes, the science of the unbroken. Discontinuities are sudden, dramatic: places where a tiny change in cause produces an enormous change in effect." [11]

The standard textbook mathematics gives a wrong impression of how the world actually is, how nature really works. "The mathematical intuition so developed," wrote Robert May, "ill equips the student to confront the bizarre behaviour exhibited by the simplest non-linear systems." [12] Whereas elementary school geometry teaches us to regard squares, circles, triangles and parallelograms as entirely separate things, in topology ("rubber-sheet geometry"), they are treated as *the same.* Traditional geometry teaches that the circle cannot be squared, however in topology this is not the case. The rigid lines of demarcation are broken down: a square can be turned ("deformed") into a circle. Despite the spectacular advances of 20th century science, it is surprising to note that a large number of what would seem to be quite simple phenomena are not properly understood and cannot be expressed in mathematical terms, for example, the weather, the flow of liquids, turbulence. The shapes of classical geometry are inadequate to express the extremely complex and irregular surfaces found in nature, as Gleick points out:

"Topology studies the properties that remain unchanged when shapes are deformed by twisting or stretching or squeezing. Whether a shape is square or round, large or small, is irrelevant in topology, because stretching can change those properties. Topologists ask whether a shape is connected, whether it has holes, whether it is knotted. They imagine surfaces not just in the one-, two-, and three-dimensional universes of Euclid, but in spaces of many dimensions, impossible to visualise. Topology is geometry on rubber sheets. It concerns the qualitative rather than the quantitative." [13]

Differential equations deal with the rate of change of position. This is more difficult and complex than what may appear at first sight. Many differential equations cannot be solved at all. These equations are able to describe motion, but only as a smooth change of position, from one point to another, with no sudden leaps or interruptions. However, in nature, change does not only occur in this way. Periods of slow, gradual, uninterrupted change are punctuated by sharp turns, breaks in continuity, explosions and catastrophes. This fact can be illustrated by innumerable examples from organic and inorganic nature, the history of society and of human thought. In a differential equation, time is assumed to be divided into a series of very small "time-steps". This gives an *approximation* of reality, but in fact there are no such "steps". As Heraclitus expressed it, "everything flows".

The inability of traditional mathematics to deal with qualitative as opposed to merely quantitative change represents a severe limitation. Within certain limits, it can suffice. But when gradual quantitative change suddenly breaks down, and becomes "chaotic", to use the current expression, the linear equations of classical mathematics no longer suffice. This is the starting point for the new non-linear mathematics, pioneered by Benoit Mandelbrot, Edward Lorenz and Mitchell Feigenbaum. Without realising it, they were following in the footsteps of Hegel, whose nodal line of measurement expresses the very same idea, which is central to dialectics.

The new attitude to mathematics developed as a reaction against the dead end of the existing schools of mathematics. Mandelbrot had been a member of the French school of mathematical Formalism known as the Bourbaki group, which advocated a purely abstract approach, proceeding from first principles and deducing everything from them. They were actually proud of the fact that their work had nothing to do with science or the real world. But the advent of the computer introduced an entirely new element into the situation. This is yet another example of how the development of technique conditions that of science. The vast number of computations which could be made at the press of a button made it possible to discover patterns and lawfulness where previously only random and chaotic phenomena appeared to exist.

Mandelbrot began by investigating unexplained phenomena of the natural world, like apparently random bursts of interference in radio transmissions, the flooding of the Nile, and crises of the stock exchange. He realised that the traditional mathematics could not deal adequately with such phenomena. In investigating

(13) J. Gleick, op. cit., p. 46.

infinity in the 19th century, Georg Cantor invented the set that is named after him. This involves a line, which is divided into an infinite number of points (Cantor "dust") the total length of which is 0. Such a manifest contradiction disturbed many 19th century mathematicians, yet it served as the starting point for Mandelbrot's new theory of fractal mathematics, which played a key role in chaos theory:

"Discontinuity, bursts of noise, Cantor dusts," Gleick explains, "—phenomena like these had no place in the geometries of the past 2,000 years. The shapes of classical geometry are lines and planes, circles and spheres, triangles and cones. They represent a powerful abstraction of reality, and they inspired a powerful philosophy of Platonic harmony. Euclid made of them a geometry that lasted two millennia, the only geometry still that most people ever learn. Aristotle found an ideal beauty in them. But for understanding complexity, they turn out to be the wrong kind of abstraction." [14]

All science involves a degree of abstraction from the world of reality. The problem with classical Euclidean measurement, dealing with length, depth and thickness, is that it failed to capture the essence of irregular shapes that are found in the real world. The science of mathematics is the science of *magnitude*. The abstractions of Euclidean geometry therefore leave aside all but the quantitative side of things. Reality is reduced to planes, lines and points. However, the abstractions of mathematics, despite the exaggerated claims made for them, remain only a rough approximation to the real world, with its irregular shapes and constant and abrupt changes. In the words of the Roman poet Horace, "You may drive out nature with a pitch-fork, yet she'll be constantly running back." James Gleick describes the difference between classical mathematics and chaos theory in the following way:

"Clouds are not spheres, Mandelbrot is fond of saying. Mountains are not cones. Lightning does not travel in a straight line. The new geometry mirrors a universe that is rough, not rounded, scabrous, not smooth. It is a geometry of the pitted, pocked, and broken up, the twisted, tangled, and intertwined. The understanding of nature's complexity awaited a suspicion that the complexity was not just random, not just accident. It required a faith that the interesting feature of a lightning bolt's path, for example, was not its direction, but rather the distribution of zigs and zags. Mandelbrot's work made a claim about the world, and the claim was that such odd shapes carry meaning. The pits and tangles are more than blemishes distorting the classic shapes of Euclidean geometry. They are often the keys to the essence of a thing." [15]

These things were seen as monstrous aberrations by traditional mathematicians. But to a dialectician, they suggest that the unity of finite and infinite, as in the infinite divisibility of matter, can also be expressed in mathematical terms. Infinity exists in nature. The universe is infinitely large. Matter can be divided into infinite-

(14) J. Gleick, op. cit., p. 94.
(15) J. Gleick, op. cit., p. 94.

ly small particles. Thus, all talk about the "beginning of the universe" and the search after the "bricks of matter" and the "ultimate particle" are based on entirely wrong assumptions. The existence of the mathematical infinite is merely a reflection of this fact. At the same time, it is a dialectical contradiction that this infinite universe consists of finite bodies. Thus, finite and infinite form a dialectical unity of opposites. The one cannot exist without the other. The question is therefore not whether the universe is finite or infinite. It is both finite and infinite as Hegel explained long ago.

The advances of modern science have permitted us to penetrate deeper and deeper into the world of matter. At each stage, an attempt has been made to "call a halt", to erect a barrier, beyond which it was allegedly impossible to go. But at each stage, the limit was overcome, revealing startling new phenomena. Ever new and more powerful particle accelerators have uncovered new and smaller particles, existing in ever-tinier time scales. There is no reason to suppose that the situation will be any different in relation to the quarks, which at present are being represented as the last of the particles.

Similarly, the attempt to establish the beginning of the universe and "time" will turn out to be a wild goose chase. There is no limit to the material universe, and all efforts to impose one will inevitably fail. The most encouraging thing about the new mathematics of chaos theory is that it represents a rejection of sterile abstractions and ivory-tower reductionism, and an attempt to move back towards nature and the world of everyday experience. And to the degree that mathematics reflects nature, it must begin to lose its one-sided character and acquire a whole new dimension which expresses the dynamic, contradictory, in a word, *dialectical* character of the real world.

17. Chaos theory

Dialectical materialism, elaborated by Karl Marx and Frederick Engels, was concerned with much more than political economy: it was a worldview. Nature, as Engels in particular sought to demonstrate in his writings, is proof of the correctness of both materialism and dialectics. "My recapitulation of mathematics and the natural sciences," he wrote, "was undertaken in order to convince myself also in detail…that in nature amid the welter of innumerable changes, the same dialectical laws of motion force their way through as those which in history govern the apparent fortuitousness of events…" [16]

Since their day, every important new advance in scientific discovery has confirmed the Marxian outlook although scientists, because of the political implications of an association with Marxism, seldom acknowledge dialectical materialism. Now, the advent of chaos theory provides fresh backing for the fundamental ideas of the founders of scientific socialism. Up to now chaos has been largely ignored by scientists, except as a nuisance or something to be avoided. A tap drips, sometimes regularly, sometimes not; the movement of a fluid is either turbulent or not; the heart beats regularly but sometimes goes into a fibrillation; the weather blows hot or cold. Wherever there is motion that appears to be chaotic—and it is all around us—there is generally little attempt to come to terms with it from a strictly scientific point of view.

What then, are the general features of chaotic systems? Having described them in mathematical terms, what application does the mathematics have? One of the features given prominence by Gleick and others is what has been dubbed "the butterfly effect". Lorenz had discovered on his computer-simulated weather a remarkable development. One of his simulations was based on twelve variables, including, as we said, non-linear relationships. He found that if he started his simulation with values that were only slightly different from the original—the difference being that one set were down to six decimal places and the second set down three places—then the

(16) Engels, *Anti-Dühring*, p. 16.

"weather" produced by the computer soon veered wildly from the original. Where perhaps a slight perturbation might have been expected, there was, only after a brief period of recognisable similarity, a completely different pattern.

This means that in a complex, non-linear system, a small change in the input could produce a huge change in the output. In Lorenz's computer world, it was equivalent to a butterfly's wing-beat causing a hurricane in another part of the world; hence the expression. The conclusion that can be drawn from this is that, given the complexity of the forces and processes that go to determine the weather, it can never be predicted beyond a short period of time ahead. In fact, the biggest weather computer in the world, in the European centre for Medium-range Weather Forecasting, does as many as 400 million calculations every second. It is fed 100 million separate weather measurements from around the world every day, and it processes data in three hours of continuous running, to produce a ten-day forecast. Yet beyond two or three days the forecasts are speculative, and beyond six or seven they are worthless. Chaos theory, then, sets definite limits to the predictability of complex non-linear systems.

It is strange, nevertheless, that Gleick and others have paid so much attention to the butterfly effect, as if it injects a strange mystique into chaos theory. It is surely well established (if not accurately modelled mathematically) that in other similarly complex systems a small input can produce a large output, that an accumulation of "quantity" can be transformed to "quality". There is only a difference of less than two per cent, for example, in the basic genetic make-up of human beings and chimpanzees—a difference that can be quantified in terms of molecular chemistry. Yet in the complex, non-linear processes that are involved in translating the genetic "code" into a living animal, this small dissimilarity means the difference between one species and another.

Marxism applies itself to perhaps the most complex of all non-linear systems—human society. With the colossal interaction of countless individuals, politics and economics constitute so complex a system that alongside it, the planet's weather systems looks like clockwork. Nevertheless, as is the case with other "chaotic" systems, society can be treated scientifically—as long as the limits, like the weather, are understood. Unfortunately, Gleick's book is not clear on the application of chaos theory to politics and economics. He cites an exercise by Mandelbrot, who fed his IBM computer with a hundred year's worth of cotton prices from the New York exchange. "Each particular price change was random and unpredictable," he writes. "But the sequence of changes was independent of scale: curves for daily and monthly price changes matched...the degree of variation had remained constant over a tumultuous 60-year period that saw two world wars and a depression." [17]

This passage cannot be taken on face value. It may be true that within certain limits, it is possible to see the same mathematical patterns that have been identified in other models or chaotic systems. But given the almost limitless complexity of human society and economics, it is inconceivable that major events like wars would not disrupt these patterns. Marxists would argue that society does lend itself to scientific study. In contrast to those who see only formlessness, Marxists see human development from the starting point of material forces, and a scientific description of social categories like classes, and so on. If the development of chaos science leads to an acceptance that the scientific method is valid in politics and economics, then it is a valuable plus. However, as Marx and Engels have always understood, theirs is an inexact science, meaning that broad trends and developments could be traced, but detailed and intimate knowledge of all influences and conditions is not possible.

Cotton prices notwithstanding, the book gives no evidence that this Marxist view is wrong. In fact, there is no explanation as to why Mandelbrot apparently saw a pattern in only 60 years' prices when he had over 100 years' of data to play with. In addition, elsewhere in the book, Gleick adds that "economists have looked for strange attractors in stock market trends but so far had not found them." Despite the apparent limitations in the fields of economics and politics, however, it is clear that the mathematical "taming" of what were thought to be random or chaotic systems has profound implications for science as a whole. It opens up many vistas for the study of processes that were largely out of bounds in the past.

Division of labour

One of the main characteristics of the great scientists of the Renaissance was that they were whole human beings. They had an all-rounded development, which enabled, for example, Leonardo da Vinci to be a great engineer, mathematician and mechanician, as well as an artist of genius. The same was true of Dührer, Machiavelli, Luther, and countless others, of whom Engels wrote:

"The heroes of that time were not yet in thrall to the division of labour, the restricting effects of which, with its production of one-sidedness, we so often notice in their successors." [18] The division of labour, of course, plays a necessary role in the development of the productive forces. However, under capitalism, this has been carried to such an extreme that it begins to turn into its opposite.

The extreme division, on the one hand, between mental and manual labour means that millions of men and women are reduced to a life of unthinking drudgery on the production line, denied of any possibility to display the creativity and inventiveness which is latent in every human being. At the other extreme, we have the development of a kind of intellectual priestly caste that has arrogated to itself the sole right to the title of "guardians of science and culture". To the degree that these people become remote from the real life of society, this has a negative effect on their

(18) Engels, *The Dialectics of Nature*, p. 31

consciousness. They develop in an entirely narrow, one-sided way. Not only is there an abyss separating "artists" from scientists, but the scientific community itself is riven with ever-increasing divisions between increasingly narrow specialisations. It is ironic that, precisely when the "lines of demarcation" between physics, chemistry and biology are breaking down, the gulf that divides even different branches of, say, physics has become virtually unbridgeable.

James Gleick describes the situation thus:

"Few laymen realise how tightly compartmentalised the scientific community had become, a battleship with bulkheads sealed against leaks. Biologists had enough to read without keeping up with the mathematical literature—for that matter, molecular biologists had enough to read without keeping up with population biology, physicists had better ways to spend their time than sifting through the meteorology journals."

In recent years, the advent of chaos theory is one of the indications that something is beginning to change in the scientific community. Increasingly, scientists from different fields feel that they have somehow reached a dead end. It is necessary to break out in a new direction. The birth of chaos mathematics, therefore, is a proof as Engels would have said, of the dialectical character of nature, a reminder that reality consists of whole dynamic systems, or even one whole system, and not of models (however useful) abstracted from them. What are the main features of chaos theory? Gleick describes them in the following way:

"To some physicists, chaos is a science of process rather than state, of becoming rather than being."

"They feel that they are turning back a trend in science towards reductionism, the analysis of systems in terms of their constituent parts: quarks, chromosomes, or neutrons. They believe that they are looking for the whole."

The method of dialectical materialism is precisely to look at "process rather than state, of becoming rather than being." "More and more over the past decade, he'd begun to sense that the old reductionist approaches were reaching a dead end, and that even some of the hard-core physical scientists were getting fed up with mathematical abstractions that ignored the real complexities of the world. They seemed to be half-consciously groping for a new approach—and in the process, he thought, they were cutting across the traditional boundaries in a way they hadn't done in years. Maybe centuries." [19]

Because chaos is a science of whole dynamic systems, rather than separate parts, it represents, in effect, an unacknowledged vindication of the dialectical view. Up to now, scientific investigation has been too much isolated into its constituent parts. In pursuit of the "parts" the scientific specialist becomes too specialised not infrequently losing all sight of the "whole". Experimentation and theoretical rationalisa-

(19) J. Gleick, op. cit., p. 31, 5, 11 and 61-2.

tions thus became increasingly removed from reality. More than a century ago, Engels criticised the narrowness of what he called the metaphysical method, which consisted of looking at things in an isolated way, which lost sight of the whole. The starting point of the supporters of chaos theory was a reaction against precisely this method, which they call "reductionism". Engels explained that the "reduction" of the study of nature to separate disciplines is to some extent necessary and inevitable.

"When we reflect on nature or the history of mankind or our own intellectual activity, at first we see the picture of an endless maze of connections in which nothing remains what, where and as it was, but everything moves, changes, comes into being and passes away...

"But this conception, correctly as it expresses the general character of the picture of phenomena as a whole, does not suffice to explain the details of which this picture is made up, and so long as we cannot do this, we are not clear about the whole picture. In order to understand these details we must detach them from their natural or historical connection and examine each one separately according to its nature, special causes and effects, etc."

But as Engels warned, too great a retreat into "reductionism" can lead to an undialectical view, or a drift to metaphysical ideas.

"The analysis of nature into its individual parts, the division of the different natural processes and objects into definite classes, the study of the internal anatomy of organic bodies in their manifold forms—these were the fundamental conditions for the gigantic strides in our knowledge of nature that have been made during the last four hundred years. But this has bequeathed us the habit of observing natural objects and processes in isolation, detached from the general context; of observing them not in their motion, but in their state of rest; not as essentially variable elements, but as constant ones; not in their life, but in their death." [20]

Now compare this with the following passage from Gleick's book:

"Scientists break things apart and look at them one at a time. If they want to examine the interaction of subatomic particles, they put two or three together. There is complication enough. The power of self-similarity, though, begins at much greater levels of complexity. It is a matter of looking at the whole." [21]

If we substitute the word "reductionism" for "the metaphysical mode of thought", we see that the central idea is identical. Now see what conclusion Engels drew from his criticism of reductionism ("the metaphysical method"):

"But for dialectics, which grasps things and their images, ideas, essentially in their interconnection, in their sequence, their movement, their birth and death, such processes as those mentioned above are so many corroborations of its own method of treatment. Nature is the test of dialectics, and it must be said for modern natural science that it has furnished extremely rich and daily increasing materials for this

(20) Engels, Anti-Dühring, pp. 24-5.
(21) J. Gleick, op. cit., p. 115.

test, and has thus proved that in the last analysis Nature's process is dialectical and not metaphysical.

"But the scientists who have learnt to think dialectically are still few and far between, and hence the conflict between the discoveries made and the old tradition-al mode of thought is the explanation of the boundless confusion which now reigns in theoretical natural science and reduces both teachers and students, writers and readers to despair." [22]

Over one hundred years ago, old Engels accurately describes the state of the physical sciences today. This is acknowledged by Ilya Prigogine (Nobel-prize win-ner for chemistry 1977) and Isabelle Stengers in their book *Order Out of Chaos, Man's New Dialogue with Nature*, where they write the following:

"To a certain extent, there is an analogy between this conflict (between Newtonian physics and the new scientific ideas) and the one that gave rise to dialec-tical materialism…The idea of a history of nature as an integral part of materialism was asserted by Marx and, in greater detail, by Engels. Contemporary developments in physics, the discovery of the constructive role played by irreversibility, have thus raised within the natural sciences a question that has long been asked by material-ists. For them, understanding nature meant understanding it as being capable of pro-ducing man and his societies.

"Moreover, at the time Engels wrote his *Dialectics of Nature*, the physical sci-ences seemed to have rejected the mechanistic world view and drawn closer to the idea of an historical development of nature. Engels mentions three fundamental dis-coveries: energy and the laws governing its qualitative transformations, the cell as the basic constituent of life, and Darwin's discovery of the evolution of species. In view of these great discoveries, Engels came to the conclusion that the mechanistic world view was dead." [23]

Despite all the wonderful advances of science and technology, there is a deep-seated feeling of malaise. An increasing number of scientists are beginning to rebel against the prevailing orthodoxies and seek new solutions to the problems facing them. Sooner or later, this is bound to result in a new revolution in science, similar to the one effected by Einstein and Planck at the beginning of the 20th century. Significantly, Einstein himself was far from being a member of the scientific estab-lishment.

"The mainstream for most of the twentieth century," Gleick remarks, "has been particle physics, exploring the building blocks of matter at higher and higher ener-gies, smaller and smaller scale, shorter and shorter times. Out of particle physics have come theories about the fundamental forces of nature and about the origin of the universe. Yet some young physicists have grown dissatisfied with the direction of the most prestigious of sciences. Progress has begun to seem slow, the naming of

(22) Engels, *Anti-Dühring*, p. 29.
(23) I. Prigogine and I. Stengers, op. cit., pp. 252-3.

new particles futile, the body of theory cluttered. With the coming of chaos, younger scientists believed they were seeing the beginnings of a course change for all of physics. The field had been dominated long enough, they felt, by the glittering abstractions of high-energy particles and quantum mechanics."

Chaos and dialectics

It is as yet too early to form a definitive view of chaos theory. However, what is clear is that these scientists are groping in the direction of a dialectical view of nature. For example, the dialectical law of the transformation of quantity into quality (and vice versa) plays a prominent sole in chaos theory:

"He [Von Neumann] recognised that a complicated dynamical system could have points of instability—critical points where a small push can have large consequences, as with a ball balanced at the top of a hill."

And again: "In science as in life, it is well known that a chain of events can have a point of crisis that could magnify small changes. But chaos meant that such points were everywhere. They were pervasive." [24]

These and many other passages reveal a striking resemblance between certain aspects of chaos theory and dialectics. Yet the most incredible thing is that most of the pioneers of "chaos" seem to have not the slightest knowledge not only of the writings of Marx and Engels, but even of Hegel! In one sense, this provides even more striking confirmation of the correctness of dialectical materialism. But in another, it is a frustrating thought that the absence of an adequate philosophical framework and methodology has been denied to science needlessly and for such a long time.

For 300 years, physics was based on linear systems. The name linear refers to the fact that if you plot such an equation on a graph, it emerges as a straight line. Indeed, much of nature appears to work precisely in this way. This is why classical mechanics is able to describe it adequately. However, much of nature is not linear, and cannot be understood through linear systems. The brain certainly does not function in a linear manner, nor does the economy, with its chaotic cycle of booms and slumps. A non-linear equation is not expressed in a straight line, but takes into account the irregular, contradictory and frequently chaotic nature of reality. There is increasing dissatisfaction among a growing layer of scientists, who are seeking alternative explanations and an alternative methodology. This implies a break with the current received wisdom. Ian Steward expresses this malaise in his well-known book *Does God Play Dice?*:

"All this makes me feel very unhappy about cosmologists who tell us that they've got the origins of the Universe pretty well wrapped up, except for the first millisecond or so of the Big Bang. And with politicians who assure us that not only

(24) J. Gleick, op. cit., pp. 6, 18-9 and 23.

is a solid dose of monetarism going to be good for us, but they're so certain about it that a few million unemployed must be just a minor hiccup. The mathematical ecologist Robert May voiced similar sentiments in 1976. 'Not only in research, but in the everyday world of politics and economics, we would all be better off if more people realised that simple systems do not necessarily possess simple dynamical properties'." [25]

The problems of modern science could be overcome far more easily by adopting a conscious (as opposed to an unconscious, haphazard, empirical) dialectical method. It is clear that the general philosophical implications of chaos theory are disputed by its scientists. Gleick quotes Ford, "a self-proclaimed evangelist of chaos" as saying that chaos means "systems liberated to randomly explore their every dynamic possibility..." Others refer to apparently random systems. Perhaps the best definition comes from Roderick V. Jensen, a theoretical physicist at Yale, who defines "chaos" as "the irregular, unpredictable behaviour of deterministic, non-linear dynamical systems."

Rather than elevate randomness to a principle of nature, as Ford seems to do, the new science does the opposite: it shows irrefutably that processes that were considered to be random (and may still be so considered, for everyday purposes) are nevertheless driven by an underlying determinism—not the crude mechanical determinism of the 18th century but *dialectical determinism*.

Some of the claims being made for the new science are very grand, and with the refinement and development of methods and techniques, may well prove true. Some of its exponents go so far as to say that the 20th century will be known for three things: relativity, quantum mechanics and chaos. Albert Einstein, although one of the founders of quantum theory, was never reconciled to the idea of a non-deterministic universe. In a letter to the physicist Niels Bohr, he insisted that "God does not play dice." Chaos theory has not only shown Einstein to be correct on this point, but even in its infancy, it is a brilliant confirmation of the fundamental world view put forward by Marx and Engels over a hundred years ago.

It is really astonishing that so many of the advocates of chaos theory, who are attempting to break with the stultifying "linear" methodology and work out a new "non-linear" mathematics, which is more in consonance with the turbulent reality of ever-changing nature, appear to be completely unaware of the only genuine revolution in logic in two millennia—the dialectical logic elaborated by Hegel, and subsequently perfected on a scientific and materialist basis by Marx and Engels. How many errors, blind alleys and crises in science could have been avoided if scientists had been equipped with a methodology which genuinely reflects the dynamic reality of nature, instead of conflicting with it at every turn!

(25) I. Stewart, *Does God Play Dice?* p. 21.

18. The theory
of knowledge

"It is the customary fate of new truths to begin as heresies and to end as superstitions." (T.H. Huxley)

The basic assumption underlying all science and rational thought in general is that the physical world exists, and that it is possible to understand the laws governing objective reality. The great majority of working scientists accept that the universe is governed by natural law, a fact pointed out by Philip Anderson:

"Indeed, it's hard to imagine how science could exist if they didn't. To believe in natural law is to believe that the universe is ultimately comprehensible—that the same forces that determine the destiny of a galaxy can also determine the fall of an apple here on earth; that the same atoms that refract the light passing through a diamond can also form the stuff of a living cell; that the same electrons, neutrons, and protons that emerged from the big bang can now give rise to the human brain, mind, and soul. To believe in natural law is to believe in the unity of nature at the deepest possible level." [26]

The same is true of the human race in general. Every new discovery of science and technique broadens and deepens our understanding, but by so doing, also poses new challenges. Every question answered immediately raises two more questions. Like a traveller who, with growing excitement, approaches the horizon, only to discover a new one, beckoning him from afar, the process of discovery unfolds with no end in sight. Scientists delve ever deeper into the mysteries of the subatomic world, in search of the "ultimate particle". But each time they reach the horizon with a triumphant cry, it stubbornly recedes into the distance.

It is the illusion of every epoch that it represents the ultimate peak of all human achievements and wisdom. The ancient Greeks thought that they had understood all the laws of the universe on the basis of Euclid's geometry. Laplace thought the same in relation to Newton's mechanics. In 1880, the chief of the Prussian patent office

(26) Quoted in M.M. Waldrop, *Complexity, The Emerging Science at the Edge of Order and Chaos,* p. 81.

declared that everything that could ever be discovered had already been invented! Nowadays, scientists tend to be slightly more circumspect in their pronouncements. Even so, tacit assumptions are made that, for example, Einstein's general relativity theory is absolutely true, and the principle of indeterminacy has a universal application.

The history of science shows how economical the human mind is. Very little is actually wasted in the process of collective learning. Even mistakes, when honestly analysed, can play a positive role. Only when thought becomes ossified into official dogma, which treats new ideas as heresy to be prohibited and punished, is the development of thought paralysed and even thrust back. The dismal history of science in the Middle Ages is sufficient proof of this. The search for the philosopher's stone was based upon a mistaken hypothesis, yet the alchemists made important discoveries, and laid the basis for the development of modern chemistry. The big bang theory, with its search for a non-existent "beginning of time", has scarcely any better scientific credentials, yet, despite this, there is no doubt about the big advances which have been, and are being, made.

As Eric J. Lerner correctly observes: "Good data, competently obtained and analysed, is of scientific value even if the theory that inspired it is wrong. Other theorists will find uses for it that were little imagined when it was first gathered. Even in theoretical work, honest efforts to compare a theory to observation almost always prove useful regardless of the theory's truth: a theoretician is bound to be upset if his idea is wrong, but time won't have been wasted in ruling it out." [27]

The development of science proceeds through an infinite series of successive approximations. Each generation arrives at a series of fundamental generalisations about the workings of nature, which serve to explain certain observed phenomena. These are invariably considered to be absolute truths, valid for all time in "all possible worlds". On further examination, however, they are found to be not absolute, but relative. Exceptions are discovered, which contradict the established rules, and, in turn, demand explanation, and so on ad infinitum.

"The first discoveries were realisation that each change of scale brought new phenomena and new kinds of behaviour. For modern particle physicists, the process has never ended. Every new accelerator, with its increase in energy and speed, extends science's field of view to tinier particles and briefer time scales, and every extension seems to bring new information." [28]

Should we therefore despair of ever achieving the whole truth? To pose the question in this way is not to understand the nature of truth and human knowledge. Thus Kant thought that the human mind could only ever know appearances. Behind the world of appearances lay the Thing-in-Itself, which we can never know. To this Hegel replied that to know the properties of a thing is to know the thing itself. There

(27) E. Lerner, *The Big Bang Never Happened*, p. 155.
(28) J. Gleick, op. cit., p. 115.

is no absolute barrier between appearance and essence. We start with the reality that presents itself to us in sense perception, but we do not stop here. Using our intellect, we penetrate ever deeper into the mysteries of matter, passing beyond appearance to essence; from the particular to the universal; from the secondary to the fundamental; from the facts to the law.

To use the terminology that Hegel used to answer Kant, the whole history of science and of human thought in general is the process of changing the Thing-in-Itself into a Thing-for-Us. In other words, what "cannot be known" at a given stage of the development of science is eventually explored and explained. Every barrier placed in the way of thought is broken down. But in solving one problem, we immediately come up against new ones which must be solved, new challenges to be overcome. And this process will never come to an end, because the properties of the material universe are indeed infinite.

"To pursue our analogy further," writes David Bohm, "we may say that with regard to the totality of natural laws we never have enough views and cross-sections to give us a complete understanding of this totality. But as science progresses, and new theories are developed, we obtain more and more views from different sides, views that are more comprehensive, views that are more detailed, etc. Each particular theory or explanation of a given set of phenomena will then have a limited domain of validity and will be adequate only in a limited context and under limited conditions. This means that any theory extrapolated to an arbitrary context and to arbitrary conditions will (like the partial views of our object) lead to erroneous predictions. *The finding of such errors is one of the most important means of making progress in science.*

"A new theory, to which the discovery of such errors will eventually give rise, does not, however invalidate the older theories. Rather, by permitting the treatment of a broader domain in which they are inadequate and, in so doing, it helps define the conditions under which they are valid (e.g. as the theory of relativity corrected Newton's laws of motion, and thus helped to define the conditions of validity of Newton's laws as those in which the velocity is small compared with that of light). Thus, we do not expect that any causal relationships will represent *absolute truths*; for to do this, they will have to apply *without approximation*, and *unconditionally*. Rather, then, we see that the mode of progress of science is, and has been, through a series of progressively more fundamental, more extensive, and more accurate conceptions of the laws of nature, each of which contributes to the definition of the conditions of validity of the older conceptions (just as broader and more detailed views of our object contribute to defining the limitations of any particular view or set of views)." [29]

In his book *The Structure of Scientific Revolution*, Professor Thomas Kuhn pictures the history of science as periodic theoretical revolutions, punctuating long periods of merely quantitative change, mainly devoted to filling in details. In such

(29) D. Bohm, op. cit., p. 32.

"normal" periods, science operates within a given set of theories which he calls *paradigms*, which are unquestioned assumptions about what the world is like. Initially, the existing paradigm stimulates the development of science, providing a coherent framework for investigation. Without such an agreed framework, scientists would be forever arguing about the fundamentals. Science, no more than society, cannot live in a permanent state of revolutionary upheaval. For this very reason, revolutions are relatively rare events, both in society and science.

For a time, science is able to advance along these well-trodden paths, piling up results. But in the meanwhile, what were originally daring new hypotheses become transformed into rigid orthodoxies. If an experiment produces results that conflict with the existing theories, scientists may suppress them, because they are subversive to the existing order. Only when the anomalies build up to the point where they cannot be ignored is the ground prepared for a new scientific revolution, which overthrows the dominant theories and opens up a new period of "normal" scientific development, on a higher level.

While it is undoubtedly over-simplified, this picture of the development of science, as a broad generalisation, can be accepted as true. In his book *Ludwig Feuerbach*, Engels explains the dialectical nature of the development of human thought, as exemplified both in the history of science and philosophy:

"Truth, the cognition of which is the business of philosophy, was in the hands of Hegel no longer an aggregate of finished dogmatic statements, which, once discovered, had merely to be learned by heart. Truth lay now in the process of cognition itself, in the long historical development of science, which mounts from lower to ever higher levels of knowledge without ever reaching, by discovering so-called absolute truth, a point at which it can proceed no further, where it would have nothing more to do than to fold its hands and gaze with wonder at the absolute truth to which it had attained."

And again: "For it [dialectical philosophy] nothing is final, absolute, sacred. It reveals the transitory character of everything and in everything; nothing can endure before it except the uninterrupted process of becoming and of passing away, of endless ascendancy from the lower to the higher. And dialectical philosophy itself is nothing more than the mere reflection of this process in the thinking brain. It has, of course, also a conservative side: it recognises that definite stages of knowledge and society are justified for their time and circumstances; but only so far. The conservatism of this mode of outlook is relative; its revolutionary character is absolute—the only absolute dialectical philosophy admits." [30]

What is the scientific method?

In the 3rd century B.C. the Greek scholar Eratosthenes read that a vertical stick, positioned in a place called Syrene, cast no shadow at midday. He then observed

(30) MESW, Vol. 3, pp. 339-340.

that in his own city, Alexandria, a vertical stick did cast a shadow. From these observations of real physical phenomena, he deduced that the earth was round. He then sent a slave to Syrene to measure the distance from Alexandria. Then, using simple geometry, he calculated the circumference of the earth. This is the real method of science in action. It is a mixture of observation, hypothesis and mathematical reasoning. Eratosthenes began with observation (both his own and that of others). Then, on the basis of this, he drew a general conclusion, the hypothesis that the earth is curved. He then made use of mathematics to give a precise form to his theory.

The brilliant achievements of Alexandrine science were eclipsed by the rise of Christianity in the Dark Ages. For centuries, the development of science was paralysed by the spiritual dictatorship of the Church. Only by freeing itself of the influence of religion did science manage to develop. Yet by a strange quirk of history, at the end of the 20th century determined attempts are being made to drag science backwards. All kinds of quasi-religious and mystical ideas are floating in the air. This strange phenomenon is closely related to two things. Firstly, the division of labour has been carried to such extremes that it has begun to cause serious harm. Narrow specialisation, reductionism, and an almost complete divorce between the theoretical and experimental side of physics has had the most negative consequences.

Secondly, there has been no adequate philosophy which could help to point science in the right direction. The philosophy of science is in a mess. This is not surprising, because the prevailing "philosophy of science"—or rather the philosophical sect of logical positivism, which set itself up in this capacity—is least of all able to help science out of its difficulties. On the contrary, it has made matters worse. In recent decades, we have seen a growing tendency in theoretical physics to approach the phenomena of the natural world from an excessively abstract and mathematical standpoint. This is clearly the case in the arbitrary attempt to reconstruct an alleged beginning of the universe. As Anderson pointed out in an article written in 1972:

"The ability to reduce everything to simple fundamental laws does not imply the ability to start from those laws and reconstruct the universe. In fact, the more the elementary particles physicists tell us about the nature of the fundamental laws, the less relevance they seem to have to the very real problems of the rest of science, much less society." [31]

In recent decades the prejudice has become deeply rooted that "pure" science, especially theoretical physics is the product of abstract thought and mathematical deduction alone. As Eric Lerner explains, Einstein was partly responsible for this tendency. Unlike earlier theories, such as Maxwell's laws of electromagnetism, or Newton's laws of gravity, which were firmly based on experiment, and soon confirmed by hundreds of thousands of independent observations, Einstein's theories

(31) Quoted in M.M. Waldrop, op. cit., p. 81.

were initially confirmed on the basis of only two—the deflection of starlight by the sun's gravitational field and a slight deviation in the orbit of Mercury. The fact that relativity theory was subsequently shown to be correct has led others, possibly not quite up to Einstein's level of genius, to assume that this is the way to proceed. Why bother with time-consuming experiments and tedious observations? Indeed, why depend upon the evidence of the senses at all, when we can get straight to the truth through the method of pure deduction?

We must remind ourselves that the great breakthrough in science came in the Renaissance, when it separated itself from religion, and began to base itself upon observation and experiment, setting out from the real material world, and always returning to it. In the 20th century, however, there has been a partial regression to idealism, both to Platonism and, still worse, to the subjective idealism of Berkeley and Hume. For all his unquestioned genius, Einstein was unable to free himself from this trend, although he frequently recoiled against the consequences that flowed from it. It is to his credit, for example, that he conducted a stubborn rear-guard action against the subjective idealist interpretation of quantum mechanics put forward by Heisenberg.

Like many scientists, Einstein did not feel at home with philosophy, and honest-ly confessed that great scientists tend to make poor philosophers of science. Nevertheless, he himself made a number of pronunciations of a philosophical or semi-philosophical character, which, given his colossal prestige, were bound to be taken seriously by many scientists—with some very unfortunate results. In 1934, for example, he wrote:

"The theory of relativity is a fine example of the fundamental character of the modern development of theoretical science. The hypotheses with which it starts are becoming steadily more abstract and remote from experience. The theoretical scien-tist is compelled in an increasing degree to be guided by purely mathematical, for-mal considerations in his search for a theory, because the physical experience of the experimenter cannot lift him into the regions of highest abstraction. The predomi-nantly inductive methods appropriate to the youth of science are giving place to ten-tative deduction." [32]

In point of fact, it is not true that Einstein arrived at his theories through a process of pure reasoning and deduction. As he himself states in his *Essays in Science*, his theory of special relativity was derived from Maxwell's work on elec-tricity and magnetism, which, in turn, was based on the work of Faraday, with its solid experimental foundations. Only after 1915, when he turned to cosmology did Einstein turn to the method of abstract deduction to obtain his results. Here he departed from the established method by taking as his fundamental hypothesis an assumption which was contradicted by observation: the notion that the universe as a whole is homogeneous (evenly spread throughout space).

(32) Quoted in E. Lerner, op. cit., p. 128.

Setting out from this proposition, Einstein used his general theory of relativity to prove that space is finite. According to this view, the greater the mass of a given density, the more it "curves space". A sufficiently large mass will lead to a situation where space curves round on itself altogether, thus producing a "closed universe". This marked, in effect, a regression to the mediaeval world outlook of a finite universe, previously rejected as unscientific. However, even in 1915, there was sufficient evidence to show that the universe was not homogeneous. The theory collided with the facts established by observation. It is no coincidence that Einstein's search for a unified theory of gravitation and electromagnetism during his last thirty years ended in failure, as he himself admitted.

Limits of empiricism

Real philosophy ended with Hegel. Since then, we have seen only a tendency to repeat old ideas, occasionally a filling out of this or that detail, but no real breakthrough, no great new idea. This is hardly surprising. The unprecedented advances of science over the past hundred years make philosophy in the old sense of the word redundant. There is very little point in speculating about the nature of the universe, when we are in a position to uncover its secrets with the aid of ever more powerful telescopes, space probes, computers and particle accelerators. Just as the debate about the nature of the solar system was decided by Galileo's telescope, so the advances in technique will settle the question of the history of the universe, only to pose new questions for future generations to solve.

"As soon as each separate science is required to clarify its position in the great totality of things and of our knowledge of things, a special science dealing with this totality is superfluous," wrote Engels. "All that remains in an independent state from all earlier philosophy is the science of thought and its laws—formal logic and dialectics. Everything else merges into the positive science of nature and history." [33]

Yet philosophy still has a role to play, in the only two areas left to it—formal logic and dialectics. Science, as we have seen, is not merely concerned with accumulating facts. It still requires the active intervention of thought, which alone can discover the inner meaning of the facts, their lawfulness. It is still necessary to make hypotheses, which can guide our investigations along the most fruitful channels, to grasp the real interrelations between apparently unrelated phenomena, to derive order from chaos. This requires training and a thorough knowledge of the history of both science and philosophy. As the American philosopher George Santayana put it, "He who does not learn from history is doomed to repeat it." One of the most pernicious consequences of the influence of logical positivism in 20th century science is that all the great schools of the past were treated like a dead dog. Now we see where this attitude leads us. Those who haughtily dismissed "metaphysics" have been punished for their pride. At no time in the history of science has mysticism been so rampant as now.

(33) Engels, *Anti-Dühring*, p. 31.

The purely empirical school of thought inevitably leads to this, as Engels pointed out long ago:

"Exclusive empiricism, which at most allows itself thinking in the form of mathematical calculation, imagines that it operates only with undeniable facts. In reality, however, it operates predominantly with traditional notions, with the largely obsolete products of thought of its predecessors, and such are positive and negative electricity, the electric force of separation, the contact theory. These serve it as the foundation of endless mathematical calculations in which, owing to the strictness of the mathematical formulation, the hypothetical nature of the premises gets comfortably forgotten. This kind of empiricism is as credulous towards the results of the thought of its predecessors as it is sceptical in its attitude to the results of contemporary thought. For it even the experimentally established facts have gradually become inseparable from their traditional interpretations...They have to resort to all kinds of subterfuges and untenable expedients, to the glossing over of irreconcilable contradictions, and thus finally land themselves into a medley of contradictions from which they have no escape." [34]

It is impossible for scientists to remain aloof from society, on the grounds that they are purely impartial. None of us live in a vacuum. As the American geneticist Theodosius Dobzhansky says:

"Scientists often have a naïve faith that if only they could discover enough facts about a problem, these facts would somehow arrange themselves in a compelling and true solution. The relation between scientific discovery and popular belief is not, however, a one-way street. Marxists are more right than wrong when they argue that the problems scientists take up, the way they go about solving them, and even the solutions they are inclined to accept, are conditioned by the intellectual, social, and economic environments in which they live and work." [35]

It is sometimes asserted that Marx and Engels considered the dialectic to be some kind of Absolute—the last word in human knowledge. Such a notion is a self-evident contradiction. The Marxian dialectic differs from the Hegelian in two fundamental ways. Firstly, it is a materialist philosophy, and therefore derives its categories from the world of physical reality. Nature is infinite, not closed. Likewise, truth itself is endless and cannot be summed up in a single all-embracing system. The negation of the negation, as Engels explains, is a kind of spiral of development—an open-ended system, not a closed circle. That is the second fundamental difference with the Hegelian philosophy, which ultimately contradicted itself by attempting to express the dialectic as a closed and absolute System.

Marx and Engels worked out the outline of a new dialectical method, the usefulness of which was brilliantly shown in the three volumes of Capital. But the enormous advances of 20th century science provide ample material with which to fill

(34) Engels, *The Dialectics of Nature*, pp. 185-6.
(35) T. Dobzhansky, *Mankind Evolving*, p. 138.

out, develop and extend the content of dialectics. The further evolution of chaos and complexity theory can provide the basis for such a development, which would be of immense benefit to both the natural and social sciences. We cannot therefore say that dialectical materialism will not in the future be overtaken by some new and more satisfactory mode of thinking. But we can certainly say that up to the present time, it is the most advanced, comprehensive and flexible method of scientific analysis available. Let Engels speak for himself on this subject:

"Further, if no philosophy as such is needed any longer, then no system, not even a natural system of philosophy, is needed any longer either. The recognition of the fact that all the processes of nature are systematically interconnected drives science on to prove this systematic interconnection throughout, both in general and in detail. But an adequate, exhaustive scientific exposition of this interconnection, the formation of an exact mental image of the world system in which we live, remains impossible for us, as it does for all times. If at any epoch in the development of mankind such a final, definitive system of the interconnections within the world—physical as well as mental and historical—were constructed, this would mean that the realm of human knowledge had reached its limit, and that further historical development would be cut short from the moment when society had been brought into accord with that system—which would be an absurdity, pure nonsense.

"Mankind therefore finds itself faced with a contradiction: on the one hand, it has to gain an exhaustive knowledge of the world system in all its interconnections, and on the other hand, this task can never be completely fulfilled because of the nature both of men and of the world system. But this contradiction not only lies in the nature of the two factors—the world and man—it is also the main lever of all intellectual advance, and constantly finds its solution, day by day, in the endless progressive development of humanity, just as for example mathematical problems find their solution in an infinite series or continued fractions. Actually, each mental image of the world system is and remains limited, objectively by the historical situation and subjectively by its author's physical and mental constitution." [36]

Prejudice against dialectics

Modern science furnishes an abundance of material which completely confirms Engels' assertion that "in the last analysis, nature works dialectically." The discoveries of science since Engels died completely confirm this view.

"When we reflect on Nature, or the history of mankind, or our own intellectual activity," Engels wrote, "the first picture presented to us is of an endless maze of relations and interactions, in which nothing remains what, where and as it was, but everything moves, changes, comes into being and passes out of existence. This primitive, naïve, yet intrinsically correct conception of the world was that of ancient

(36) Engels, *Anti-Dühring*, pp. 45-6.

Greek philosophy, and was first clearly formulated by Heraclitus: everything is and also is not, for everything is in flux, is constantly changing, constantly coming into being and passing away." [37]

Let us compare this to another quotation from Hoffmann: "In the world of quantum, particles are incessantly appearing and disappearing. What we would think of as empty space is a teeming, fluctuating nothingness, with photons appearing from nowhere and vanishing almost as soon as they were born, with electrons frothing up for brief moments from the monstrous ocean to create evanescent electron-proton pairs and sundry other particles adding to the confusion." [38]

The rise of chaos and complexity theory indicates a welcome reaction against the stultifying reductionism of the past. Yet very little attention has been paid to the pioneering work of Hegel, Marx and Engels. This astonishing fact is largely to be explained by the widespread prejudice against dialectics, partly as a reaction against the mystical way that dialectics was presented by the idealist school after Hegel's death, but mainly because of its connection with Marxism. Hegel's dialectics have been described as the "algebra of revolution". If the law of quantity and quality is accepted as valid for chemistry and physics, the next step would be to apply it to existing society, with most unfortunate consequences for the defenders of the status quo.

The scientific writings of Marx and Engels cannot be separated from their revolutionary theory of history in general (historical materialism), and their analysis of the contradictions of capitalism. These are evidently not very popular with those who currently possess a monopoly of economic and political power, and who control, not only the newspapers and television companies, but also hold in their hands the purse strings that determine the fate of universities, research-projects, and academic careers. Is it surprising that dialectical materialism is a taboo subject, which is systematically passed over in silence, except when it is denounced as unscientific mumbo-jumbo, by people who have clearly never read a single line of Marx or Engels? True, a small number of brave souls have raised the question of the contribution of Marxism to the philosophy of science, but even then, such mentions are frequently hedged round with all kinds of qualifications, aiming to show that dialectics may be valid for a given field of science, but cannot be accepted as a general proposition.

Nowadays, the idea of change, of evolution, has deeply penetrated the popular consciousness. But evolution is generally understood as a slow, gradual, uninterrupted process. As Trotsky put it, "Hegel's logic is the logic of evolution. Only one must not forget that the concept of 'evolution' itself has been completely corrupted and emasculated by university professors and liberal writers to mean peaceful 'progress'."

(37) Engels, *Anti-Dühring*, p. 24.
(38) B. Hoffmann, op. cit., p. 210.

In politics, this common prejudice finds its expression in the theory of reformist gradualism, where today is better than yesterday and tomorrow will be better than today. Sadly, human history in general, and the history of the 20th century in particular, provides precious little comfort for the supporters of this tranquillising view of the social process. History knows long periods of gradual change but this is by no means a continuous and smooth process. It is interrupted by all kinds of explosions and catastrophes: wars, economic crises, revolutions and counter-revolutions. To deny this is to deny what everyone knows to be true. So how do we regard these phenomena? As sudden, inexplicable outbreaks of collective madness? As accidental "deviations" from the gradualist "norm"? Or, on the contrary, are they to be seen as an integral part of the process of social development—not accidents but the necessary outcome of tensions and stresses that build up gradually and unseen within society and which, sooner or later, must force their way to the surface, just as the pressures that accumulate along a fault-line in the earth's crust result in an earthquake?

Any attempt to banish contradiction from nature, to smooth out its rough edges, to subject it to the neat rules of formal logic, as the gardeners at Versailles subjected rude nature to the rules of classical geometry, is doomed to fail. Such efforts may well have a soothing effect upon the nerves, but will prove to be utterly useless to arrive at an understanding of the real world. And what is true for inanimate and animate nature is also true for the history of human society itself, despite the stubborn attempts to demonstrate the contrary. The history of society reveals the selfsame tendencies—the inner contradictions that impel development; the rise and fall of different socioeconomic systems; the long periods of gradual "evolutionary" change, punctuated by sudden upheavals, wars and revolutions, which stand at the crossroads of every great historical development. Are such striking phenomena merely to be shrugged off as accidents, temporary and unfortunate deviations from the alleged evolutionary "norm"? Or irrefutable proof of the stupidity or inherent wickedness of human beings?

If this is the case, then all attempts to arrive at a rational understanding of human development must be abandoned. We are compelled to echo the opinion of Edward Gibbon, author of *The Decline and Fall of the Roman Empire* who described history as "little more than the register of the crimes, follies, and misfortunes of mankind." But if, as we firmly believe, human history proceeds according to the same dialectical laws that we observe throughout nature (and why should the human race claim the unlikely "privilege" of being entirely exempt from objective laws of development?) then the pattern of human history for the first time begins to make sense. It can be explained. It can even—within certain limits—be predicted, although predictions of complex phenomena are not as straightforward as ones involving simple linear processes. This applies just as much to predicting an earthquake or the weather as it does to anticipating the movement of society. No one can say for certain when the city of Los Angeles will fall victim to a catastrophic earth-quake, but one can predict with absolute certainty that such a thing will happen.

Despite the most strenuous efforts to deny the validity of dialectics, the latter always takes its revenge on its most hardened detractors. The conservative geological community has been compelled to accept continental drift, the birth and death of continents, which they once laughed out of court. Biologists have been compelled to accept that the old idea of evolution as a gradual, uninterrupted process of adaptation is one-sided and false; that evolution takes place through catastrophic qualitative leaps, in which death (extinction) becomes the precondition for birth (new species).

At every turn, the wealth of material furnished by the natural sciences compels scientists to adopt dialectical conclusions. However, they soon become uncomfortably aware of the potentially "subversive" implications of such ideas. It is at this point that they hasten to resort to all kinds of embarrassed disclaimers and subterfuges in order to cover up their tracks. The usual get-out is to protest ignorance concerning philosophy in general. Like Oscar Wilde's "love that dare not speak its name", these authors who wax eloquent about everything under the sun, find themselves utterly unable to pronounce the words dialectical materialism. At best, they insist, in effect, that *dialectical materialism* is valid for their own narrow speciality but has no application to the broader field of science or (perish the thought!) to society at large.

It is surprising that even those proponents of the theory of chaos who come quite close to a dialectical position display a complete lack of knowledge about Marxism. Thus, Ian Stewart and Tim Poston could write in *Analog* (November 1981) the following lines:

"So the 'inexorable laws of physics' on which—for instance—Marx tried to model his laws of history, were never really there. If Newton could not predict the behaviour of three balls, could Marx predict that of three people? Any regularity in the behaviour of large assemblies of particles or people must be statistical, and that has quite a different philosophical taste." [39]

This is completely off the mark. Marx did not base his model of history on the laws of physics at all. The laws of social development must be derived from a painstaking study of society itself. Marx and Engels devoted the whole of their lives to such a study, based upon a colossal amount of carefully collected empirical data, as even the most superficial examination of the three volumes of *Capital* alone will reveal. Incidentally, both Marx and Engels were highly critical of mechanical determinism in general and Newton in particular. The attempt to establish some parallel between Marx's method and that of Newton and Laplace is without the slightest foundation.

(39) Quoted in I. Stewart, op. cit., p. 40.

The closer chaos and complexity theory moves to an examination of existing society, the greater is the potential for arriving at an understanding of the contradictions of capitalism:

"But in the United States, the ideal is maximum individual freedom—or, as [Brian] Arthur puts it, 'letting everybody be their own John Wayne and run around with guns.' However much that ideal is compromised in practice, it still holds mythic power.

"But increasing returns cut to the heart of that myth. If small chance events can lock you into any of several possible outcomes, then the outcome that's actually selected may *not* be the best. And that means that maximum individual freedom—and the free market—might *not* produce the best of all possible worlds. So by advocating increasing returns, Arthur was innocently treading into a minefield." [40] (Brian Arthur is an economist and one of the theoreticians of complexity.)

Stephen Jay Gould, who has made an important contribution to current evolutionary theory, is one of the few Western scientists who has openly recognised the parallels between his theory of "punctuated equilibria" and dialectical materialism. In his book, *The Panda's Thumb*, he says the following:

"If gradualism is more a product of Western thought than a fact of nature, then we should consider alternative philosophies of change to enlarge our realm of constraining prejudices. In the Soviet Union, for example, scientists are trained with a very different philosophy of change—the so-called dialectical laws, reformulated by Engels from Hegel's philosophy. The dialectical laws are explicitly punctuational. They speak, for example, of the 'transformation of quantity into quality.' This may sound like mumbo jumbo, but it suggests that change occurs in large leaps following a slow accumulation of stresses that a system resists until it reaches the breaking point. Heat water and it eventually boils. Oppress the workers more and more and bring on the revolution. Eldredge and I were fascinated to learn that many Russian palaeontologists support a model similar to our punctuated equilibria."

Palaeontology and anthropology are, after all, only separated by a very thin wall from the historical and social sciences, which have potentially dangerous political implications for the defenders of the status quo. As Engels pointed out, the nearer one gets to the social sciences, the less objective and the more reactionary they become. It is therefore encouraging that Stephen J. Gould has come quite close to a dialectical point of view, despite his obvious caution:

"Nonetheless, I will confess to a personal belief that a punctuational view may prove to map tempos of biological and geologic change more accurately and more often than any of its competitors—if only because complex systems in a steady state are both common and highly resistant to change." [41]

---

(40) M.M. Waldrop, op. cit., p. 48.
(41) S. J. Gould, *The Panda's Thumb*, pp. 153 and 154.

In the 19th century, Marx ironically pointed out that most of the natural scientists were "shamefaced materialists". In the last half of the 20th century, we have a still greater paradox. Scientists who have never read a word of Marx or Hegel, have independently arrived at many of the ideas of dialectical materialism. We are firmly convinced that the future development of science will confirm the importance of the dialectical method, and that those who pioneered it will finally obtain the recognition which has been denied them.

Stalinist caricature

A serious obstacle in the path of many who approached the ideas of Marxism in the past was the caricature presented by Stalinism. This played a contradictory role. On the one hand, the tremendous successes of the nationalised planned economy in the Soviet Union powerfully attracted many workers and intellectuals in the West. Prominent scientists such as the celebrated biologist J.B.S. Haldane in Britain were drawn to Marxism, and began to apply it to their own fields with promising results. A large number of works appeared which attempted to explain the latest discoveries of science in a comprehensible language. The results were uneven, but this literature was infinitely preferable to the mystifying stuff produced for popular consumption today.

There is no doubt that the unprecedented advances of culture, education and science in Russia served as a point of reference not just for the international labour movement, but for the best of the intellectuals and scientists in the West. These achievements showed the potential of a nationalised planned economy, despite all the monstrous bureaucratic distortions that ultimately undermined it. They stand in stark contrast to the present situation. The fall of the Soviet Union, and the attempt to move in the direction of a "market economy" has produced a frightful collapse of the productive forces and culture. Overnight, a colossal ideological counter-offensive has been launched on a world scale against the idea of a planned economy, Marxism and socialism in general. The enemies of socialism have taken advantage of the crimes of Stalinism to attempt to blacken the name of Marxism. They aim to convince people that revolution does not pay and that, consequently, it is better to put up with the rule of the big banks and monopolies, accept mass unemployment and falling living standards, because, they say there is "no alternative".

In reality, what failed in Russia was not socialism, but a bureaucratic caricature of socialism. A totalitarian and bureaucratic system is incompatible with a regime of nationalised planned economy, which as Leon Trotsky explained in 1936 needs democracy as the human body needs oxygen. Without the active and conscious participation of the population at all levels, without complete freedom of criticism, discussion and debate, it would inevitably lead to a nightmare of bureaucracy, corruption, red tape, bungling and mismanagement, which would undermine the basis of the planned economy in the end. This is precisely what happened in the former Soviet Union, as predicted by Marxists decades ago.

The totalitarian regime of Stalinism, with its inevitable companions, corruption, conformism and toadyism, had its most negative effects in the fields of science and the arts. Despite the enormous impulse given to education and culture by the October revolution and the nationalised planned economy that issued from it, the free development of science was held back by the suffocating bureaucratic regime. More than any other section of society, science and the arts need to develop in an atmosphere of intellectual freedom, freedom to think, to speak, to explore, to make mistakes. In the absence of such conditions, creative thought will wither and die. Thus the USSR, with more scientists than America and Japan together (and they were good scientists), was unable to get the same results as in the West, and gradually fell behind in a whole series of fields.

One of the things that created all kinds of misconceptions about Marxism was the way that it was presented by the Stalinists. The ruling elite in Russia could not tolerate freedom of thought and criticism in any sphere. In the hands of the bureaucracy, Marxist philosophy ("diamat" as they called it) was twisted into a sterile dogma, or a variety of sophism used to justify all the twists and turns of the leadership. According to Lefebvre, at one point things got so bad that the Soviet army high command insisted that lessons on formal logic be put back on the curriculum of military academies because of the shameful confusion caused by the teachers of so-called diamat. At least lessons in logic would teach the cadets the ABCs of reasoning. This little incident is enough to expose the caricature nature of the "Marxism" of the Stalinists.

Under Stalin, scientists were forced to accept without question this rigid and lifeless caricature, as well as a number of false theories with no scientific basis that happened to suit the bureaucracy, such as Lysenko's "theory" of genetics. This discredited the idea of dialectical materialism in the scientific community to a certain extent, and prevented a fruitful and creative application of the method of dialectics to different fields of science, which would have made possible serious advances both in the sciences themselves and in the further elaboration of the philosophical ideas which Marx and Engels explained in outline, but left to future generations to develop and fill out in detail.

It is a condemnation of the Stalinist regime that, for more than six decades, with all the resources of the Soviet state at its disposal, the bureaucracy was unable to introduce a single original idea into the theoretical arsenal of Marxism. In spite of the tremendous advantages of the nationalised planned economy, which created a powerful industry and technology, they proved incapable of adding anything new to the discoveries of Karl Marx, working alone in the library of the British Museum.

Despite everything, the benefits of a planned economy permitted outstanding progress in many fields, a fact which the present avalanche of propaganda would like to conceal. Moreover, where scientists did apply the dialectical method to different fields, interesting results were obtained. This is shown precisely by chaos theory, one area in which Soviet scientists, undoubtedly influenced by dialectical materialism, were in advance of the West by at least two decades. It is not generally realised that the original research into chaos theory was done in the Soviet Union, and this gave an impulse to those Western scientists who were independently coming to the same conclusions, and whose ideas in turn stimulated the further development of Soviet research into chaos, as Gleick admits:

"The blossoming of chaos in the United States and Europe has inspired a huge body of parallel work in the Soviet Union; on the other hand, it also inspired considerable bewilderment, because much of the new science was not so new in Moscow. Soviet mathematicians and physicists had strong tradition in chaos research, dating back to the work of A.N. Kolmogorov in the fifties. Furthermore, they had a tradition of working together that had survived the divergence of mathematics and physics elsewhere." [42]

(42) J. Gleick, op. cit., p. 76.

19. Alienation and the future of humanity

Capitalism in a blind alley

In the period from 1948 to 1973-74, we witnessed a fireworks display of industrial and technological innovation the like of which has never been seen. Yet the very successes of the capitalist system are now turning into their opposite. At this time of writing, there are officially 22 million unemployed in the advanced capitalist economies of the OECD alone, even without considering the hundreds of millions of unemployed and under-employed in Africa, Asia and Latin America. Moreover, this is not the temporary cyclical unemployment of the past. It is a chronic ulcer gnawing at the bowels of society. Like some dreadful epidemic, it strikes down even sections of society which believed themselves safe in the past.

Despite all the advances of science and technology, society finds itself at the mercy of forces it cannot control. At the beginning of the 21st century people look to the future with growing anxiety. In place of the old certainty there is uncertainty. The general malaise affects first and foremost the ruling class and its strategists, who are increasingly aware that their system is in serious difficulties. The crisis of the system finds its reflection in a crisis of ideology, reflected in the political parties, official churches, morality, science and even what passes nowadays for philosophy.

Private ownership and the nation state are the two straitjackets that hamper and restrict the development of society. From an objective point of view, the conditions for world socialism have existed for decades. However, the decisive factor that permitted capitalism partially to overcome its fundamental contradictions was the development of world trade. After 1945 the domination of the world by the United States, dictated by the need to stave off revolution in Europe and Japan and contain the Soviet Bloc, gave them the opportunity, through the Bretton Woods agreement and GATT, to compel the other capitalist powers to lower tariffs and remove other obstacles to the free flow of trade.

This was in complete contrast with the economic chaos of the inter-war period when the intensification of national rivalries expressed itself through competitive devaluation and trade wars that led to the strangling of the productive forces within the narrow confines of private ownership and the nation state. As a consequence of this, the period between the Wars was one of crisis, revolutions and counter-revolutions, culminating in the new imperialist slaughter of 1939-45.

In the post-war period, capitalism partially succeeded in overcoming the fundamental crisis of their system through the integration of world trade, creating a largely unified world market. This provided the basic premise for the massive upswing of the economy in the period of 1948-73, which in turn led to increased living standards, at least for a sizable section of the population of the advanced capitalist countries. Thus, a dying man can, at times, experience a sudden access of energy, which appears to presage a complete recovery, but in reality is only the prelude to a new and fatal relapse.

Periods such as this are not only possible, but inevitable, even in an epoch of capitalist decline, if the existing social order is not overthrown. However, the massive fireworks display of economic growth, amounting to many trillions of dollars over a period of four decades, has in no way changed the nature of capitalism or obliterated the contradictions within it. The long period of economic upswing from 1948 to 1973 is over. Full employment, rising living standards and the welfare state are things of the past. In place of growth we now face economic stagnation, recession and a crisis of the productive forces.

The owners of capital are no longer interested in investing in productive activity. The late Akio Morita, who was chairman of Sony Corporation, repeatedly warned in the 1980s of the mortal danger to the capitalist system of the trend away from productive industry towards services. Since 1950, the USA has lost over half its manufacturing jobs, while three quarters of all jobs are oriented to the service sector. A similar trend exists in Britain, now relegated to a third rate capitalist power. In an article in the *Director* (February 1988), Morita stated:

"What I would like to suggest is that this trend, far from being the matured progression of a maturing economy and something to be encouraged, is destructive. For in the long run an economy that has lost its manufacturing base has lost its vital centre. A service-based economy has no engine to drive it. Thus, complacency about moving from manufacturing to a haven of hi-tech services, where workers sit at computers and exchange information all day, is entirely misplaced.

"This is because it is only manufacturing that creates something new, which takes raw materials and fashions them into products that are of more value than the raw materials they are made from. It would seem obvious that the service elements of an economy are subsidiary and dependent upon manufacturing."

Instead of creating jobs and increasing the wealth of society, the big monopolies are dedicating huge resources to speculating in the money markets, organising predatory takeovers, and other kinds of parasitic activity. Morita pointed out that "Businessmen have become fascinated with the foreign exchange game. They have discovered it can bring quick returns without the need to invest in a productive enterprise. Even some industrial concerns have gone over to the FX Empire. The people who spend their lives hunched over a monitor displaying the latest exchange transactions live in a world all their own. They have no allegiances. They do not make any products. They do not create any new ideas. They trade US $200 billion each day in London, New York and Tokyo. That is a lot of poker chips, significantly more than the value of the actual goods bought and sold in a day. "That is a lot of water to be sloshing around in the engine room," Morita wrote.

Morita compared the situation of world capitalism to playing poker on a sinking ship, and concluded:

"It is a heady game, full of excitement, but wins and losses at the poker table don't obscure the frightening fact that the ship is sinking and no one realises it."

Since Morita wrote these lines, the situation has got worse. The gigantic world market in "derivatives" has now reached the staggering total of US$ 25 trillion and is completely out of control. This amounts to gambling on a colossal scale. It makes the South Sea Bubble look like a mere trifle. This shows the fundamental unsoundness of world capitalism, which could end up in a new 1929-style financial crash.

Contradictions remain

In 1848, Marx and Engels predicted that capitalism would develop as a world system. This has been borne out in almost laboratory fashion in the 20th century. The crushing domination of the world market is the most important fact of the epoch. We have a world economy, world politics, world diplomacy, world culture, world wars—there have been two of those in the past hundred years, and the second came close to extinguishing the light of human civilisation. Yet the globalisation of the economy does not mean a lessening of the problems, but, on the contrary, an enormous intensification of the contradictions.

In the last decade of the 20th century, despite all the wonders of modern science, two thirds of humanity lives on the border line of barbarism. Common diseases such as diarrhoea and measles kill seven million children a year. Yet this can be prevented by a cheap and simple vaccination. 500,000 women die each year from complications during pregnancy, and perhaps another 200,000 die from abortions. The ex-colonial countries spent only 4 per cent of their GDP on health—an average of $41 a head, compare with $1900 in the advanced capitalist countries.

According to United Nations reports, more than six billion people will inhabit the earth by the year 2,000. About half of them will be under the age of 20. Yet most suffer from unemployment, lack of basic education and health care, overcrowding and bad living conditions. An estimated 100 million children aged 6 to 11 are not in school. Two-thirds are girls. Incidentally, even in the USA, UNICEF estimates that

20 per cent of children live below the national poverty line. However, the situation in Third World countries has reached a horrific level. As many as a 100 million children live on the streets. In Brazil, this problem is being "solved" by a campaign by the police and murder squads to exterminate children for the crime of being poor. Similar atrocities are being carried out against homeless people in Colombia. Not long ago it was discovered that a large number of men, women and children living on the street had been murdered and their bodies sold to the University of Bogota for dissection by medical students. Such stories fill all civilised people with horror. But it is only the most extreme expression of the morality of a society that treats human beings as mere commodities.

One million children have been killed, four million seriously injured, and five million have become refugees or orphaned as a result of wars in the past decade. In many ex-colonial countries, we have the phenomenon of child labour, often amounting to slavery. The hypocritical protests in the Western media do not prevent the products of this labour from reaching Western markets and increasing the capital of "respectable" western companies. A typical example was the recently published case of a match factory where children, mostly girls, work a 6 day-60 hour-week, with toxic chemicals, for three dollars. A letter to *The Economist* of the 15th September 1993 pointed out that: "Parents do realise the value of education for the future of their children but often their poverty is so desperate that they cannot do without the wages of their labouring children."

The main reason for the grinding poverty of the third world is the two-fold looting of the resources through the terms of trade, and the trillion dollars debt owed by the third world to the big western banks. Just to pay the interest on the debt, these countries have to export food needed by their own people and sacrifice the health and education of the people. According to UNICEF, debt repayments have caused incomes in the third world to fall by a quarter, health expenditure by 50 per cent and educational expenditure by 25 per cent. Despite the hypocritical outcry against the destruction of the Amazonian rainforest, Brazilian economists have proved that this is mainly motivated by the need to raised cash for agricultural exports, such as beef, raised on reclaimed land. The financing for such export projects comes from the World Bank and other international financial organisations.

In a very literal sense of the word, humanity stands at the crossroads. On the one hand, all the potential exists to build a paradise in this world. On the other, the elements of barbarism threaten to engulf the entire planet. In addition to everything else, we have the threat to the environment. In their frantic search after profit, the big multinationals are destroying the planet. The tropical rain forest is being devastated at a rate of 29,000 square miles a year. That is an area the size of Scotland. People may speculate on what caused the extinction of the dinosaurs 65 million years ago. But there is no doubt about what is the cause of the present catastrophe—the uncontrolled pursuit of profit and the anarchy of capitalist production.

Even scientists who have nothing in common with socialism have been driven to the conclusion (perfectly logical, if one thinks for a moment) that the only solution is some kind of world planned economy. However, this is not possible on the basis of capitalism. Forty-one nations formally endorsed the "World Conservation Strategy". But, in the absence of a world socialist federation, this is mainly an exercise on paper. The interests of the big monopolies decide.

Yet there is no inevitability about this. All the dire predictions about the hopeless plight of humanity, starting with Malthus, have been shown to be false. The potential for human development is limitless. The capacity exists even now to eliminate hunger from the face of the earth. In Western Europe and the United States, agricultural productivity has reached such heights that farmers are paid not to produce food. Good land is taken out of commission. Wheat is thrown into the sea, or mixed with dye to make it inedible. There are mountains of beef, butter and powdered milk. Spanish olive trees are deliberately uprooted. And there are 450 million people in the world who are malnourished, or actually starving.

By early next century, the Pacific Rim countries will probably account for half of world output. The world economy will have come into its own. For centuries, Europeans have regarded themselves as the centre of the globe. Objectively speaking, this has no more basis than the idea of Ptolemy that the earth stood at the centre of the universe. Already in the 1920s Trotsky predicted that the centre of gravity of world history would pass from the Atlantic to the Pacific. The next stage of human history will see the multi-millioned masses of Asia realise their full potential, as part of a Socialist World Federation.

The scourge of unemployment

Work is our main life's activity. From the earliest age, we prepare for it. Our schooling is geared to it. We spend all our active life involved in it. Work is the basis upon which society rests. Without it, there would be no food, no clothing, no shelter, no schools, no culture, no art and no science. In a very real sense, work is life. To deny a person the right to work is not just to deny him or her the right to a minimum standard of living. It is to deprive a person of human dignity, to cut them off from civilised society, to render their lives futile and meaningless. Unemployment is a crime against humanity. The creation of a kind of under-class in the inner cities of the United States and other countries is a condemnation of modern society. The following quotations reveal the fears of the most conscious strategists of capital about the tendency towards social disintegration in the West:

"The concentration of growing populations of disgruntled and impoverished people in cities dependent upon vulnerable infrastructure is fraught with dangers. Not the least of these is a strong likelihood that the social solidarity that underlies the welfare state will be broken apart in the years to come. The steadily escalating costs of supporting dependent populations will try the patience of the more successful in an economic downturn...But that is the problem for the next century."

"The welfare state has made failure pay in evolutionary terms. Underclass women give birth to 60 per cent more children than middle-class women—black or white. But even this statistic underestimates the impact on the population. Underclass women not only have more children, they also give birth at a younger age, leading to a geometric rise in the underclass population over time."

Rees-Mogg, who comforts himself with the delusion that "Marxism is dead", gives voice to the politics of open reaction, which vividly recalls the pronouncements of Victorian Malthusians a hundred years ago:

"They [the poor] are abetted in the wasting of their lives by the perverse incentives of entitlement programmes that impose effective tax rates of 100 per cent or more on those who shun welfare to take a job. In many cases, the total value of food stamps, rent subsidies, welfare payments, income supplements, and free medical care and other services exceeds the after-tax income that can be earned in unskilled work. And welfare entitlements, by definition, can be realised with little or no daily effort. You don't have to rise in the morning and rush through a crowd of commuters to secure your livelihood... Lax law enforcement also makes illiteracy, idleness, and illegitimacy more attractive. Children who can make one hundred dollars per hour as thieves or drug dealers are less likely to be impressed with the rigours of learning to read or keeping a minimum-wage job that may pay off in a better life only in the future." [43]

On the other side of the Atlantic, the same feeling of foreboding is spreading among the strategists of capital. The well-known American author and economist, John Kenneth Galbraith, unlike Rees-Mogg, is a liberal in politics, but has come to similar conclusions. In his latest book *The Culture of Contentment*, he issues a stark warning of explosive social conflict arising out of class divisions in American society:

"Yet the possibility of an underclass revolt, deeply disturbing to contentment, exists and grows stronger. There have been outbreaks in the past, notably the major inner city riots in the latter 1960s, and there are several factors that might lead to a repetition.

"In particular, it has been made clear, tranquillity has depended on the comparison with previous discomfort. With time, that comparison fades, and also with time the past promise of escape from relative privation—of upward movement—diminishes. This especially could be the consequence of a slowing or shrinking economy and even more of a prolonged recession or depression. The successive waves of workers who served the Detroit auto factories and body shops—the refugees from the adjacent farmlands of Michigan and Ontario and later the poor whites from Appalachia—went up and on. Many of those who came from the South to replace them are now stalled in endemic unemployment. No one should be surprised if this

---

(43) W. Rees-Mogg and J. Davidson, op. cit., pp. 294-5, 183 and 273.

should, someday, breed a violent reaction. It has always been one of the high tenets of comfort that the uncomfortable accept peacefully, even gladly, their fate. Such a belief today may be suddenly and surprisingly disproved." [44]

Alienation

"The world is not a collection of isolated individuals; all are somehow connected one with another." (Aristotle)

"No man is an Iland, intire of itselfe; every man is a peece of the Continent, a part of the maine; if a Clod bee washed away by the sea, Europe is the lesse, as well as if a Promontorie were, as well as if a Mannor of thy friends or thine own were; any man's death diminishes me, because I am involved in Mankind; and therefore never send to know for whom the bell tolls; it tolls for thee." (John Donne, *Devotions upon Emergent Occasions*, no. xvii.)

Human beings became human by separating themselves from their purely animal, that is to say, unconscious, nature. Even the most complex animals cannot match the accomplishments of humankind, which enable it to survive and prosper in the most varied conditions and climates, under the sea, in the skies, and even in space. Human beings have so far raised themselves above their "natural", that is, zoological state, that they have mastered their environment to an unparalleled degree. Yet, paradoxically, humans are still controlled by blind forces beyond their control. The so-called market economy is based upon the premise that people do not control their lives and destinies, but are puppets in the hands of invisible forces, which, like the capricious and insatiable gods of old, rule everything with neither rhyme nor reason. These gods have their high priests, who dedicate their lives to their service. They inhabit the banks and stock exchanges, with their elaborate rituals, and make fat profits out of it. But when the gods get angry, the priests panic, like a herd of frightened beasts, and just as unconscious.

The ancient Romans described a slave as "a tool with a voice" (*instrumentum vocale*). Nowadays, many workers might feel that this description could equally apply to them. We are supposed to live in a post-modern, post-industrial, post-Fordist world. But, as far as the conditions of working people are concerned, what has changed? Everywhere, the gains of the past are under attack. In the West living standards, for the majority of people, are being squeezed. The welfare state is being undermined, and full employment is a thing of the past.

In all countries, society is afflicted with a deep sense of malaise. This starts on the top and percolates down to every level. The feeling of insecurity bred by permanent mass unemployment has spread to sections of the workforce who previously believed themselves immune—teachers, doctors, nurses, civil servants, factory

(44) J. K. Galbraith, *The Culture of Contentment*, pp. 170-1.

managers—nobody is safe. The savings of the middle class, the value of their houses, are likewise threatened by the uncontrolled movements of the money markets and the stock exchange. The lives of billions of human beings are at the mercy of blind forces, which operate with a caprice that makes the gods of old seem rational by comparison.

Decades ago, it was confidently predicted that the forward march of science and technology would solve all the problems of humanity. In the future, men and women would no longer be concerned with the class struggle, but with the problem of leisure. These predictions were not at all unreasonable. From a strictly scientific point of view, there is no reason why we should not be in a position to bring about a general reduction in the hours of labour, while simultaneously increasing output and living standards, on the basis of the improved productivity gained from the application of new technology. But the real situation is very different.

Marx explained long ago that, under capitalism, the introduction of machinery, far from reducing the working day, tends to lengthen it. In all the main capitalist countries, we see a merciless pressure on workers to work longer hours for less pay. In its issue of October 24, 1994, *Time* reported a sharp up-turn in the American economy, with booming profits: "But workers complain that for them expansion spells exhaustion. Throughout American industry, companies are using overtime to wring the most out of the US labour force: the factory workweek currently is averaging a near record 42 hours, including 4.6 hours of overtime. 'Americans', observes Audrey Freedman, a labour economist and member of *Time*'s board, 'are the workingest people in the world.' The big-three automakers have pushed this trend to an extreme. Their workers are putting in an average of 10 hours overtime a week and labouring an average of six eight-hour Saturdays a year."

The same article quotes numerous examples of both blue-collar and white-collar workers from many different industries, who complain of chronic overwork:

"'I'm doing the work of three people,' says Joseph Kelterborn, 44, who works for the Nynex telephone company in New York City. His department, which installs and maintains fiber-optic networks, has been reduced from 27 people to 20 in recent years, in part by combining what were once three separate positions—switchman, powerman and tester—into his job of carrier switchman. As a result, says Kelterborn, he often works up to four extra hours a day and one weekend in three. 'By the time I get home,' he complains, 'all I have time for is a shower, dinner and a little sleep; then it's time to turn around and do it all over again'."

As Marx pointed out, increased use of machinery under capitalism means longer hours of toil for those who still have a job. Since the recovery from the previous recession began in March 1991, the US economy has created almost six million new jobs, but in such a way that leaves it two million jobs short. If US companies had hired workers at the same rate as in past expansions, the increase in jobs would have been eight million or more.

The *Time* article adds: "There is much evidence, in fact, that the US is developing something of a two-tiered society. While corporate profits and executive salaries are rising rapidly, real wages (that is, discounted for inflation) are not growing at all. Indeed, the government has reported that last year real median household income in the US fell by $312, while a million more people slipped into poverty; those officially defined as poor were 15.1 per cent of the US population vs. 14.8 per cent in 1992. Those were astonishing developments for the fourth year of a business recovery that is steadily gaining strength."

In *The Communist Manifesto*, Marx and Engels pointed out that "owing to the extensive use of machinery and to division of labour, the work of the proletarians has lost all individual character, and, consequently, all charm for the workman. He becomes an appendage of the machine, and it is only the most simple, most monotonous, and most easily acquired knack, that is required of him. Hence, the cost of production of a workman is restricted, almost entirely, to the means of subsistence that he requires for his maintenance, and for the propagation of his race. But the price of a commodity, and therefore also of labour, is equal to its cost of production. In proportion, therefore, as the repulsiveness of the work increases, the wage decreases. Nay more, in proportion as the use of machinery and division of labour increases, in the same proportion the burden of toil also increases, whether by prolongation of the working hours, by increase of the work exacted in a given time or by increased speed of the machinery, etc." [45]

In one of Charles Chaplin's most famous films *Modern Times*, we have a graphic picture of life on the assembly line of a big plant in the 1930s. The mindless drudgery of an endless repetition of the same monotonous tasks indeed changes a human being into an appendage of the machine, a "tool with a voice". Despite all the fancy talk about "participation", conditions in most factories remain much the same. Indeed, the pressure on workers has been steadily stepped up in recent years. The little things that made life a bit more bearable are being ruthlessly whittled away. In Britain, where the strength of the unions achieved notable advances in the past, the lunch-hour has largely passed into history. Chancellor Kohl informs the German workers that they must begin to work weekends. It is the same picture everywhere.

Instead of new technology improving the lot of the worker in industry, it has been used to worsen the conditions of the white-collar worker. In most banks, hospitals and large offices, the position of the employees is more and more similar to that which exists in big factories. The same insecurity, the same relentless pressure on the nervous system, the same stress, leading to medical problems, depression, the break-up of marriages.

In recent years scientists have returned to the idea of a "man-machine", in relation to the field of robotics and the question of artificial intelligence. It has even

(45) MESW, Vol. 1, pp. 114-5.

penetrated the popular imagination, as witnessed by a spate of films of the *Terminator* type, where human beings are pitted against ingeniously constructed automata. This latter phenomenon tells us quite a lot about the psychology of the present period, characterised by the general dehumanising of society, mixed with a sensation that human beings are not in charge of their own destiny, and fear of uncontrollable forces that dominate people's lives. By contrast, the attempt to create artificial intelligence represents a further advance of the science of robotics, which, in a genuinely rational society, opens up a truly marvellous vista of human advancement.

The substitution of human toil by advanced machinery is the key to the greatest cultural revolution in history, on the basis of a generalised reduction in the hours of work. Nevertheless, there can be no question of ever exactly reproducing human thought in a machine, although specific operations can be done more efficiently by them. This is not for any mystical reasons, or because of an "immortal soul" which allegedly makes us a unique product of Creation, but because of the nature of thought itself, which cannot be separated from all the other bodily activities of human beings, beginning with labour.

Marx and alienation

Even for those fortunate enough to have a job, nine times out of ten, work is meaningless drudgery. The hours of labour are not thought of as part of one's life. They are nothing to do with you as a human being. The product of your labour belongs to someone else, for whom you are just a "factor of production". Life begins the moment you step outside the workplace, and ceases the moment you re-enter it. This phenomenon was well explained by Marx in his *Economic and Philosophic Manuscripts of 1844*:

"What, then, constitutes the alienation of labour?

"First, the fact that labour is external to the worker, i.e., it does not belong to his intrinsic nature; that in his work, therefore, he does not affirm himself but denies himself, does not feel content but unhappy, does not develop freely his physical and mental energy but mortifies his body and ruins his mind. The worker therefore only feels himself outside his work, and in his work feels outside himself. He feels at home when he is not working, and when he is working he does not feel at home. His labour is therefore not voluntary, but coerced; it is *forced labour*. It is merely a *means* to satisfy needs external to it. Its alien character emerges clearly in the fact that as soon as no physical or other compulsion exists, labour is shunned like the plague.

"External labour, labour in which man alienates himself, is a labour of self-sacrifice, of mortification. Lastly, the external character of labour for the worker appears in the fact that it is not his own, but someone else's, that it does not belong to him, that in it he belongs, not to himself, but to another. Just as in religion the spontaneous activity of the human imagination, of the human brain and the human heart, operates on the individual independently of him—that is, operates as an alien, divine or diabolical activity—so is the worker's activity not his spontaneous activity. It belongs to another; it is the loss of his self." [46]

Thus, for the great majority, life is mainly taken up in an activity which has very little meaning for the individual; at best, it is tolerable; at worse, a living torment. Even those who take a job like teaching children or nursing sick people are finding that the satisfaction they get is being taken away, as the laws of the market-place force their way into the classroom and the hospital ward.

The feeling that society has reached an impasse is not confined to the "lower orders". In the ruling class also there is an increasing feeling of malaise and pessimism with regard to the future. One looks in vain for the great ideas of the past, the confidence, the optimism. The constant bragging about the supposed wonders of the "free market economy" have an increasingly empty ring about them, as people begin to take stock of the real situation—the millions of unemployed, the attacks on living standards, the fabulous fortunes made through speculation, greed, and corruption.

It is ironical that the defenders of the existing order accuse Marxism of "materialism", when the bourgeois themselves practise the most gross and vulgar kind of materialism, in the dictionary, not the philosophical, sense of the word. The mindless pursuit of wealth, the elevation of greed as the dominant principle of all things, is at the centre of their whole culture. It is their real religion. In the past, they took care to conceal this from view as much as possible, hiding behind a screen of hypocritical moralising about duty, patriotism, honest toil, and all the rest. Now it is all out in the open. In every country, we see an unprecedented epidemic of corruption, swindling, lying, cheating, theft—not the petty theft of ordinary criminals, but looting on a massive scale, perpetrated by businessmen, politicians, police chiefs and judges. And why not? Is it not our duty to get rich?

The creed of monetarism elevates egotism and greed to a principle. Grab as much as you can, however you can, and may the devil take the hindmost! This is the distilled essence of capitalism. The law of the jungle, translated into the language of voodoo economics. At least it has the merit of simplicity. It says bluntly and clearly what the capitalist system is all about.

Yet what an empty philosophy! What a miserable conception of human life! Though they do not know it, the lords of the planet are themselves mere slaves, blind servants of forces they do not control. They have no more real command of the system than ants in an anthill. The point is that they are quite satisfied with this state of affairs, which gives them position, power and wealth. And they grimly resist all attempts to carry out a radical change in society.

(46) MECW, Vol. 3, p. 274.

If there is a single thread running through human history, it is the struggle of men and women to gain control over their lives, to become free in the true sense of the word. All the advances of science and technique, all that humans have learned about nature and ourselves, means that the potential now exists to gain full mastery over the conditions in which we live. Yet, in the last decade of the 20th century, the world seems to be in the grip of a strange madness. Human beings feel even less in control of their destinies than before. The economy, the environment, the air we breathe, the water we drink, the food we eat—all seems to be under threat. Gone is the old sense of security. Gone is the feeling that history represents an uninterrupted march towards something better than the present.

Under these circumstances, sections of society look for a way out in such things as drugs and alcohol. When society is no longer rational, men and women turn to the irrational for solace. Religion is, as Marx said, an opium, and its effects are no less harmful than other drugs. We have seen how religious and mystical ideas have penetrated even the world of science. This is a reflection of the nature of the period through which we are passing.

Morality

> "Seek to strengthen your moral commitments and religious faith. Reread the *Ten Commandments* and the *Book of Ecclesiastes*. A Bible is not a bad teacher of history and a guide to survival in hard times." (Rees-Mogg)

> "Whoever does not care to return to Moses, Christ or Mohammed; whoever is not satisfied with eclectic *hodgepodges* must acknowledge that morality is a product of social development; that there is nothing immutable about it; that it serves social interests; that these interests are contradictory; that morality more than any other form of ideology has a class character." (Trotsky)

"Marxism denies morality!" How often have we heard expressions of this type, which merely reveal ignorance of the ABCs of Marxism. True, Marxism denies the existence of a supra-historical morality. But it does not require much effort to show that the moral codes that have regulated human conduct have varied substantially from one historical period to another. At one time, it was not considered immoral to eat prisoners of war. Later on, cannibalism was regarded with abhorrence, but prisoners of war could be turned into slaves. Even the great Aristotle was prepared to justify slavery, on the grounds that slaves did not possess souls and therefore were not fully human (the same argument was used in relation to women). Still later, it was considered morally wrong for one person to own another as a piece of property, but perfectly acceptable for feudal lords to have serfs who were chained to the land and entirely subject to the master, to the point of giving up his bride to the lord on her wedding night.

Nowadays, all these things are regarded as barbarous and immoral, but the institution of *wage-labour*, where a human being sells himself piecemeal to an employer, who uses his labour-power as he pleases, is never called into question. This is, after all, free labour. Unlike the serf and the slave, the worker and employer arrive at an agreement of their own free will. Nobody obliges the worker to work for a particular boss. If he does not like it, he may leave and seek employment elsewhere. Moreover, in a free market economy, the law is the same for everyone. The French writer Anatole France wrote about the "majestic egalitarianism of the law, which forbids rich and poor alike to sleep under bridges, to beg in the streets, and to steal bread."

In modern society, in place of the old open forms of exploitation, we have disguised, hypocritical exploitation, in which the real relation between men and women is translated into a relation between things—little bits of paper which give their owners the power of life and death; which can make what is ugly beautiful; what is weak, strong; what is stupid, intelligent; what is old, young.

Trotsky wrote that money relations have sunk so deep into people's minds that we refer to a man as being "worth" so many million dollars. It is a measure of the degree of alienation that exists in present-day society that such expressions are taken for granted. Nor is anyone surprised when, during, a monetary crisis, the television talks about the currency as if it were a person recovering from an illness ("The pound/dollar/Deutschmark was a little stronger today..."). Human beings are regarded as things, while objects, especially money, are regarded with superstitious awe, recalling the religious attitudes of savages to their totems and fetishes. The reason for this *fetishism of commodities* was explained by Marx in the first volume of *Capital*.

The search for an absolute morality proves to be completely futile. Here again, the immutable laws of logic can offer us no help. Formal logic basis itself on a fixed antithesis between truth and falsehood. An idea is either right or wrong. Yet truth, as the German poet Lessing pointed out, is not like a stamped coin that is issued ready from the mint and can be used under all circumstances. What is true at one time and under one set of circumstances becomes false in another. The same is the case with concepts like "good" and "evil". What is "good" and praiseworthy in one society is abhorrent in another. Moreover, even within a given society, the concept of what is good and bad frequently changes, according to circumstances, and to the interests of a particular class.

If we exclude incest, which appears to have been taboo in virtually all societies, there are very few moral injunctions that can be shown to have been eternal and absolute. "Thou shalt not steal" does not make much sense in a society not based on private property. "Thou shalt not commit adultery" only has meaning for a male-dominated society, where men wished to be sure that private property was handed down to their own sons. "Thou shalt not kill" has always been surrounded by so many qualifications that it immediately becomes transformed into something quite different, or even its opposite; for example, thou shalt not kill, except in self-defence; or, thou shalt not kill, unless it is somebody from another tribe/nation/religion, and so on.

In every war, the armies of the nation are blessed by the priests as they go out to slaughter the armies of other nations. The *absolute* moral injunction not to kill suddenly turns out to be relative to other considerations, which, on closer examination, are found to be related to the economic, territorial, political, or strategic interests of the states involved in the fighting. The hypocrisy of all this was well expressed in a little verse by the great Scottish poet Robert Burns *On Thanksgiving For a National Victory*:

"Ye hypocrites! are these your pranks?
To murder men, and give God thanks?
Desist for shame! Proceed no further:
God won't accept your thanks for Murther."

War is a fact of life (and death). There have been many wars throughout human history. The fact may be deplored, but not denied. Moreover, all the most important issues between nations have ultimately been settled by war. Pacifism has never been a fashionable doctrine with governments, except as the small change of diplomacy, the exclusive aim of which is to deceive everyone concerning the real intentions of the government it represents. Lying is the stock-in-trade of diplomats. It is what they are paid for. "Thou shalt not bear false witness" simply does not come into it. An army commander who did not do everything in his power to deceive the enemy about his intentions would be considered a fool or worse. Here, however, a lie becomes something praiseworthy—*a military ruse*. A general who told the truth about his plans to the enemy would be shot as a traitor. A worker who revealed details of a strike to the employer would be regarded in the same way by his or her workmates.

From these few examples, it is clear that morality is not a supra-historical abstraction, but a something that has evolved historically, and undergone considerable changes. In the Middle Ages, the Roman Catholic Church condemned usury as a deadly sin. Nowadays, the Vatican has a bank of its own, and raises very large sums of money by lending at interest. In other words, morality has a class basis. It reflects the values, interests and outlook of the dominant social class. Of course, it cannot succeed in maintaining the necessary degree of social cohesion if it is not accepted by the great majority of citizens. Hence, it must appear to consist of absolute and unquestionable truths, the violation of which must bring the whole social edifice crashing down.

There are few sights more repulsive than the sight of well-to-do ladies and gentlemen lecturing the public on the need for morality, religion, family planning and thrift. The same individuals, whose selfish greed is manifested every day in huge salary increases for boardroom directors, lecture workers on the need for sacrifice. The same speculators, who do not hesitate to plunge the currency of their own country into chaos in order to increase their already swollen bank balances, lecture us on the need for patriotic values. The same banks, multinationals and governments that have been responsible for the merciless squeezing of millions in Africa, Asia and Latin America throw up their hands in horror whenever the workers and peasants take up arms to fight for their rights. They lecture the world on the need for peace. But the stocks of murderous weaponry upon which they continue to lavish fabulous sums show that their pacifism is also quite relative. Violence is only a crime when it is resorted to by the poor and oppressed. The whole of history shows that the ruling class will always defend its power and privileges by the most brutal means, if necessary.

Family, Order, Private Property and Religion have always been inscribed on the banners of conservative defenders of the status quo. Yet of these supposedly inviolate institutions, only one, private property, is of real interest to the ruling class. Religion is, as Rees-Mogg bluntly points out, a necessary weapon to keep the poor in order. Most of the upper class do not believe a word of it, and go to Church, much the same as they go to the opera, in order to show off the latest fashion. Their understanding of theology is as scanty as their appreciation of Wagner's *Ring* cycle. In their private life, the bourgeois show scant consideration for the "eternal laws of morality". The epidemic of scandals, which have rocked the political establishment in Italy, France, Spain, Britain, Belgium, Japan and the United States, is just the tip of the iceberg. Yet they prate endlessly on about "eternal moral truths" and are surprised when they are greeted with a resounding guffaw.

Does this mean that morality does not exist? Or that Marxists do not have a morality? Far from it. Morality exists, and plays a necessary role in society. Every society has an ethical code, which serves as a powerful bond, to the degree that it is recognised and respected by the great majority. Ultimately, existing morality and the legal code which seeks to put it into practice is backed by the full force of the state, reflecting the interests of the ruling class or caste, although it does so in a disguised way. While the existing socioeconomic order carries society forward, the values, ideas and outlook of the ruling stratum are accepted without question by the great majority. The class basis of morality was explained by Trotsky:

"The ruling class forces its end upon society and habituates it into considering all those means which contradict its ends as immoral. That is the chief function of official morality. It pursues the idea of the 'greatest possible happiness' not for the majority but for a small and ever-diminishing minority. Such a regime could not have endured for even a week through force alone. It needs the cement of morality." [47]

(47) Trotsky, *Their Morals and Ours*, p. 13.

Those few individuals who dare to question it are branded as heretics and persecuted. They are regarded as "immoral" people—not because they do not possess a moral standpoint, but because they do not conform to the *existing* morality. Socrates was declared to be a harmful influence on the Athenian youth, before being made to drink hemlock. The early Christians were accused of all manner of immoral acts by the slave state that persecuted them mercilessly before it decided it would be better to recognise the new faith, in order to corrupt the leaders of the Church. Martin Luther was denounced as an evil man, when he opened up an attack on the corruption of the mediaeval Church.

The crime of Marxists is to point out that capitalist society has entered into conflict with the needs of social development; that it has become an intolerable obstacle to human progress; that it is shot through with contradictions; that it is economically, politically, culturally and morally bankrupt; and that the further survival of this sick system puts the future of the planet in grave danger. From the standpoint of those who own and control the wealth of society, these ideas are "bad". From the standpoint of what is needed to find a way out of the impasse, they are correct, necessary, and good.

The long drawn-out crisis of capitalism is having a most negative effect on morality and culture. Everywhere, the symptoms of social disintegration are palpable. The bourgeois family is breaking down, but, in the absence of anything to put in its place, this is leading to a nightmare of poverty and degradation for millions of needy families. The decaying inner cities of the United States and Europe, with their huge pools of unemployment and deprivation, are a spawning-ground for drug abuse, crime, and every kind of nightmare.

In capitalist society, people are regarded as dispensable commodities. Goods which cannot be sold lie idle until they rot. Why should human beings be any different? Only it is not so simple with people. They cannot be allowed to starve to death in large numbers, for fear of the social consequences. So, in the ultimate contradiction of capitalism, the bourgeois is obliged to feed the unemployed, instead of being fed by them. A truly insane situation, where men and women wish to work, to add to the wealth of society, and are prevented from doing so by the "laws of the market".

This is an inhuman society, where people are subordinated to things. Is it any wonder that some of these people behave in an inhuman manner? Every day the tabloid press is full of horror stories about the terrible abuses committed against the weakest, most defenceless sections of the community—women, children, old people. This is an accurate barometer of the moral state of society. The law sometimes punishes these offences, although in general crimes against (big) property are more energetically pursued by the police than crimes against the person. But in any case, the profound social roots of crimes are outside the powers of courts and police. Unemployment breeds crimes of all sorts. But there are other, more subtle factors.

The culture of egotism, greed and indifference to the sufferings of others has flourished, particularly since de 1980s, when it was given the stamp of approval by Thatcher and Reagan, and has undoubtedly played a role, though it is not so easy to quantify. This is the real face of capitalism, more accurately of monopoly and finance capital—ruthless, crude, grasping and cruel. This is capitalism in its period of senile decay, attempting to recover the vigour of its youth. It is parasitic capitalism, with a marked preference for the fleshpots of financial and monetary speculation, instead of the production of real wealth. It prefers "services" to industry. It closes factories like matchboxes, ruthlessly destroying whole communities and industries, and recommends miners and steelworkers to find work in hamburger bars. It is the 20th century equivalent of "Let them eat cake".

Quite apart from the monstrous social and economic consequences of this doctrine, it spreads a deadly moral poison through the fabric of society. People with no prospect of even finding a job are confronted with the spectacle of the "consumer society", where getting and spending money are presented as the only worthwhile activity in life. The role models of this society are the pushy parvenus, the get-rich-quick mob, prepared to go to any lengths to "get on". This is the true face of "free enterprise", of monetarist reaction—it is the face of an unprincipled adventurer, a crook and a swindler, a shallow ignoramus, a bully in an expensive suit, the personification of greed and selfishness. These are the people who applaud the closure of schools and hospitals, the cutting of pensions and other "unprofitable" items of expenditure, while they make fortunes by lifting a phone, without ever producing anything of use for the benefit of society.

It is often asserted that people "naturally" act according to their interests. This is then interpreted in a narrow way, as personal egotism. Such an interpretation suits the defenders of the present socioeconomic system, in which greed and the pursuit of self-interest are held up as great moral principles, equivalent to the exercise of "personal freedom". If this had been the case, human society could never have developed. The word "interest" itself comes from the Latin "inter-esse" which means "to take part in". The whole basis of the intellectual and moral evolution of the child is the movement away from "egotism" and towards a greater sense of the needs and requirements of others. Human society is based on the necessity of social production, co-operation and communication.

It is the impasse of capitalism which threatens to push human culture back to a childish level, in the worst sense of the word—the childishness of senile decay. An atomised, self-centred society without a vision, without a morality, without a philosophy, without a soul, a society "sans teeth, sans eyes, sans taste, sans everything."

Limitless possibilities

Every social system imagines itself to be the last word in historical development. All previous history was supposed to be only a preparation for this particular mode of production, and all the legal property forms, moral code, religion and philosophy that accompany it. Yet any system of society only exists to the degree that it shows it is capable of satisfying the needs of the population, and giving people hope for the future. The moment it fails to do this, it enters into an irreversible process of decline, not only economically, but morally, culturally, and in every respect. Such a society is dead, even though its defenders will never admit it.

At the beginning of the new milenium, there is a palpable and all-pervasive feeling of weariness and exhaustion in capitalist society. It is as if a whole way of life has become old and decrepit. This is not just what writers refer to as the *mal du siecle*. It is a vague realisation that the "market economy" has reached its limits. Yet, though a given form of society has outlived itself, this does not mean that the development of humankind is similarly limited. Not only has history not ended—it has not even begun. If we envisage history as a calendar in which 1st January represents the origin of the earth and 31st December represents the present day, taking a round figure of 5,000 million years as the age of the earth, each second will represent about 167 years, each minute 10,000 years. The Lower Cambrian would then begin on 18 November. Man would appear at about 11.50 pm on 31st December. The whole of recorded human history would fall within the final forty seconds before midnight.

Ilya Prigogine has wisely remarked that "Scientific understanding of the world around us is just beginning." Human civilisation, which seems to us to be very old, is actually very young. In fact, real civilisation, in the sense of a society where humans consciously control their own lives, and are able to live a truly human existence, as opposed to the animal struggle for survival, has not yet commenced. What is true is that a particular form of society has become old and exhausted. It clings to life, though it has no longer anything to offer. Pessimism about the future, mingled with superstition and unfounded hopes for salvation, are entirely characteristic of such a period.

In 1972, the Club of Rome published a gloomy report entitled *The Limits of Growth*, which predicted that the world's supply of fossil fuels would run out in a few decades. This provoked panic, soaring oil prices and a frantic search for alternative sources of energy. More than twenty years later, there is no shortage of oil or gas, and few now bother to look for alternatives. This shortsightedness is a characteristic of capitalism, which is motivated by the search for short-term profits. Everyone knows that sooner or later the supply of fossil fuels will dry up. A long-term plan is absolutely necessary to find a cheap, clean alternative.

Nature provides a literally limitless supply of potential energy—the sun, the wind, the sea, and, above all, matter itself, which contains vast quantities of untapped energy. Nuclear fusion (unlike nuclear fission) provides a potential for limitless amounts of cheap, clean energy. But the development of alternative fuels is not in the interests of the big oil monopolies. Here again, private ownership of the means of production acts as a gigantic barrier in the path of human development. The future of the planet comes a poor second to the cause of the enrichment of a few.

The solution to the pressing problems of the world can only be found in a socioeconomic system which is under the conscious control of people. The problem is not that there is an inherent limit to development. The problem is an out-dated and anarchic system of production which squanders lives and resources, destroys the environment, and prevents the potential of science and technology being developed to the full. "There is no necessary connection between great science and great business opportunities," one commentator wrote recently, "the general theory of relativity has yet to be turned into a money-spinner." (*The Economist*, 25th February 1995.)

Yet even at the present time, the possibilities implicit in technology are breathtaking. Technological innovations open the door to a genuine cultural revolution. Interactive television is already a feasible proposition. The possibility of actively participating in the elaboration of television programmes has tremendous potential, far more than merely deciding what programmes you want to watch. It opens the door to democratic participation in the running of society and the economy in a way that could only have been dreamed of in the past.

The birth of capitalism was characterised by the breakdown of the old parochial relations, and the birth of the nation states. Now the growth of the productive forces, science and technique, have made the nation state itself redundant. As Marx predicted, even the biggest nation state is compelled to participate on the world market. The old national one-sidedness has become impossible.

Back to the future?

Early humans were closely bound to nature. This bond was gradually broken with the development of urban life, and the division between town and country, which has reached monstrous proportions under capitalism. The rupture between human beings and nature has created an unnatural world of alienation. A further manifestation of this is the complete divorce between mental and manual labour, that unwholesome social apartheid which separates the modern priest-caste of knowledge from the "hewers of wood and drawers of water". It is not just the alienation of humans from nature. It is the alienation of humanity from itself. To break out of the condition of utter dependence on nature, to rise above the merely animal nature, to acquire consciousness—these are what define us as human. But this gain is also a loss, and one that is felt ever more keenly as time goes on. The process has gone so far that it has turned into its opposite. As cities become ever vaster, more overcrowded, more polluted, a nightmare is in the making. In the next few decades, Shanghai alone will have more inhabitants than Great Britain, on present trends. Bad housing, crime, drugs, and a general process of dehumanisation faces millions of people on the eve of the 21st century.

The suffocating one-sided, artificial nature of this "civilisation" becomes increasingly oppressive, even for those who do not suffer the worst conditions. The yearning for a simpler form of life, where men and women could live more natural lives, free from the intolerable pressures of competition and conflict expresses itself in a trend among a layer of young people to "drop out" of society, in an attempt to re-discover a lost paradise. There is a misunderstanding here. In the first place, the life of primitive people was not as idyllic as some imagine. The "noble savage" was always a fiction of Romantic writers, with very little in common with reality. Our early ancestors were close to nature, only because they were the slaves of nature.

However, there is another side to this. These "primitive" people lived quite happily without rent, interest and profit. Women were not regarded as private property, but occupied a highly respected position in the community. Money was unknown. So was the state, with its monstrous bureaucracy, and special bodies of armed men, soldiers, policemen, prison warders and judges. In primitive tribal communism, there was no state in the sense of an apparatus of coercion, but the elders had the respect of all, and their word was law. Later, the tribal chieftain ruled through the voluntary respect of the community. Coercion was not necessary, because all shared a common interest. This was the basis for a deep social bond of co-operation and unity. No modern ruler could ever know the respect enjoyed by the heads of the old gens, underwritten by a sense of mutual identity and duty, which was "codified" in oral tradition as tribal lore, known to all and universally accepted. This respect must have been similar to the feelings of a child for its parents.

In our supposedly enlightened age, many people, including those who like to think themselves educated, find it unthinkable that men and women could ever have got along without such necessary phenomena as money, policemen, prisons, armies, merchants, tax-collectors, judges and archbishops. And if they did manage to do so, it can only be explained in terms of the fact that, being "primitive", they had not yet come to realise the blessings that such institutions bestow upon humanity. Even some anthropologists, who do not have this mentality, are not immune from introducing into early human society entirely alien concepts, like prostitution, derived from the "civilised" world where everything is for sale, including people.

Anyone who has seen films of the life of tribes still living in stone-age conditions in the Amazon cannot fail to be impressed by their naturalness and spontaneity, resembling that of children, before it is crushed out of them by the rat-race of life under capitalism. In Matthew's Gospel, Jesus says: "Except ye be converted, and become as little children, ye shall not enter into the kingdom of heaven." (18:3) In the process of growing up, something important is lost, never to be regained. It is the Fall from innocence, which in the book of *Genesis* is identified with men and women gaining knowledge. Modern society can no more go back to primitive tribal communism than a grown man or woman can become a child again.

It is considered unnatural and unhealthy for an adult to wish to go back to childhood. The word "childish" is used as an insult, a synonym for incongruous ignorance. In any case, it is a futile wish, because it is impossible. But alongside ignorance, the child also displays other qualities—a spontaneous gaiety and naturalness, which is foreign to most adults. The same is true of "primitive" peoples, before the advent of class society, and the one-sided and stultifying division of labour twisted human nature inside out. What modern artist would be capable of producing paintings of such breathtaking immediacy and natural beauty as the work of the cave-artists of Lascaux and Altamira?

It is not a question of going back, but going forward. Not a return to primitive tribal communism, but forward to the future socialist world commonwealth. The negation of the negation brings us back to the starting-point of human development, but only in appearance. The socialism of the future will base itself on all the marvellous discoveries of the past, and place them at the disposal of humanity. To use the language of Hegel, it is a case of the "universal, filled with the wealth of the particular."

"A man cannot become a child again, or he becomes childish," writes Marx. "But does he not find joy in the child's naïveté, and must he himself not strive to reproduce its truth at a higher stage? Does not the true character of each epoch come alive in the nature of its children? Why should not the historic childhood of humanity, its most beautiful unfolding, as a stage never to return, exercise an eternal charm? There are unruly children and precocious children. Many of the old peoples belong in this category. The Greeks were normal children. The charm of their art for us is not in contradiction to the undeveloped stage of society on which it grew. [It] is its result, rather, and is inextricably bound up, rather, with the fact that the unripe social conditions under which it arose, and could alone arise, can never return." [48]

Socialism and aesthetics

In present day society, architecture is the poor relation of the arts. People are accustomed to living in ugly surroundings, in bad housing, in congested cities, surrounded by noise and pollution. At weekends, some of them go to art galleries, where, for a few hours, they can gaze upon paintings hanging on walls—islands of beauty in a sea of monotonous ugliness. Thus beauty is boxed off from life, an unattainable dream, a fiction, as remote from reality as the furthest galaxy from the earth. So remote has art become from life that many people regard it as a useless irrelevance. Hostility towards art, which is seen as the privileged preserve of the middle class, is a further consequence of the extreme division between mental and manual labour. Barbaric conditions breed barbaric attitudes.

(48) Marx, *Grundrisse*, p. 111.

It was not always so. In earlier human societies, music, epic poetry and fine speaking were the common property of all men and women. The monopoly of culture by a small minority is the product of class society, which deprives the great majority, not only of property, but of the right to a free development of their minds and personalities. Yet, if we delve a little beneath the surface, we find a great desire to learn, to experience new ideas, to seek broader horizons. The thirst of the masses for culture, deeply repressed under "normal" conditions, comes to the surface in any revolution.

The Russian Revolution of 1917, that allegedly barbarous act, was in fact the starting-point for a great upsurge in culture, poetry, art and music. This cannot be expunged because the blossom was later crushed under the jackboot of Stalinist reaction. In the Spanish revolution of 1931-37, there was a similar artistic renaissance—the poetry of Lorca, Machado, Alberti, and above all, Miguel Hernandez was inspired by the struggle, and in turn was listened to with rapt attention by audiences of millions who had never before had access to the marvellous world of art and culture.

In a revolution, ordinary men and women begin to see themselves as human beings, capable of controlling their own destinies, not mere "tools with voices". With true humanity comes dignity, a sense of self-respect and its necessary companion, respect for others. The waiters put up notices in the restaurants of Barcelona in 1936 saying: "Just because a man has to work here, it does not mean you have to insult him by offering a tip." This is the birth of culture—real human culture, which is part of life itself. The same phenomenon, in embryo, can be seen in every strike, where men and women reveal qualities they never dreamed they possessed. Of course, if the movement does not lead to a complete transformation of society, the dead weight of habit and routine once more predominates. Material conditions determine consciousness. But a socialist society based on a high level of technology and culture would completely transform the outlook of people.

It is often alleged by logicians and mathematicians that the kind of perfect symmetries that they admire possess an intrinsic aesthetic value. Some even go so far as to claim that the most important thing about equations is not whether they tell us anything about reality, but whether they are aesthetically pleasing. Whereas no-one will deny that symmetry can be beautiful, there is symmetry and symmetry. The harmonious buildings of classical Athens are considered by many to be one of the high points of the history of architecture. There is certainly a most satisfying symmetry here, and one that recalls the linear relations of Euclidean geometry. The importance of architecture in the Athens of Pericles is a graphic expression of the public-spirited outlook of Athenian democracy (based, of course on the labour of the slaves, who were totally excluded from it). The great buildings of the Acropolis and the Agora were, without exception, *public buildings*, not private residences. In our own day and age, such splendours are extremely rare. The low priority given to architecture in comparison to other arts is no accident.

In the name of "utility", which is a polite synonym for stinginess, people are forced to live in uniform high-rise concrete boxes, devoid of all artistic merit or human warmth. These monstrosities are designed by architects, inspired by strictly geometrical principles, who nevertheless prefer to live in quaint 15th century cottages in the countryside, far away from the urban nightmares they have helped to create. Yet human beings do not generally like living in boxes. And nature knows of symmetries very far removed from straight lines and simple circles.

It is the other side of the coin of the mechanised idiocy of the production line, where human beings, in the words of Marx, are treated as mere appendages of the machines. Why, then, should they not live, herded together on big estates in concrete boxes, which are built on similarly sound "industrial" principles? The same arid reductionism, the same empty formalism, the same linear approach has characterised architecture most of this century. Here the alienation of late capitalist society expresses itself in the soulless treatment of people's most basic need, for a clean, attractive, and genuinely human environment to live in. When life itself is stripped of all humanity, when it is made unnatural in a thousand different ways, how can we be surprised if some of the products of our so-called civilisation behave in an unnatural and inhuman way?

Here too, we are witnessing a revolt against soulless conformism and rigidity. The high-rise blocks and skyscrapers, aptly described by an English writer as the "topless towers of idiocy", are rapidly falling into disfavour. And no wonder. They are a monument to alienation on a massive scale, a progressive slide into dehumanised conditions of life, which breeds all kinds of monstrosities.

"Why is it," asked the German physicist Gert Eilenberger, "that the silhouette of a storm-bent leafless tree against an evening sky in winter is perceived as beautiful, but the corresponding silhouette of any multi-purpose university building is not, in spite of all efforts of the architect? The answer seems to me, even if somewhat speculative, to follow from the new insights into dynamical systems. Our feeling for beauty is inspired by the harmonious arrangement of order and disorder as it occurs in natural objects—in clouds, trees, mountain ranges, or snow crystals. The shapes of all these are dynamical processes jelled into physical forms, and particular combinations of order and disorder are typical for them."

As James Gleick correctly observes, "Simple shapes are inhuman. They fail to resonate with the way nature organises itself or with the way human perception sees the world." [49]

Long ago Karl Marx pointed to the harmful consequences of the extreme division between town and countryside. It is not a question of "going back to nature", in the utopian sense advocated by certain ecologists, who dream of escaping from the ugliness of the present by retreating into the alleged charms of a non-existent

---

(49) Quoted in J. Gleick, op. cit., pp. 116-7.

rural paradise in a mythical past. There is no going back. It is not a question of denying technology, but of fighting against the abuse of technology in the cause of private gain, which destroys the environment and creates a hell, where an earthly paradise ought to exist. That is the central task facing humanity in the last decade of the 20th century.

'Thinkers' and 'doers'

> "Nec manus, nisi intellectus, sibi permissus, multum valent." (Neither hand nor intellect left each to itself is worth much—Francis Bacon.)

The total divorce between theory and practice in present day society has become harmful in the extreme. The increasingly fantastic character of many of the "theories" put in circulation by certain cosmologists and theoretical physicists is undoubtedly a consequence of this fact. Freed from the constraints of having to furnish any concrete proof of their theories, and relying ever more on complicated equations and arcane interpretations of relativity theory, the results of this wholly speculative thinking are increasingly bizarre.

It is time to re-examine the whole system of education, and the class system of society upon which it rests. It is time to re-consider the validity of dividing humanity into the "thinkers" and "doers", not from the standpoint of some abstract moral justice, but simply because it has now become a hindrance to the development of culture and society. The future development of humanity cannot be based on the old rigid divisions. New complex technology demands an educated workforce capable of a creative approach to work. That can never be achieved in a society split down the middle by class apartheid. In a very perceptive passage, Margaret Donaldson points out the unsatisfactory situation that exists in universities today:

"Consider the engineering departments of our universities. They teach mathematics and physics and so they should. But they do not teach people to make things. You can emerge as a graduate in mechanical engineering without ever having used a lathe or a milling-machine. *These* things are considered suitable only for the technicians. And for most of *them*, on the other hand, mathematics and physics beyond an elementary level are quite simply out of reach."

The English philosopher and educationalist Alfred North Whitehead was deeply concerned at this situation, and, in his article *Technical Education and its Relation to Science and Literature*, wrote that "in teaching you come to grief as soon as you forget that your pupils have bodies," and added: "It is a moot point whether the human hand created the human brain, or the brain created the hand. Certainly the connection is intimate and reciprocal."

Donaldson correctly points out that, while abstract thought (she calls it "disembodied thinking") calls for the ability to step back from life, it yields its greatest results when linked to doing. The whole history of the Renaissance is proof of this assertion. True, the field of modern science is infinitely more vast and complicated than at that time, but does this really mean that it is impossible for scientists to learn from different disciplines? Rather than being a result of the increasing complexity of the subject, is the present state of intellectual apartheid not a product of the way present society is structured, and the attitudes, prejudices, and material interests which flow from it, and seek at all costs to preserve it?

Reactionaries try to justify the present state of affairs by the now obligatory references to genetic determinism: if some of "us" are clever, and have good jobs and large salaries, that is because we were born under a lucky star (read "with the right genes"—it comes out about the same). The fact that the rest of humankind are not so fortunate must be because there is something wrong with their genes. Answering this rubbish, Donaldson writes:

"Are only a few of us *able* to learn to move beyond the bounds of human sense and function successfully there? I doubt it. While it may make some sense to postulate that we each possess some genetically determined 'intellectual potential', in which case individuals will surely differ in this respect as in others, there is no reason to suppose that most of us—or any of us for that matter—manage to come close to realising what we are capable of. And it is not even certain that it makes a great deal of sense to think in terms of upper limits at all. For, as Jerome Bruner points out, there are tools of the mind as well as tools of the hand—and in either case the development of a powerful new tool brings with it the possibility of leaving old limitations behind. In a similar vein, David Olson says: 'Intelligence is not something we have that is immutable; it is something we cultivate by operating with a technology, or something we create by inventing new technology'." [50]

The great Soviet educationalist Vygotsky did not believe that the teacher should operate a rigid control over exactly what the child learns. Like Piaget, he considered *activity* by the children as central to education. Instead of chaining children to desks, where they mechanically go through the motions of learning things which are meaningless to them, Vygotsky stressed the need for genuine intellectual development. This, however, cannot be considered in a social vacuum. In a genuinely socialist society, education would be linked with creative practical activity from the beginning, thus breaking down the stultifying barrier between mental and manual labour. In many ways, Vygotsky was ahead of his time. His educational methods showed great imagination, for example, in allowing the children to learn from each other:

"Vygotsky advocated using a more advanced child to help a less advanced child. For a long time this was used as a basis of egalitarian Marxist education in the Soviet Union. The socialist rationale was one of all children working for the general good rather than the capitalist one of each child trying to get out of school as much benefit as he can without putting anything back into it. The brighter child is

(50) M. Donaldson, *Children's Minds*, pp. 83 and 85.

helping society by helping the less able one, since the latter will (it is hoped) be more of an asset to society as a literate than as an illiterate adult. Vygotsky argued that this act is not necessarily one of self-sacrifice on the part of the more advanced child. By explaining and helping the other child, he may well gain a greater explicit understanding of his own learning, on metacognitive lines. And, by teaching a topic, he consolidates his own learning." [51]

A democratic socialist society would abolish the difference between mental and manual labour through the general increase in the cultural level of society. This is closely linked to a reduction in the working day as a consequence of a rational plan of production. Education will be transformed by combining learning with creative activity and play. The development of all kinds of new techniques will be used to the full. V. R. (virtual reality) devices, which are at present little more than novelties, have tremendous potential, not only for production and design, but for education. This will make lessons come to life, stimulating the imagination and creativity of children, not just to experience history and geography, but to learn mechanical engineering, or how to paint and play musical instruments. Freedom from the humiliating struggle for the necessities of life, access to culture and the time to develop oneself as a human being, these are the bases upon which human society can realise its full potential.

Humanity and the universe

> "He said, 'What's the time? Leave Now for dogs and apes! Man has Forever'." (Robert Browning, *A Grammarian's Funeral*.)

The achievements of the Soviet and American space programmes provided just an inkling of what would be possible. But the space programmes of the great powers were really a by-product of the arms race during the Cold War. Since the collapse of the Soviet Union, the question of space travel no longer occupies the centre stage, although there is still the possibility of building a space station that will orbit the earth, making travel to the moon a lot easier. In the future world socialist commonwealth, space travel will cease to be the stuff of science fiction, and become a fact of life, as common as air travel is now. The exploration of the solar system, and later other galaxies, will provide the same kind of challenge and stimulus to humankind as that which came to Europe from the discovery of America.

The possibility of long distance space travel beyond the confines of our own solar system will not forever remain in the realms of science fiction. Let us not forget that only a hundred years ago, the idea of flying faster than the speed of sound seemed beyond the bounds of credibility, let alone travelling to the moon. The history of the human race in general, and that of the last 40 years in particular, shows that there is no problem so great that men and women cannot solve it, given time.

(51) P. Sutherland, *Cognitive Development Today: Piaget and his Critics*, p. 45.

In about four billion years from now, our sun will begin to swell in size, as its helium core slowly shrinks. The planets near the sun will be subjected to unimaginable temperatures. Life on earth will become impossible, as the oceans boil away, and the atmosphere is destroyed. Yet the end of life in one small corner of the universe is not the end of the story. Even as our star dies, other stars will be born. Among the billions of galaxies in the visible universe, there are a vast quantity of suns and planets like our own where the conditions for life exist. Beyond doubt, many of these will be inhabited by advanced forms of life, including thinking beings like ourselves. Very few scientists now doubt this proposition, and fewer still since the complicated molecules needed to create living organisms have been found even in space itself.

At the end of *The Dialectics of Nature*, Engels expresses a vibrant optimism about the future of life:

"It is an eternal cycle in which matter moves, a cycle that certainly only completes its orbit in periods of time for which our terrestrial year is no adequate measure, a cycle in which the time of highest development, the time of organic life and still more that of the life of beings conscious of nature and of themselves, is just as narrowly restricted as the space in which life and self-consciousness come into operation; a cycle in which every finite mode of existence of matter, whether it be sun or nebular vapour, single animal or genus of animals chemical combination or dissociation, is equally transient, and wherein nothing is eternal but eternally changing, eternally moving matter and the laws according to which it moves and changes.

"But however often, and however relentlessly, this cycle is completed in time and space; however many millions of suns and earths may arise and pass away, however long it may last before, in one solar system and only on *one* planet, the conditions for organic life develop; however innumerable the organic beings, too, that have to arise and to pass away before animals with a brain capable of thought are developed from their midst, and for a short span of time find conditions suitable for life, only to be exterminated later without mercy—we have the certainty that matter remains eternally the same in all its transformations, that none of its attributes can ever be lost, and therefore, also, that with the same iron necessity that it will exterminate on the earth its highest creation, the thinking mind, it must somewhere else and at another time again produce it." [52]

Now, however, we are entitled to go further than this. The staggering advances of science over the hundred years since Engels died mean that the death of the sun will not necessarily mean the death of the human race. The development of powerful spacecraft, capable of travelling at speeds which at present seem impossible, could prepare the ground for the ultimate adventure, involving emigration to other parts of the solar system, and, eventually, other galaxies. Even at one per cent of the

(52) Engels, *Dialectics of Nature*, p. 54.

speed of light—a clearly attainable goal—it would be possible to reach inhabitable planets in the course of a few hundred years.

If this seems a long time, we should remember that it took early humans millions of years to colonise the world, setting out from Africa. Moreover, the journey would probably take place in stages, establishing colonies and staging posts along the way, like the early Polynesian settlers who colonised the Pacific, island by island, over several centuries. The technological problems will be immense, but we will have at least three billion years to resolve them. If we consider that *Homo sapiens sapiens* has only been in existence for about 100,000 years, that civilisation has only existed for about 5,000 years of that, and that the pace of technological advance has tended to increase ever more rapidly, there is no reason whatever to draw pessimistic conclusions about the future of humanity—on one condition: that class rule, that atrocious relic of barbarism, is replaced by a system of co-operation and planning, which will unite all the resources of the globe in one common cause.

Engels described socialism as humanity's leap from the realm of necessity into the realm of freedom. For the first time, it will be possible for the majority of humankind to escape from the humiliating struggle for existence, and raise their sights to a higher level. The elimination of disease, illiteracy and homelessness in themselves important aims, will only be the starting point. By combining all the resources of the planet that are now being shamelessly squandered humankind can literally reach out to the stars.

Last, but not least, humans will at last become masters of themselves, their lives and their destinies, even their genetic make-up. The relations between men and women will be relations between free human beings, not slaves. Aristotle pointed out that man begins to philosophise when the needs of life are provided. That mighty thinker understood that the development of culture was closely linked to the material conditions of life. In a truly remarkable passage, he shows how men and women begin to philosophise, to dedicate themselves to the pursuit of knowledge for its own sake, only when they are freed from the need to struggle for the necessities of existence:

"This is shown by the actual course of events; for philosophy arose only when the necessities and the physical and mental comforts of life had been provided for. Clearly, therefore, Wisdom is desired for no advantage extrinsic to itself; for just as we call a man free who exists for himself and not in the interests of another, so philosophy alone of the sciences is free since it alone is pursued for its own sake." [53]

For the whole history of civilisation to the present day, culture has been a monopoly of a small minority. In a genuinely democratic socialist society, it would be possible to ensure a general reduction in the working day, and increased living standards for everyone on the basis of a tremendous upswing of production. Freed

(53) Aristotle, op. cit., p. 55.

from the pressures of necessity, men and women can devote their lives to a full and all-round development of their personality, intellect and physique. Art, literature, music, science and philosophy will occupy a similar position as party politics at present.

On the basis of a rational democratically run planned economy, the colossal potential of science and technique could be placed at the disposal of humankind. In the last 100 years, improved diet and medical care have doubled the life expectancy in many industrialised countries. Further improvements in lifestyle could prolong active life still further. To live a fully active life for a hundred years would be commonplace. The proper use of genetic engineering could even permit scientists to counteract the ageing process and prolong life far beyond what was regarded as "man's natural span". The possibilities for the future of humankind will be as limitless as the universe itself.

"The blind elements have settled most heavily in economic relations, but man is driving them out from there also, by means of the Socialist organisation of economic life. This makes it possible to reconstruct fundamentally the traditional family life. Finally, the nature of man himself is hidden in the deepest and darkest corner of the unconscious, of the elemental, of the sub-soil. Is it not self-evident that the greatest efforts of investigative thought and of creative initiative will be in that direction? The human race will not have ceased to crawl on all fours before God, kings and capital, in order later to submit humbly before the dark laws of heredity and a blind sexual selection! Emancipated man will want to attain a greater equilibrium in the work of his organs and a more proportional developing and wearing out of his tissues, in order to reduce the fear of death to a rational reaction of the organism towards danger. There can be no doubt that man's extreme anatomical and physiological disharmony, that is, the extreme disproportion in the growth and wearing out of organ and tissues, give the life instinct the form of a pinched, morbid and hysterical fear of death, which darkens reason and which feeds the stupid and humiliating fantasies about life after death.

"Man will make it his purpose to master his own feelings, to raise his instincts to the heights of consciousness, to make them transparent, to extend the wires of his will into hidden recesses, and thereby to raise himself to a new plane, to create a higher social biologic type, or, if you please, a superman.

"It is difficult to predict the extent of self-government which the man of the future may reach or the heights to which he may carry his technique. Social construction and psychophysical self-education will become two aspects of one and the same process. All the arts—literature, drama, painting, music and architecture will lend this process beautiful form. More correctly, the shell in which the cultural construction and self-education of Communist man will be enclosed, will develop all the vital elements of contemporary art to the highest point. Man will become immeasurably stronger, wiser and subtler; his body will become more harmonised, his movements more rhythmic, his voice more musical. The forms of life will become dynamically dramatic. The average human type will rise to the heights of an Aristotle, a Goethe, or a Marx. And above the ridge new peaks will rise." [54]

(54) Trotsky, *Literature and Revolution*, pp. 255-6.

Bibliography

Aristotle, *Metaphysics*, London, 1961

Asimov, I., *New Guide to Science*, London, 1987

Barrow, J.D., *The Origin of the Universe*, London, 1994

Berkeley, G., *The Principles of Human Knowledge*, London & Glasgow, 1962

Bernal, J.D., *The Origin of Life*, 1967

Bernal, J.D., *Science in History*, London, 1954

Blackmore, V. A., and Page, *Evolution: The Great Debate*, 1989

Bohm, D., *Causality and Chance in Modern Physics*, London, 1984

Bruner, J.S., *Beyond the Information Given*, London, 1974

Bruner, J.S. and Haste, H. (eds), *Making Sense*, London & New York, 1987

Buchsbaum, R., *Animals Without Backbones*, 2 vols., London, 1966

Bukharin, N.I. and others, *Marxism and Modern Thought*, London, 1935

Burn, A.R., *The Pelican History of Greece*, London, 1966

Calder, N., *Einstein's Universe*, London, 1986

Caudwell, C., *The Crisis in Physics*, London, 1949

Childe, V.G., *Man Makes Himself*, London, 1965

Childe, V.G., *What Happened in History*, London, 1965

Chomsky, N., *Language and Mind*, New York, 1972

Cohen, Morris R. and Nagel, Ernest, *An Introduction to Logic and the Scientific Method*, London, 1972

Cornforth, M., *The Open Philosophy and The Open Society*, London, 1977

Cornforth, M., *Dialectical Materialism, an Introduction*, London, 1974

Darwin, C., *The Origin of Species*, London, 1929

Davies, P., *The Last Three Minutes*, London, 1994

Dawkins, R., *The Extended Phenotype: The Long Reach of the Gene*, 1982

Dawkins, R., *The Selfish Gene*, Oxford, 1976

Dietzgen, J., *Philosophical Essays*, Chicago, 1917

Dietzgen, J., *The Positive Outcome of Philosophy*, Chicago, 1906

Dobzhansky, T., *Mankind Evolving*, New York, 1962

Donaldson, M., *Children's Minds*, London, 1978

Donaldson, M., *Making Sense*

Engels, F., *The Dialectics of Nature*, Moscow, 1954

Engels, F., *Anti-Dühring*, Peking, 1976 (See also under Marx)

Farrington, B., *Greek Science*, London, 1963

Farrington, B., *What Darwin Really Said*, London, 1969

Ferris, T., The *World Treasury of Physics, Astronomy and Mathematics*, Boston, 1991

Feuerbach, L., *The Essence of Christianity*, New York, 1957

Feynman, R. P., *Lectures on Physics*, London, 1969

Forbes, R.J. and Dijksterhuis, E.J., *A History of Science and Technology*, Vol. 1, London, 1963

Frazer, Sir J., *The Golden Bough*, London, 1959

Freud, S., *The Psychopathology of Everyday Life*, London, 1960

Galbraith, J.K., *The Culture of Contentment*, London, 1992

Gleick, J., *Chaos, Making a New Science*, New York, 1988

Gould, S.J., *An Urchin in the Storm*, London, 1987

Gould, S.J., *Ever Since Darwin*, London, 1977

Gould, S.J., *The Panda's Thumb*, London, 1980

Gould, S.J., *Wonderful Life*, London, 1990

Haldane, J.B.S., *The Marxist Philosophy and the Sciences*, London, 1938

Haldane, J.B.S., *The Rationalist Annual*, 1929.

Hawking, S., *A Brief History of Time, From the Big Bang to Black Holes*, London, 1994

Hegel, G.W.F., *Science of Logic*, 2 vols., London, 1961

Hegel, G.W.F., *Logic*, Part 1 of the Encyclopaedia of the Philosophical Sciences, Oxford, 1978

Hegel, G.W.F., *The Phenomenology of Mind*, London, 1961

Hegel, G.W.F., *Philosophy of Right*, Oxford, 1942

Hegel, G.W.F., *Lectures of the History of Philosophy*, 3 vols., London

Hobbes, T., *Leviathan*, London, 1962

Hoffmann, B., *The Strange Story of the Quantum*, London, 1963

Hooper, A., *Makers of Mathematics*, London

Huizinga, J., *The Waning of the Middle Ages*, London, 1972

Huxley, J., *Evolution in Action*, London, 1963

Ilyenkov, E.V., *Dialectical Logic*, Moscow, 1977

Johanson, D.C. and Edey, M.A., *Lucy, The Beginnings of Humankind*, London, 1981

Johnson, P., *Ireland, a Concice History*, London, 1981

Kant, I., *Critique of Pure Reason*, London, 1959

Kline, M., *Mathematics, the Loss of Certainty*, London, 1980

Kneale, W. and Kneale, M., *The Development of Logic*, Oxford, 1962

Landau, L.D. and Rumer, G.B., *What is Relativity?* Edinburgh & London, 1964

Leakey, R., *The Origin of Humankind*, London, 1994

Lefebvre, H., *Lógica formal, Lógica dialéctica*, Madrid, 1972

Lenin, V.I., *Collected Works*, Moscow, 1961

Lerner, E.J., *The Big Bang Never Happened*, London & Sydney, 1992

Lewin, R., *Complexity, Life at the Edge of Chaos*, London, 1993

Luce, A.A., *Logic*, London, 1966

Lucretius, T., *The Nature of the Universe*, London, 1952

Lukacs, G., *History and Class Consciousness*, London, 1971

Marx, K., *Capital*, Vol. 1, Moscow, 1961

Marx, K., *Grundrisse*, London, 1973

Marx, K. and Engels, F., *Selected Correspondence*, Moscow, 1965

Marx, K. and Engels, F., *Collected Works*, Moscow

Marx, K. and Engels, F., *Selected Works*, 3 vols, Moscow, 1969-70

Oparin, A.I., *The Origin of Life on Earth*, 1959

Piaget, J., *The Mental Development of the Child*

Plekhanov, G., *The Devolopment of the Monist View of History*, 1947

Plekhanov, G., *Selected Philosophical Works*, Moscow, 1976

Popper, K., *Unended Quest*, Glasgow, 1982

Prigogine, I. and Stengers, I., *Order Out of Chaos, Man's New Dialogue with Nature*, London, 1985

Rees-Mogg, W. and Davidson, J., *The Great Reckoning: How the World Will Change in the Depression of the 1990s*, London, 1992

Regan, D. *For the record*, 1988

Rhodes, F.H.T., *The Evolution of Life*, London, 1962

Romer, A.S., *Man and the Vertebrates*, 2 vols., London, 1970

Rose, S. and Appignanesi, L. (eds), *Science and Beyond*, Oxford, 1986

Rose, S., Kamin, L.J. and Lewontin, R.C., *Not in Our Genes*, London, 1984

Rose, S., *The Conscious Brain*, London, 1976

Rose, S., *The Making of Memory*, London, 1992

Rose, S., *Molecules and Minds*, 1987

Savage-Rumbaugh, S. and Lewin, R., *Kanzi - The Ape at the Brink of the Human Mind*, London, 1994

Shakespeare, William, Sonnets,

Spinoza, *Ethics*, London, 1993

Stepanova, Y., *Frederick Engels*, Moscow, 1958

Stewart, I., *Does God Play Dice?* London, 1990

Sutherland, P., *Cognitive Development Today: Piaget and his Critics*, London, 1992

Toulmin, S. and Goodfield, J., *The Fabric of the Heavens*, London, 1961

Trotsky, L.D., *In Defence of Marxism*, London, 1982

Trotsky, L.D., *My Life*, New York, 1960

Trotsky, L.D., *Literature and Revolution*, Michigan, 1960

Trotsky, L.D., *The Living Thoughts of Karl Marx*, New York, 1963

Trotsky, L.D., *Their Morals and Ours*

Trotsky, L.D., *Problems of Everyday Life*, New York, 1979

Trotsky, L.D., *The Struggle Against Fascism in Germany*, New York, 1971

Trotsky, L.D., *Writings, 1939-1940*, New York, 1973

Waldrop, M.M., *Complexity, The Emerging Science at the Edge of Order and*

Chaos, London, 1992
Walter, W.G., *The Living Brain*, London, 1963
Washburn, S.L., and Moore, Ruth E., *Ape into Man: A Study of Human Evolution*, Boston 1973
Westbroek, P., *Life as a Geological Force: Dynamics of the Eath,* 1991
White, M. and Gribbin, J., *Einstein, A Life in Science*, London, 1993
Whitehead, A.N., *Adventures of Ideas*, London, 1942
Wills, C., *The Runaway Brain, The Evolution of Human Uniqueness,* 1994
Wilson, E.O., *Sociobiology – The New Synthesis*, Cambridge, 1975

Magazines and periodicals:

Scientific American
Director
Time
New Scientist
The Economist
Financial Times
The Guardian

Glossary of Terms

Please note that this glossary is not intended, for reasons of space, to be exhaustive. To avoid repetition, terms explained in the text are not generally included here.

Adaptive radiation.- Evolution, from a primitive type of organism, of several divergent forms adapted to distinct modes of life.

Allopatric Theory.- The theory that the evolutionary divergence of populations into separate species, which no longer interbreed, takes place in geographically separate places.

Amino Acids.- Organic compound containing both basic amino and acidic carobxyl groups. Amino acid molecules combine to make protein molecules and are therefore a fundamental constituent of living matter.

Causality, Law of.- The law defining the interdependence of cause and effect— the necessary connections between phenomena. Causality is an essential question in the struggle between materialism and idealism.

Chromosomes.- A chain of genes found in cells. They are present in all cells in the body and consist of DNA and a supporting structure of protein.

Cognition.- The process by which human thought reflects and observes the real world.

Convergent Series.- Number series in which the successive partial sums obtained by taking more and more terms approach some fixed number or limit.

Cytoplasm.-All the protoplasm of a cell excluding the nucleus.

Determinism.- A belief that all processes are predetermined by definite causes and natural laws and can therefore be predicted. Biological determinism and mechanical determinism are two variations of this premise. Indeterminism is the reverse of this—a belief that events are governed not by laws but by pure chance.

Dialectics.- From the Greek words for dispute and debate, this is the science of the general laws governing the development of nature, science, society and thought. It considers all phenomena to be in movement and in perpetual change. Marxism linked this concept to materialism and showed the process of development in all things through struggle, contradiction and the replacement on one form by another.

Diploid.- Cell with chromosomes in pairs.

DNA.- The molecule that carries the genetic information in organisms (except RNA viruses).

Dogma.- A blind belief in things often without a material base.

Eclecticism.- A mechanical and/or arbitrary collecting of concepts or facts without any pre-established principles or structures. Eclecticism is often used to attempt to reconcile the irreconcilable such as idealism and materialism.

Electromagnetism.- The study of the effects of the relationship and interplay between a magnetic field and an electric current. For example the electrical creation of a magnetic field in a conductor.

Electrons.- Elementary particles that possess one unit of negative charge and are a constituent of all atoms.

Entropy.- One of the main notions of thermodynamics, where it is normally viewed as a measure of disorder. In isolated systems, it is used to determine the way in which the system will change if heated or cooled, compressed or expanded. Thermodynamics holds that the entropy of a system can never decrease but only increase and that a state of maximum entropy is marked by a state of balance in which no further conversion of energy is possible. This has been used to justify the erroneous idea of the "heat death of the universe". In recent years, I. Prigogine has reinterpreted the Second Law of Thermodynamics in a way which defines entropy differently. According to Prigogine, entropy does not mean higher disorder in the generally accepted sense, but an irreversible process of change which generally leads to more highly ordered states.

Empiricism.- A teaching on the theory of knowledge which holds that sensory experience is the only source of knowledge and affirms that all knowledge is founded on experience and is obtained through experience. The opposite to rationalism. The main failing of this is a tendency to reject reason as a means of deduction in favour of a metaphysical exaggeration of the role of experience alone.

Eugenics.- A doctrine which holds that the human race can be "improved" by selective control of breeding to eradicate less "desirable" traits in society. The supporters of eugenics argue that social problems are caused by inherited genetic traits in people which can be bred out to resolve the problem for future generations. The logical conclusion of this theory is deeply racist and reactionary based on dubious research and prejudice.

Eukaryotes.- One of the two major groups of organisms on Earth (the other being Prokaryotes). Characterised by the possession of a cell nucleus and other membrane-bounded cell organelles.

Gene.- A unit of heredity; a sequence of base pairs in a DNA molecule that contains information for the construction of protein molecule.

Genome.- The entire collection of genes possessed by one organism.

Genotype.- Genetic constitution (the particular set of alleles present in each cell of an organism) as contrasted with the characteristics manifested by the organism.

Gradualism.- The theory that all evolutionary change is gradual rather than occurring in leaps and jumps.

Haploid.- Cell with single set of chromosomes.

Lamarckism.- The theory that acquired characteristics can be inherited and that any new genetic variation tends to be adaptively directed rather than 'random' as stated by Darwin.

Logical Positivists.- A variation on positivism which attempts to combine subjective-idealist empiricism with a method of logical analysis.

Lysenkoism.- A revival of Lamarckism in the USSR under Lysenko who sought to affect the hereditary modification of plants by certain treatments. His research was subsequently discredited but was heavily touted by Stalinists in its day.

Malthusian Theory.- The theory developed by Thomas Malthus which claimed that population levels were responsible for social problems and should be checked to resolve them since uncontrolled population increases occur on a geometrical ratio whereas the increase in resources occurs on an arithmetical basis. This is not so but laid the basis for the belief that nothing could be done about the problems of the world. In its most extreme form it was the basis for an acceptance of famines etc. as unavoidable and socially necessary.

Meiosis.- Cell division in which a cell gives rise to daughter cells with half as many chromosomes.

Metaphysics.- There are two definitions of this word: the one used by Marx and Engels, and the other more traditional conception. In Marxist terminology, metaphysics is a method which holds that things are immutable and immutable, independent of one another and denies that inherent contradictions are the source of the development of nature and society but rather that nature is at rest, unchanging and static. All things can be investigated as separate from each other. Nowadays, the word reductionism would often be used instead.

The more traditional philosophical definition derives from Aristotle who used the word metaphysics to describe the branch of philosophy dealing with universal concepts as opposed to the observation of nature (in Greek, "meta ta physika" means "that which comes after physics"). Later on it became a synonym for abstract idealist speculation.

Mitosis.- Cell division in which a cell gives rise to daughter cells with a complete set of chromosomes.

Mutation.- An inherited change in the genetic material; a change in the genotype

Neutron.- One of the two types of particle which form the nucleus of an atom—the other being the proton.

Nodes.- The points in a wave system where the amplitude of the wave is zero. In Hegel, the nodal line of measurement was one where the line is interrupted by sudden leaps, denoting qualitative change ("node" here means "knot").

Nucleotide.- A biochemical molecule used as the basic building block of DNA and RNA.

Phenotype.- Manifested attributes of an organism (e.g., eye colour).

Photon.- Units or 'packets' of electromagnetic radiation.

Plasma.- A gas that contains a large number of positively and negatively charged particles (ions and electrons). This can occur when a gas is raised to extremely high temperatures (e.g., the outer regions of the sun) or in an intense electrical field. Plasma physics is an important branch of modern science.

Polymorphism.- The coexistence of several well-defined distinct phenotypes or alleles in a population.

Positivism.- An idealistic current which believes in "positive" facts rather than abstract deductions. It denies that philosophy is a world outlook and states that belief should be concentrated on a description of facts rather than an analysis of them. Positivism claims to be neutral and above philosophical outlooks, interested in processes but not willing to go beyond the boundaries of the status quo. In effect they confirm the maintenance of existing social structures.

Positrons.- The antiparticles of electrons—having the same mass but a positive charge.

Prokaryotes.- One of the two major groups of organisms on Earth (the other being Eukaryotes).They have no structured cell nucleus and no membrane-bounded organelles.

Proton.- One of the two types of particles which form the nucleus of an atom—the other being neutrons.

Protoplasm.- Substance within and including plasma-membrane of a cell or protoplasm.

Quantum Mechanics.- The mathematical description of the workings of the atomic and sub-atomic structures.

Quarks.- According to particle physics these sub-atomic particles are believed to be the constituents of elementary particles known as hadrons. Five or possibly six different sorts are thought to exist, but new discoveries are being made all the time.

Quasars.- Quasi-stellar radio sources (quasars) were first detected by virtue of their radio transmissions and appear to show the small bright centres of distant galaxies (although some believe that they are not as far away as people imagine but are moving at high speeds).

Rationalism.- The theory which holds that reason is the unique source of knowledge as against empiricism which holds that perception is the source of knowledge.

Reductionism.- A belief that all scientific laws and processes relating to complex systems can be reduced down to basic scientific laws. Physicalism was a version of this.

Relativity, Theory of.- The laws of relativity (relationship between an object and an observer or another object) considered and developed by Einstein. Einstein's general theory deals with motion, gravity, time and the concept of curved space. The theory which deals with constant velocities is called the special theory. The most famous part of these laws is that which shows the relationship between mass and energy ($E = mc2$).

Speciation.- The process of evolutionary divergence i.e., two species being produced from one source.

Stasis.- A period in which no evolutionary change takes place in the development of a species.

Sufficient Reason, Law of.- A principle that holds that a proposition can only be considered true if sufficient reason for it can be formulated.

Syllogism.- A doctrine of inference, historically the first logical system of deduction, formulated by Aristotle. Every syllogism consists of a triad of propositions: two premises and a conclusion.

Systematics.- Study of the diversity of organisms.

Taxonomy.- Study of classifying organisms.

Thermodynamics.- The branch of physics concerned with the nature of heat and its transformations. The First Law of Thermodynamics is generally referred to as the Law of the Conservation of Energy. The Second Law deals with the concept of increasing entropy (see under entropy).

Index of Names

A

Alfvén, Hannes, 174, 186
Alvarez, Luis, 263, 264
Anaximander, 355
Anderson, Carl David, 379
Archimedes, 354, 356
Aristotle, 40, 44, 45, 47, 51, 53, 85, 87, 89, 90, 91, 93, 94, 102, 103, 136, 138, 145, 182, 208, 209, 222, 225, 242, 288, 352, 356, 369, 401, 406, 422, 424
Arrhenius, Svente, 243
Arthur, Brian, 391
Asimov, Isaac, 114, 164, 425
Augustine, Saint, 124, 141, 142
Avery, Oswald, 325

B

Bacon, Francis, 25, 45, 217, 418
Bak, Per, 54
Berkeley, Bishop George, 46, 115, 358, 384
Bernal, John Desmond, 149, 163, 240, 244, 247, 422
Binet, Alfred, 332, 336
Binford, Lewis, 275,
Bohm, David, 50, 63, 64, 116, 121, 125, 126, 127, 128, 130, 174, 381, 425
Bohr, Niels, 72, 73, 110, 116, 118, 193, 209, 362, 378
Bolanzo, Bernhard, 359
Boltzmann, Ludwig, 125, 147, 166, 168, 169, 170, 176, 177, 178, 180
Bondi, Herman, 213
Boyle, George, 101
Breggin, Peter, 339
Brinton, Daniel G.,323
Broglie, Louis de, 108, 117
Browning, Robert, 420
Bruner, Jerome, 269, 300, 302, 419
Brunner, Hans, 343
Buck, Carrie, 335, 336
Bukharin, Nikolai, 287
Burns, Robert, 173
Burt, Cyril Lodowic, 333, 334
Butler, Samuel, 343

Gleick, James, 59, 126, 363, 364, 365, 366, 367, 369, 371, 372, 373, 374, 375, 376, 378, 394, 417
Gödel, Kurt, 361
Gold, Thomas, 186
Goldman, David, 342
Gould, Stephen J., 61, 249, 253, 280, 311, 312, 313, 314, 315, 316, 317, 324, 343, 346
Grant, Ted, 15, 19, 198
Grenville, Charles, 321
Guth, Alan, 188, 189, 190, 192, 222

H

Haldane, John B.S., 239, 240, 241, 245, 325, 326, 341
Hawking, Stephen,195, 207, 208, 210, 211, 212, 213, 214, 215, 216, 217, 218, 219,
Hebb, Donald, 298
Hegel, Georg W.F., 16, 20, 27, 39, 46, 47, 48, 50, 53, 56, 57, 59, 71, 77, 78, 79, 80, 81, 86, 89, 90, 91, 92, 93, 95, 96, 97, 101, 102, 130, 131, 132, 133, 134, 139, 142, 146, 147, 148, 149, 154, 156, 157, 166, 211, 218, 222, 229, 282, 299, 300, 308, 312, 354, 356, 358, 359, 368, 370, 377, 378, 380, 381, 382, 385, 386, 388, 391, 392, 415
Heisenberg, Werner, 100, 107, 113, 114, 115, 116, 117, 118, 119, 128, 133, 168, 209, 220, 389
Helvétius, Claude Adrien 45
Heraclitus, , 46, 48, 69, 70, 71, 79, 101, 143, 144, 147, 368, 388
Herrnstein, Richard, 332
Hertz, Heinrich Rudolf, 105, 106
Hilbert, David, 360, 362
Hobbes, Thomas, 20, 45, 295, 323, 344, 352
Hoffmann, Banesh, 72, 107, 108, 129, 193, 388
Holbach, Paul-Henri Thiry, Baron d', 45
Holmes, O.W., 335
Hooper, Alfred, 353, 356
Horace, 369
Hoyle, Fred, 186, 188, 198, 205, 206, 213, 224, 243
Hubble, Edwin Powell, 184, 185, 189, 196, 197, 201, 202
Hume, David, 46, 115, 212
Hunter, G.W., 335, 339, 384
Huxley, Thomas Henry, 243, 379
Huygens, Christiaan, 105

I

Ilyenkov, Evald V., 93

Isaac, Glynn Llywelyn, 279

Other titles from Wellred

▶ **In the Cause of Labour -
History of British Trade Unionism**
By Rob Sewell
Price: £ 14.99

Pub. Date: 2003
Format: Paperback
No. Pages: 480
ISBN: 1900007142

History of British Trotskyism ◀
By Ted Grant
Price: £ 9.99

Pub. Date: 2002
Format: Paperback
No. Pages: 310
ISBN: 190000710X

▶ **Lenin and Trotsky -
What they really stood for**
By Alan Woods and Ted Grant
Price: £ 8.95

Pub. Date: 2000
Format: Paperback
No. Pages: 221
ISBN: 8492183268

Bolshevism - The Road to Revolution ◀
By Alan Woods
Price: £ 15.00
Pub. Date: 1999
Format: Paperback
No. Pages: 636
ISBN: 1900007053

▶ History of the Russian Revolution
By Leon Trotsky

Pub. Date: 2007
Format: Paperback

Vol 1
No. Pages: 530
ISBN: 1 9000 07 26 6
Price £11.99

Vol2
No. Pages: 349
ISBN: 1 9000 07 27 4
Price £10.99

Vol3
No. Pages: 413
ISBN: 1 9000 07 28 2
Price £11.99

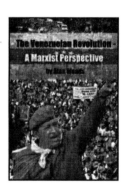

The Venezuelan Revolution - A Marxist Perspective ◀
By Alan Woods
Price: £ 7.99
Pub. Date: April 2005
Format: Paperback
No. Pages: 180
ISBN: 1 9000 0721 5

▶ Ireland - Republicanism and Revolution
By Alan Woods
Price: £ 6.99

Pub. Date: April 2005
Format: Paperback
No. Pages: 137
ISBN: 1 9000 07 20 7

▶ Russia - From Revolution to Counter-Revolution
By Ted Grant
out of print

Pub. Date: 1999
Format: Paperback
No. Pages: 636
ISBN: 1900007053

My Life ◀
By Leon Trotsky
Price: £ 14.99
Pub. Date: 2004
Format: Paperback
No. Pages: 512

▶ The Permanent Revolution and Results and Prospects
By Leon Trotsky
Price: £ 9.99

Pub. Date: 2004
Format: Paperback
No. Pages: 277
ISBN: 8492183268

1905 ◀
By Leon Trotsky
Publisher: Wellred Publications
Pub. Date: 2005
Format: Paperback
No. Pages: 350
ISBN: 1900007223

Price £11.99

▶ Not Guilty - Dewey Commission Report
Price £14.99

Pub. Date: January 2005
Format: Paperback
No. Pages: 432
ISBN: 1 9000 07 19 3

Marxism and the USA ◀
By Alan Woods
Price: £ 9.99
Pub. Date: 2006
Format: Paperback
No. Pages: 154
ISBN: 1 90000724 X

▶ Dialectics of Nature
By Frederick Engels
Price £14.99

Pub. Date: 2006
Format: Paperback
No. Pages: 410
ISBN: 1 9000 0723 1

07 85 445 448 8 18